8.50

DRIVER'S RECEIPT

I acknowledge receipt of the Compliance Pocketbook (5733 responsibilities and duties in hazardous materials, as pre Department of Transportation in 171-180 and 390-397.

D0197733

Date

Driver's Name (Please Print)

Driver's Signature

Supervisor or Carrier Representative Signature

11/20

NOTE: This receipt shall be read and signed by the driver. A responsible company supervisor or carrier representative shall countersign the receipt and place in the driver's file.

1

9/24

$8.50

HAZARDOUS MATERIALS COMPLIANCE POCKETBOOK

This hazmat pocketbook includes all revisions issued on or before October 2, 2020.
Featured revisions include:

TAB	SUBJECT	DATE
EXCEPTIONS	Changes from RIN 2137-AF32 (HM-215O)	7/2020
ID CROSS REFERENCE CHART	Changes from RIN 2137-AF32 (HM-215O)	7/2020
HAZMAT TABLE and HAZMAT TABLE SPECIAL PROVISIONS	Changes from RIN 2137-AF32 (HM-215O)	7/2020
	Changes from RIN 2137-AF40 (HM-264)	8/2020
	2020 ERG changes	9/2020

Copyright 2020

J. J. Keller & Associates, Inc.
3003 Breezewood Lane, P.O. Box 368
Neenah, Wisconsin 54957-0368 USA
Phone: (800) 327-6868
JJKeller.com
Library of Congress Catalog Card Number: 2016959236
ISBN: 978-1-68008-950-9

Canadian Goods and Services Tax (GST) Number: R123-317687

(57333)

11/20

TABLE OF CONTENTS

Reserved

The Law Affects You Directly

The current Hazardous Materials Regulations can be traced to the Transportation Safety Act of 1974, the hazardous materials regulations "consolidation" of 1976, the Hazardous Materials Transportation Uniform Safety Act of 1990, and the numerous amendments issued to date. Carriers are subject to both the Hazardous Materials Regulations and Motor Carrier Safety Regulations (49 CFR Parts 105–107, 109, 110, 130, 171–180 & 390–397).

In turn, carriers (employers) are responsible for training, testing and certifying drivers and other employees in proper hazardous materials handling, and for providing necessary documents and information to drivers hauling hazardous materials loads.

Drivers are responsible for following the requirements prescribed in the hazmat regulations. Drivers can be fined for not complying with parts of the hazmat regulations that relate to them. **A person who violates a requirement in the regulations is liable for a penalty of not more than $81,993 for each violation. However, if the violation results in death, serious illness or injury, or substantial destruction of property the maximum penalty is $191,316. There is no minimum penalty, except if the violation is related to training, then the minimum penalty is $493.** When the violation is a continuing one, each day is considered a separate offense.

The regulations for transporting hazardous materials are based on good common sense, and are designed to protect the safety of all concerned. It makes good sense for you to follow them carefully!

Besides obeying requirements specifically aimed at them, responsible drivers can do a lot to ensure that hazardous materials shipments are handled properly by all concerned. The following checklist for drivers rounds up the ways you can help.

Checklist

1. **Be able to recognize discrepancies in documents, packaging, labeling and compatibility.**

2. **Inspect all hazardous material shipments before loading and contact carrier management for instructions if there are any suspicious shipments offered.**

3. **Refuse to accept hazardous material freight from shippers or interline carriers, if the shipping papers are improperly prepared or don't check out with the freight. Also refuse leaking containers, those that might be damaged or any that appear improper.**

4. **Be sure that packages bearing POISON (TOXIC) or POISON INHALATION HAZARD labels are not loaded with foodstuffs, animal feeds or any other edible cargo intended for consumption by humans or animals unless they are packaged and loaded according to the regulations.**

5. Be sure that all hazardous material is properly blocked and secured for transportation. Be sure containers won't be damaged by any other freight or by nails, rough floors, etc.

6. Be sure any required placards are in place before starting.

7. Have all necessary shipping papers (bills of lading, hazardous waste manifest, etc.) in good order, in your possession and available for immediate use in case of an incident, accident or inspection.

8. Know your responsibilities for attending your vehicle while carrying hazardous materials.

9. Know the procedures (and have them in writing if possible) for disposing of (or decontaminating) the hazardous cargo if there is an accident or some incident involving your hazardous cargo.

10. Be prepared to provide the required information to police, firemen, or other authorities in case of emergency.

11. Report the full details on any hazardous materials incident to your superior as quickly as possible. Include detailed information on cause, container damage, identification of specific containers and any corrective action which was taken.

How to Comply With the Law

How can you be sure that you can successfully comply with the provisions of the Hazardous Materials Regulations? It does take some study and responsibility on your part and you should have received training and testing from your employer. Requirements vary somewhat, depending on the type of operation you are working for. The following brief descriptions cover various types of operations which might be involved at some time with hauling hazardous goods.

Road Drivers

You should have a broad knowledge of the hazardous materials regulations.

You must have proper shipping papers for any hazardous shipment (except for ORM-D Consumer Commodity, or a Limited Quantity, or Materials of Trade). The papers must be properly stored and be available for immediate reference in case of an incident, accident, or inspection.

You should be able to recognize improper shipping papers, and take appropriate action to get the situation corrected.

You should be able to match the freight being hauled with the correct documents, and be able to question the shipment if it does not appear to comply with the rules for hazardous shipments.

You must understand and comply with the attendance requirements for vehicles hauling hazardous materials.

You must report leaking containers, defective valves, etc. or any incident that occurs during a trip. If you receive written instructions from the carrier on emergency procedures, etc., you are required to follow them carefully.

Pick-Up and Delivery Drivers

If you fall into this category, you also need to be acquainted with the regulations concerning transportation of hazardous materials. Knowing the basics will help you identify any discrepancies you might find in shipments.

You should be advised in advance that you will be picking up hazardous materials.

Before the vehicle is loaded, you must inspect the hazardous materials to be hauled. If you suspect that the shipment may not be in compliance with regulations, you should contact the terminal for instructions before proceeding.

You must comply with any special blocking and securing requirements for the type of cargo you will be hauling.

You should also know the procedures to follow for incidents, accidents or emergencies during transit. Finally, you must comply with attendance requirements for vehicles hauling hazardous materials.

HOW TO COMPLY

Passenger-Carrying Vehicles

In general, no hazardous materials at all should be hauled on any for-hire passenger-carrying vehicle, if any other practicable means of transportation is available. Extremely dangerous Division 6.1 (poison) or Division 2.3 (poison gas), or any paranitroaniline (poison) must not be hauled in passenger-carrying vehicles.

However, in instances where there is no other means of transportation available, certain quantities of some types of hazardous materials may be hauled in passenger-carrying vehicles. In general, any hazardous material (with the exception of small arms ammunition) hauled on a passenger-carrying vehicle must be hauled outside the passenger compartment. The following may be hauled:

- **Up to 99 lb (45 kg) gross weight of Class 1 (explosive) materials that are permitted to be transported by passenger-carrying aircraft or rail car.**

- **Not more than 100 detonators, of Division 1.4 (explosive) materials per vehicle.**

- **Not more than 2 lab samples of Class 1 (explosive) materials per vehicle.**

- **Not more than 496 lb (225 kg) of other types of hazardous materials, with no more than 99 lb (45 kg) of any class.**

- **A cylinder not exceeding 250 lb (113 kg) that is secured against movement.**

- **Not more than 99 lb (45 kg) of non-liquid, less dangerous, Division 6.1 (poison) materials.**

- **Class 7 (radioactive) materials requiring labels, when no other practicable means of transportation is available, and then only in full compliance with specific loading requirements.**

- **Emergency shipments of drugs, chemicals, and hospital supplies.**

- **Department of Defense materials under special circumstances.**

Definitions

Having a broad knowledge of the Hazardous Materials Regulations includes understanding hazmat definitions. The following definitions are some that you should be familiar with.

Bulk Packaging

A bulk packaging has no intermediate form of containment and has:

1. A maximum capacity greater than 119 gal (450 L) as a receptacle for a liquid;

2. A maximum net mass greater than 882 lb (400 kg) and a maximum capacity greater than 119 gal (450 L) as a receptacle for a solid; or

3. A water capacity greater than 1,000 lb (454 kg) as a receptacle for a gas.

Combustible Liquid

See Combustible Liquids in the next section of this pocketbook "Exceptions."

Consumer Commodity

See Consumer Commodities in the next section of this pocketbook "Exceptions."

Elevated Temperature Material

An elevated temperature material is a material offered for transportation in a BULK packaging and meets one of the following criteria:

1. Is a liquid at a temperature at or above 212°F (100°C);

2. Is a liquid with a flash point at or above 100°F (37.8°C) that is intentionally heated and transported at or above its flash point; or

3. Is in a solid phase and at a temperature at or above 464°F (240°C).

Gross Weight

Gross weight or gross mass means the weight of a packaging plus the weight of its contents.

Hazardous Material

A hazardous material is a substance or material which has been determined by the Secretary of Transportation to be capable of posing an unreasonable risk to health, safety, and property when transported in commerce, and which has been so designated. This includes hazardous substances, hazardous wastes, marine pollutants, and elevated temperature materials.

DEFINITIONS

Hazardous materials fall into the following categories:

<u>**Class 1 (explosives)**</u> — is divided into six divisions as follows:

Division 1.1 — explosives that have a mass explosion hazard.

Division 1.2 — explosives that have a projection hazard.

Division 1.3 — explosives that have a fire hazard and either a minor blast hazard or a minor projection hazard or both.

Division 1.4 — explosive devices that present a minor blast hazard.

Division 1.5 — very insensitive explosives.

Division 1.6 — extremely insensitive detonating substances.

<u>**Class 2 (gases)**</u> — is divided into three divisions as follows:

Division 2.1 — gases that are flammable.

Division 2.2 — gases that are non-flammable and non-poisonous.

Division 2.3 — gases that are poisonous by inhalation.

<u>**Class 3 (flammable and combustible liquids)**</u> — A flammable liquid has a flash point of not more than 140°F (60°C). A combustible liquid has a flash point above 140°F (60°C) and below 200°F (93°C).

<u>**Class 4 (flammable solids)**</u> — is divided into three divisions as follows:

Division 4.1 — solids that are flammable.

Division 4.2 — material that is spontaneously combustible.

Division 4.3 — material that is dangerous when wet.

<u>**Class 5 (oxidizers and organic peroxides)**</u> — is divided into two divisions as follows:

Division 5.1 — oxidizer.

Division 5.2 — organic peroxide.

<u>**Class 6 (poisons)**</u> — is divided into two divisions as follows:

Division 6.1 — material that is poisonous.

Division 6.2 — material that is an infectious substance (etiologic agent).

<u>**Class 7 (radioactives)**</u> — material having a specific radioactive activity greater than 0.002 microcuries per gram.

<u>**Class 8 (corrosives)**</u> — material that causes visible destruction or irreversible alteration to human skin or a liquid that has a severe corrosion rate on steel or aluminum.

<u>**Class 9 (miscellaneous)**</u> — material which presents a hazard during transport, but which is not included in any other hazard class (such as a hazardous substance or a hazardous waste).

ORM-D (other regulated material) — material which although otherwise subject to the regulations, presents a limited hazard during transportation due to its form, quantity and packaging (Consumer Commodities. See the next section of this pocketbook "Exceptions.").

Hazardous Substance

A hazardous substance is a material, including its mixtures or solutions, that is listed in Appendix A to §172.101 and is in a quantity, in one package, that equals or exceeds the reportable quantity (RQ) listed in Appendix A.

Hazardous Waste

A hazardous waste is any material that is subject to the hazardous waste manifest requirements of the U.S. Environmental Protection Agency specified in 40 CFR 262.

Limited Quantity

See Limited Quantities in the next section of this pocketbook "Exceptions."

Marine Pollutant

A marine pollutant is a material that is listed in Appendix B to §172.101 and when in a solution or mixture of one or more marine pollutants, is packaged in a concentration which equals or exceeds:

1.   Ten percent by weight of the solution or mixture; or

2.   One percent by weight of the solution or mixture for materials that are identified as severe marine pollutants (PP) in Appendix B.

Marine pollutants transported by water, in any size packaging, are subject to all the applicable requirements. Marine pollutants transported by highway, rail or air are subject to the requirements when transported in **BULK** packaging.

Materials of Trade

See Materials of Trade in the next section of this pocketbook "Exceptions."

Non-Bulk Packaging

A non-bulk packaging has:

1.   A maximum capacity of 119 gal (450 L) or less as a receptacle for a liquid;

2.   A maximum net mass of 882 lb (400 kg) or less and a maximum capacity of 119 gal (450 L) or less as a receptacle for a solid;

3.   A water capacity of 1,000 lb (454 kg) or less as a receptacle for a gas; or

4.   A maximum net mass of 882 lb (400 kg) or less for a bag or box conforming to the specification packaging requirements in subpart L of part 178.

Overpack

An overpack is an enclosure used by a single shipper to provide protection or convenience in handling a package or to consolidate two or more packages. This does not include a transport vehicle, freight container, or aircraft unit load device. Overpacks are one or more packages:

1.   Placed or stacked onto a load board or pallet and secured by strapping, shrink wrapping, stretch wrapping, or other suitable means; or

2.   Placed in a protective outer packaging such as a box or crate.

Packing Group

A packing group indicates the degree of danger presented by a hazardous material. Packing Group I indicates great danger, Packing Group II indicates medium danger, and Packing Group III indicates minor danger. No packing groups are assigned to Class 1, Class 2, Class 7, and ORM-D materials. Also, some Division 4.1, 5.1, 5.2, 6.2, Class 8, and most Class 9 materials do not have packing groups.

Proper Shipping Name

The description/proper shipping name shown in Roman type (not italics) in Column 2 of the §172.101 Hazmat Table.

Reportable Quantity (RQ)

Reportable quantity is the quantity of a hazardous substance specified in Column 2 of Table 1 or Column 3 of Table 2 in Appendix A to §172.101, for the substance identified in Column 1.

Residue

Residue is the hazardous material remaining in a packaging after its contents have been removed to the maximum extent practicable and before the packaging is either refilled or cleaned and purged of hazardous material.

Reverse Logistics

See Reverse Logistics in the next section of this pocketbook "Exceptions."

Shipping Paper

A shipping paper is a shipping document, such as a shipping order, bill of lading, or manifest that is prepared in compliance with the hazardous materials regulations.

Technical Name

A recognized chemical name or microbiological name currently used in scientific and technical handbooks, journals, and texts. Except for names that appear in the Hazmat Table or Special Provisions, trade names may not be used.

Exceptions

Exceptions to the Hazardous Materials Regulations are found throughout the regulations. Exceptions provide relief from the regulations if certain requirements for the exception are met. You do not have to receive special permission to use an exception; you only have to meet the requirements specified in the regulations for the exception.

A few of the most common exceptions that you may encounter are covered here, including **Materials of Trade, Limited Quantities, Consumer Commodities, Combustible Liquids, Batteries, and Reverse Logistics.**

Materials of Trade

Materials of Trade (MOTs) are hazardous materials that are carried on a motor vehicle:

- For the purpose of protecting the health and safety of the motor vehicle operator or passengers (such as insect repellant or self-contained breathing apparatus);

- For the purpose of supporting the operation or maintenance of a motor vehicle, including its auxiliary equipment (such as a spare battery, gasoline, or engine starting fluid); or

- By a private motor carrier (including vehicles operated by a rail carrier) in direct support of a principal business that is other than transportation by motor vehicle (such as lawn care, plumbing, welding, or painting operations).

A material of trade (not including self-reactive material, poisonous by inhalation material, or hazardous waste) is limited to:

- A Class 3, 8, 9, Division 4.1, 5.1, 5.2, 6.1, or ORM–D material contained in a packaging having a gross mass or capacity not over—

  - 1 lb (0.5 kg) or 1 pt (0.5 L) for Packing Group I material,

  - 66 lb (30 kg) or 8 gal (30 L) for a Packing Group II, III, or ORM–D material,

  - 400 gal (1500 L) for a diluted mixture, not to exceed 2 percent concentration, of a Class 9 material;

- A Division 2.1 or 2.2 material in a cylinder with a gross weight not over 220 lb (100 kg);

- A Division 2.1 or 2.2 material in a Dewar flask meeting the requirements in section 173.320;

- A non-liquefied Division 2.2 material with no subsidiary hazard in a permanently mounted tank manufactured to the ASME Code at not more than 70 gallons water capacity; or

- A Division 4.3 material in Packing Group II or III contained in a packaging having a gross capacity not exceeding 1 oz (30 mL).

- A Division 6.2 material, other than a Category A infectious substance, contained in patient or animal samples, including but not limited to, secreta, excreta, blood and its components, tissue and tissue fluids, and body parts) being transported for research, diagnosis, investigational activities, or disease treatment or prevention, or is a biological product or regulated medical waste.

  The material must be contained in a combination packaging. For liquids, the inner packaging must be leakproof, and the outer packaging must contain sufficient absorbent material to absorb the entire contents of the inner packaging. For sharps, the inner packaging (sharps container) must be constructed of a rigid material resistant to punctures and securely closed to prevent leaks or punctures, and the outer packaging must be securely closed to prevent leaks or punctures.

  For solids, liquids, and sharps, the outer packaging must be a strong, tight packaging securely closed and secured against shifting, including relative motion between packages, within the vehicle on which it is being transported.

  For other than a regulated medical waste, the amount of Division 6.2 material in a combination packaging must conform to the following:

  - One or more inner packagings, each of which may not contain more than 1.1 lb (0.5 kg) or 17 oz (0.5 L), and an outer packaging containing not more than 8.8 lb (4 kg) or 1 gal (4 L); or

  - A single inner packaging containing not more than 35.2 lb (16 kg) or 4.2 gal (16 L) in a single outer packaging.

  For a regulated medical waste, a combination packaging must consist of one or more inner packagings, each of which may not contain more than 8.8 lb (4 kg) or 1 gal (4 L), and an outer packaging containing not more than 35.2 lb (16 kg) or 4.2 gal (16 L).

- A limited quantity package prepared in accordance with the regulations. Class 7 (radioactive) substances, instruments, and articles are not authorized.

- For a material or article that does not have a packing group in column 5 of the Hazardous Materials Table: for Classes 3, 8, 9, Division 4.1, 5.1, 5.2, 6.1, or ORM–D listed above, the amounts specified there; and for Division 4.3 materials, packaging having a gross capacity not exceeding 30 mL.

The **gross weight of all MOTs** on a motor vehicle **may not exceed 440 lb (200 kg)**, not including 400 gal (1,500 L) or less of a diluted mixture of Class 9 material, as mentioned above.

A non-bulk packaging, other than a cylinder, must be marked with a common name or proper shipping name to identify the material it contains (such as spray paint or Isopropyl Alcohol). The letters "RQ" must be included if the packaging contains a reportable quantity of a hazardous substance.

A bulk packaging containing a diluted mixture (≤ 2%) of a Class 9 material must be marked on two opposing sides with the identification number.

Packaging for MOTs must be leak tight for liquids and gases, sift proof for solids, and be securely closed, secured against shifting, and protected against damage. Each material must be packaged in the manufacturer's original packaging or a packaging of equal or greater strength and integrity. Packaging for gasoline must be made of metal or plastic and conform to the Hazardous Materials Regulations or OSHA regulations.

Outer packagings are not required for receptacles (e.g. cans and bottles) or articles that are secured against shifting in cages, carts, bins, boxes, or compartments, or by other means.

A cylinder or other pressure vessel containing a Division 2.1 or 2.2 material must conform to the marking, labeling, packaging, qualification, maintenance, and use requirements of the Hazardous Materials Regulations, except that outer packagings are not required. Manifolding of cylinders is authorized provided all valves are tightly closed.

The operator of a motor vehicle that contains MOTs must be informed of the presence of the material and must be informed of the MOTs regulations in §173.6 of the Hazardous Materials Regulations.

The MOTs regulations <u>require</u>:

- General knowledge of the MOTs regulations;
- Quantity limitations;
- Packaging requirements;
- Marking requirements;
- Labeling requirements;
- Closure requirements; and
- Securement requirements.

The MOTs regulations <u>do not require</u>:

- Shipping papers;
- Emergency response information;
- Placarding;
- Formal hazmat training; or
- Retention of hazmat training records.

EXAMPLES OF MATERIALS OF TRADE

CLASS OR DIVISION	EXAMPLES
Flammable Gases (Division 2.1)	acetylene, propane
Non-flammable Gases (Division 2.2)	oxygen, nitrogen
Flammable or Combustible Liquids (Class 3)	paint, PVC glue, gasoline
Flammable Solids (Division 4.1)	charcoal
Dangerous When Wet Materials (Division 4.3)	some fumigants
Oxidizers (Division 5.1)	bleaching compounds
Organic Peroxides (Division 5.2)	benzoyl peroxide
Poisons (Division 6.1)	pesticides
Some Infectious Substances (Division 6.2)	diagnostic specimens
Corrosive Materials (Class 8)	muriatic acid, drain cleaners, battery acid
Miscellaneous Hazardous Materials (Class 9)	asbestos, self-inflating lifeboats
Consumer Commodities (ORM-D)	hair spray, spray paints

Limited Quantities

Limited quantities are smaller amounts of hazmat in non-bulk combination packages. Limited quantities are generally excepted from specification packaging, shipping papers, labeling and placarding. However, labeling is required if the material is to be transported by air. Shipping papers are required if the material is a hazardous substance, hazardous waste, marine pollutant, or is to be transported by air or water.

A limited quantity exception can only be used for a material if Column 8A of the Hazardous Materials Table references the specific section in Part 173 that contains the exception. In each instance, the combination packaging must conform to the specifications, quantity and weight limits specified for limited quantities for each hazard class/division and packing group.

When shipping papers are required, the words "Limited Quantity" or "Ltd Qty" must follow the basic description for the material.

Non-air packages containing a limited quantity must display the square-on-point limited quantity marking. A package displaying the limited quantity marking is not required to be marked with the proper shipping name or identification number, unless the material is a hazardous substance or hazardous waste.

Packages meeting the requirements for air transport must display the square-on-point "Y" limited quantity marking. A package displaying the "Y" limited quantity marking is required to be marked with the proper shipping name and identification number when transported by air.

Packages displaying the square-on-point "Y" limited quantity marking (for air transport) are also authorized for transportation by the other modes (highway, rail, and water).

See Marking Illustrations at the back of this pocketbook.

Consumer Commodities

A consumer commodity is a limited quantity of a hazardous material that is packaged and distributed In a form intended or suitable for sale through retail sales agencies or instrumentalities for consumption by individuals for purposes of personal care or household use. Consumer commodities are products you can purchase at grocery, hardware, and discount stores. This includes products such as bleach, aerosols, drain cleaners, lighter fluid, cosmetics, etc.

Materials meeting the consumer commodity definition as well as the limited quantity provisions, may be renamed a consumer commodity and reclassified as an ORM–D. In each instance, the combination packaging must conform to the specifications, quantity and weight limits specified for limited quantities for each hazard class/division and packing group.

Consumer commodities are generally excepted from specification packaging, labeling, placarding and shipping papers. Some of these exceptions are not allowed if transport is by air or the material is a hazardous substance, hazardous waste, or marine pollutant.

The ORM–D classification and markings are being phased out of the Hazardous Materials Regulations. They are being replaced with the limited quantity requirements and markings.

Before January 1, 2021, packages of ORM–D material may be marked with the ORM–D marking. Starting on January 1, 2021, only the square-on-point limited quantity marking may be used.

See Marking Illustrations at the back of this pocketbook.

Combustible Liquids

The classification of a material as a combustible liquid is strictly for transportation within the United States. Combustible liquids do not meet the definition of any other hazard class and have a flashpoint above 140°F (60°C) and below 200°F (93°C).

Class 3 materials with flashpoints at or above 100°F (38°C) that do not meet the definition of any other hazard class, may be reclassified as a "combustible liquid" for transportation by highway and rail. For shipments involving air, water, or international movement, these materials are Class 3 materials.

Combustible liquids in non-bulk packaging which are not a hazardous substance, hazardous waste, or marine pollutant are not subject to the hazardous materials regulations. Combustible liquids in bulk packaging or non-bulk combustible liquids that are a hazardous substance, hazardous waste, or marine pollutant are subject to most of the hazardous materials regulations. This does not include labeling or security plans.

Batteries

Non-spillable batteries are excepted from all other requirements in the hazardous materials regulations if in compliance with section 173.159a. Non-spillable batteries must be securely packed in strong outer packaging and the battery and outer packaging must be marked with "NON-SPILLABLE" or "NON-SPILLABLE BATTERY." Non-spillable batteries must be securely fastened in a battery holder when on equipment. Non-spillable batteries are subject to the incident reporting requirements.

When transported by highway or rail, storage batteries containing electrolyte or corrosive battery fluid are not subject to the hazardous materials regulations if all of the following are met:

• No other hazardous materials are transported in the vehicle.

• Batteries must be loaded or braced to prevent damage and short circuits in transit.

• Other material loaded in the vehicle must be blocked, braced, or otherwise secured to prevent contact with or damage to the batteries.

• The vehicle may not carry material shipped by any person other than the shipper of the batteries.

Reverse Logistics

Reverse logistics is the offering or transporting of goods by motor vehicle from a retail store for return to the manufacturer, supplier, or distribution facility for the purpose of capturing value (credit), recall, replacement, recycling, or similar reason. This does not include hazardous waste.

Reverse logistics materials are excepted from many of the Hazmat Regulations. However, shipments of reverse logistics materials must:

• Meet the definition for reverse logistics;

• Meet the materials specific packaging requirements;

• Comply with the segregation requirements;

• Comply with the incident reporting requirements; and

• Be marked with the limited quantity marking or the words "REVERSE LOGISTICS – HIGHWAY TRANSPORT ONLY – UNDER 49 CFR 173.157."

Employees who prepare reverse logistics material must have training that includes clear instructions from the supplier, manufacturer, or distributor on preparing the shipment. This includes information to properly classify, package, mark, offer, and transport.

Employers must:

- Identify the reverse logistics materials;

- Verify compliance with the appropriate conditions and limitations;

- Ensure they have clear instructions from the supplier, manufacturer, or distributor;

- Ensure the clear instructions are known and accessible to the employees preparing the shipment; and

- Document that employees are familiar with the reverse logistics regulations and the specific return instructions for the materials. Documentation must be retained while the employee is employed and for 60-days thereafter.

Reserved

General Requirements When Hauling Hazardous Materials

This chapter briefly details the requirements for vehicles transporting hazardous materials. Areas covered include **hazmat endorsement, shipping papers, emergency response information, markings, labels, placards, cargo heaters, and special documents.**

Hazardous Materials Endorsement

The driver of a commercial motor vehicle that is required to be placarded for hazardous materials or that transports any quantity of a material listed as a select agent or toxin in 42 CFR part 73, must have a hazardous materials endorsement on their Commercial Driver's License.

Shipping Papers

Most hazardous materials shipments must be accompanied by proper shipping papers, such as bills of lading, hazardous waste manifests, etc. During the course of the trip, the driver is responsible for maintaining the shipping papers according to requirements, so that they are easily accessible to authorities in case of accidents or inspection.

Shipping papers are not required for a material (unless it is a hazardous substance, hazardous waste, or marine pollutant) that:

- Has "A" in Col. (1) of the hazmat table, except by air;
- Has "W" in Col. (1) of the hazmat table, except by water;
- Is a limited quantity material, except by air or water;
- Is a ORM-D material by highway, rail, or water (Before January 1, 2021); or
- Is a Category B infectious substance (prepared per §173.199).

Also, shipping papers are not required for materials transported as Materials of Trade.

Hazardous materials shipping papers must be retained by the shipper for **two years** after the material is accepted by the initial carrier and by carriers for **one year** after the material is accepted. The date of acceptance must be included. This may be a paper copy or an electronic image of the shipping paper. Hazardous waste manifests must be retained for **three years**.

Hazardous materials are required to be indicated on shipping papers in one of three ways when non-hazardous materials are also listed.

1. Listed **first**, before any non-hazardous materials, or

Number and Type of Packages	Description of Articles	Total Quantity
10 drums	UN1203, Gasoline, 3, II	3,400 lb
3 skids	100# Sorex paper 36" x 40"	3,000 lb

2. Listed in a **color** that clearly contrasts with entries for materials that are not subject to the hazardous materials regulations (hazardous material entries may be highlighted only on reproductions of the shipping paper), or

Number and Type of Packages	Description of Articles	Total Quantity
3 skids	100# Sorex paper 36" x 40"	3,000 lb
10 drums	UN1203, Gasoline, 3, II	3,400 lb
100 skids	36" x 40" wooden skids	3,000 lb

3. Listed with an "**X**" in a column captioned "HM."

Number and Type of Packages	HM	I.D. Number	Description of Articles	Hazard Class	PG	Total Quantity
10 drums	X	UN1203	Gasoline	3	II	3,400 lb
3 skids			100# Sorex paper 36" x 40"			3,000 lb

Each hazardous material that is offered for transport must be clearly described on the shipping paper using the applicable information from the Hazardous Materials Table. This shipping description must include the material's:

- Identification number;
- Proper shipping name;
- Hazard class or division number;
- Subsidiary Hazard Class(es) or Division number(s) entered in parentheses, if required;
- Packing group, if any;
- Total quantity (mass or volume or activity for Class 7 or net explosive mass for Class 1) and unit of measurement; and
- Number and type of packages.

Example:
2 drums, UN1717, Acetyl chloride, 3, (8), II, 180 lb

The identification number for each proper shipping name is listed in Column 4 of the Hazardous Materials Table. The identification number must include the letters "UN," or "ID," or "NA," as appropriate.

Proper shipping names are limited to those shown in Roman type (*not italics*) in Column 2 of the Hazardous Materials Table. Punctuation and words in italics may be used. Proper shipping names may be singular or plural and in either capital or lower case letters.

Column 3 of the Hazardous Materials Table lists the hazard class or division number that corresponds to a proper shipping name. The word "Forbidden" is listed when the material is too hazardous to transport.

A subsidiary hazard Class or Division must be included, in parenthesis, when a subsidiary label is required. Unless excepted, a subsidiary label is required when indicated in Column 6 of the Hazardous Materials Table or by §172.402.

Column 5 of the Hazardous Materials Table lists the packing groups which correspond to the proper shipping name and hazard class of the material. The packing group must be shown in Roman numerals and may be preceded by the letters "PG."

There are no packing groups for Class 1, Class 2, Class 7, and ORM-D materials. Also, some Division 4.1, 5.1, 5.2, 6.2, Class 8, and most Class 9 materials do not have packing groups.

The first five (5) items — often referred to as the material's basic description — must be shown in sequence, with no additional information interspersed unless authorized by the regulations.

Examples: UN1203, Gasoline, 3, PG II
                  UN2359, Diallylamine, 3, (6.1, 8), II
                  NA1911, Diborane mixtures, 2.1

The total quantity for each hazardous material must be included along with a unit of measurement (pounds, kilograms, liters, gallons, etc.). The unit of measurement may be abbreviated.

The total quantity is **not** required for hazardous material packaging containing only **residue** (i.e., one that has not been cleaned/purged or refilled with a non-hazardous material), **cylinders**, and **bulk packagings**. However, some indication of total quantity must be shown for cylinders and bulk packagings (10 cylinders or 1 cargo tank). Total quantity is also not required for hazardous materials that are household wastes (40 CFR 261.4) and not subject to the EPA's hazardous waste regulations in 40 CFR 262 and 263.

The number and type of packages must be indicated. This may be entered before or after the basic description. Placing this information before the basic description is recommended. Abbreviations may be used for the types of packages provided they are commonly accepted and recognizable.

Most proper shipping names with a "G" in Column 1 of the Hazardous Materials Table must have the technical name of the hazardous material entered in parentheses in association with the basic description. If a hazardous material is a mixture or solution the technical names of at least two components most predominately contributing to the hazards of the mixture or solution must be entered.

Examples: UN1760, Corrosive liquids, n.o.s. (Caprylyl chloride), 8, II
                  UN2924, Flammable liquid, corrosive, n.o.s., 3, (8), II
                  (methanol, potassium hydroxide)

Except for some Class 7 descriptions, if the name of a hazardous substance is not identified in the proper shipping name for a material, the name of the hazardous substance must be entered in parentheses in association with the basic description. If a material contains two or more hazardous substances only the names of the two substances with the lowest RQ's must be entered. For hazardous waste, the waste code (such as D001) if appropriate, may be used to identify the hazardous substance.

Examples: RQ, UN1760, Corrosive Liquids, n.o.s. (Hydrofluoric acid,
Phosphoric acid), 8, II

NA3082, Hazardous waste, liquid, n.o.s. (D001), 9, III, RQ

Although there are a number of additional descriptions which may be required
on shipping papers, there are several of special significance.

1.   If the material is a hazardous substance, the letters "**RQ**" must appear
either before or after the basic description. The letters "RQ" may be
entered in the HM Column in place of the "X."

Number and Type of Packages	HM	I.D. Number	Description of Articles	Hazard Class	PG	Total Quantity
10 drums	RQ	UN1114	Benzene	3	II	2,000 lb

2.   When shipping papers are required for materials being shipped under a
limited quantity exception, the words "Limited Quantity" or the abbreviation "Ltd Qty" must be entered following the basic description.

3.   For all materials meeting the poisonous by inhalation criteria, the words
"Poison-Inhalation Hazard" or "Toxic-Inhalation Hazard" and the words
"Zone A", "Zone B", "Zone C", or "Zone D", for gases or "Zone A" or "Zone
B" for liquids, as appropriate, must be added on the shipping paper immediately following the shipping description. For anhydrous ammonia
transported within the U.S., only the words "Inhalation Hazard" must be
added in association with the shipping description.

4.   The fact that a material is an elevated temperature material must be indicated in the shipping name or the word "HOT" must immediately precede
the proper shipping name.

5.   If a material is a marine pollutant the words "Marine Pollutant" must be
entered in association with the basic shipping description, unless the
proper shipping name indicates that it is a marine pollutant.

6.   Materials shipped under a special permit must have on the shipping
papers the notation DOT-SP followed by the number issued for the special permit. The notation must be clearly associated with the description
to which the special permit applies.

Each shipping paper should include the date of acceptance by the carrier.
Although the date is not required to be on the shipping paper for transport, the
date is a required part of the shipping paper retention requirements.

Finally, check for the **Shipper's Certification** which states the shipment has
been properly classified, described, packaged, marked and labeled/placarded.

The following Shipper's Certifications are authorized by the regulations.

"This is to certify that the above-named materials are properly classified,
described, packaged, marked and labeled, and are in proper condition for
transportation according to the applicable regulations of the Department of
Transportation."

"I hereby declare that the contents of this consignment are fully and accurately
described above by the proper shipping name, and are classified, packaged,

marked and labelled/placarded, and are in all respects in proper condition for transport according to applicable international and national governmental regulations."

The certification must be legibly signed by an authorized representative of the shipper. The signature may be applied manually, by typewriter, or other mechanical means. On hazardous waste manifests the signature must be handwritten.

Emergency Response Information

Most hazardous material shipments (except those that do not require shipping papers or ORM-D materials) must have **emergency response information on or in association with the shipping paper**. If the information is in association with the shipping paper it may be in the form of the Emergency Response Guidebook, a Safety Data Sheet (SDS), or any other form that provides all the information required in §172.602.

In most cases, a numeric **emergency response telephone number** must be entered on the shipping paper. It can be immediately following the description of each hazardous material or if the number applies to every hazardous material entered on the shipping paper, entered once on the shipping paper in a clearly visible location and identified as an emergency response information number.

Near the emergency response telephone number, the **name** of the offeror providing emergency response information or who is registered with an emergency response information (ERI) provider or their ERI service provider contract number or other **unique identifier** must be entered. This is not required if the name or identifier is entered elsewhere on the shipping paper in a prominent, readily identifiable, and clearly visible manner to be easily and quickly found.

Markings

Markings provide important information about the hazardous contents of a packaging, freight container, or transport vehicle. The type of marking(s) displayed is often different for non-bulk and bulk packagings.

Non-Bulk Packagings

Almost all non-bulk packagings (119 gallons or less for liquids) **must be marked with the proper shipping name and** the four digit **identification number** (preceded by "UN," "NA," or "ID" as appropriate) as shown in the Hazardous Materials Table. The identification numbers must be at least 0.47 inches (12 mm) high. On smaller packages, 8 gallons (30 L) or less, 66 pounds (30 kg) maximum, or cylinders with a water capacity of 16 gallons (60 L) or less, the numbers must be at least 0.24 inches (6 mm) high. For even smaller packages, capacity of 1.32 gallons (5 L) or 11 pounds (5 kg) or less, the size of the numbers must be a size appropriate for the size of the package.

Non-bulk packagings manufactured and permanently marked before January 1, 2017, with ID numbers not meeting the above size requirements, may continue to be used until the end of their useful life.

Limited quantity materials do not require the shipping name or identification number if marked with a square-on-point limited quantity marking. Identification numbers are not required on packages marked as ORM-D materials. Most n.o.s. and other generic proper shipping names must also have the technical name(s) entered in parentheses in association with the proper shipping name.

Several other important markings may also be required, such as package orientation arrows. Each non-bulk combination package having inner packagings containing liquid hazmat, or single packaging fitted with vents, or open cryogenic receptacles must be marked with orientation arrows.

If the non-bulk package contains a hazardous substance (meets or exceeds the reportable quantity) the letters "RQ" must be marked in association with the proper shipping name or the identification number, as applicable.

A package containing a limited quantity of hazardous materials is required to be marked with one of the following:

1. Non-air packages containing a limited quantity must display the square-on-point limited quantity marking. A package displaying the limited quantity marking is not required to be marked with the proper shipping name or identification number, unless the material is a hazardous substance or hazardous waste.

2. Packages meeting the requirements for air transport must display the square-on-point "Y" limited quantity marking. A package displaying the "Y" limited quantity marking is required to be marked with the proper shipping name and identification number when transported by air. Packages displaying the square-on-point "Y" limited quantity marking are authorized for transport by all modes of transportation.

3. Except for air transport, before January 1, 2021, packagings that contain a material classed as "ORM-D" may be marked with the ORM-D marking. Starting on January 1, 2021, only the appropriate square-on-point limited quantity marking may be used.

A package containing a limited quantity (except for Class 1 and 7, and Division 6.1 and 6.2) that is transported by a private motor carrier is not required to have the limited quantity marking if:

*   The materials are in packing group II or III;

*   The materials meet the limited quantity packaging requirements;

- Inner packagings for liquids do not exceed 0.3 gallons (1 L) net capacity each;

- Inner packagings for solids do not exceed 2.2 pounds (1.0 kg) net capacity each;

- No more than 0.6 gallons (2 L) or 4.4 pounds (2 kg) aggregate net quantity of any one material per vehicle;

- The total gross weight of all limited quantity packages on a vehicle does not exceed 132 pounds (60 kg);

- Each package is marked with the name and address of the offeror;

- Each package is marked with a 24-hour emergency response telephone number; and

- Each package is marked "Contains Chemicals" with letters at least one inch (25 mm) high on a contrasting background.

For those materials meeting the poisonous by inhalation criteria, the words "Inhalation Hazard" must appear in association with the hazard warning labels or shipping name, when required. The INHALATION HAZARD marking is not required on packages that display a label with the words "INHALATION HAZARD" on the label.

Non-bulk packagings of marine pollutants transported by motor vehicle, rail car, or aircraft are not subject to the marine pollutant requirements.

Non-spillable batteries and outer packagings must be plainly and durably marked "NONSPILLABLE" or "NONSPILLABLE BATTERY."

keep away from heat

For transportation by aircraft, packages containing self-reactive substances of Division 4.1 or organic peroxides of Division 5.2 must be marked with the KEEP AWAY FROM HEAT handling mark.

For transportation by aircraft, excepted quantities of hazardous materials must be marked with the excepted quantities marking. This marking indicates that the shipper is certifying compliance with the requirements in section 173.4a.

A package marked with "THIS PACKAGE CONFORMS TO 49 CFR 173.4 FOR DOMESTIC HIGHWAY OR RAIL TRANSPORT ONLY" indicates that the shipper is certifying conformance with the requirements in section 173.4 for small quantity exceptions.

Proper shipping names marked on non-bulk packages of hazardous waste are not required to include the word "waste" if the package displays the EPA marking prescribed by 40 CFR 262.32.

Finally, packagings (except for cylinders, Class 7 packagings and bulk packagings) for most hazardous materials must meet the United Nations Performance-Oriented Packaging Standards and be marked by the manufacturer in a manner such as illustrated below for a fiberboard box with an inner packaging.

4G/Y145/S/99
USA/RA

Large Quantities of Non-Bulk Packagings

A transport vehicle or freight container containing only a single hazardous material in non-bulk packages must be marked, on each side and each end with the material's identification number, subject to the following:

- Each package must be marked with the same proper shipping name and identification number;

- The aggregate gross weight of the hazardous material is 8,820 lb (4,000 kg) or more;

- All of the hazardous material is loaded at one loading facility; and

- The transport vehicle or freight container contains no other material, hazardous or non-hazardous.

This does not apply to Class 1 materials, Class 7 materials, or non-bulk packagings for which identification numbers are not required (such as limited quantities or ORM-D).

A transport vehicle or freight container loaded at one loading facility with 2,205 lb (1,000 kg) or more of non-bulk packages containing material that is poisonous by inhalation (in Hazard Zone A or B), having the same proper shipping name and identification number, must be marked on each side and each end with the identification number for the material. If the transport vehicle or freight container contains more than one inhalation hazard material that meets this requirement, it must be marked with the identification number for only one material. That one identification number is determined by the following:

- For different materials in the same hazard zone, the identification number of the material having the greatest aggregate gross weight.

- For different materials in both Hazard Zone A or B, the identification number for the Hazard Zone A material.

Bulk Packagings

Unless excepted, all bulk packagings (capacity more than 119 gallons for liquids) of hazardous materials must be marked with the UN or NA identification number(s) of the contents. The identification number marking may be displayed on an orange panel, primary hazard placard, or a white square-on-point configuration.

When the four digit identification number is required to be displayed on vehicles, containers, or bulk packagings it may be displayed on an "Orange Panel" [6.3 inches (160 mm) by 15.7 inches (400 mm)], or on a white square-on-point display configuration having the same outside dimensions as a placard, or across the center of the proper placard in place of the hazard wording. Identification numbers must not be displayed on DANGEROUS, subsidiary, RADIOACTIVE, EXPLOSIVES 1.1, 1.2, 1.3, 1.4, 1.5, or 1.6 placards.

Identification numbers must be displayed on bulk packagings such as portable tanks, cargo tanks, and tank cars. Identification numbers are required to be displayed on each side and each end of a bulk packaging which has a capacity of 1,000 gal (3,785 L) or more. Bulk packagings that have a capacity of less than 1,000 gal (3,785 L) need the identification numbers displayed on two opposing sides.

If the identification number markings on a portable tank or cargo tank are not visible, the transport vehicle or freight container used to transport the tank must also be marked with the numbers, on each side and each end. When a tank is permanently installed within an enclosed cargo body of a transport vehicle or freight container, the identification number marking need only be displayed on the sides and ends of the tank that are visible when the enclosed cargo body is opened or entered.

Identification numbers are not required on the ends of portable tanks or cargo tanks having more than one compartment, if hazardous materials having different identification numbers are transported in the compartments. The identification numbers on the sides of the tank must be displayed in the same sequence as the compartments containing the materials they identify.

When a bulk packaging is labeled instead of placarded, the identification number markings may be displayed on the bulk packaging in the same manner as would be required for a non-bulk packaging. These smaller markings may be used in place of the identification number on an orange panel, placard, or white square-on-point configuration.

In addition to displaying the identification number, portable tanks must be marked with the material's proper shipping name on two sides and the owner or lessee's name.

In addition to the identification number, cargo tanks (except for certain nurse tanks) which are used to transport gases (Class 2 material) must be marked on each side and each end with the proper shipping name or appropriate common name of the gas.

Examples: CARBON DIOXIDE, REFRIGERATED LIQUID or
REFRIGERANT GAS

Each specification cargo tank that successfully completes a test/inspection must be marked with the date (month and year) and the type of test/inspection completed. This marking must be displayed near the specification plate or anywhere on the front head.

A bulk package containing Poison Inhalation Hazard material must be marked "Inhalation Hazard" in association with any required labels, placards, or shipping name, when required. The INHALATION HAZARD marking is not required on packages that display a label or placard with the words "INHALATION HAZARD" on the label or placard.

This marking must be at least 1.0 inch (25 mm) in height for portable tanks with capacities of less than 1,000 gal (3,785 L) and at least 2.0 inches (50 mm) in height for cargo tanks and other bulk packages. Bulk packaging must be marked on two opposing sides with this marking.

Bulk packagings of anhydrous ammonia transported in the U.S. must be marked with "INHALATION HAZARD" on two opposing sides.

Most bulk packages containing elevated temperature materials must be marked on two opposing sides with the word "HOT." However, if the package contains molten aluminum or molten sulfur the package must be marked "MOLTEN ALUMINUM" or "MOLTEN SULFUR" instead of the word "HOT."

The "HOT" marking must be on the package itself or in black lettering on a white square-on-point configuration that is the same size as a placard. The lettering must be at least 2.0 inches (50 mm) high.

The word "HOT" may be displayed in the upper corner of a white-square-on-point configuration that also displays the required identification number.

A package containing **solid** elevated temperature material **is not subject** to any of the Hazardous Materials Regulations, **except** that the word "HOT" must be on the package.

Bulk packages containing marine pollutants must be marked, on all four sides, with the MARINE POLLUTANT marking, unless they are labeled or placarded.

A bulk packaging containing a regulated medical waste must be marked with the BIOHAZARD marking, visible from the direction it faces:

- on two opposing sides or ends if the packaging has a capacity of less than 1,000 gal (3,785 L), or

- on each end and each side if the packaging has a capacity of 1,000 gal (3,785 L) or more.

If the BIOHAZARD markings on a bulk packaging are not visible, the vehicle or freight container containing the bulk packaging must be marked on each side and each end with the BIOHAZARD marking. The BIOHAZARD marking may be displayed on a white square-on-point configuration.

IBCs and Large Packagings must be marked with the appropriate stacking marking. If stacking is allowed, the stacking marking will appear and it will include the maximum stacking load in kilograms. If stacking is not allowed, the no stacking marking will appear. The stacking markings must be at least 3.9 inches (100 mm) by 3.9 inches (100 mm).

Stacking Allowed

All IBCs manufactured, repaired or remanufactured after January 1, 2011, must have a stacking marking. All Large Packagings manufactured, repaired or remanufactured after January 1, 2015, must have a stacking marking.

No Stacking

Other Markings

Additional markings may be required depending on the hazardous material being transported or the type of package that is used.

A package authorized for use under a special permit must be marked with DOT-SP followed by the special permit number.

A package of Class 1 material must be marked with the EX number for each substance, article or device contained therein, unless excepted by the regulations. In some situations no marking is required, for others a national stock number or product code may be used. When more than five different Class 1 materials are packed in the same package, no more than five of the numbers, codes, or a combination thereof are required to be marked on the package.

Each overpack must be marked with the proper shipping names and identification numbers of the materials contained within, unless the markings on the inside packages are visible. Each overpack must be marked with the word "OVERPACK" indicating that the inner packages comply with prescribed specifications (when specification packagings are required), unless the specification markings on the inside packages are visible.

Each overpack that contains packages subject to the orientation marking requirements must be marked with orientation arrows on two opposite vertical sides, with the arrows pointing in the correct upward direction.

Each overpack containing packages of limited quantity materials or ORM-D materials must be marked "OVERPACK," unless all required markings are visible through the overpack. Each overpack containing excepted quantities must be marked with the required markings for the inside packages, unless all the required markings are visible through the overpack. Overpacks of excepted quantities are not required to be marked "OVERPACK."

No person may offer or transport certain specification cylinders, a portable tank, cargo tank, or tank car containing liquefied petroleum gas (LPG) that is unodorized unless the words "NON-ODORIZED" or "NOT ODORIZED" appear near the proper shipping name. This marking must appear on two opposing sides on portable tanks, cargo tanks, and tank cars.

Each truck body or trailer, rail car or freight container containing lading that has been fumigated or treated with any material must have a FUMIGANT marking displayed so that it can be seen by any person attempting to enter the vehicle or container.

DANGER

THIS UNIT IS UNDER FUMIGATION
WITH_____ APPLIED ON
Date _____
Time _____
Ventilated on ____

DO NOT ENTER

Marking illustrations can be found at the back of this pocketbook.

Labels

Labels are placed on packages containing hazardous materials. Labels are diamond-shaped and should measure at least 3.9 inches (100 mm) on each side.

When hazard warning labels are required on packages, the shipper is required to affix the labels before offering the shipment. The driver should not accept the shipment unless the required labels are properly affixed to the packages.

The Hazardous Materials Table in this book provides a ready reference to the labels required for each proper shipping name, see Column 6 of the Table.

If more than one label is indicated by the label codes listed in Column 6 of the Hazardous Materials Table, the first one listed is the primary label and any others are subsidiary labels. When primary and subsidiary labels are required to be displayed, they must be placed next to each other (within 6 inches).

Labels must be printed on or affixed to a surface (other than the bottom) of the package containing the hazardous material. If possible, the label should be located on the same surface and near the proper shipping name marking. Labels must be clearly visible and not obscured by markings or attachments. The package pictured, has labels properly affixed.

A label may be printed on or placed on a securely affixed tag, or may be affixed by other suitable means to:

- A package that contains no radioactive material and which has dimensions less than those of the required label; or

- A cylinder; or

- A package which has such an irregular surface that a label cannot be satisfactorily affixed.

Generally, only one of each different required label must be displayed on a package. However, duplicate labels must be displayed on at least two sides or two ends (other than the bottom) of the following:

- Each package or overpack having a volume of 64 ft^3 (1.8 m^3) or more;

- Each non-bulk package containing a radioactive material;

- Each DOT 106 or 110 multi-unit tank car tank. Labels must be displayed on each end;

- Each portable tank of less than 1,000 gal (3,785 L) capacity;

- Each freight container or aircraft unit load device having a volume of 64 ft³ (1.8 m³) or more, but less than 640 ft³ (18 m³). One of each required label must be displayed on or near the closure; and

- Each IBC having a volume of 64 ft³ (1.8 m³) or more.

When two or more packages containing compatible hazardous materials are placed within the same unit load device or overpack, the unit load device or overpack must be labeled for each class of material contained within, unless the labels on the inside packages are visible.

Text is not required on a label for Classes 1, 2, 3, 4, 5, 6, and 8. However, the label must meet the other specifications in the hazmat regulations.

For a package containing oxygen, the OXIDIZER label may be modified to display the word "OXYGEN" instead of "OXIDIZER" and the class number "2" instead of "5.1." This OXYGEN label may be used in place of the NON-FLAMMABLE and OXIDIZER labels specified in the Hazmat Table. The word "OXYGEN" must appear on the label.

The POISON label may be modified by displaying the text "TOXIC" instead of "POISON."

A package containing a Division 6.1, packing group III material may display a POISON label that has been modified to display the text "PG III" instead of "POISON" or "TOXIC" below the mid line of the label.

Label illustrations can be found at the back of this pocketbook.

Placards

The Hazardous Materials Regulations require most vehicles hauling hazardous materials to be placarded. In most situations **the shipper is responsible for providing the appropriate placards** to the carrier for a shipment. **The carrier is responsible for applying them correctly to the vehicle** and maintaining them during transport. In addition, carriers are responsible for any placarding necessitated by aggregate shipments. Large freight containers (640 cubic feet or more) must be placarded by the shipper.

Placards are diamond-shaped and should measure at least 9.84 inches (250 mm) on each side. Placards must be displayed on-point with the words or identification number displayed horizontally, reading from left to right.

In most situations placards must be affixed on all four sides of the vehicle, trailer or cargo carrier. The front placard may be on the front of the tractor or the cargo body. Placards must be removed when the hazardous materials are no longer present.

In general, some basic rules apply to placards:

- **Placards must be securely attached to the vehicle or placed in a proper placard holder.**

- **Placards must be located at least 3 inches (76.0 mm) from any other type of marking on the vehicle.**

- **Words and numbers on placards must read horizontally.**

- **Placards must be clearly visible and maintained in a legible condition throughout the trip.**

As a rule, a driver may not move a vehicle that is not properly placarded, if placards are required for the cargo carried in the vehicle. However, in certain emergency situations, a vehicle not properly placarded may be moved if at least one of these three conditions is met:

- **Vehicle is escorted by a state or local government representative.**

- **Carrier has received permission from the Department of Transportation.**

- **Movement is necessary to protect life and property.**

Placards are chosen according to tables found in §172.504. Table 1 lists categories of hazardous materials which require placarding no matter what amount of material is being hauled. **Any quantity of hazardous material covered by Table 1 must be placarded** as specified in Table 1.

Table 2 also lists categories of hazardous materials and the placards required, but, there are some exceptions.

When the gross weight of hazardous materials in non-bulk packages covered by Table 2 is **less than 1,001 lb (454 kg), no placard is required** on a transport vehicle or freight container. This does not apply to bulk packagings (such as portable tanks or cargo tanks) or hazardous materials subject to §172.505, placarding for subsidiary hazards.

Non-bulk packaging that contains only the residue of Table 2 materials does not have to be included in determining placarding, except for materials subject to §172.505, placarding for subsidiary hazards.

A transport vehicle or freight container which contains non-bulk packagings with two or more categories of materials, requiring different placards specified in Table 2, may be placarded DANGEROUS in place of the separate placarding specified for each of the categories in Table 2. However, when 2,205 lb (1,000 kg) or more of **one category** of materials is loaded at **one loading facility** on **one transport vehicle** or container, the placard specified for that category in Table 2 must be applied.

In the following tables the **bold face entry** describes the category of the hazardous material, the light face entry indicates the placard required for that type of shipment.

GENERAL REQUIREMENTS

TABLE 1

CATEGORY OF MATERIAL	PLACARD
1.1	EXPLOSIVES 1.1
1.2	EXPLOSIVES 1.2
1.3	EXPLOSIVES 1.3
2.3	POISON GAS
4.3	DANGEROUS WHEN WET
5.2 (Organic peroxide, Type B, liquid *or* solid, temperature controlled)	ORGANIC PEROXIDE
6.1 (material poisonous by inhalation (see §171.8 of this subchapter))	POISON INHALATION HAZARD
7 (Radioactive Yellow III label only)	RADIOACTIVE[1]

[1]RADIOACTIVE placards are also required for: All shipments of unpackaged LSA-I material or SCO-I; all shipments required by §§173.427, 173.441, and 173.457 of this subchapter to be operated under exclusive use; and all closed vehicles used in accordance with §173.443(d).

TABLE 2

CATEGORY OF MATERIAL	PLACARD
1.4	EXPLOSIVES 1.4
1.5	EXPLOSIVES 1.5
1.6	EXPLOSIVES 1.6
2.1	FLAMMABLE GAS
2.2	NON-FLAMMABLE GAS
3	FLAMMABLE
Combustible liquid	COMBUSTIBLE
4.1	FLAMMABLE SOLID
4.2	SPONTANEOUSLY COMBUSTIBLE
5.1	OXIDIZER
5.2 (Other than organic peroxide, Type B, liquid or solid, temperature controlled)	ORGANIC PEROXIDE
6.1 (other than material poisonous by inhalation)	POISON
6.2	(None)
8	CORROSIVE
9	CLASS 9
ORM-D	(None)

Placarding Exceptions

1. When more than one division placard is required for Class 1 materials on a transport vehicle, rail car, freight container or unit load device, only the placard representing the lowest division number must be displayed.

2. A FLAMMABLE placard may be used in place of a COMBUSTIBLE placard on—

   (i) A cargo tank or portable tank.

   (ii) A compartmented tank car which contains both flammable and combustible liquids.

3. A NON-FLAMMABLE GAS placard is not required on a transport vehicle which contains non-flammable gas if the transport vehicle also contains flammable gas or oxygen and it is placarded with FLAMMABLE GAS or OXYGEN placards, as required.

4. OXIDIZER placards are not required for Division 5.1 materials on freight containers, unit load devices, transport vehicles or rail cars which also contain Division 1.1 or 1.2 materials and which are placarded with EXPLOSIVES 1.1 or 1.2 placards, as required.

5. For transportation by transport vehicle or rail car only, an OXIDIZER placard is not required for Division 5.1 materials on a transport vehicle, rail car or freight container which also contains Division 1.5 explosives and is placarded with EXPLOSIVES 1.5 placards, as required.

6. The EXPLOSIVE 1.4 placard is not required for those Division 1.4 Compatibility Group S (1.4S) materials that are not required to be labeled 1.4S.

7. For domestic transportation of oxygen, compressed or oxygen, refrigerated liquid, the OXYGEN placard in §172.530 of this subpart may be used in place of a NON-FLAMMABLE GAS placard.

8. For domestic transportation, a POISON INHALATION HAZARD placard is not required on a transport vehicle or freight container that is already placarded with the POISON GAS placard.

9. For Class 9, a CLASS 9 placard is not required for domestic transportation, including that portion of international transportation, defined in §171.8 of this subchapter, which occurs within the United States. However, a bulk packaging must be marked with the appropriate identification number on a CLASS 9 placard, an orange panel, or a white square-on-point display configuration as required by subpart D of this part.

10. For Division 6.1, PG III materials, a POISON placard may be modified to display the text "PG III" below the mid line of the placard.

11. For domestic transportation, a POISON placard is not required on a transport vehicle or freight container required to display a POISON INHALATION HAZARD or POISON GAS placard.

The compatibility group letter must be displayed on placards for shipments of Class 1 materials when transported by aircraft or vessel. When more than one compatibility group placard is required for Class 1 materials, only one placard is required to be displayed as follows:

1. Explosive articles of compatibility groups C, D or E may be placarded displaying compatibility group E.

2. Explosive articles of compatibility groups C, D, or E, when transported with those in compatibility group N, may be placarded displaying compatibility group D.

3. Explosive substances of compatibility groups C and D may be placarded displaying compatibility group D.

4. Explosive articles of compatibility groups C, D, E or G, except for fireworks, may be placarded displaying compatibility group E.

Each transport vehicle, portable tank, freight container, or unit load device that contains a material subject to the Poison-Inhalation Hazard shipping paper description must be placarded POISON INHALATION HAZARD or POISON GAS, as appropriate, on each side and each end if not so placarded under §172.504.

Placards for subsidiary hazards are required when certain hazardous materials are transported. The subsidiary placards that you will most likely encounter are DANGEROUS WHEN WET, POISON INHALATION HAZARD, POISON GAS, POISON, and CORROSIVE.

Text indicating the hazard (such as CORROSIVE) is not required on most placards. Text is required on RADIOACTIVE and DANGEROUS placards. Text is also required on the OXYGEN placard, unless the text is replaced with an identification number.

A white square background must be displayed behind each placard when the transport vehicle transports a highway route-controlled quantity of Class 7 (radioactive) material.

Identification numbers may be displayed on most placards. However, identification numbers must not be displayed on DANGEROUS, subsidiary, RADIOACTIVE, EXPLOSIVES 1.1, 1.2, 1.3, 1.4, 1.5, or 1.6 placards.

A COMBUSTIBLE placard used to display an identification number is required to have a white bottom for rail transportation. A white-bottom COMBUSTIBLE placard displaying an identification number **may be used** for highway transportation.

Placard illustrations can be found at the back of this pocketbook.

Cargo Heaters

If a cargo heater is located in a vehicle that will be used to transport hazardous materials, various restrictions apply.

When transporting Class 1 (explosives), any cargo heater must be made inoperable by draining or removing the heater's fuel tank and disconnecting its power source.

When transporting Class 3 (flammable liquid) or Division 2.1 (flammable gas), any cargo heater in the vehicle must meet the following:

1. If the heater is powered by diesel fuel or propane the following must be met:

- **Electrical apparatus in cargo compartment is non-sparking or explosion proof.**

- **Combustion apparatus is not in cargo compartment.**

- **System will not heat any part of the cargo to more than 130°F (54°C).**

- **Heater and fuel supply are externally mounted.**

- **Combustion must be retained in a sealed combustion unit.**

- Must use outside air for combustion.

- Combustion gases must be exhausted to the outside.

- Complies with vehicle heater requirements in section 393.77.

2. If the heater is catalytic the following must be met:

- Surface cannot exceed 130°F (54°C) when the outside temperature is 61°F (16°C) or less.

- Is not ignited in a loaded vehicle.

- No flame on the catalyst or anywhere in the heater.

- Permanently marked by the manufacturer with "MEETS DOT REQUIREMENTS FOR CATALYTIC HEATERS USED WITH FLAMMABLE LIQUID AND GAS" and also "DO NOT LOAD INTO OR USE IN CARGO COMPARTMENTS CONTAINING FLAMMABLE LIQUID OR GAS IF FLAME IS VISIBLE ON CATALYST OR IN HEATER."

- Complies with vehicle heater requirements in section 393.77.

There are also special restrictions on the use of **automatic cargo space heating temperature control devices.** Such devices may be used in transporting Class 3 (flammable liquid) or Division 2.1 (flammable gas) materials only if all the following conditions are met:

- Electrical apparatus in the cargo compartment is explosion-proof or non-sparking.

- No combustion apparatus is located in the cargo compartment.

- No air-return connection exists between the cargo compartment and the combustion apparatus.

- The system is not capable of heating any part of the cargo to more than 129°F (54°C).

If the temperature control device in question does not meet the previous four specifications, the following steps must be taken before the vehicle can be used to transport flammable liquid or flammable gas:

- Any cargo heater fuel tank (other than LPG) must be emptied or removed.

- LPG tanks must have all discharge valves closed and fuel feed lines disconnected.

Special Documents

Certificate of Registration

Any person who offers for transport, or transports in foreign, interstate or intrastate commerce, any of the following, is subject to the PHMSA hazardous materials registration and fee requirements.

- Any highway route-controlled quantity of a Class 7 (radioactive) material;

- **More than 55 lb (25 kg) of a Division 1.1, 1.2, 1.3 (explosive) material;**

- **More than 1.06 qt (1 L) per package of a material extremely toxic by inhalation (i.e., "material poisonous by Inhalation," as defined in §171.8, that meets the criteria for "hazard zone A," as specified in §§173.116(a) or 173.133(a));**

- **A hazardous material in a bulk packaging having a capacity equal to or greater than 3,500 gal (13,248 L) for liquids or gases, or more than 468 ft³ (13.24 m³) for solids;**

- **A shipment in other than a bulk packaging (being offered or loaded at one loading facility using one transport vehicle) of 5,000 lb (2,268 kg) gross weight or more of one class of hazardous materials for which placarding is required; or**

- **A quantity of hazardous material that requires placarding.** Except farmers in direct support of farming operations.

Motor carriers subject to the registration requirements must carry, on board **each** vehicle that is transporting a hazardous material requiring registration:

- **A copy of the carriers' current Certificate of Registration; or**

- **Another document bearing the registration number identified as the "U.S. DOT Hazmat Reg. No.".**

Safety Permit

A motor carrier may not transport in interstate or intrastate commerce any of the following unless the motor carrier holds a FMCSA safety permit:

- **A highway route-controlled quantity of a Class 7 (radioactive) material;**

- **More than 55 lb (25 kg) of a Division 1.1, 1.2, or 1.3 (explosive) material;**

- **An amount of a Division 1.5 (explosive) material requiring placarding;**

- **More than 1.08 qt (1 L) per package of a "material poisonous by inhalation," that meets the criteria for "hazard zone A;"**

- **A "material poisonous by inhalation," that meets the criteria for "hazard zone B," in a bulk packaging;**

- **A "material poisonous by inhalation," that meets the criteria for "hazard zone C" or "hazard zone D," in a packaging having a capacity equal to or greater than 3,500 gal (13,248 L); or**

- **A shipment of compressed or refrigerated liquefied methane or liquefied natural gas, or other liquefied gas with a methane content of at least 85 percent, in a bulk packaging having a capacity equal to or greater than 3,500 gal (13,248 L).**

Each motor vehicle that transports a hazardous material requiring a safety permit must carry:

- **A copy of the safety permit or another document showing the carrier's safety permit number clearly identified as the FMCSA Safety Permit Number;**

- **A written route plan; and**

- **The telephone number to contact the motor carrier or a representative of the motor carrier familiar with the routing plan.**

The driver must follow the communications plan required by the regulations, to contact the carrier at the beginning and end of each duty tour and at the pickup and delivery of each load. The motor carrier or the driver must maintain a record of communications for 6 months after the initial acceptance of a shipment.

Class 1 (Explosive) Shipments

Some special documents are required to be carried by drivers of vehicles transporting Division 1.1, 1.2, or 1.3 (explosive) materials:

- **A copy of Part 397, Transportation of Hazardous Materials; Driving and Parking Rules (Federal Motor Carrier Safety Regulations).** Part 397 can be found at the back of this pocketbook.

- **Instructions on procedures to be followed in case of an accident or delay. This must include the nature of the explosives being hauled, the names and phone numbers of persons to be contacted, and precautions to be taken.**

Drivers are required to sign a receipt for these documents. The carrier must maintain the receipt for one year.

In addition to the above documents drivers must also have the following documents:

- **Proper shipping papers.**

- **A written route plan for the shipment. (In some cases, this plan may be prepared by the driver, if the trip begins at some other point than the carrier's terminal.)**

Class 7 (Radioactive) Shipments

A driver transporting a package that contains a highway route controlled quantity of Class 7 (radioactive) materials must have within immediate possession a written route plan and operate the vehicle in accordance with the route plan. The driver must also have within immediate possession a certificate of training for the Class 7 training required by §397.101(e).

Hazardous Waste Shipments

A driver **must not** accept a shipment of hazardous waste unless it is accompanied by a properly prepared Uniform Hazardous Waste Manifest!

Delivery of hazardous wastes **must be** made ONLY to the facility or alternate facility designated on the hazardous waste manifest. If delivery can not be made, the driver should contact his dispatcher or other designated official, immediately.

Reserved

Loading and Unloading Rules for Hazardous Materials Shipments

There are some regulations for the safe and secure loading and unloading of hazardous materials shipments which apply to all hazardous commodities shipments. They are included in this chapter, and should be interpreted as general common sense rules to follow in the operation of your vehicle. Specifics on loading and unloading certain particular hazardous materials are contained in a later chapter.

Securing Packages

Any package containing any hazardous material that is not permanently attached to a vehicle must be secured against any movement, including motion between packages, within the vehicle during normal transportation conditions. Packages having valves or other fittings must be loaded in a manner to minimize the likelihood of damage during transportation

Each package bearing orientation arrow markings must be loaded on a vehicle or within a freight container in accordance with the arrow markings. The package must remain in this position during transportation.

No Smoking

Smoking on or near any vehicle while loading or unloading any Class 1 (explosive), Class 3 (flammable liquid), Class 4 (flammable solid), Class 5 (oxidizer), or Division 2.1 (flammable gas) materials is forbidden. Further, care should be taken to keep all fire sources — matches and smoking materials in particular — away from vehicles hauling any of the above materials.

Set Handbrake

During the loading and unloading of any hazardous materials shipment the handbrake on the vehicle must be set, and all precautions taken to prevent movement of the vehicle.

Tools

Any tools used in loading or unloading hazardous material must be used with care not to damage the closures on any packages or containers, or to harm packages of Class 1 (explosive) material and other hazardous materials in any way.

Attending Vehicles

There are attendance requirements for cargo tanks that are being loaded or unloaded with hazardous materials. Such a tank must be attended at all times during loading and unloading by a qualified person. The person who is responsible for loading the cargo is also responsible for seeing that the vehicle is attended. However, the carrier's obligation to oversee unloading ceases when all these conditions are met:

- **The carrier's transportation obligation is completed;**

- **The cargo tank is placed on the consignee's premises; and**

- **The motive power is removed from the cargo tank and the premises.**

A qualified person attends the loading or unloading of a cargo tank only if, throughout the process:

1. Except for specific unloading operations for Combustible Liquids, Liquefied Petroleum Gas, and Anhydrous Ammonia, the person:

    - **Is alert;**

    - **Is within 25 ft (7.62 m) of the cargo tank; and**

    - **Has an unobstructed view of the cargo tank and delivery hose to the maximum extent practicable during unloading.**

    OR

2. The qualified person observes all loading or unloading operations by electronic surveillance from a remote control station and the following are met:

    - **The video monitoring camera provides an unobstructed view of all equipment involved;**

    - **The surveillance system provides surveillance at least equal to a human observer;**

    - **Shut-off valves are operable from a remote control station;**

    - **Upon loss of electronic surveillance, the operations are immediately terminated;**

    - **A containment area must be capable of holding the contents of as many cargo tanks that might be loaded at one time; and**

    - **The qualified person must conduct a visual inspection of the cargo tank motor vehicle after it is loaded and prior to departure.**

    OR

3. Hoses are equipped with devices at each end that are able to stop the flow of product from both the source and the receiving tank within one second without human intervention in the event of an incident and the following are met:

    - **Each hose must be visually inspected prior to each use, and**

    - **The loading/unloading operation must be physically inspected at least once every 60 minutes.**

A person is qualified if they are:

- **Aware of the nature of the hazardous material;**

- **Instructed in emergency procedures; and**

- **Except for persons observing by electronic surveillance and those inspecting hoses equipped with stop devices, is authorized to move and is capable of moving the cargo tank.**

Forbidden Articles

No motor carrier may accept for transportation or transport any goods classed as "Forbidden" in the §172.101 Hazardous Materials Table or goods not prepared in accordance with the regulations.

Carrier personnel are also responsible for rejecting packages of hazardous materials which show signs of leakage or other damage.

Commodity Compatibility

The Hazardous Materials Regulations contain segregation requirements which indicate which hazardous materials may not be loaded, transported or stored together.

Materials which are in packages that require labels or placards, in a compartment within a multi-compartmented cargo tank, or in a portable tank loaded in a transport vehicle or freight container are subject to the segregation requirements. In addition to the following Tables and §173.12(e), cyanides or cyanide mixtures or solutions may not be stored, loaded and transported with acids if a mixture of the materials would generate hydrogen cyanide; Division 4.2 materials may not be stored, loaded and transported with Class 8 liquids; and Division 6.1 Packing Group I, Hazard Zone A material may not be stored, loaded and transported with Class 3 material, Class 8 liquids, and Division 4.1, 4.2, 4.3, 5.1 or 5.2 materials.

Except as mentioned in the previous paragraph, hazardous materials may not be stored, loaded, or transported together, except as provided in the following Tables:

SEGREGATION TABLE FOR HAZARDOUS MATERIALS

Class or Division		Notes	1.1, 1.2	1.3	1.4	1.5	1.6	2.1	2.2	2.3 gas Zone A	2.3 gas Zone B	3	4.1	4.2	4.3	5.1	5.2	6.1 liquids PG I Zone A	7	8 liquids only
Explosives.	1.1 and 1.2	A	*	*	*	*	*	X	X	X	X	X	X	X	X	X	X	X	X	X
Explosives.	1.3		*	*	*	*	*	X	X	X	X	X	X	X	X	X	X	X	X	X
Explosives.	1.4		*	*	*	*	*	O		O		O	O	O	O	O	O	O	O	O
Very insensitive explosives.	1.5	A	*	*	*	*	*	X	X	X	X	X	X	X	X	X	X	X	X	X
Extremely insensitive explosives.	1.6		*	*	*	*	*													
Flammable gases.	2.1		X	X	O	X				X					X		O	X		O
Non-toxic, non-flammable gases.	2.2		X	X		X									O					
Poisonous gas Zone A.	2.3		X	X	O	X		X							O					
Poisonous gas Zone B.	2.3		X	X	O	X									O					
Flammable liquids.	3		X	X	O	X		X		O	O									
Flammable solids.	4.1		X	X	O	X										O				
Spontaneously combustible materials.	4.2		X	X	O	X														
Dangerous when wet materials.	4.3		X	X	O	X		X	O	O	O							X		
Oxidizers.	5.1	A	X	X	O	X		O		O	O	O	O							O
Organic peroxides.	5.2		X	X	O	X		O		O	O	X						X		
Poisonous liquids PG I Zone A.	6.1		X	X	O	X		X				X			X					X
Radioactive materials.	7		X	X	O	X									O					
Corrosive liquids.	8		X	X	O	X		O		O	O				O	O	O	X		

Instructions for using the segregation table for hazardous materials are as follows:

1. The absence of any hazard class or division or a blank space in the Table indicates that no restrictions apply.

2. The letter "X" in the Table indicates that these materials may not be loaded, transported, or stored together in the same transport vehicle or storage facility during the course of transportation.

3. The letter "O" in the Table indicates that these materials may not be loaded, transported, or stored together in the same transport vehicle or storage facility during the course of transportation unless separated in a manner that, in the event of leakage from packages under conditions normally incident to transportation, commingling of hazardous materials would not occur. Notwithstanding the methods of separation employed, Class 8 (corrosive) liquids may not be loaded above or adjacent to Class 4 (flammable) or Class 5 (oxidizing) materials; except that shippers may load truckload shipments of such materials together when it is known that the mixture of contents would not cause a fire or a dangerous evolution of heat or gas.

4. The "*" in the Table indicates that segregation among different Class 1 (explosive) materials is governed by the compatibility table for Class 1 (explosive) materials.

5. The note "A" in the second column of the Table means that, notwithstanding the requirements of the letter "X", ammonium nitrate (UN1942) and ammonium nitrate fertilizer may be loaded or stored with Division 1.1 (explosive) or Division 1.5 materials.

6. When the §172.101 Table or §172.402 of this subchapter requires a package to bear a subsidiary hazard label, segregation appropriate to the subsidiary hazard must be applied when that segregation is more restrictive than that required by the primary hazard. However, hazardous materials of the same class may be stowed together without regard to segregation required for any secondary hazard if the materials are not capable of reacting dangerously with each other and causing combustion or dangerous evolution of heat, evolution of flammable, poisonous, or asphyxiant gases, or formation of corrosive or unstable materials.

Class 1 (explosive) materials shall not be loaded, transported, or stored together, except as provided in this section, and in accordance with the following Table:

COMPATIBILITY TABLE FOR CLASS 1 (EXPLOSIVE) MATERIALS

Compatibility group	A	B	C	D	E	F	G	H	J	K	L	N	S
A		X	X	X	X	X	X	X	X	X	X	X	X
B	X		X	X$_{(4)}$	X	X	X	X	X	X	X	X	4/5
C	X	X		2	2	X	6	X	X	X	X	3	4/5
D	X	X$_{(4)}$	2		2	X	6	X	X	X	X	3	4/5
E	X	X	2	2		X	6	X	X	X	X	3	4/5

COMPATIBILITY TABLE FOR CLASS 1 (EXPLOSIVE) MATERIALS, Continued

Compatibility group	A	B	C	D	E	F	G	H	J	K	L	N	S
F	X	X	X	X	X		X	X	X	X	X	X	4/5
G	X	X	6	6	6	X		X	X	X	X	X	4/5
H	X	X	X	X	X	X	X		X	X	X	X	4/5
J	X	X	X	X	X	X	X	X		X	X	X	4/5
K	X	X	X	X	X	X	X	X	X		X	X	4/5
L	X	X	X	X	X	X	X	X	X	X	1	X	X
N	X	X	3	3	3	X	X	X	X	X	X		4/5
S	X	4/5	4/5	4/5	4/5	4/5	4/5	4/5	4/5	4/5	X	4/5	

Instructions for using the compatibility table for Class 1 (explosive) materials are as follows:

1. A blank space in the Table indicates that no restrictions apply.

2. The letter "X" in the Table indicates that explosives of different compatibility groups may not be carried on the same transport vehicle.

3. The numbers in the Table mean the following:

    1   means an explosive from compatibility group L shall only be carried on the same transport vehicle with an identical explosive.

    2   means any combination of explosives from compatibility groups C, D, or E is assigned to compatibility group E.

    3   means any combination of explosives from compatibility groups C, D, or E with those in compatibility group N is assigned to compatibility group D.

    4   means 'see §177.835(g)' when transporting detonators.

    5   means Division 1.4S fireworks may not be loaded on the same transport vehicle with Division 1.1 or 1.2 (explosive) materials.

    6   means explosive articles in compatibility group G, other than fireworks and those requiring special handling, may be loaded, transported and stored with other explosive articles of compatibility groups C, D and E, provided that explosive substances (such as those not contained in articles) are not carried in the same transport vehicle.

Except as provided in the next paragraph, explosives of the same compatibility group but of different divisions may be transported together provided that the whole shipment is transported as though its entire contents were of the lower numerical division (i.e., Division 1.1 being lower than Division 1.2). For example, a mixed shipment of Division 1.2 (explosive) materials and Division 1.4 (explosive) materials, both of compatibility group D, must be transported as Division 1.2 (explosive) materials.

When Division 1.5 materials, compatibility group D, are transported in the same freight container as Division 1.2 (explosive) materials, compatibility group D, the shipment must be transported as Division 1.1 (explosive) materials, compatibility group D.

On the Road With Hazardous Materials

Some general rules apply to drivers hauling hazardous materials during the actual time on the road. The following covers these driving rules for all hazardous materials shipments.

Shipping Papers

Hazardous materials shipments must be accompanied by proper shipping papers, such as bills of lading, hazardous waste manifests, etc. During the course of the trip, the driver is responsible for maintaining the shipping papers according to requirements, so that they are easily accessible to authorities in case of an incident, accident, or inspection.

1. If the hazardous material shipping paper is carried with any other papers, it must be clearly distinguished, either by tabbing it or having it appear first.

2. When the driver is at the controls, the shipping papers must be within immediate reach when the driver is restrained by the seat belt.

3. The shipping papers must be readily visible to someone entering the driver's compartment, or in a holder mounted on the inside of the door on the driver's side.

4. If the driver is not in the vehicle, the shipping papers must be either in the holder on the door or on the driver's seat.

Emergency Response Information

Most hazardous material shipments (except those that do not require shipping papers or ORM-D materials) must have **emergency response information** on or in association with the shipping paper. If the information is in association with the shipping paper it may be in the form of the Emergency Response Guidebook, a Safety Data Sheet (SDS), or any other form that provides all the information required in §172.602.

In most cases, a numeric **emergency response telephone number** must be entered on the shipping paper. It can be immediately following the description of each hazardous material or if the number applies to every hazardous material entered on the shipping paper, entered once on the shipping paper in a clearly visible location and identified as an emergency response information number.

Near the emergency response telephone number, the **name** of the offeror providing emergency response information or who is registered with an emergency response information (ERI) provider or their ERI service provider contract number or other **unique identifier** must be entered. This is not required if the name or identifier is entered elsewhere on the shipping paper in a prominent, readily identifiable, and clearly visible manner to be easily and quickly found.

Registration

Motor carriers that are subject to the federal DOT hazmat registration requirements (§107.601) must carry, on board **each** vehicle that is transporting a hazardous material requiring registration:

- A copy of the carriers' current Certificate of Registration; OR

- Another document bearing the registration number identified as the "U.S. DOT Hazmat Reg. No."

Safety Permit

Each motor vehicle that transports a hazardous material requiring a safety permit (§385.403) must carry:

- **A copy of the safety permit or another document showing the carrier's safety permit number clearly identified as the FMCSA Safety Permit Number;**

- **A written route plan for certain Class 1 (explosive) and Class 7 (radioactive) material; and**

- **A telephone number to contact the motor carrier or a representative of the motor carrier who is familiar with the expected route for the material.**

The driver must follow the communications plan required by the regulations, to contact the carrier at the beginning and end of each duty tour and at the pickup and delivery of each load. Contact may be by telephone, radio, or via an electronic tracking or monitoring system.

The motor carrier or the driver must maintain a record of communications for 6 months after the initial acceptance of a shipment. The record must contain the name of the driver, identification of the vehicle, material transported, and the date, location, and time of each required contact.

Railroad Crossings

Any marked or placarded vehicle (except for Divisions 1.5 (explosive), 1.6 (explosive), 4.2 (spontaneously combustible), 6.2 (infectious substance), and Class 9 (miscellaneous)); any cargo tank motor vehicle, loaded or empty, used to transport any hazardous material; or a vehicle carrying any amount of chlorine, must stop at railroad crossings.

Stops must be made within 50 feet of the crossing, but no closer than 15 feet. When you determine it is safe to cross the tracks, you may do so, but do not shift gears while crossing the tracks.

Stops need not be made at:

1. **Streetcar crossings or industrial switching tracks within a business district.**

2. **Crossings where a police officer or flagman is directing traffic.**

3. **Crossings which are controlled by a stop-and-go traffic light which is green.**

4. **Abandoned rail lines marked with a sign and industrial or spur line crossings clearly marked "exempt."**

Only drive onto a railroad crossing if there is sufficient space to drive completely through the crossing without stopping. Vehicles not required to stop at crossings, must approach crossings at a speed that permits stopping before reaching the nearest rail. Vehicles must not be driven on or over until the course is clear.

Tunnels

Unless there is no other practicable route, marked or placarded shipments of hazardous materials should not be driven through tunnels. Operating convenience cannot be used as a determining factor in such decisions.

In addition, the provisions of the Hazardous Materials Regulations do not supersede state or local laws and ordinances which may be more restrictive concerning hazardous materials and urban vehicular tunnels used for mass transportation.

Routing

A motor carrier transporting hazardous materials required to be marked or placarded shall operate the vehicle over routes which do not go through or near heavily populated areas, places where crowds are assembled, tunnels, narrow streets, or alleys, except when:

- There is no practicable alternative;

- It is necessary to reach a terminal, points of loading or unloading, facilities for food, fuel, rest, repairs, or a safe haven; or

- A deviation is required by emergency conditions;

Operating convenience is not a basis for determining if a route can be used. A motor carrier shall also comply with the routing designations of States or Indian tribes as authorized by federal regulations.

Attending Vehicles

Any marked or placarded vehicle containing hazardous materials which is on a public street or highway or the shoulder of any such road must be attended by the driver. Except when transporting Division 1.1, 1.2, or 1.3 (explosive) material, the vehicle does not have to be attended when the driver is performing duties necessary to the operation of the vehicle.

What exactly does "attended" mean? In terms of the regulations a motor vehicle is attended when the person in charge is on the vehicle and awake (cannot be in the sleeper berth) or is within 100 feet of the vehicle and has an unobstructed view of it.

ON THE ROAD

Fueling

When a marked or placarded vehicle is being fueled, the engine must be shut off and a person must be in control of the fueling process at the point where the fuel tank is filled.

Parking

Marked or placarded vehicles containing hazardous materials should not be parked on or within five feet of the traveled portion of any roadway. If the vehicle does not contain Division 1.1, 1.2, or 1.3 (explosive) material, it may be stopped for brief periods when operational necessity requires parking the vehicle, and it would be impractical to stop elsewhere. Further restrictions apply to vehicles hauling Division 1.1, 1.2, or 1.3 (explosive) materials. Standard warning devices are to be set out as required by law when a vehicle is stopped along a roadway.

Warning Devices

Vehicles must be equipped with emergency warning devices such as reflective triangles, red lanterns, fusees or liquid-burning flares. Liquid-burning flares, fusees, oil lanterns, or any signal produced by a flame must not be carried on or used for any vehicle transporting Division 1.1, 1.2, 1.3 (explosive) materials, any cargo tank motor vehicle transporting Division 2.1 (flammable gas) or Class 3 (flammable liquid) materials, loaded or empty.

Emergency Carrier Information Contact

If a transport vehicle (semi-trailer or freight container-on-chassis) contains hazardous materials that require shipping papers and the vehicle is separated from its motive power and parked at a location, the carrier must:

- Mark the vehicle with the telephone number of the motor carrier on the front exterior near the brake hose and electrical connections, or on a label, tag, or sign attached to the vehicle at the brake hose or electrical connection; or

- Have the shipping paper and emergency response information readily available on the transport vehicle.

The above requirements **do not apply** if the vehicle is marked on an orange panel, a placard, or a plain white square-on-point configuration with the identification number of each hazardous material contained within. The identification number(s) must be visible on the outside of the vehicle.

The above requirements **also do not apply** if the vehicle is parked at a:

- Shipper's (consignors's) facility;

- Recipient's (consignee's) facility; or

- Facility that has the emergency response information immediately available.

If you are transporting hazardous materials that require shipping papers, your carrier must instruct you to contact them (e.g., by telephone or radio) in the event of an incident involving the hazardous material.

Tire Checks

The driver of any vehicle which must be marked or placarded because it contains hazardous materials, must examine each tire on their vehicle at the beginning of each trip and each time the vehicle is parked.

If any defect is found in a tire, it should be repaired or replaced immediately. The vehicle may, however, be driven a short distance to the nearest safe place for repair.

If a hot tire is found, it must be removed from the vehicle immediately and taken to a safe distance. Such a vehicle may not be operated until the cause of the overheating is corrected.

No Texting or Phoning

A person transporting a quantity of hazardous materials that requires placarding or any quantity of a material listed as a select agent or toxin in 42 CFR part 73 must not engage in, allow, or require texting or use of a hand-held mobile telephone while driving.

No Smoking

No person may smoke or carry any lighted smoking materials on or within 25 foot of marked or placarded vehicles containing any Class 1 (explosive) materials, Class 5 (oxidizer) materials or flammable materials classified as Division 2.1, Class 3, Divisions 4.1 and 4.2, or any empty tank vehicle that has been used to transport Class 3 (flammable liquid) or Division 2.1 (flammable gas) materials.

Fires

A marked or placarded vehicle containing hazardous materials should not be driven near an open fire, unless careful precautions have been taken to be sure the vehicle can completely pass the fire without stopping. In addition, a marked or placarded vehicle containing hazardous materials should not be parked within 300 feet of any open fire.

Fire Extinguisher

If a power unit or a vehicle pulled by a power unit requires the display of markings or placards, the power unit must be equipped with a fire extinguisher having an Underwriters' Laboratories (UL) rating of 10 B:C or more. The fire extinguisher must be properly filled, securely mounted, and located so that it is readily accessible for use. It must be designed, constructed, and maintained to permit visual determination of whether it is fully charged.

ON THE ROAD

Vehicle Maintenance

No person may use heat, flame or spark producing devices to repair or maintain the cargo or fuel containment system of a motor vehicle required to be placarded, other than COMBUSTIBLE. The containment system includes all vehicle components intended physically to contain cargo or fuel during loading or filling, transport, or unloading.

Damaged Packages

Packages of hazardous materials that are damaged or found leaking during transportation, and hazardous materials that have spilled or leaked during transportation, may be forwarded to their destination or returned to the shipper in a salvage drum in accordance with the regulations.

Packages may be repaired in accordance with the best and safest practice known and available.

Any package repaired in accordance with the requirements in the regulations may be transported to the nearest place where it may safely be disposed. This may be done only if the following requirements are met:

1. The package must be safe for transportation.

2. The repair of the package must be adequate to prevent contamination of other lading or producing a hazardous mixture with other lading transported on the same motor vehicle.

3. If the carrier is not the shipper, the consignee's name and address must be plainly marked on the repaired package.

In the event any leaking package or container cannot be safely and adequately repaired for transportation or transported, it shall be stored pending proper disposition in the safest and most expeditious manner possible.

Incident Reporting

As soon as possible, report any incident involving hazardous materials during transportation (including loading, unloading, and temporary storage) to your carrier.

Any incident subject to the immediate notification requirements or any unintentional release of hazardous materials must be reported in writing to the DOT by the person (such as the carrier) in physical possession of the hazardous material. This written or electronic report to the DOT must be on Form F 5800.1 (Hazardous Materials Incident Report). The report must be submitted to the DOT within 30 days of the date of discovery.

In some cases, immediate notification to the National Response Center is required, no later than 12 hours after the incident. In these cases, contact your carrier as soon as possible, so the immediate notification can be made to the National Response Center (800-424-8802 or 202-267-2675). Incidents which require this immediate notification include those in which:

- **As a direct result of hazardous materials**

  1. **A person is killed;**

  2. **A person receives an injury requiring hospitalization;**

  3. **An evacuation of the general public occurs lasting one or more hours;**

  4. **A major transportation artery or facility is closed or shut down for one hour or more; or**

  5. **The operational flight pattern or routine of an aircraft is altered.**

- **Fire, breakage, spillage or suspected radioactive contamination occurs involving radioactive material.**

- **Fire, breakage, spillage or suspected contamination occurs involving infectious substances, other than a diagnostic specimen or regulated medical waste.**

- **There has been a release of a marine pollutant in a quantity exceeding 119 gal (450 L) for liquids or 882 lb (400 kg) for solids.**

- **Fire, violent rupture, explosion or dangerous evolution of heat occurs as a direct result of a battery or battery-powered device transported by air.**

- **Some other situation occurs which the person in possession of the hazardous material considers important enough to warrant immediate reporting.**

Reserved

Shipments of CLASS 1 (Explosives)

General loading, transportation and unloading requirements that apply to all hazardous materials shipments can be found in the two preceding chapters. The following information is specific to Class 1 materials.

Combination Vehicles

Division 1.1 or 1.2 (explosive) materials may not be loaded on any vehicle of a combination of vehicles if:

1. More than two cargo carrying vehicles are in the combination;

2. Any full trailer in the combination has a wheel base of less than 184 inches;

3. Any vehicle in the combination is a cargo tank which is required to be marked or placarded; or

4. The other vehicle in the combination contains any:

   • Substances, explosive, n.o.s., Division 1.1A (explosive) material (Initiating explosive),

   • Packages of Class 7 (radioactive) materials bearing "Yellow III" labels,

   • Division 2.3 (poison gas) Hazard Zone A or B or Division 6.1 (poison) PG I, Hazard Zone A materials, or

   • Hazardous materials in a portable tank or a DOT Spec. 106A or 110A tank.

Vehicle Condition

Vehicles transporting any Class 1 (explosive) materials must be free of sharp projections into the body which could damage packages of explosives.

Vehicles carrying Division 1.1, 1.2, or 1.3 (explosive) materials must have tight floors. They must be lined with non-metallic material or non-ferrous material in any portion that comes in contact with the load.

Motor vehicles carrying Class 1 (explosive) materials should have either a closed body or have the body covered with a tarpaulin, so that the load is protected from moisture and sparks. However, explosives other than black powder may be hauled on flat-bed vehicles if the explosive portions of the load are packed in fire and water-resistant containers or are covered by a fire and water-resistant tarpaulin.

If the vehicle assigned to haul Class 1 (explosive) materials is equipped with any kind of cargo heater, **it must be inoperable for the duration of that shipment.** Check to be sure the heater's fuel tank has been completely drained and the power source disconnected.

Loading & Unloading

Rules for loading Class 1 (explosive) materials are based on good common sense. They include:

1. **Be sure the engine of your vehicle is stopped before loading or unloading any Class 1 materials.**

2. **Don't use bale hooks or any other metal tool to handle Class 1 materials.**

3. **Don't roll any Class 1 materials packages, except barrels or kegs.**

4. **Be careful not to throw or drop packages of Class 1 materials.**

5. **Keep Class 1 materials well clear of any vehicle exhaust pipes at all times.**

6. **Be sure any tarpaulins are well-secured with ropes or wire tie-downs.**

7. **Loads of Class 1 materials must be contained entirely within the body of the vehicle, with no projection or overhang.**

8. **If there is a tailgate or tailboard, it should be securely in place throughout the trip.**

9. **Don't load Class 1 materials with any other materials that might damage packages during transit. In an allowable mixed load, bulkheads or other effective means must be used to separate cargo.**

Emergency Transfers

Division 1.1, 1.2, or 1.3 (explosive) materials may not be transferred (from container to container, motor vehicle to motor vehicle, another vehicle to a motor vehicle) on any street, road or highway, except in emergencies.

In such cases all possible precautions must be taken to alert other drivers of the hazards involved in the transfer. Specifically, red electric lanterns, emergency reflectors or flags must be set out as prescribed for stopped or disabled vehicles.

Liquid-burning flares, fusees, oil lanterns, or any signal produced by a flame must not be used for protecting any stopped or disabled vehicle transporting Division 1.1, 1.2, or 1.3 (explosive) materials.

Parking

Marked or placarded vehicles carrying Division 1.1, 1.2, or 1.3 (explosive) materials must not be parked in the following locations:

*   **On a public street or highway, or within five feet of the traveled portion of such a roadway.**

- **On private property (including truck stops and restaurants) without the knowledge and consent of the person in charge of the property and who is aware of the nature of the materials.**

- **Within 300 feet of any bridge, tunnel, dwelling, building or place where people work or assemble, except for brief periods necessary to the operation of the vehicle when parking elsewhere is not practical.**

Marked or placarded vehicles containing Division 1.4, 1.5, or 1.6 (explosive) materials should not be parked on or within five feet of the traveled portion of any public street or highway, except for brief periods necessary to vehicle operation.

Attending Vehicles

Marked or placarded vehicles containing Division 1.1, 1.2, or 1.3 (explosive) materials must be attended at all times by their drivers or some qualified representative of the motor carrier, except in those situations where all the following conditions are met:

1. **Vehicle is located on the property of a carrier, shipper or consignee; in a safe haven; or on a construction or survey site (if the vehicle contains 50 pounds or less of Division 1.1, 1.2, or 1.3 (explosive) materials).**

2. **A lawful bailee knows the nature of the vehicle's cargo and has been instructed in emergency procedures.**

3. **Vehicle is within the unobstructed field of vision of the bailee, or is in a safe haven.**

Marked or placarded vehicles containing Division 1.4, 1.5, or 1.6 (explosive) materials, located on a public street or highway or the shoulder of the roadway, must be attended by the driver, except when the driver is performing necessary duties as operator of the vehicle.

No Smoking

An extra reminder! Don't smoke or carry a lighted cigarette, cigar or pipe on or within 25 feet of any vehicle containing Class 1 (explosive) materials.

Required Documents

Motor carriers transporting Division 1.1, 1.2, or 1.3 (explosive) materials must furnish drivers with the following required documents:

- **A copy of Part 397 — Transportation of Hazardous Materials; Driving and Parking Rules (Federal Motor Carrier Safety Regulations).** Part 397 can be found at the back of this pocketbook.

- **Instructions on procedures to be followed in case of an accident or delay. This must include the nature of the explosives being hauled, the names and phone numbers of persons to be contacted and precautions to be taken.**

Drivers are required to sign a receipt for these documents.

The carrier must maintain the receipt for one year.

In addition to the above documents drivers must also have the following documents:

- **Proper shipping papers.**

- **A written route plan for the shipment. (In some cases, this plan may be prepared by the driver, if the trip begins at some other point than the carrier's terminal.)**

The driver must be in possession of, be familiar with, and be in compliance with all four of the documents described above.

Class 1 Do's

1. Check vehicle thoroughly to be sure it meets specifications.

2. Stop engine while loading or unloading.

3. Handle cargo as specified.

4. Deliver only to authorized persons.

5. Know the vehicle attendance requirements.

6. Have all required documents in order before starting.

Class 1 Don'ts

1. Don't transfer Class 1 (explosive) materials, except in emergencies.

2. Don't park a Class 1 (explosive) materials vehicle in prohibited areas.

3. Don't smoke on or within 25 feet of a Class 1 (explosive) materials vehicle.

Shipments of CLASS 2 (Gases)

General loading, transportation and unloading requirements that apply to all hazardous materials shipments can be found after the General Requirements section of this handbook. The following information is specific to Class 2 materials. For information on shipments of Division 2.3 (Poisonous Gases), see shipments of Division 6.1 & Division 2.3.

Vehicle Condition

Before any cylinders of Class 2 materials are loaded onto a motor vehicle, that vehicle should be inspected to determine that the floor or loading platform is essentially flat. If a solid floor or platform is not provided in the vehicle, there must be securely-fastened racks which will secure the cargo.

Loading & Unloading

Cylinders — To prevent shifting, overturning, or ejection from the vehicle under normal transport conditions, cylinders of Class 2 materials must be securely attached to the motor vehicle by one of the following ways:

1. **Securely restrained in an upright or horizontal position.**

2. **Loaded into racks.**

3. **Packed in boxes or crates.**

A pressure relief device, when installed, must be in communication with the vapor space of a cylinder containing a Division 2.1 (flammable) material.

Bulk packagings — Portable tank containers may be loaded on the flat floor or platform of a vehicle or onto a suitable frame. In either case, the containers must be blocked or held down in some way to prevent movement during transportation, including sudden starts or stops and changes in direction of the vehicle. Containers may even be stacked, if they are secured to prevent any motion.

If a Division 2.1 (flammable gas) material is being loaded or unloaded from a tank motor vehicle, the engine must be stopped. The only exception occurs if the engine is used to operate the transfer pump. The engine must also be off while filling or discharge connections are disconnected, unless the delivery hose is equipped with a shut-off valve.

Liquid discharge valves on cargo tanks must be closed securely after loading or unloading, before any movement of the vehicle.

Special handling provisions are specified for certain kinds of Class 2 materials. Information on these follows.

Liquefied Hydrogen

Specification DOT-4L cylinders filled with liquefied hydrogen, cryogenic liquid must be carried on vehicles with open bodies equipped with racks or supports having clamps or bands to hold the cylinders securely upright. These arrangements must be capable of withstanding acceleration of 2 "g" in any horizontal direction.

Cylinders of liquefied hydrogen are marked with venting rates. The combined total venting rates on all cylinders on a single motor vehicle must not exceed 60 standard cubic feet per hour.

Only private and contract carriers may haul liquefied hydrogen on the highway and the transportation must be a direct movement from origin to destination.

Vehicles hauling liquefied hydrogen may not be driven through tunnels.

Chlorine

Any shipment of chlorine in a cargo tank must be accompanied by a gas mask (approved for chlorine service by the National Institute of Occupational Safety and Health (NIOSH)) and an emergency kit to control leaks in the fittings on the dome cover plate.

Do not move, couple or uncouple any chlorine tank vehicle while loading or unloading connections are attached.

Do not leave any trailer or semitrailer without a power unit, unless it has been chocked or some adequate means provided to prevent it from moving.

No Smoking

Smoking on or near the vehicle while you are loading or unloading Division 2.1 material is forbidden.

Cargo Heaters

Vehicles equipped with combustion cargo heaters may transport Division 2.1 materials only if:

1. The heater is powered by diesel fuel or propane and the following are met:

- **Electrical apparatus in cargo compartment is non-sparking or explosion proof.**

- **Combustion apparatus is not in cargo compartment.**

- **System will not heat any part of the cargo to more than 130°F (54°C).**

- **Heater and fuel supply are externally mounted.**

- **Combustion must be retained in a sealed combustion unit.**

- **Must use outside air for combustion.**

- **Combustion gases must be exhausted to the outside.**

- **Complies with vehicle heater requirements in section 393.77.**

2. The heater is catalytic and the following are met:

- **Surface cannot exceed 130°F (54°C) when the outside temperature is 61°F (16°C) or less.**

- **Is not ignited in a loaded vehicle.**

- **No flame on the catalyst or anywhere in the heater.**

- **Permanently marked by the manufacturer with "MEETS DOT REQUIREMENTS FOR CATALYTIC HEATERS USED WITH FLAMMABLE LIQUID AND GAS" and also "DO NOT LOAD INTO OR USE IN CARGO COMPARTMENTS CONTAINING FLAMMABLE LIQUID OR GAS IF FLAME IS VISIBLE ON CATALYST OR IN HEATER."**

- **Complies with vehicle heater requirements in section 393.77.**

Attending Vehicles

Marked or placarded vehicles located on a public street or highway or the shoulder of the roadway, must be attended by the driver, except when the driver is performing necessary duties as operator of the vehicle.

In addition, cargo tanks must be attended by a qualified person at all times during loading and unloading.

Parking

Marked or placarded vehicles containing Class 2 materials should not be parked on or within five feet of the traveled portion of any public roadway, except for brief periods necessary to vehicle operation.

Warning Devices

Liquid-burning flares, fusees, oil lanterns, or any signal produced by a flame must not be carried on or used for protecting any stopped cargo tank motor vehicle transporting Division 2.1 materials, loaded or empty.

Class 2 Do's

1. Be sure vehicle is adequately equipped to haul Class 2 materials safely.

2. Stop engine while loading or unloading Division 2.1 materials.

3. Be sure liquid discharge valves are closed before moving vehicle.

4. Know special provisions for handling liquefied hydrogen and chlorine.

Class 2 Don'ts

1. Don't drive a vehicle hauling liquefied hydrogen through a tunnel.

2. Don't move chlorine tanks with loading or unloading connections attached.

3. Don't smoke on or near vehicles containing Division 2.1 materials.

Reserved

Shipments of CLASS 3
(Flammable Liquids)

General loading, transportation and unloading requirements that apply to all hazardous materials shipments can be found after the General Requirements section of this handbook. The following information is specific to Class 3 materials.

Loading & Unloading

There are some common sense rules to follow when loading and unloading Class 3 materials:

- **Engine should be stopped. Two possible exceptions are:**

  - **If the engine is used to operate a pump used in the loading or unloading process, or**

  - **A diesel engine may be left running during loading or unloading if the temperature is at or below 10°F (-12°C).**

- **Tanks, barrels, drums, cylinders or other types of packaging containing Class 3 materials (and not permanently attached to the vehicle) must be secured to prevent movement during transportation.**

- **Keep fires (of all kinds and sizes) away!**

Bonding & Grounding

Containers other than cargo tanks not in metallic contact with each other must have metallic bonds or ground conductors attached to avoid the possibility of static charge. Attach bonding first to the vehicle to be filled, then to the container from which the flammable liquid will be loaded. **Attachment must be done in this order!** To prevent ignition of vapors, connection should be made at some distance from the opening where Class 3 material is discharged.

For cargo tanks, similar provisions apply, but they vary depending on loading procedure.

When loading through an open filling hole, attach one end of a bond wire to the stationary system piping or integral steel framing, the other end to the cargo tank shell. Make the connection before any filling hole is opened, and leave it in place until the last hole has been closed.

If nonmetallic flexible connections exist in the stationary system piping, additional bond wires are required.

When unloading from open filling holes using a suction piping system, electrical connection must be maintained from cargo tank to receiving tank.

When loading through a vaportight top or bottom connection, and where there is no release of vapor at any point where a spark could occur, no bonding or grounding is required. However, contact of the closed connection must be made before flow starts and must not be broken until flow is complete.

CLASS 3

When unloading through a non-vaportight connection, into a stationary tank, no bonding or grounding is required if the metallic filling connection is in contact with the filling hole at all times.

No Smoking

Smoking on or within 25 feet of any vehicle containing Class 3 materials is forbidden during the loading and unloading process, as well as the rest of the trip. Keep anyone with any kind of smoking materials away from the vehicle! The rule also applies to empty tank vehicles used to transport Class 3 materials.

Cargo Tank Attendance

A cargo tank must be attended by a qualified person at all times while it is being loaded or unloaded. The person responsible for loading the tank is also responsible for seeing that the tank is attended. The person attending must be awake, have an unobstructed view and be within 25 ft (7.62 m) of the tank. The person must also know the nature of the hazard, be instructed in emergency procedures and be able to move the vehicle, if necessary.

Cargo Heaters

Vehicles equipped with combustion cargo heaters may transport Class 3 materials only if:

1. The heater is powered by diesel fuel or propane and the following are met:

- **Electrical apparatus in cargo compartment is non-sparking or explosion proof.**

- **Combustion apparatus is not in cargo compartment.**

- **System will not heat any part of the cargo to more than 130°F (54°C).**

- **Heater and fuel supply are externally mounted.**

- **Combustion must be retained in a sealed combustion unit.**

- **Must use outside air for combustion.**

- **Combustion gases must be exhausted to the outside.**

- **Complies with vehicle heater requirements in section 393.77.**

2. The heater is catalytic and the following are met:

- **Surface cannot exceed 130°F (54°C) when the outside temperature is 61°F (16°C) or less.**

- **Is not ignited in a loaded vehicle.**

- **No flame on the catalyst or anywhere in the heater.**

- **Permanently marked by the manufacturer with "MEETS DOT REQUIREMENTS FOR CATALYTIC HEATERS USED WITH FLAMMABLE LIQUID AND GAS" and also "DO NOT LOAD INTO OR USE IN CARGO COMPARTMENTS CONTAINING FLAMMABLE LIQUID OR GAS IF FLAME IS VISIBLE ON CATALYST OR IN HEATER."**

- **Complies with vehicle heater requirements in section 393.77.**

There are also restrictions on the use of automatic cargo-space-heating temperature control devices. Such devices may be used in vehicles transporting Class 3 materials if the following conditions are met:

- **Any electrical apparatus in the cargo area must be non-sparking or explosive-proof.**

- **No combustion apparatus is located in the cargo area, and there is no connection for air return between the cargo area and the combustion apparatus.**

- **The heating system will not heat any part of the cargo to more than 129°F (54°C).**

If the above conditions are not met, the vehicle may still be used to transport Class 3 materials, if the device is rendered inoperable.

Parking & Attending Vehicles

Marked or placarded vehicles containing Class 3 materials should not be parked on or within five feet of the traveled portion of any public highway, except for brief periods necessary to vehicle operation. While such a vehicle is on the highway, it must be attended by the driver, except when the driver is performing necessary duties as operator of the vehicle.

Warning Devices

Liquid-burning flares, fusees, oil lanterns, or any signal produced by a flame must not be carried on or used for protecting any stopped cargo tank motor vehicle transporting Class 3 materials, loaded or empty.

Class 3 Do's

1. Stop engine while loading and unloading.

2. Know the bonding and grounding procedures.

3. Check smaller cargo packages to be sure they are secure.

Class 3 Don'ts

1. Don't smoke or allow others to smoke while handling flammable liquids.

2. Don't leave vehicle unattended while unloading.

3. Don't use any cargo heater without knowing the restrictions.

Reserved

Shipments of
CLASS 4 (Flammable Solids)
& CLASS 5 (Oxidizers)

General loading, transportation and unloading requirements that apply to all hazardous materials shipments can be found after the General Requirements section of this handbook. The following information is specific to Class 4 and Class 5 materials.

Loading & Unloading

Logic dictates the rules that apply to the loading and unloading of Class 4 and Class 5 materials:

- **The entire load must be contained within the body of the vehicle.**

- **The load must be covered either by the vehicle body or tarpaulins or other similar means.**

- **If there is a tailgate or board, it must be closed securely.**

- **Care must be taken to load cargo while dry and to keep it dry.**

- **Provide adequate ventilation for cargos which are known to be subject to heating and/or spontaneous combustion, in order to prevent fires.**

- **Shipments of water-tight bulk containers do not have to be covered by a tarpaulin or other means.**

Pick-Up & Delivery

Provisions concerning Class 4 and Class 5 loads being completely contained inside the body of the vehicle with the tailgate closed do not apply to pick-up and delivery vehicles used entirely for that purpose in and around cities.

Special provisions are necessary for some particular commodities. The following sections detail those requirements.

Charcoal

Charcoal screenings and ground, crushed, pulverized or lump charcoal become more hazardous when wet. Extra care should be taken to keep packages completely dry during loading and carriage.

In addition, these commodities must be loaded so that bags lay horizontally in the vehicle and piled so that there are spaces at least 3.9 inches (10 cm) wide for effective air circulation. These spaces must be maintained between rows of bags. No bags may be piled closer than 5.9 inches (15 cm) from the top of a vehicle with a closed body.

Smokeless Powder

Smokeless powder for small arms, Division 4.1, in quantities not exceeding 100 lb (45.4 kg) net mass of material may be transported in a motor vehicle.

CLASS 4 & 5

Nitrates

All nitrates (except ammonium nitrate with organic coating) must be loaded in vehicles that have been swept clean and are free of projections which could damage the bags. The vehicles may be closed or open-type. If open, the cargo must be covered securely.

Ammonium nitrate with organic coating should not be loaded in all-metal closed vehicles, except those made of aluminum or aluminum alloys.

No Smoking

Don't smoke or carry a lighted cigarette, cigar or pipe on or within 25 feet of a vehicle containing Class 4 or Class 5.

Parking & Attending Vehicles

A marked or placarded vehicle containing Class 4 and/or Class 5 materials should not be parked on or within five feet of the traveled portion of any public roadway, except for brief periods necessary to vehicle operation. While such a vehicle is on the highway, it must be attended by the driver, except when the driver is performing necessary duties as operator of the vehicle.

Class 4 & Class 5 Do's

1. Know loading and covering requirements for cargo.

2. Be sure ventilation is adequate for the cargo you're hauling.

3. Know the special handling requirements for your commodity, if any.

Class 4 & Class 5 Don'ts

1. Don't leave vehicle unattended for long periods.

2. Don't reload damaged cargo without following correct safety procedures to determine if all hazards have been eliminated.

3. Don't smoke on or near vehicle.

Shipments of
DIVISION 6.1 (Poisons) &
DIVISION 2.3 (Poisonous Gases)

General loading, transportation and unloading requirements that apply to all hazardous materials shipments can be found after the General Requirements section of this handbook. The following information is specific to Division 6.1 or Division 2.3 materials.

Loading & Unloading

No Division 6.1 or 2.3 materials may be hauled if there is any interconnection between packagings.

Except as provided in the following paragraph, a motor carrier may not transport a package bearing or required to bear a POISON (TOXIC) or POISON INHALATION HAZARD label or placard in the same motor vehicle with material that is marked as or known to be a foodstuffs, feed or edible material intended for consumption by humans or animals unless the poisonous material is:

(i) Overpacked in a metal drum as specified in §173.25(c) of the regulations, or

(ii) Loaded into a closed unit load device and the foodstuffs, feed, or other edible material are loaded into another closed unit load device.

A motor carrier may not transport a package bearing a POISON label displaying the text "PG III" or bearing a "PG III" mark adjacent to a POISON label, with materials marked as, or known to be, foodstuffs, feed or any other edible material intended for consumption by humans or animals, unless the package containing the Division 6.1, PG III material is separated in a manner that, in the event of leakage from packages under conditions normally incident to transportation, commingling of hazardous materials with foodstuffs, feed or any other edible material will not occur.

A motor carrier may not transport a package bearing or required to bear a POISON (TOXIC), POISON GAS or POISON INHALATION HAZARD label in the driver's compartment (including a sleeper berth) of a motor vehicle.

For highway transport by private or contract motor carrier a Division 6.1, PG I, Hazard Zone A toxic-by-inhalation material that is a hazardous waste may be transported on the same vehicle with Class 3, 4, 5, and 8 materials if the Division 6.1, PG I, Hazard Zone A, hazardous waste is:

• **Filled and packed by the offeror**

• **Packaged in combination packagings as specified in §173.226(c)**

• **On pallets**

• **Separated from Class 3, 4, 5, and 8 materials by a minimum horizontal distance (buffer zone) of 9 feet (2.74 m)**

The buffer zone may be established by a load lock, empty drums, or drums containing hazardous material or non-hazardous material that is compatible with materials in all the drums immediately around them.

Arsenical Materials

Bulk arsenical compounds loaded and unloaded under certain conditions demand extra caution. These materials include:

- **arsenical dust**
- **arsenic trioxide**
- **sodium arsenate**

These materials may be loaded in siftproof steel hopper or dump vehicle bodies, if they are equipped with waterproof and dustproof covers secured on all openings. They must be loaded carefully, using every means to minimize the spread of the compounds into the atmosphere. Loading and unloading may not be done in any area where there might be persons not connected with the transportation. This includes all highways and other public places.

After a vehicle is used for transporting arsenicals, and before it may be used again for any other materials, the vehicle must be flushed with water or use other appropriate means to remove all traces of arsenical material.

Parking & Attending Vehicles

A marked or placarded vehicle containing Division 6.1 or 2.3 materials should not be parked on or within five feet of the traveled portion of any public roadway, except for brief periods necessary to vehicle operation. While such a vehicle is on the highway, it must be attended by the driver, except when the driver is performing necessary duties as an operator of the vehicle.

Division 6.1 & Division 2.3 Do's

1. Know provisions for hauling Division 6.1 materials with foodstuffs.
2. Know special provisions for hauling arsenicals.
3. Be aware of vehicle parking and attendance rules.

Division 6.1 & Division 2.3 Don'ts

1. Don't transport any package labeled poison, poison gas or poison inhalation hazard in the driver's compartment.
2. Don't haul any arsenical material unless vehicle is properly loaded and marked.

Shipments of CLASS 7 (Radioactives)

General loading, transportation and unloading requirements that apply to all hazardous materials shipments can be found after the General Requirements section of this handbook. The following information is specific to Class 7 materials.

Loading & Unloading

The number of packages or overpacks of Class 7 material which may be carried in a transport vehicle is limited by the total transport index number. This number is determined by adding together the transport index numbers given on the labels of individual packages and overpacks. The total may not exceed 50, except in certain special "exclusive use" shipments that the regulations describe.

Class 7 material in a package labeled "RADIOACTIVE YELLOW-II" or "RADIO-ACTIVE YELLOW-III" may not be positioned closer to any area which may be continuously occupied by passengers, employees, animals, or packages of undeveloped film than indicated in the following table. If several packages are involved, distances are determined by the total transport index number.

Total transport index	Minimum separation distance in meters (feet) to nearest undeveloped film for various times of transit					Minimum distance in meters (feet) to area of persons, or minimum distance in meters (feet) from dividing partition of cargo compartments
	Up to 2 hours	2-4 hours	4-8 hours	8-12 hours	Over 12 hours	
None	0.0 (0)	0.0 (0)	0.0 (0)	0.0 (0)	0.0 (0)	0.0 (0)
0.1 to 1.0	0.3 (1)	0.6 (2)	0.9 (3)	1.2 (4)	1.5 (5)	0.3 (1)
1.1 to 5.0	0.9 (3)	1.2 (4)	1.8 (6)	2.4 (8)	3.4 (11)	0.6 (2)
5.1 to 10.0	1.2 (4)	1.8 (6)	2.7 (9)	3.4 (11)	4.6 (15)	0.9 (3)
10.1 to 20.0	1.5 (5)	2.4 (8)	3.7 (12)	4.9 (16)	6.7 (22)	1.2 (4)
20.1 to 30.0	2.1 (7)	3.0 (10)	4.6 (15)	6.1 (20)	8.8 (29)	1.5 (5)
30.1 to 40.0	2.4 (8)	3.4 (11)	5.2 (17)	6.7 (22)	10.1 (33)	1.8 (6)
40.1 to 50.0	2.7 (9)	3.7 (12)	5.8 (19)	7.3 (24)	11.0 (36)	2.1 (7)

Note: The distance in this table must be measured from the nearest point on the nearest packages of Class 7 (radioactive) material.

Shipments of low specific activity materials and surface contaminated objects must be loaded to avoid spilling and scattering loose materials.

Be sure packages are blocked and braced so they cannot change position during normal transportation conditions.

Fissile material, controlled shipments must be shipped as described in §173.457 and §173.459 of the hazardous materials regulations.

Exclusive use condition shipments may not exceed 0.02 mSv per hour (2 mrem per hour) in any position normally occupied in the transport vehicle.

Keep the time spent in a vehicle carrying radioactive materials at an absolute minimum.

Vehicle Contamination

Vehicles used to transport Class 7 materials under exclusive use conditions must be checked after each use with radiation detection instruments. These vehicles may not be returned to use until the radiation dose at every accessible surface is 0.005 mSv per hour (0.5 mrem per hour) or less, and the non-fixed contamination is not greater than prescribed in §173.443.

These contamination limitations do not apply to vehicles used only for transporting Class 7 materials, provided certain conditions are met:

- **Interior surface shows a radiation dose of no more than 0.1 mSv per hour (10 mrem per hour).**

- **At a distance of 3.3 feet (1 m) from any interior surface shows a dose no more than 0.02 mSv per hour (2 mrem per hour).**

- **The vehicle must be stenciled with "For Radioactive Materials Use Only" in letters at least 3 inches (7.6 cm) high in a conspicuous place, on both sides of the exterior of the vehicle.**

- **Vehicles must be kept closed at all times except during loading and unloading.**

Parking & Attending Vehicles

A marked or placarded vehicle containing Class 7 materials should not be parked on or within five feet of the traveled portion of any public roadway except for brief periods necessary to vehicle operation. While such a vehicle is on the highway, it must be attended by the driver, except when the driver is performing necessary duties as operator of the vehicle.

Special Documents

A driver transporting a package that contains a highway route controlled quantity of Class 7 (radioactive) materials must have within immediate possession a written route plan and operate the vehicle in accordance with the route plan. The driver must also have within immediate possession a certificate of training for the Class 7 training required by §397.101(e).

Class 7 Do's

1.   Know how the transport index system works in limiting Class 7 shipments.

2.   Be sure packages are blocked and braced correctly for shipment.

3.   If your vehicle transports Class 7 materials only, know the special provisions for marking and acceptable radiation dose.

4.   Be sure to keep all special documents within immediate possession.

Class 7 Don'ts

1. Don't spend more time than absolutely necessary in a vehicle used for transporting Class 7 materials.

2. Don't leave vehicle unattended for long periods of time.

3. Don't handle damaged cargo unless you have been instructed in disposal procedures by authorized personnel.

4. Don't transport highway route controlled quantities without all required documents.

Reserved

Shipments of CLASS 8 (Corrosives)

General loading, transportation and unloading requirements that apply to all hazardous materials shipments can be found after the General Requirements section of this handbook. The following information is specific to Class 8 materials.

Loading & Transport

Division 4.2 (Spontaneously Combustible) materials must not be loaded and transported with Class 8 (corrosive) liquids.

Nitric Acid

No package of nitric acid of 50 percent or greater concentration may be loaded above any packaging containing any other kind of material.

Storage Batteries

Storage batteries containing any electrolyte and hauled in a mixed load must be loaded so that they are protected from the possibility of other cargo falling on or against them. Battery terminals must be insulated and protected from the possibility of short circuits.

Parking & Attending Vehicles

A marked or placarded vehicle containing Class 8 materials should not be parked on or within five feet of the traveled portion of any public roadway, except for brief periods necessary for vehicle operation. While such a vehicle is on the highway, it must be attended by the driver, except when the driver is performing necessary duties as operator of the vehicle.

Class 8 Do's

1. Be sure vehicle condition meets requirements.

2. Know container handling requirements for loading by hand.

3. Be sure cargo is loaded in accordance with specifications.

4. If you are hauling batteries, be sure they are adequately protected during transit.

Class 8 Don'ts

1. Don't load nitric acid above other commodities.

2. Don't load or transport Division 4.2 (Spontaneously Combustible) materials with corrosive liquids. .

3. Don't park on or near the roadway, or leave your vehicle unattended for more than very brief periods necessary to your duties.

CLASS 8

Reserved

ID Cross Reference

The identification number cross reference index to proper shipping names is useful in determining a shipping name when only an identification number is known. It is also useful in checking if an identification number is correct for a specific shipping description. This listing is for information purposes only, the §172.101 Hazardous Materials Table should be consulted for authorized shipping names and identification numbers.

IDENTIFICATION NUMBER CROSS REFERENCE TO PROPER SHIPPING NAMES IN THE §172.101 HAZARDOUS MATERIALS TABLE

ID Number	Description
UN0004	Ammonium picrate
UN0005	Cartridges for weapons
UN0006	Cartridges for weapons
UN0007	Cartridges for weapons
UN0009	Ammunition, incendiary
UN0010	Ammunition, incendiary
UN0012	Cartridges for weapons, inert projectile or Cartridges, small arms
UN0014	Cartridges for weapons, blank or Cartridges, small arms, blank or Cartridges for tools, blank
UN0015	Ammunition, smoke
UN0016	Ammunition, smoke
UN0018	Ammunition, tear-producing
UN0019	Ammunition, tear-producing
UN0020	Ammunition, toxic
UN0021	Ammunition, toxic
NA0027	Black powder for small arms
UN0027	Black powder or Gunpowder
UN0028	Black powder, compressed or Gunpowder, compressed or Black powder, in pellets or Gunpowder, in pellets
UN0029	Detonators, non-electric
UN0030	Detonators, electric
UN0033	Bombs
UN0034	Bombs
UN0035	Bombs
UN0037	Bombs, photo-flash
UN0038	Bombs, photo-flash
UN0039	Bombs, photo-flash
UN0042	Boosters
UN0043	Bursters
UN0044	Primers, cap type
UN0048	Charges, demolition
UN0049	Cartridges, flash
UN0050	Cartridges, flash
UN0054	Cartridges, signal
UN0055	Cases, cartridge, empty with primer
UN0056	Charges, depth
UN0059	Charges, shaped
UN0060	Charges, supplementary explosive
UN0065	Cord, detonating
UN0066	Cord, igniter
UN0070	Cutters, cable, explosive
UN0072	Cyclotrimethylenetrinitramine, wetted or Cyclonite, wetted or Hexogen, wetted or RDX, wetted

ID CROSS REFERENCE

ID Number	Description
UN0073	Detonators for ammunition
UN0074	Diazodinitrophenol, wetted
UN0075	Diethyleneglycol dinitrate, desensitized
UN0076	Dinitrophenol
UN0077	Dinitrophenolates
UN0078	Dinitroresorcinol
UN0079	Hexanitrodiphenylamine or Dipicrylamine or Hexyl
UN0081	Explosive, blasting, type A
UN0082	Explosive, blasting, type B
UN0083	Explosive, blasting, type C
UN0084	Explosive, blasting, type D
UN0092	Flares, surface
UN0093	Flares, aerial
UN0094	Flash powder
UN0099	Fracturing devices, explosive
UN0101	Fuse, non-detonating
UN0102	Cord, detonating or Fuse, detonating
UN0103	Fuse, igniter
UN0104	Cord, detonating, mild effect or Fuse, detonating, mild effect
UN0105	Fuse, safety
UN0106	Fuzes, detonating
UN0107	Fuzes, detonating
UN0110	Grenades, practice
UN0113	Guanyl nitrosaminoguanylidene hydrazine, wetted
UN0114	Guanyl nitrosaminoguanyltetrazene, wetted or Tetrazene, wetted
UN0118	Hexolite or Hexotol
UN0121	Igniters
NA0124	Jet perforating guns, charged
UN0124	Jet perforating guns, charged
UN0129	Lead azide, wetted
UN0130	Lead styphnate, wetted or Lead trinitroresorcinate, wetted
UN0131	Lighters, fuse
UN0132	Deflagrating metal salts of aromatic nitroderivatives, n.o.s
UN0133	Mannitol hexanitrate, wetted or Nitromannite, wetted
UN0135	Mercury fulminate, wetted
UN0136	Mines
UN0137	Mines
UN0138	Mines
UN0143	Nitroglycerin, desensitized
UN0144	Nitroglycerin, solution in alcohol
UN0146	Nitrostarch
UN0147	Nitro urea
UN0150	Pentaerythrite tetranitrate wetted or Pentaerythritol tetranitrate wetted or PETN, wetted, or Pentaerythrite tetranitrate, or Pentaerythritol tetranitrate, or PETN, desensitized
UN0151	Pentolite
UN0153	Trinitroaniline or Picramide
UN0154	Trinitrophenol or Picric acid
UN0155	Trinitrochlorobenzene or Picryl chloride
UN0159	Powder cake, wetted or Powder paste, wetted
UN0160	Powder, smokeless
UN0161	Powder, smokeless
UN0167	Projectiles
UN0168	Projectiles

ID Number	Description
UN0169	Projectiles
UN0171	Ammunition, illuminating
UN0173	Release devices, explosive
UN0174	Rivets, explosive
UN0180	Rockets
UN0181	Rockets
UN0182	Rockets
UN0183	Rockets
UN0186	Rocket motors
UN0190	Samples, explosive
UN0191	Signal devices, hand
UN0192	Signals, railway track, explosive
UN0193	Signals, railway track, explosive
UN0194	Signals, distress
UN0195	Signals, distress
UN0196	Signals, smoke
UN0197	Signals, smoke
UN0204	Sounding devices, explosive
UN0207	Tetranitroaniline
UN0208	Trinitrophenylmethylnitramine or Tetryl
UN0209	Trinitrotoluene or TNT
UN0212	Tracers for ammunition
UN0213	Trinitroanisole
UN0214	Trinitrobenzene
UN0215	Trinitrobenzoic acid
UN0216	Trinitro-m-cresol
UN0217	Trinitronaphthalene
UN0218	Trinitrophenetole
UN0219	Trinitroresorcinol or Styphnic acid
UN0220	Urea nitrate
UN0221	Warheads, torpedo
UN0222	Ammonium nitrate
UN0224	Barium azide
UN0225	Boosters with detonator
UN0226	Cyclotetramethylenetetranitramine, wetted or HMX, wetted or Octogen, wetted
UN0234	Sodium dinitro-o-cresolate
UN0235	Sodium picramate
UN0236	Zirconium picramate
UN0237	Charges, shaped, flexible, linear
UN0238	Rockets, line-throwing
UN0240	Rockets, line-throwing
UN0241	Explosive, blasting, type E
UN0242	Charges, propelling, for cannon
UN0243	Ammunition, incendiary, white phosphorus
UN0244	Ammunition, incendiary, white phosphorus
UN0245	Ammunition, smoke, white phosphorus
UN0246	Ammunition, smoke, white phosphorus
UN0247	Ammunition, incendiary
UN0248	Contrivances, water-activated
UN0249	Contrivances, water-activated
UN0250	Rocket motors with hypergolic liquids
UN0254	Ammunition, illuminating
UN0255	Detonators, electric
UN0257	Fuzes, detonating

ID Number	Description
UN0266	Octolite or Octol
UN0267	Detonators, non-electric
UN0268	Boosters with detonator
UN0271	Charges, propelling
UN0272	Charges, propelling
UN0275	Cartridges, power device
NA0276	Model rocket motor
UN0276	Cartridges, power device
UN0277	Cartridges, oil well
UN0278	Cartridges, oil well
UN0279	Charges, propelling, for cannon
UN0280	Rocket motors
UN0281	Rocket motors
UN0282	Nitroguanidine or Picrite
UN0283	Boosters
UN0284	Grenades
UN0285	Grenades
UN0286	Warheads, rocket
UN0287	Warheads, rocket
UN0288	Charges, shaped, flexible, linear
UN0289	Cord, detonating
UN0290	Cord, detonating or Fuse, detonating
UN0291	Bombs
UN0292	Grenades
UN0293	Grenades
UN0294	Mines
UN0295	Rockets
UN0296	Sounding devices, explosive
UN0297	Ammunition, illuminating
UN0299	Bombs, photo-flash
UN0300	Ammunition, incendiary
UN0301	Ammunition, tear-producing
UN0303	Ammunition, smoke
UN0305	Flash powder
UN0306	Tracers for ammunition
UN0312	Cartridges, signal
UN0313	Signals, smoke
UN0314	Igniters
UN0315	Igniters
UN0316	Fuzes, igniting
UN0317	Fuzes, igniting
UN0318	Grenades, practice
UN0319	Primers, tubular
UN0320	Primers, tubular
UN0321	Cartridges for weapons
UN0322	Rocket motors with hypergolic liquids
NA0323	Model rocket motor
UN0323	Cartridges, power device
UN0324	Projectiles
UN0325	Igniters
UN0326	Cartridges for weapons, blank
UN0327	Cartridges for weapons, blank or Cartridges, small arms, blank
UN0328	Cartridges for weapons, inert projectile
UN0329	Torpedoes

ID Number	Description
UN0330	Torpedoes
NA0331	Ammonium nitrate-fuel oil mixture
UN0331	Explosive, blasting, type B or Agent blasting, Type B
UN0332	Explosive, blasting, type E or Agent blasting, Type E
UN0333	Fireworks
UN0334	Fireworks
UN0335	Fireworks
UN0336	Fireworks
NA0337	Toy caps
UN0337	Fireworks
UN0338	Cartridges for weapons, blank or Cartridges, small arms, blank
UN0339	Cartridges for weapons, inert projectile or Cartridges, small arms
UN0340	Nitrocellulose
UN0341	Nitrocellulose
UN0342	Nitrocellulose, wetted
UN0343	Nitrocellulose, plasticized
UN0344	Projectiles
UN0345	Projectiles
UN0346	Projectiles
UN0347	Projectiles
UN0348	Cartridges for weapons
UN0349	Articles, explosive, n.o.s.
UN0350	Articles, explosive, n.o.s.
UN0351	Articles, explosive, n.o.s.
UN0352	Articles, explosive, n.o.s.
UN0353	Articles, explosive, n.o.s.
UN0354	Articles, explosive, n.o.s.
UN0355	Articles, explosive, n.o.s.
UN0356	Articles, explosive, n.o.s.
UN0357	Substances, explosive, n.o.s.
UN0358	Substances, explosive, n.o.s.
UN0359	Substances, explosive, n.o.s.
UN0360	Detonator assemblies, non-electric
UN0361	Detonator assemblies, non-electric
UN0362	Ammunition, practice
UN0363	Ammunition, proof
UN0364	Detonators for ammunition
UN0365	Detonators for ammunition
UN0366	Detonators for ammunition
UN0367	Fuzes, detonating
UN0368	Fuzes, igniting
UN0369	Warheads, rocket
UN0370	Warheads, rocket
UN0371	Warheads, rocket
UN0372	Grenades, practice
UN0373	Signal devices, hand
UN0374	Sounding devices, explosive
UN0375	Sounding devices, explosive
UN0376	Primers, tubular
UN0377	Primers, cap type
UN0378	Primers, cap type
UN0379	Cases, cartridges, empty with primer
UN0380	Articles, pyrophoric
UN0381	Cartridges, power device

ID Number	Description
UN0382	Components, explosive train, n.o.s.
UN0383	Components, explosive train, n.o.s.
UN0384	Components, explosive train, n.o.s.
UN0385	5-Nitrobenzotriazol
UN0386	Trinitrobenzenesulfonic acid
UN0387	Trinitrofluorenone
UN0388	Trinitrotoluene and Trinitrobenzene mixtures or TNT and trinitrobenzene mixtures or TNT and hexanitrostilbene mixtures or Trinitrotoluene and hexanitrostilnene mixtures
UN0389	Trinitrotoluene mixtures containing Trinitrobenzene and Hexanitrostilbene or TNT mixtures containing trinitrobenzene and hexanitrostilbene
UN0390	Tritonal
UN0391	RDX and HMX mixtures, wetted, or RDX and HMX mixtures, desensitized
UN0392	Hexanitrostilbene
UN0393	Hexotonal
UN0394	Trinitroresorcinol, wetted or Styphnic acid, wetted
UN0395	Rocket motors, liquid fueled
UN0396	Rocket motors, liquid fueled
UN0397	Rockets, liquid fueled
UN0398	Rockets, liquid fueled
UN0399	Bombs with flammable liquid
UN0400	Bombs with flammable liquid
UN0401	Dipicryl sulfide
UN0402	Ammonium perchlorate
UN0403	Flares, aerial
UN0404	Flares, aerial
UN0405	Cartridges, signal
UN0406	Dinitrosobenzene
UN0407	Tetrazol-1-acetic acid
UN0408	Fuzes, detonating
UN0409	Fuzes, detonating
UN0410	Fuzes, detonating
UN0411	Pentaerythrite tetranitrate or Pentaerythritol tetranitrate or PETN
UN0412	Cartridges for weapons
UN0413	Cartridges for weapons, blank
UN0414	Charges, propelling, for cannon
UN0415	Charges, propelling
UN0417	Cartridges for weapons, inert projectile or Cartridges, small arms
UN0418	Flares, surface
UN0419	Flares, surface
UN0420	Flares, aerial
UN0421	Flares, aerial
UN0424	Projectiles
UN0425	Projectiles
UN0426	Projectiles
UN0427	Projectiles
UN0428	Articles, pyrotechnic
UN0429	Articles, pyrotechnic
UN0430	Articles, pyrotechnic
UN0431	Articles, pyrotechnic
UN0432	Articles, pyrotechnic
UN0433	Powder cake, wetted or Powder paste, wetted
UN0434	Projectiles
UN0435	Projectiles
UN0436	Rockets

ID Number	Description
UN0437	Rockets
UN0438	Rockets
UN0439	Charges, shaped
UN0440	Charges, shaped
UN0441	Charges, shaped
UN0442	Charges, explosive, commercial
UN0443	Charges, explosive, commercial
UN0444	Charges, explosive, commercial
UN0445	Charges, explosive, commercial
UN0446	Cases, combustible, empty, without primer
UN0447	Cases, combustible, empty, without primer
UN0448	5-Mercaptotetrazol-1-acetic acid
UN0449	Torpedoes, liquid fueled
UN0450	Torpedoes, liquid fueled
UN0451	Torpedoes
UN0452	Grenades practice
UN0453	Rockets, line-throwing
UN0454	Igniters
UN0455	Detonators, non-electric
UN0456	Detonators, electric
UN0457	Charges, bursting, plastics bonded
UN0458	Charges, bursting, plastics bonded
UN0459	Charges, bursting, plastics bonded
UN0460	Charges, bursting, plastics bonded
UN0461	Components, explosive train, n.o.s.
UN0462	Articles, explosive, n.o.s.
UN0463	Articles, explosive, n.o.s.
UN0464	Articles, explosive, n.o.s.
UN0465	Articles, explosive, n.o.s.
UN0466	Articles, explosive, n.o.s.
UN0467	Articles, explosive, n.o.s.
UN0468	Articles, explosive, n.o.s.
UN0469	Articles, explosive, n.o.s.
UN0470	Articles, explosive, n.o.s.
UN0471	Articles, explosive, n.o.s.
UN0472	Articles, explosive, n.o.s.
UN0473	Substances, explosive, n.o.s.
UN0474	Substances, explosive, n.o.s.
UN0475	Substances, explosive, n.o.s.
UN0476	Substances, explosive, n.o.s.
UN0477	Substances, explosive, n.o.s.
UN0478	Substances, explosive, n.o.s.
UN0479	Substances, explosives, n.o.s.
UN0480	Substances, explosives, n.o.s.
UN0481	Substances, explosive, n.o.s.
UN0482	Substances, explosive, very insensitive, n.o.s., or Substances, EVI, n.o.s.
UN0483	Cyclotrimethylenetrinitramine, desensitize or Cyclonite, desensitized or Hexogen, desensitized or RDX, desensitized
UN0484	Cyclotetramethylenetetrani-tramine, desensitized or Octogen, desensitized or HMX, desensitized
UN0485	Substances, explosive, n.o.s.
UN0486	Articles, explosive, extremely insensitive or Articles, EEI
UN0487	Signals, smoke
UN0488	Ammunition, practice

ID Number	Description
UN0489	Dinitroglycoluril or Dingu
UN0490	Nitrotriazolone or NTO
UN0491	Charges, propelling
UN0492	Signals, railway track, explosive
UN0493	Signals, railway track, explosive
NA0494	Jet perforating guns, charged
UN0494	Jet perforating guns, charged
UN0495	Propellant, liquid
UN0496	Octonal
UN0497	Propellant, liquid
UN0498	Propellant, solid
UN0499	Propellant, solid
UN0500	Detonator assemblies, non-electric
UN0501	Propellant, solid
UN0502	Rockets
UN0503	Safety devices, pyrotechnic
UN0504	1H-Tetrazole
UN0505	Signals, distress
UN0506	Signals, distress
UN0507	Signals, smoke
UN0508	1-Hydroxybenzotriazole, anhydrous
UN0509	Powder, smokeless
UN0510	Rocket motors
UN1001	Acetylene, dissolved
UN1002	Air, compressed
UN1003	Air, refrigerated liquid
UN1005	Ammonia, anhydrous
UN1006	Argon
UN1008	Boron trifluoride
UN1009	Bromotrifluoromethane or Refrigerant gas R 13B1
UN1010	Butadienes, stabilized or Butadienes and Hydrocarbon mixture, stabilized
UN1011	Butane
UN1012	Butylene
UN1013	Carbon dioxide
UN1016	Carbon monoxide, compressed
UN1017	Chlorine
UN1018	Chlorodifluoromethane or Refrigerant gas R22
UN1020	Chloropentafluoroethane or Refrigerant gas R115
UN1021	1-Chloro-1,2,2,2-tetrafluoroethane or Refrigerant gas R 124
UN1022	Chlorotrifluoromethane or Refrigerant gas R 13
UN1023	Coal gas, compressed
UN1026	Cyanogen
UN1027	Cyclopropane
UN1028	Dichlorodifluoromethane or Refrigerant gas R 12
UN1029	Dichlorofluoromethane or Refrigerant gas R 21
UN1030	1, 1-Difluoroethane or Refrigerant gas R 152a
UN1032	Dimethylamine, anhydrous
UN1033	Dimethyl ether
UN1035	Ethane
UN1036	Ethylamine
UN1037	Ethyl chloride
UN1038	Ethylene, refrigerated liquid
UN1039	Ethyl methyl ether
UN1040	Ethylene oxide or Ethylene oxide with nitrogen

ID Number	Description
UN1041	Ethylene oxide and Carbon dioxide mixtures
UN1043	Fertilizer ammoniating solution
UN1044	Fire extinguishers
UN1045	Fluorine, compressed
UN1046	Helium, compressed
UN1048	Hydrogen bromide, anhydrous
UN1049	Hydrogen, compressed
UN1050	Hydrogen chloride, anhydrous
UN1051	Hydrogen cyanide, stabilized
UN1052	Hydrogen fluoride, anhydrous
UN1053	Hydrogen sulfide
UN1055	Isobutylene
UN1056	Krypton, compressed
NA1057	Lighters
UN1057	Lighters or Lighter refills
UN1058	Liquefied gases
UN1060	Methyl acetylene and propadiene mixtures, stabilized
UN1061	Methylamine, anhydrous
UN1062	Methyl bromide
UN1063	Methyl chloride or Refrigerant gas R 40
UN1064	Methyl mercaptan
UN1065	Neon, compressed
UN1066	Nitrogen, compressed
UN1067	Dinitrogen tetroxide
UN1069	Nitrosyl chloride
UN1070	Nitrous oxide
UN1071	Oil gas, compressed
UN1072	Oxygen, compressed
UN1073	Oxygen, refrigerated liquid
UN1075	Petroleum gases, liquefied or Liquefied petroleum gas
UN1076	Phosgene
UN1077	Propylene
UN1078	Refrigerant gases, n.o.s.
UN1079	Sulfur dioxide
UN1080	Sulfur hexafluoride
UN1081	Tetrafluoroethylene, stabilized
UN1082	Trifluorochloroethylene, stabilized or Refrigerant gas R 1113
UN1083	Trimethylamine, anhydrous
UN1085	Vinyl bromide, stabilized
UN1086	Vinyl chloride, stabilized
UN1087	Vinyl methyl ether, stabilized
UN1088	Acetal
UN1089	Acetaldehyde
UN1090	Acetone
UN1091	Acetone oils
UN1092	Acrolein, stabilized
UN1093	Acrylonitrile, stabilized
UN1098	Allyl alcohol
UN1099	Allyl bromide
UN1100	Allyl chloride
UN1104	Amyl acetates
UN1105	Pentanols
UN1106	Amylamines
UN1107	Amyl chlorides

ID Number	Description
UN1108	1-Pentene
UN1109	Amyl formates
UN1110	n-Amyl methyl ketone
UN1111	Amyl mercaptans
UN1112	Amyl nitrate
UN1113	Amyl nitrites
UN1114	Benzene
UN1120	Butanols
UN1123	Butyl acetates
UN1125	n-Butylamine
UN1126	1-Bromobutane
UN1127	Chlorobutanes
UN1128	n-Butyl formate
UN1129	Butyraldehyde
UN1130	Camphor oil
UN1131	Carbon disulfide
UN1133	Adhesives
UN1134	Chlorobenzene
UN1135	Ethylene chlorohydrin
UN1136	Coal tar distillates, flammable
UN1139	Coating solution
UN1143	Crotonaldehyde or Crotonaldehyde, stabilized
UN1144	Crotonylene
UN1145	Cyclohexane
UN1146	Cyclopentane
UN1147	Decahydronaphthalene
UN1148	Diacetone alcohol
UN1149	Dibutyl ethers
UN1150	1,2-Dichloroethylene
UN1152	Dichloropentanes
UN1153	Ethylene glycol diethyl ether
UN1154	Diethylamine
UN1155	Diethyl ether or Ethyl ether
UN1156	Diethyl ketone
UN1157	Diisobutyl ketone
UN1158	Diisopropylamine
UN1159	Diisopropyl ether
UN1160	Dimethylamine solution
UN1161	Dimethyl carbonate
UN1162	Dimethyldichlorosilane
UN1163	Dimethylhydrazine, unsymmetrical
UN1164	Dimethyl sulfide
UN1165	Dioxane
UN1166	Dioxolane
UN1167	Divinyl ether, stabilized
UN1169	Extracts, aromatic, liquid
UN1170	Ethanol or Ethyl alcohol or Ethanol solutions or Ethyl alcohol solutions
UN1171	Ethylene glycol monoethyl ether
UN1172	Ethylene glycol monoethyl ether acetate
UN1173	Ethyl acetate
UN1175	Ethylbenzene
UN1176	Ethyl borate
UN1177	2-Ethylbutyl acetate
UN1178	2-Ethylbutyraldehyde

ID Number	Description
UN1179	Ethyl butyl ether
UN1180	Ethyl butyrate
UN1181	Ethyl chloroacetate
UN1182	Ethyl chloroformate
UN1183	Ethyldichlorosilane
UN1184	Ethylene dichloride
UN1185	Ethyleneimine, stabilized
UN1188	Ethylene glycol monomethyl ether
UN1189	Ethylene glycol monomethyl ether acetate
UN1190	Ethyl formate
UN1191	Octyl aldehydes
UN1192	Ethyl lactate
UN1193	Ethyl methyl ketone or Methyl ethyl ketone
UN1194	Ethyl nitrite solutions
UN1195	Ethyl propionate
UN1196	Ethyltrichlorosilane
UN1197	Extracts, flavoring, liquid
UN1198	Formaldehyde solutions, flammable
UN1199	Furaldehydes
UN1201	Fusel oil
UN1202	Gas oil or Diesel fuel or Heating oil, light
UN1203	Gasoline
UN1204	Nitroglycerin solution in alcohol
UN1206	Heptanes
UN1207	Hexaldehyde
UN1208	Hexanes
UN1210	Printing ink or Printing ink related material
UN1212	Isobutanol or isobutyl alcohol
UN1213	Isobutyl acetate
UN1214	Isobutylamine
UN1216	Isooctenes
UN1218	Isoprene, stabilized
UN1219	Isopropanol or isopropyl alcohol
UN1220	Isopropyl acetate
UN1221	Isopropylamine
UN1222	Isopropyl nitrate
UN1223	Kerosene
UN1224	Ketones, liquid, n.o.s.
UN1228	Mercaptans, liquid, flammable, toxic, n.o.s. or Mercaptan mixtures, liquid, flammable, toxic, n.o.s.
UN1229	Mesityl oxide
UN1230	Methanol
UN1231	Methyl acetate
UN1233	Methylamyl acetate
UN1234	Methylal
UN1235	Methylamine, aqueous solution
UN1237	Methyl butyrate
UN1238	Methyl chloroformate
UN1239	Methyl chloromethyl ether
UN1242	Methyldichlorosilane
UN1243	Methyl formate
UN1244	Methylhydrazine
UN1245	Methyl isobutyl ketone
UN1246	Methyl isopropenyl ketone, stabilized

ID Number	Description
UN1247	Methyl methacrylate monomer, stabilized
UN1248	Methyl propionate
UN1249	Methyl propyl ketone
UN1250	Methyltrichlorosilane
UN1251	Methyl vinyl ketone, stabilized
UN1259	Nickel carbonyl
UN1261	Nitromethane
UN1262	Octanes
UN1263	Paint
UN1263	Paint related material
UN1264	Paraldehyde
UN1265	Pentanes
UN1266	Perfumery products
UN1267	Petroleum crude oil
UN1268	Petroleum distillates, n.o.s. or Petroleum products, n.o.s.
NA1270	Petroleum oil
UN1272	Pine oil
UN1274	n-Propanol or Propyl alcohol, normal
UN1275	Propionaldehyde
UN1276	n-Propyl acetate
UN1277	Propylamine
UN1278	1-Chloropropane
UN1278	Propyl chloride
UN1279	1,2-Dichloropropane
UN1280	Propylene oxide
UN1281	Propyl formates
UN1282	Pyridine
UN1286	Rosin oil
UN1287	Rubber solution
UN1288	Shale oil
UN1289	Sodium methylate solutions
UN1292	Tetraethyl silicate
UN1293	Tinctures, medicinal
UN1294	Toluene
UN1295	Trichlorosilane
UN1296	Triethylamine
UN1297	Trimethylamine, aqueous solutions
UN1298	Trimethylchlorosilane
UN1299	Turpentine
UN1300	Turpentine substitute
UN1301	Vinyl acetate, stabilized
UN1302	Vinyl ethyl ether, stabilized
UN1303	Vinylidene chloride, stabilized
UN1304	Vinyl isobutyl ether, stabilized
UN1305	Vinyltrichlorosilane
UN1306	Wood preservatives, liquid
UN1307	Xylenes
UN1308	Zirconium suspended in a liquid
UN1309	Aluminum powder, coated
UN1310	Ammonium picrate, wetted
UN1312	Borneol
UN1313	Calcium resinate
UN1314	Calcium resinate, fused
UN1318	Cobalt resinate, precipitated

ID Number	Description
UN1320	Dinitrophenol, wetted
UN1321	Dinitrophenolates, wetted
UN1322	Dinitroresorcinol, wetted
UN1323	Ferrocerium
UN1324	Films, nitrocellulose base
NA1325	Fusee
UN1325	Flammable solids, organic, n.o.s.
UN1326	Hafnium powder, wetted
UN1328	Hexamethylenetetramine
UN1330	Manganese resinate
UN1331	Matches, strike anywhere
UN1332	Metaldehyde
UN1333	Cerium
UN1334	Naphthalene, crude or Naphthalene, refined
UN1336	Nitroguanidine, wetted or Picrite, wetted
UN1337	Nitrostarch, wetted
UN1338	Phosphorus, amorphous
UN1339	Phosphorus heptasulfide
UN1340	Phosphorus pentasulfide
UN1341	Phosphorus sesquisulfide
UN1343	Phosphorus trisulfide
UN1344	Trinitrophenol, wetted
UN1345	Rubber scrap or shoddy
UN1346	Silicon powder, amorphous
UN1347	Silver picrate, wetted
UN1348	Sodium dinitro-o-cresolate, wetted
UN1349	Sodium picramate, wetted
NA1350	Sulfur
UN1350	Sulfur
UN1352	Titanium powder, wetted
UN1353	Fibers or Fabrics inpregnated with weakly nitrated nitrocellulose, n.o.s.
UN1354	Trinitrobenzene, wetted
UN1355	Trinitrobenzoic acid, wetted
UN1356	Trinitrotoluene, wetted or TNT, wetted
UN1357	Urea nitrate, wetted
UN1358	Zirconium powder, wetted
UN1360	Calcium phosphide
NA1361	Charcoal
UN1361	Carbon
UN1362	Carbon, activated
UN1363	Copra
UN1364	Cotton waste, oily
NA1365	Cotton
UN1365	Cotton, wet
UN1369	p-Nitrosodimethylaniline
UN1370	Dimethylzinc
UN1372	Fibers, animal or Fibers, vegetable
UN1373	Fibers or Fabrics, animal or vegetable or Synthetic, n.o.s.
UN1374	Fish meal, unstablized or Fish scrap, unstablized
UN1376	Iron oxide, spent, or Iron sponge, spent
UN1378	Metal catalyst, wetted
UN1379	Paper, unsaturated oil treated
UN1380	Pentaborane

ID Number	Description
UN1381	Phosphorus, white dry or Phosphorus, white, under water or Phosphorus white, in solution or Phosphorus, yellow dry or Phosphorus, yellow, under water or Phosphorus, yellow, in solution
UN1382	Potassium sulfide, anhydrous or Potassium sulfide
UN1383	Pyrophoric metals, n.o.s., or Pyrophoric alloys, n.o.s.
UN1384	Sodium dithionite or Sodium hydrosulfite
UN1385	Sodium sulfide, anhydrous or Sodium sulfide
UN1386	Seed cake
UN1387	Wool waste, wet
UN1389	Alkali metal amalgam, liquid
UN1390	Alkali metal amides
UN1391	Alkali metal dispersions, or Alkaline earth metal dispersions
UN1392	Alkaline earth metal amalgams, liquid
UN1393	Alkaline earth metal alloys, n.o.s.
UN1394	Aluminum carbide
UN1395	Aluminum ferrosilicon powder
UN1396	Aluminum powder, uncoated
UN1397	Aluminum phosphide
UN1398	Aluminum silicon powder, uncoated
UN1400	Barium
UN1401	Calcium
UN1402	Calcium carbide
UN1403	Calcium cyanamide
UN1404	Calcium hydride
UN1405	Calcium silicide
UN1407	Cesium or Caesium
UN1408	Ferrosilicon
UN1409	Metal hydrides, water reactive, n.o.s.
UN1410	Lithium aluminum hydride
UN1411	Lithium aluminum hydride, ethereal
UN1413	Lithium borohydride
UN1414	Lithium hydride
UN1415	Lithium
UN1417	Lithium silicon
UN1418	Magnesium, powder or Magnesium alloys, powder
UN1419	Magnesium aluminum phosphide
UN1420	Potassium, metal alloys, liquid
UN1421	Alkali metal alloys, liquid, n.o.s.
UN1422	Potassium sodium alloys, liquid
UN1423	Rubidium
UN1426	Sodium borohydride
UN1427	Sodium hydride
UN1428	Sodium
UN1431	Sodium methylate
UN1432	Sodium phosphide
UN1433	Stannic phosphide
UN1435	Zinc ashes
UN1436	Zinc powder or Zinc dust
UN1437	Zirconium hydride
UN1438	Aluminum nitrate
UN1439	Ammonium dichromate
UN1442	Ammonium perchlorate
UN1444	Ammonium persulfate
UN1445	Barium chlorate, solid

ID Number	Description
UN1446	Barium nitrate
UN1447	Barium perchlorate, solid
UN1448	Barium permanganate
UN1449	Barium peroxide
UN1450	Bromates, inorganic, n.o.s.
UN1451	Cesium nitrate or Caesium nitrate
UN1452	Calcium chlorate
UN1453	Calcium chlorite
UN1454	Calcium nitrate
UN1455	Calcium perchlorate
UN1456	Calcium permanganate
UN1457	Calcium peroxide
UN1458	Chlorate and borate mixtures
UN1459	Chlorate and magnesium chloride mixture solid
UN1461	Chlorates, inorganic, n.o.s.
UN1462	Chlorites, inorganic, n.o.s.
UN1463	Chromium trioxide, anhydrous
UN1465	Didymium nitrate
UN1466	Ferric nitrate
UN1467	Guanidine nitrate
UN1469	Lead nitrate
UN1470	Lead perchlorate, solid
UN1471	Lithium hypochlorite, dry or Lithium hypochlorite mixture
UN1472	Lithium peroxide
UN1473	Magnesium bromate
UN1474	Magnesium nitrate
UN1475	Magnesium perchlorate
UN1476	Magnesium peroxide
UN1477	Nitrates, inorganic, n.o.s.
UN1479	Oxidizing, solid, n.o.s.
UN1481	Perchlorates, inorganic, n.o.s.
UN1482	Permanganates, inorganic, n.o.s.
UN1483	Peroxides, inorganic, n.o.s.
UN1484	Potassium bromate
UN1485	Potassium chlorate
UN1486	Potassium nitrate
UN1487	Potassium nitrate and sodium nitrite mixtures
UN1488	Potassium nitrite
UN1489	Potassium perchlorate
UN1490	Potassium permanganate
UN1491	Potassium peroxide
UN1492	Potassium persulfate
UN1493	Silver nitrate
UN1494	Sodium bromate
UN1495	Sodium chlorate
UN1496	Sodium chlorite
UN1498	Sodium nitrate
UN1499	Sodium nitrate and potassium nitrate mixtures
UN1500	Sodium nitrite
UN1502	Sodium perchlorate
UN1503	Sodium permanganate
UN1504	Sodium peroxide
UN1505	Sodium persulfate
UN1506	Strontium chlorate

ID Number	Description
UN1507	Strontium nitrate
UN1508	Strontium perchlorate
UN1509	Strontium peroxide
UN1510	Tetranitromethane
UN1511	Urea hydrogen peroxide
UN1512	Zinc ammonium nitrite
UN1513	Zinc chlorate
UN1514	Zinc nitrate
UN1515	Zinc permanganate
UN1516	Zinc peroxide
UN1517	Zirconium picramate, wetted
UN1541	Acetone cyanohydrin, stabilized
UN1544	Alkaloids, solid, n.o.s. or Alkaloid salts, solid, n.o.s.
UN1545	Allyl isothiocyanate, stabilized
UN1546	Ammonium arsenate
UN1547	Aniline
UN1548	Aniline hydrochloride
UN1549	Antimony compounds, inorganic, solid, n.o.s.
UN1550	Antimony lactate
UN1551	Antimony potassium tartrate
UN1553	Arsenic acid, liquid
UN1554	Arsenic acid, solid
UN1555	Arsenic bromide
NA1556	Methyldichloroarsine
UN1556	Arsenic compounds, liquid, n.o.s.
UN1557	Arsenic compounds, solid, n.o.s.
UN1558	Arsenic
UN1559	Arsenic pentoxide
UN1560	Arsenic trichloride
UN1561	Arsenic trioxide
UN1562	Arsenical dust
UN1564	Barium compounds, n.o.s.
UN1565	Barium cyanide
UN1566	Beryllium compounds, n.o.s.
UN1567	Beryllium, powder
UN1569	Bromoacetone
UN1570	Brucine
UN1571	Barium azide, wetted
UN1572	Cacodylic acid
UN1573	Calcium arsenate
UN1574	Calcium arsenate and calcium arsenite, mixtures, solid
UN1575	Calcium cyanide
UN1577	Chlorodinitrobenzenes, liquid
UN1578	Chloronitrobenzenes, solid
UN1579	4-Chloro-o-toluidine hydrochloride, solid
UN1580	Chloropicrin
UN1581	Chloropicrin and methyl bromide mixtures
UN1582	Chloropicrin and methyl chloride mixtures
UN1583	Chloropicrin mixtures, n.o.s.
UN1585	Copper acetoarsenite
UN1586	Copper arsenite
UN1587	Copper cyanide
UN1588	Cyanides, inorganic, solid, n.o.s.
UN1589	Cyanogen chloride, stabilized

ID Number	Description
UN1590	Dichloroanilines, liquid
UN1591	o-Dichlorobenzene
UN1593	Dichloromethane
UN1594	Diethyl sulfate
UN1595	Dimethyl sulfate
UN1596	Dinitroanilines
UN1597	Dinitrobenzenes, liquid
UN1598	Dinitro-o-cresol
UN1599	Dinitrophenol solutions
UN1600	Dinitrotoluenes, molten
UN1601	Disinfectants, solid, toxic, n.o.s.
UN1602	Dyes, liquid, toxic, n.o.s. or Dye intermediates, liquid, toxic, n.o.s.
UN1603	Ethyl bromoacetate
UN1604	Ethylenediamine
UN1605	Ethylene dibromide
UN1606	Ferric arsenate
UN1607	Ferric arsenite
UN1608	Ferrous arsenate
UN1611	Hexaethyl tetraphosphate
UN1612	Hexaethyl tetraphosphate and compressed gas mixtures
NA1613	Hydrocyanic acid, aqueous solutions
UN1613	Hydrocyanic acid, aqueous solutions or Hydrogen cyanide, aqueous solutions
UN1614	Hydrogen cyanide, stabilized
UN1616	Lead acetate
UN1617	Lead arsenates
UN1618	Lead arsenites
UN1620	Lead cyanide
UN1621	London purple
UN1622	Magnesium arsenate
UN1623	Mercuric arsenate
UN1624	Mercuric chloride
UN1625	Mercuric nitrate
UN1626	Mercuric potassium cyanide
UN1627	Mercurous nitrate
UN1629	Mercury acetate
UN1630	Mercury ammonium chloride
UN1631	Mercury benzoate
UN1634	Mercury bromides
UN1636	Mercury cyanide
UN1637	Mercury gluconate
UN1638	Mercury iodide
UN1639	Mercury nucleate
UN1640	Mercury oleate
UN1641	Mercury oxide
UN1642	Mercury oxycyanide, desensitized
UN1643	Mercury potassium iodide
UN1644	Mercury salicylate
UN1645	Mercury sulfates
UN1646	Mercury thiocyanate
UN1647	Methyl bromide and ethylene dibromide mixtures, liquid
UN1648	Acetonitrile
UN1649	Motor fuel anti-knock mixtures
UN1650	beta-Naphthylamine, solid
UN1651	Naphthylthiourea

ID Number	Description
UN1652	Naphthylurea
UN1653	Nickel cyanide
UN1654	Nicotine
UN1655	Nicotine compounds, solid, n.o.s. or Nicotine preparations, solid, n.o.s.
UN1656	Nicotine hydrochloride liquid or solution
UN1657	Nicotine salicylate
UN1658	Nicotine sulfate solution
UN1659	Nicotine tartrate
UN1660	Nitric oxide, compressed
UN1661	Nitroanilines
UN1662	Nitrobenzene
UN1663	Nitrophenols
UN1664	Nitrotoluenes, liquid
UN1665	Nitroxylenes, liquid
UN1669	Pentachloroethane
UN1670	Perchloromethyl mercaptan
UN1671	Phenol, solid
UN1672	Phenylcarbylamine chloride
UN1673	Phenylenediamines
UN1674	Phenylmercuric acetate
UN1677	Potassium arsenate
UN1678	Potassium arsenite
UN1679	Potassium cuprocyanide
UN1680	Potassium cyanide, solid
UN1683	Silver arsenite
UN1684	Silver cyanide
UN1685	Sodium arsenate
UN1686	Sodium arsenite, aqueous solutions
UN1687	Sodium azide
UN1688	Sodium cacodylate
UN1689	Sodium cyanide, solid
UN1690	Sodium fluoride, solid
UN1691	Strontium arsenite
UN1692	Strychnine or Strychnine salts
NA1693	Tear gas devices
UN1693	Tear gas substances, liquid, n.o.s.
UN1694	Bromobenzyl cyanides, liquid
UN1695	Chloroacetone, stabilized
UN1697	Chloroacetophenone, solid
UN1698	Diphenylamine chloroarsine
UN1699	Diphenylchloroarsine, liquid
UN1700	Tear gas candles
UN1701	Xylyl bromide, liquid
UN1702	1,1,2,2-Tetrachloroethane
UN1704	Tetraethyl dithiopyrophosphate
UN1707	Thallium compounds, n.o.s.
UN1708	Toluidines, liquid
UN1709	2,4-Toluylenediamine, solid or 2,4-Toluenediamine, solid
UN1710	Trichloroethylene
UN1711	Xylidines, liquid
UN1712	Zinc arsenate or Zinc arsenite or Zinc arsenate and zinc arsenite mixtures
UN1713	Zinc cyanide
UN1714	Zinc phosphide
UN1715	Acetic anhydride

ID Number	Description
UN1716	Acetyl bromide
UN1717	Acetyl chloride
UN1718	Butyl acid phosphate
UN1719	Caustic alkali liquids, n.o.s.
UN1722	Allyl chloroformate
UN1723	Allyl iodide
UN1724	Allyltrichlorosilane, stabilized
UN1725	Aluminum bromide, anhydrous
UN1726	Aluminum chloride, anhydrous
UN1727	Ammonium hydrogendifluoride, solid
UN1728	Amyltrichlorosilane
UN1729	Anisoyl chloride
UN1730	Antimony pentachloride, liquid
UN1731	Antimony pentachloride, solutions
UN1732	Antimony pentafluoride
UN1733	Antimony trichloride, liquid
UN1733	Antimony trichloride, solid
UN1736	Benzoyl chloride
UN1737	Benzyl bromide
UN1738	Benzyl chloride
UN1739	Benzyl chloroformate
UN1740	Hydrogendifluoride, solid, n.o.s.
UN1741	Boron trichloride
UN1742	Boron trifluoride acetic acid complex, liquid
UN1743	Boron trifluoride propionic acid complex, liquid
UN1744	Bromine or Bromine solutions
UN1745	Bromine pentafluoride
UN1746	Bromine trifluoride
UN1747	Butyltrichlorosilane
UN1748	Calcium hypochlorite, dry or Calcium hypochlorite mixture, dry
UN1749	Chlorine trifluoride
UN1750	Chloroacetic acid, solution
UN1751	Chloroacetic acid, solid
UN1752	Chloroacetyl chloride
UN1753	Chlorophenyltrichlorosilane
UN1754	Chlorosulfonic acid
UN1755	Chromic acid solution
UN1756	Chromic fluoride, solid
UN1757	Chromic fluoride, solution
UN1758	Chromium oxychloride
NA1759	Ferrous chloride, solid
UN1759	Corrosive solids, n.o.s.
NA1760	Chemical kit
NA1760	Compounds, cleaning liquid
NA1760	Compounds, tree killing, liquid or Compounds, weed killing, liquid
NA1760	Ferrous chloride, solution
UN1760	Corrosive liquids, n.o.s.
UN1761	Cupriethylenediamine solution
UN1762	Cyclohexenyltrichlorosilane
UN1763	Cyclohexyltrichlorosilane
UN1764	Dichloroacetic acid
UN1765	Dichloroacetyl chloride
UN1766	Dichlorophenyltrichlorosilane
UN1767	Diethyldichlorosilane

ID Number	Description
UN1768	Difluorophosphoric acid, anhydrous
UN1769	Diphenyldichlorosilane
UN1770	Diphenylmethyl bromide
UN1771	Dodecyltrichlorosilane
UN1773	Ferric chloride, anhydrous
UN1774	Fire extinguisher charges
UN1775	Fluoroboric acid
UN1776	Fluorophosphoric acid anhydrous
UN1777	Fluorosulfonic acid
UN1778	Fluorosilicic acid
UN1779	Formic acid
UN1780	Fumaryl chloride
UN1781	Hexadecyltrichlorosilane
UN1782	Hexafluorophosphoric acid
UN1783	Hexamethylenediamine solution
UN1784	Hexyltrichlorosilane
UN1786	Hydrofluoric acid and Sulfuric acid mixtures
UN1787	Hydriodic acid
UN1788	Hydrobromic acid
UN1789	Hydrochloric acid
UN1790	Hydrofluoric acid
UN1791	Hypochlorite solutions
UN1792	Iodine monochloride, solid
UN1793	Isopropyl acid phosphate
UN1794	Lead sulfate
UN1796	Nitrating acid mixtures
UN1798	Nitrohydrochloric acid
UN1799	Nonyltrichlorosilane
UN1800	Octadecyltrichlorosilane
UN1801	Octyltrichlorosilane
UN1802	Perchloric acid
UN1803	Phenolsulfonic acid, liquid
UN1804	Phenyltrichlorosilane
UN1805	Phosphoric acid solution
UN1806	Phosphorus pentachloride
UN1807	Phosphorus pentoxide
UN1808	Phosphorus tribromide
UN1809	Phosphorus trichloride
UN1810	Phosphorus oxychloride
UN1811	Potassium hydrogendifluoride solid
UN1812	Potassium fluoride, solid
UN1813	Potassium hydroxide, solid
UN1814	Potassium hydroxide, solution
UN1815	Propionyl chloride
UN1816	Propyltrichlorosilane
UN1817	Pyrosulfuryl chloride
UN1818	Silicon tetrachloride
UN1819	Sodium aluminate, solution
UN1823	Sodium hydroxide, solid
UN1824	Sodium hydroxide solution
UN1825	Sodium monoxide
UN1826	Nitrating acid mixtures spent
UN1826	Nitrating acid mixtures, spent
UN1827	Stannic chloride, anhydrous

ID Number	Description
UN1828	Sulfur chlorides
UN1829	Sulfur trioxide, stabilized
UN1830	Sulfuric acid
UN1831	Sulfuric acid, fuming
UN1832	Sulfuric acid, spent
UN1833	Sulfurous acid
UN1834	Sulfuryl chloride
UN1835	Tetramethylammonium hydroxide solution
UN1836	Thionyl chloride
UN1837	Thiophosphoryl chloride
UN1838	Titanium tetrachloride
UN1839	Trichloroacetic acid
UN1840	Zinc chloride, solution
UN1841	Acetaldehyde ammonia
UN1843	Ammonium dinitro-o-cresolate, solid
UN1845	Carbon dioxide, solid or Dry ice
UN1846	Carbon tetrachloride
UN1847	Potassium sulfide, hydrated
UN1848	Propionic acid
UN1849	Sodium sulfide, hydrated
UN1851	Medicine, liquid, toxic, n.o.s.
UN1854	Barium alloys, pyrophoric
UN1855	Calcium, pyrophoric or Calcium alloys, pyrophoric
UN1856	Rags, oily
UN1857	Textile waste, wet
UN1858	Hexafluoropropylene, compressed or Refrigerant gas R 1216
UN1859	Silicon tetrafluoride
UN1860	Vinyl fluoride, stabilized
UN1862	Ethyl crotonate
UN1863	Fuel, aviation, turbine engine
UN1865	n-Propyl nitrate
UN1866	Resin Solution
UN1868	Decaborane
UN1869	Magnesium or Magnesium alloys
UN1870	Potassium borohydride
UN1871	Titanium hydride
UN1872	Lead dioxide
UN1873	Perchloric acid
UN1884	Barium oxide
UN1885	Benzidine
UN1886	Benzylidene chloride
UN1887	Bromochloromethane
UN1888	Chloroform
UN1889	Cyanogen bromide
UN1891	Ethyl bromide
UN1892	Ethyldichloroarsine
UN1894	Phenylmercuric hydroxide
UN1895	Phenylmercuric nitrate
UN1897	Tetrachloroethylene
UN1898	Acetyl iodide
UN1902	Diisooctyl acid phosphate
UN1903	Disinfectant, liquid, corrosive, n.o.s. or Disinfectants, liquid, corrosive, n.o.s.
UN1905	Selenic acid
UN1906	Sludge, acid

ID Number	Description
UN1907	Soda lime
UN1908	Chlorite solution
UN1910	Calcium oxide
NA1911	Diborane mixtures
UN1911	Diborane
UN1912	Methyl chloride and methylene chloride mixtures
UN1913	Neon, refrigerated liquid
UN1914	Butyl propionates
UN1915	Cyclohexanone
UN1916	2,2'-Dichlorodiethyl ether
UN1917	Ethyl acrylate, stabilized
UN1918	Isopropylbenzene
UN1919	Methyl acrylate, stabilized
UN1920	Nonanes
UN1921	Propyleneimine, stabilized
UN1922	Pyrrolidine
UN1923	Calcium dithionite or Calcium hydrosulfite
UN1928	Methyl magnesium bromide, in ethyl ether
UN1929	Potassium dithionite or Potassium hydrosulfite
UN1931	Zinc dithionite or Zinc hydrosulfite
UN1932	Zirconium scrap
UN1935	Cyanide solutions, n.o.s.
UN1938	Bromoacetic acid solution
UN1939	Phosphorus oxybromide
UN1940	Thioglycolic acid
UN1941	Dibromodifluoromethane
UN1942	Ammonium nitrate
UN1944	Matches, safety
UN1945	Matches, wax, Vesta
UN1950	Aerosols
UN1950	Aerosols, flammable, n.o.s.
UN1951	Argon, refrigerated liquid
UN1952	Ethylene oxide and carbon dioxide mixtures
UN1953	Compressed gas, toxic, flammable, n.o.s.
NA1954	Refrigerant gases, n.o.s. or Dispersant gases, n.o.s.
UN1954	Compressed gas, flammable, n.o.s.
NA1955	Organic phosphate, mixed with compressed gas or Organic phosphate compound, mixed with compressed gas or Organic phosphorus compound, mixed with compressed gas
UN1955	Compressed gas, toxic, n.o.s.
UN1956	Compressed gas, n.o.s.
UN1957	Deuterium, compressed
UN1958	1,2-Dichloro-1,1,2,2-tetrafluoroethane or Refrigerant gas R 114
UN1959	1,1-Difluoroethylene or Refrigerant gas R 1132a
NA1961	Ethane-Propane mixture, refrigerated liquid
UN1961	Ethane, refrigerated liquid
UN1962	Ethylene
UN1963	Helium, refrigerated liquid
UN1964	Hydrocarbon gas mixture, compressed, n.o.s.
UN1965	Hydrocarbon gas mixture, liquefied, n.o.s.
UN1966	Hydrogen, refrigerated liquid
NA1967	Parathion and compressed gas mixture
UN1967	Insecticide gases, toxic, n.o.s.
UN1968	Insecticide gases, n.o.s.

ID Number	Description
UN1969	Isobutane
UN1970	Krypton, refrigerated liquid
UN1971	Methane, compressed or Natural gas, compressed
UN1972	Methane, refrigerated liquid or Natural gas, refrigerated liquid
UN1973	Chlorodifluoromethane and chloropentafluoroethane mixture or Refrigerant gas R502
UN1974	Chlorodifluorobromomethane or Refrigerant gas R12B1
UN1975	Nitric oxide and dinitrogen tetroxide mixtures or Nitric oxide and nitrogen dioxide mixtures
UN1976	Octafluorocyclobutane or Refrigerant gas RC 318
UN1977	Nitrogen, refrigerated liquid
UN1978	Propane
UN1982	Tetrafluoromethane or Refrigerant gas R 14
UN1983	1-Chloro-2,2,2-trifluoroethane or refrigerant gas R 133a
UN1984	Trifluoromethane or Refrigerant gas R 23
UN1986	Alcohols, flammable, toxic, n.o.s.
NA1987	Denatured alcohol
UN1987	Alcohols, n.o.s.
UN1988	Aldehydes, flammable, toxic, n.o.s.
UN1989	Aldehydes, n.o.s.
UN1990	Benzaldehyde
UN1991	Chloroprene, stabilized
UN1992	Flammable liquids, toxic, n.o.s.
NA1993	Combustible liquid, n.o.s.
NA1993	Compounds, cleaning liquid
NA1993	Compounds, tree killing, liquid or Compounds, weed killing, liquid
NA1993	Diesel fuel
NA1993	Fuel oil
UN1993	Flammable liquids, n.o.s.
UN1994	Iron pentacarbonyl
NA1999	Asphalt
UN1999	Tars, liquid
UN2000	Celluloid
UN2001	Cobalt naphthenates, powder
UN2002	Celluloid, scrap
UN2004	Magnesium diamide
UN2006	Plastics, nitrocellulose-based, self-heating, n.o.s.
UN2008	Zirconium powder, dry
UN2009	Zirconium, dry
UN2010	Magnesium hydride
UN2011	Magnesium phosphide
UN2012	Potassium phosphide
UN2013	Strontium phosphide
UN2014	Hydrogen peroxide, aqueous solutions
UN2015	Hydrogen peroxide, stabilized or Hydrogen peroxide aqueous solutions, stabilized
UN2016	Ammunition, toxic, non-explosive
UN2017	Ammunition, tear-producing, non-explosive
UN2018	Chloroanilines, solid
UN2019	Chloroanilines, liquid
UN2020	Chlorophenols, solid
UN2021	Chlorophenols, liquid
UN2022	Cresylic acid
UN2023	Epichlorohydrin
UN2024	Mercury compound, liquid, n.o.s.

ID Number	Description
UN2025	Mercury compound, solid, n.o.s.
UN2026	Phenylmercuric compounds, n.o.s.
UN2027	Sodium arsenite, solid
UN2028	Bombs, smoke, non-explosive
UN2029	Hydrazine, anhydrous
UN2030	Hydrazine aqueous solution
UN2031	Nitric acid
UN2032	Nitric acid, red fuming
UN2033	Potassium monoxide
UN2034	Hydrogen and Methane mixtures, compressed
UN2035	1,1,1,-Trifluoroethane or Refrigerant gas, R 143a
UN2036	Xenon, compressed
UN2037	Gas cartridges
UN2037	Receptacles, small, containing gas or gas cartridges
UN2038	Dinitrotoluenes
UN2044	2,2-Dimethylpropane
UN2045	Isobutyraldehyde or isobutyl aldehyde
UN2046	Cymenes
UN2047	Dichloropropenes
UN2048	Dicyclopentadiene
UN2049	Diethylbenzene
UN2050	Diisobutylene, isomeric compounds
UN2051	2-Dimethylaminoethanol
UN2052	Dipentene
UN2053	Methyl isobutyl carbinol
UN2054	Morpholine
UN2055	Styrene monomer, stabilized
UN2056	Tetrahydrofuran
UN2057	Tripropylene
UN2058	Valeraldehyde
UN2059	Nitrocellulose, solution, flammable
UN2067	Ammonium nitrate based fertilizer
UN2071	Ammonium nitrate based fertilizer
UN2073	Ammonia solution
UN2074	Acrylamide, solid
UN2075	Chloral, anhydrous, stabilized
UN2076	Cresols, liquid
UN2077	alpha-Naphthylamine
UN2078	Toluene diisocyanate
UN2079	Diethylenetriamine
UN2186	Hydrogen chloride, refrigerated liquid
UN2187	Carbon dioxide, refrigerated liquid
UN2188	Arsine
UN2189	Dichlorosilane
UN2190	Oxygen difluoride, compressed
UN2191	Sulfuryl fluoride
UN2192	Germane
UN2193	Hexafluoroethane or Refrigerant gas R 116
UN2194	Selenium hexafluoride
UN2195	Tellurium hexafluoride
UN2196	Tungsten hexafluoride
UN2197	Hydrogen iodide, anhydrous
UN2198	Phosphorus pentafluoride
UN2199	Phosphine

ID Number	Description
UN2200	Propadiene, stabilized
UN2201	Nitrous oxide, refrigerated liquid
UN2202	Hydrogen selenide, anhydrous
UN2203	Silane
UN2204	Carbonyl sulfide
UN2205	Adiponitrile
UN2206	Isocyanates, toxic, n.o.s. or Isocyanate solutions, toxic, n.o.s.
UN2208	Calcium hypochlorite mixture, dry
UN2209	Formaldehyde solutions
UN2210	Maneb or Maneb preparations
UN2211	Polymeric beads expandable
NA2212	Asbestos
UN2212	Asbestos, amphibole
UN2213	Paraformaldehyde
UN2214	Phthalic anhydride
UN2215	Maleic anhydride
UN2215	Maleic anhydride, molten
UN2216	Fish meal, stabilized or Fish scrap, stabilized
UN2217	Seed cake
UN2218	Acrylic acid, stabilized
UN2219	Allyl glycidyl ether
UN2222	Anisole
UN2224	Benzonitrile
UN2225	Benzene sulfonyl chloride
UN2226	Benzotrichloride
UN2227	n-Butyl methacrylate, stabilized
UN2232	2-Chloroethanal
UN2233	Chloroanisidines
UN2234	Chlorobenzotrifluorides
UN2235	Chlorobenzyl chlorides, liquid
UN2236	3-Chloro-4-methylphenyl isocyanate, liquid
UN2237	Chloronitroanilines
UN2238	Chlorotoluenes
UN2239	Chlorotoluidines, solid
UN2240	Chromosulfuric acid
UN2241	Cycloheptane
UN2242	Cycloheptene
UN2243	Cyclohexyl acetate
UN2244	Cyclopentanol
UN2245	Cyclopentanone
UN2246	Cyclopentene
UN2247	n-Decane
UN2248	Di-n-butylamine
UN2249	Dichlorodimethyl ether, symmetrical
UN2250	Dichlorophenyl isocyanates
UN2251	Bicyclo[2,2,1]hepta-2,5-diene, stabilized or 2,5-Norbornadiene, stabilized
UN2252	1,2-Dimethoxyethane
UN2253	N,N-Dimethylaniline
UN2254	Matches, fusee
UN2256	Cyclohexene
UN2257	Potassium
UN2258	1,2-Propylenediamine
UN2259	Triethylenetetramine
UN2260	Tripropylamine

ID Number	Description
UN2261	Xylenols, solid
UN2262	Dimethylcarbamoyl chloride
UN2263	Dimethylcyclohexanes
UN2264	N,N-Dimethylcyclohexylamine
UN2265	N,N-Dimethylformamide
UN2266	Dimethyl-N-propylamine
UN2267	Dimethyl thiophosphoryl chloride
UN2269	3,3'-Iminodipropylamine
UN2270	Ethylamine, aqueous solution
UN2271	Ethyl amyl ketone
UN2272	N-Ethylaniline
UN2273	2-Ethylaniline
UN2274	N-Ethyl-N-benzylaniline
UN2275	2-Ethylbutanol
UN2276	2-Ethylhexylamine
UN2277	Ethyl methacrylate, stabilized
UN2278	n-Heptene
UN2279	Hexachlorobutadiene
UN2280	Hexamethylenediamine, solid
UN2281	Hexamethylene diisocyanate
UN2282	Hexanols
UN2283	Isobutyl methacrylate, stabilized
UN2284	Isobutyronitrile
UN2285	Isocyanatobenzotrifluorides
UN2286	Pentamethylheptane
UN2287	Isoheptenes
UN2288	Isohexenes
UN2289	Isophoronediamine
UN2290	Isophorone diisocyanate
UN2291	Lead compounds, soluble, n.o.s.
UN2293	4-Methoxy-4-methylpentan-2-one
UN2294	N-Methylaniline
UN2295	Methyl chloroacetate
UN2296	Methylcyclohexane
UN2297	Methylcyclohexanone
UN2298	Methylcyclopentane
UN2299	Methyl dichloroacetate
UN2300	2-Methyl-5-ethylpyridine
UN2301	2-Methylfuran
UN2302	5-Methylhexan-2-one
UN2303	Isopropenylbenzene
UN2304	Naphthalene, molten
UN2305	Nitrobenzenesulfonic acid
UN2306	Nitrobenzotrifluorides, liquid
UN2307	3-Nitro-4-chlorobenzotrifluoride
UN2308	Nitrosylsulfuric acid, liquid
UN2309	Octadiene
UN2310	Pentane-2,4-dione
UN2311	Phenetidines
UN2312	Phenol, molten
UN2313	Picolines
UN2315	Polychlorinated biphenyls, liquid
UN2316	Sodium cuprocyanide, solid
UN2317	Sodium cuprocyanide, solution

ID Number	Description
UN2318	Sodium hydrosulfide
UN2319	Terpene hydrocarbons, n.o.s.
UN2320	Tetraethylenepentamine
UN2321	Trichlorobenzenes, liquid
UN2322	Trichlorobutene
UN2323	Triethyl phosphite
UN2324	Triisobutylene
UN2325	1,3,5-Trimethylbenzene
UN2326	Trimethylcyclohexylamine
UN2327	Trimethylhexamethylenediamines
UN2328	Trimethylhexamethylene diisocyanate
UN2329	Trimethyl phosphite
UN2330	Undecane
UN2331	Zinc chloride, anhydrous
UN2332	Acetaldehyde oxime
UN2333	Allyl acetate
UN2334	Allylamine
UN2335	Allyl ethyl ether
UN2336	Allyl formate
UN2337	Phenyl mercaptan
UN2338	Benzotrifluoride
UN2339	2-Bromobutane
UN2340	2-Bromoethyl ethyl ether
UN2341	1-Bromo-3-methylbutane
UN2342	Bromomethylpropanes
UN2343	2-Bromopentane
UN2344	Bromopropanes
UN2345	3-Bromopropyne
UN2346	Butanedione
UN2347	Butyl mercaptan
UN2348	Butyl acrylates, stabilized
UN2350	Butyl methyl ether
UN2351	Butyl nitrites
UN2352	Butyl vinyl ether, stabilized
UN2353	Butyryl chloride
UN2354	Chloromethyl ethyl ether
UN2356	2-Chloropropane
UN2357	Cyclohexylamine
UN2358	Cyclooctatetraene
UN2359	Diallylamine
UN2360	Diallylether
UN2361	Diisobutylamine
UN2362	1,1-Dichloroethane
UN2363	Ethyl mercaptan
UN2364	n-Propyl benzene
UN2366	Diethyl carbonate
UN2367	alpha-Methylvaleraldehyde
UN2368	alpha-Pinene
UN2370	1-Hexene
UN2371	Isopentenes
UN2372	1,2-Di-(dimethylamino)ethane
UN2373	Diethoxymethane
UN2374	3,3-Diethoxypropene
UN2375	Diethyl sulfide

ID Number	Description
UN2376	2,3-Dihydropyran
UN2377	1,1-Dimethoxyethane
UN2378	2-Dimethylaminoacetonitrile
UN2379	1,3-Dimethylbutylamine
UN2380	Dimethyldiethoxysilane
UN2381	Dimethyl disulfide
UN2382	Dimethylhydrazine, symmetrical
UN2383	Dipropylamine
UN2384	Di-n-propyl ether
UN2385	Ethyl isobutyrate
UN2386	1-Ethylpiperidine
UN2387	Fluorobenzene
UN2388	Fluorotoluenes
UN2389	Furan
UN2390	2-Iodobutane
UN2391	Iodomethylpropanes
UN2392	Iodopropanes
UN2393	Isobutyl formate
UN2394	Isobutyl propionate
UN2395	Isobutyryl chloride
UN2396	Methacrylaldehyde, stabilized
UN2397	3-Methylbutan-2-one
UN2398	Methyl tert-butyl ether
UN2399	1-Methylpiperidine
UN2400	Methyl isovalerate
UN2401	Piperidine
UN2402	Propanethiols
UN2403	Isopropenyl acetate
UN2404	Propionitrile
UN2405	Isopropyl butyrato
UN2406	Isopropyl isobutyrate
UN2407	Isopropyl chloroformate
UN2409	Isopropyl propionate
UN2410	1,2,3,6-Tetrahydropyridine
UN2411	Butyronitrile
UN2412	Tetrahydrothiophene
UN2413	Tetrapropylorthotitanate
UN2414	Thiophene
UN2416	Trimethyl borate
UN2417	Carbonyl fluoride
UN2418	Sulfur tetrafluoride
UN2419	Bromotrifluoroethylene
UN2420	Hexafluoroacetone
UN2421	Nitrogen trioxide
UN2422	Octafluorobut-2-ene or Refrigerant gas R 1318
UN2424	Octafluoropropane or Refrigerant gas R 218
UN2426	Ammonium nitrate, liquid
UN2427	Potassium chlorate, aqueous solution
UN2428	Sodium chlorate, aqueous solution
UN2429	Calcium chlorate aqueous solution
UN2430	Alkylphenols, solid, n.o.s.
UN2431	Anisidines
UN2432	N,N-Diethylaniline
UN2433	Chloronitrotoluenes, liquid

ID Number	Description
UN2434	Dibenzyldichlorosilane
UN2435	Ethylphenyldichlorosilane
UN2436	Thioacetic acid
UN2437	Methylphenyldichlorosilane
UN2438	Trimethylacetyl chloride
UN2439	Sodium hydrogendifluoride
UN2440	Stannic chloride pentahydrate
UN2441	Titanium trichloride, pyrophoric or Titanium trichloride mixtures, pyrophoric
UN2442	Trichloroacetyl chloride
UN2443	Vanadium oxytrichloride
UN2444	Vanadium tetrachloride
UN2446	Nitrocresols, solid
UN2447	Phosphorus white, molten
NA2448	Sulfur, molten
UN2448	Sulfur, molten
UN2451	Nitrogen trifluoride
UN2452	Ethylacetylene, stabilized
UN2453	Ethyl fluoride or Refrigerant gas R161
UN2454	Methyl fluoride or Refrigerant gas R 41
UN2456	2-Chloropropene
UN2457	2,3-Dimethylbutane
UN2458	Hexadiene
UN2459	2-Methyl-1-butene
UN2460	2-Methyl-2-butene
UN2461	Methylpentadienes
UN2463	Aluminum hydride
UN2464	Beryllium nitrate
UN2465	Dichloroisocyanuric acid, dry or Dichloroisocyanuric acid salts
UN2466	Potassium superoxide
UN2468	Trichloroisocyanuric acid, dry
UN2469	Zinc bromate
UN2470	Phenylacetonitrile, liquid
UN2471	Osmium tetroxide
UN2473	Sodium arsanilate
UN2474	Thiophosgene
UN2475	Vanadium trichloride
UN2477	Methyl isothiocyanate
UN2478	Isocyanates, flammable, toxic, n.o.s. or Isocyanate solutions, flammable, toxic, n.o.s.
UN2480	Methyl isocyanate
UN2481	Ethyl isocyanate
UN2482	n-Propyl isocyanate
UN2483	Isopropyl isocyanate
UN2484	tert-Butyl isocyanate
UN2485	n-Butyl isocyanate
UN2486	Isobutyl isocyanate
UN2487	Phenyl isocyanate
UN2488	Cyclohexyl isocyanate
UN2490	Dichloroisopropyl ether
UN2491	Ethanolamine or Ethanolamine solutions
UN2493	Hexamethyleneimine
UN2495	Iodine pentafluoride
UN2496	Propionic anhydride
UN2498	1,2,3,6-Tetrahydrobenzaldehyde

ID Number	Description
UN2501	Tris-(1-aziridinyl)phosphine oxide, solution
UN2502	Valeryl chloride
UN2503	Zirconium tetrachloride
UN2504	Tetrabromoethane
UN2505	Ammonium fluoride
UN2506	Ammonium hydrogen sulfate
UN2507	Chloroplatinic acid, solid
UN2508	Molybdenum pentachloride
UN2509	Potassium hydrogen sulfate
UN2511	2-Chloropropionic acid
UN2512	Aminophenols
UN2513	Bromoacetyl bromide
UN2514	Bromobenzene
UN2515	Bromoform
UN2516	Carbon tetrabromide
UN2517	1-Chloro-1,1-difluoroethane or Refrigerant gas R 142b
UN2518	1,5,9-Cyclododecatriene
UN2520	Cyclooctadienes
UN2521	Diketene, stabilized
UN2522	2-Dimethylaminoethyl methacrylate
UN2524	Ethyl orthoformate
UN2525	Ethyl oxalate
UN2526	Furfurylamine
UN2527	Isobutyl acrylate, stabilized
UN2528	Isobutyl isobutyrate
UN2529	Isobutyric acid
UN2531	Methacrylic acid, stabilized
UN2533	Methyl trichloroacetate
UN2534	Methylchlorosilane
UN2535	4-Methylmorpholine or n-methylmorpholine
UN2536	Methyltetrahydrofuran
UN2538	Nitronaphthalene
UN2541	Terpinolene
UN2542	Tributylamine
UN2545	Hafnium powder, dry
UN2546	Titanium powder, dry
UN2547	Sodium superoxide
UN2548	Chlorine pentafluoride
UN2552	Hexafluoroacetone hydrate, liquid
UN2554	Methyl allyl chloride
UN2555	Nitrocellulose with water
UN2556	Nitrocellulose with alcohol
UN2557	Nitrocellulose mixture with or without plasticizer or Nitrocellulose mixture with or without pigment
UN2558	Epibromohydrin
UN2560	2-Methylpentan-2-ol
UN2561	3-Methyl-1-butene
UN2564	Trichloroacetic acid, solution
UN2565	Dicyclohexylamine
UN2567	Sodium pentachlorophenate
UN2570	Cadmium compounds
UN2571	Alkylsulfuric acids
UN2572	Phenylhydrazine
UN2573	Thallium chlorate

ID Number	Description
UN2574	Tricresyl phosphate
UN2576	Phosphorus oxybromide, molten
UN2577	Phenylacetyl chloride
UN2578	Phosphorus trioxide
UN2579	Piperazine
UN2580	Aluminum bromide, solution
UN2581	Aluminum chloride, solution
UN2582	Ferric chloride, solution
UN2583	Alkyl sulfonic acids, solid or Aryl sulfonic acids, solid
UN2584	Alkyl sulfonic acids, liquid or Aryl sulfonic acids, liquid
UN2585	Alkyl sulfonic acids, solid or Aryl sulfonic acids, solid
UN2586	Alkyl sulfonic acids, liquid or Aryl sulfonic acids, liquid
UN2587	Benzoquinone
UN2588	Pesticides, solid, toxic, n.o.s.
UN2589	Vinyl chloroacetate
UN2590	Asbestos, chrysotile
UN2591	Xenon, refrigerated liquid
UN2599	Chlorotrifluoromethane and trifluoromethane azeotropic mixture or Refrigerant gas R 503
UN2601	Cyclobutane
UN2602	Dichlorodifluoromethane and difluoroethane azeotropic mixture or Refrigerant gas R 500
UN2603	Cycloheptatriene
UN2604	Boron trifluoride diethyl etherate
UN2605	Methoxymethyl isocyanate
UN2606	Methyl orthosilicate
UN2607	Acrolein dimer, stabilized
UN2608	Nitropropanes
UN2609	Triallyl borate
UN2610	Triallylamine
UN2611	Propylene chlorohydrin
UN2612	Methyl propyl ether
UN2614	Methallyl alcohol
UN2615	Ethyl propyl ether
UN2616	Triisopropyl borate
UN2617	Methylcyclohexanols
UN2618	Vinyl toluenes, stabilized
UN2619	Benzyldimethylamine
UN2620	Amyl butyrates
UN2621	Acetyl methyl carbinol
UN2622	Glycidaldehyde
UN2623	Firelighters, solid
UN2624	Magnesium silicide
UN2626	Chloric acid aqueous solution
UN2627	Nitrites, inorganic, n.o.s.
UN2628	Potassium fluoroacetate
UN2629	Sodium fluoroacetate
UN2630	Selenates or Selenites
UN2642	Fluoroacetic acid
UN2643	Methyl bromoacetate
UN2644	Methyl iodide
UN2645	Phenacyl bromide
UN2646	Hexachlorocyclopentadiene
UN2647	Malononitrile

ID Number	Description
UN2648	1,2-Dibromobutan-3-one
UN2649	1,3-Dichloroacetone
UN2650	1,1-Dichloro-1-nitroethane
UN2651	4,4'-Diaminodiphenyl methane
UN2653	Benzyl iodide
UN2655	Potassium fluorosilicate
UN2656	Quinoline
UN2657	Selenium disulfide
UN2659	Sodium chloroacetate
UN2660	Nitrotoluidines (mono)
UN2661	Hexachloroacetone
UN2664	Dibromomethane
UN2667	Butyltoluenes
UN2668	Chloroacetonitrile
UN2669	Chlorocresols solution
UN2670	Cyanuric chloride
UN2671	Aminopyridines
UN2672	Ammonia solution
UN2673	2-Amino-4-chlorophenol
UN2674	Sodium fluorosilicate
UN2676	Stibine
UN2677	Rubidium hydroxide solution
UN2678	Rubidium hydroxide
UN2679	Lithium hydroxide, solution
UN2680	Lithium hydroxide
UN2681	Caesium hydroxide solution
UN2682	Caesium hydroxide
UN2683	Ammonium sulfide solution
UN2684	3-Diethylamino-propylamine
UN2685	N,N-Diethylethylenediamine
UN2686	2-Diethylaminoethanol
UN2687	Dicyclohexylammonium nitrite
UN2688	1-Bromo-3-chloropropane
UN2689	Glycerol alpha-monochlorohydrin
UN2690	N-n-Butyl imidazole
UN2691	Phosphorus pentabromide
UN2692	Boron tribromide
UN2693	Bisulfites, aqueous solutions, n.o.s.
UN2698	Tetrahydrophthalic anhydrides
UN2699	Trifluoroacetic acid
UN2705	1-Pentol
UN2707	Dimethyldioxanes
UN2709	Butyl benzenes
UN2710	Dipropyl ketone
UN2713	Acridine
UN2714	Zinc resinate
UN2715	Aluminum resinate
UN2716	1,4-Butynediol
UN2717	Camphor
UN2719	Barium bromate
UN2720	Chromium nitrate
UN2721	Copper chlorate
UN2722	Lithium nitrate
UN2723	Magnesium chlorate

ID Number	Description
UN2724	Manganese nitrate
UN2725	Nickel nitrate
UN2726	Nickel nitrite
UN2727	Thallium nitrate
UN2728	Zirconium nitrate
UN2729	Hexachlorobenzene
UN2730	Nitroanisole, liquid
UN2732	Nitrobromobenzenes, liquid
UN2733	Amine, flammable, corrosive, n.o.s. or Polyamines, flammable, corrosive, n.o.s.
UN2734	Amine, liquid, corrosive, flammable, n.o.s. or Polyamines, liquid, corrosive, flammable, n.o.s.
UN2735	Amines, liquid, corrosive, n.o.s. or Polyamines, liquid, corrosive, n.o.s.
UN2738	N-Butylaniline
UN2739	Butyric anhydride
UN2740	n-Propyl chloroformate
UN2741	Barium hypochlorite
UN2742	Chloroformates, toxic, corrosive, flammable, n.o.s.
UN2743	n-Butyl chloroformate
UN2744	Cyclobutyl chloroformate
UN2745	Chloromethyl chloroformate
UN2746	Phenyl chloroformate
UN2747	tert-Butylcyclohexylchloroformate
UN2748	2-Ethylhexyl chloroformate
UN2749	Tetramethylsilane
UN2750	1,3-Dichloropropanol-2
UN2751	Diethylthiophosphoryl chloride
UN2752	1,2-Epoxy-3-ethoxypropane
UN2753	N-Ethylbenzyltoluidines liquid
UN2754	N-Ethyltoluidines
UN2757	Carbamate pesticides, solid, toxic
UN2758	Carbamate pesticides, liquid, flammable, toxic
UN2759	Arsenical pesticides, solid, toxic
UN2760	Arsenical pesticides, liquid, flammable, toxic
UN2761	Organochlorine, pesticides, solid, toxic
UN2762	Organochlorine pesticides liquid, flammable, toxic
UN2763	Triazine pesticides, solid, toxic
UN2764	Triazine pesticides, liquid, flammable, toxic
UN2771	Thiocarbamate pesticides, solid, toxic
UN2772	Thiocarbamate pesticide, liquid, flammable, toxic
UN2775	Copper based pesticides, solid, toxic
UN2776	Copper based pesticides, liquid, flammable, toxic
UN2777	Mercury based pesticides, solid, toxic
UN2778	Mercury based pesticides, liquid, flammable, toxic
UN2779	Substituted nitrophenol pesticides, solid, toxic
UN2780	Substituted nitrophenol pesticides, liquid, flammable, toxic
UN2781	Bipyridilium pesticides, solid, toxic
UN2782	Bipyridilium pesticides, liquid, flammable, toxic
UN2783	Organophosphorus pesticides, solid, toxic
UN2784	Organophosphorus pesticides, liquid, flammable, toxic
UN2785	4-Thiapentanal
UN2786	Organotin pesticides, solid, toxic
UN2787	Organotin pesticides, liquid, flammable, toxic
UN2788	Organotin compounds, liquid, n.o.s.
UN2789	Acetic acid, glacial or Acetic acid solution

ID Number	Description
UN2790	Acetic acid solution
UN2793	Ferrous metal borings or Ferrous metal shavings or Ferrous metal turnings or Ferrous metal cuttings
UN2794	Batteries, wet, filled with acid
UN2795	Batteries, wet, filled with alkali
UN2796	Battery fluid, acid
UN2796	Sulfuric acid
UN2797	Battery fluid, alkali
UN2798	Phenyl phosphorus dichloride
UN2799	Phenyl phosphorus thiodichloride
UN2800	Batteries, wet, non-spillable
UN2801	Dyes, liquid, corrosive n.o.s. or Dye intermediates, liquid, corrosive, n.o.s.
UN2802	Copper chloride
UN2803	Gallium
UN2805	Lithium hydride, fused solid
UN2806	Lithium nitride
NA2810	Compounds, tree killing, liquid or Compounds, weed killing, liquid
UN2810	Toxic, liquids, organic, n.o.s.
UN2811	Toxic, solids, organic, n.o.s.
UN2812	Sodium aluminate, solid
UN2813	Water-reactive solid, n.o.s.
UN2814	Infectious substances, affecting humans
UN2815	N-Aminoethylpiperazine
UN2817	Ammonium hydrogendifluoride, solution
UN2818	Ammonium polysulfide, solution
UN2819	Amyl acid phosphate
UN2820	Butyric acid
UN2821	Phenol solutions
UN2822	2-Chloropyridine
UN2823	Crotonic acid, solid
UN2826	Ethyl chlorothioformate
UN2829	Caproic acid
UN2830	Lithium ferrosilicon
UN2831	1,1,1-Trichloroethane
UN2834	Phosphorous acid
UN2835	Sodium aluminum hydride
UN2837	Bisulfate, aqueous solution
UN2838	Vinyl butyrate, stabilized
UN2839	Aldol
UN2840	Butyraldoxime
UN2841	Di-n-amylamine
UN2842	Nitroethane
UN2844	Calcium manganese silicon
NA2845	Ethyl phosphonous dichloride, anhydrous
NA2845	Methyl phosphonous dichloride
UN2845	Pyrophoric liquids, organic, n.o.s.
UN2846	Pyrophoric solids, organic, n.o.s.
UN2849	3-Chloropropanol-1
UN2850	Propylene tetramer
UN2851	Boron trifluoride dihydrate
UN2852	Dipicryl sulfide, wetted
UN2853	Magnesium fluorosilicate
UN2854	Ammonium fluorosilicate
UN2855	Zinc fluorosilicate

ID Number	Description
UN2856	Fluorosilicates, n.o.s.
UN2857	Refrigerating machines
UN2858	Zirconium, dry
UN2859	Ammonium metavanadate
UN2861	Ammonium polyvanadate
UN2862	Vanadium pentoxide
UN2863	Sodium ammonium vanadate
UN2864	Potassium metavanadate
UN2865	Hydroxylamine sulfate
UN2869	Titanium trichloride mixtures
UN2870	Aluminum borohydride or Aluminum borohydride in devices
UN2871	Antimony powder
UN2872	Dibromochloropropane
UN2873	Dibutylaminoethanol
UN2874	Furfuryl alcohol
UN2875	Hexachlorophene
UN2876	Resorcinol
UN2878	Titanium sponge granules or Titanium sponge powders
UN2879	Selenium oxychloride
UN2880	Calcium hypochlorite, hydrated or Calcium hypochlorite, hydrated mixture
UN2881	Metal catalyst, dry
UN2900	Infectious substances, affecting animals
UN2901	Bromine chloride
UN2902	Pesticides, liquid, toxic, n.o.s.
UN2903	Pesticides, liquid, toxic, flammable, n.o.s.
UN2904	Chlorophenolates, liquid or Phenolates, liquid
UN2905	Chlorophenolates, solid or Phenolates, solid
UN2907	Isosorbide dinitrate mixture
UN2908	Radioactive material, excepted package-empty packaging
UN2909	Radioactive material, excepted package-articles manufactured from natural uranium or depleted uranium or natural thorium
UN2910	Radioactive material, excepted package-limited quantity of material
UN2911	Radioactive material, excepted package-instruments or articles
UN2912	Radioactive material, low specific activity (LSA-I)
UN2913	Radioactive material, surface contaminated objects (SCO-I or SCO-II)
UN2915	Radioactive material, Type A package
UN2916	Radioactive material, Type B(U) package
UN2917	Radioactive material, Type B(M) package
UN2919	Radioactive material, transported under special arrangement
UN2920	Corrosive liquids, flammable, n.o.s.
UN2921	Corrosive solids, flammable, n.o.s.
UN2922	Corrosive liquids, toxic, n.o.s.
UN2923	Corrosive solids, toxic, n.o.s.
UN2924	Flammable liquids, corrosive, n.o.s.
UN2925	Flammable solids, corrosive, organic, n.o.s.
UN2926	Flammable solids, toxic, organic, n.o.s.
NA2927	Ethyl phosphonothioic dichloride, anhydrous
NA2927	Ethyl phosphorodichloridate
UN2927	Toxic liquids, corrosive, organic, n.o.s.
UN2928	Toxic solids, corrosive, organic n.o.s.
UN2929	Toxic liquids, flammable, organic, n.o.s.
UN2930	Toxic solids, flammable, organic, n.o.s.
UN2931	Vanadyl sulfate
UN2933	Methyl 2-chloropropionate

ID Number	Description
UN2934	Isopropyl 2-chloropropionate
UN2935	Ethyl 2-chloropropionate
UN2936	Thiolactic acid
UN2937	alpha-Methylbenzyl alcohol, liquid
UN2940	9-Phosphabicyclononanes or Cyclooctadiene phosphines
UN2941	Fluoroanilines
UN2942	2-Trifluoromethylaniline
UN2943	Tetrahydrofurfurylamine
UN2945	N-Methylbutylamine
UN2946	2-Amino-5-diethylaminopentane
UN2947	Isopropyl chloroacetate
UN2948	3-Trifluoromethylaniline
UN2949	Sodium hydrosulfide
UN2950	Magnesium granules, coated
UN2956	5-tert-Butyl-2,4,6-trinitro-m-xylene or Musk xylene
UN2965	Boron trifluoride dimethyl etherate
UN2966	Thioglycol
UN2967	Sulfamic acid
UN2968	Maneb stabilized or Maneb preparations, stabilized
UN2969	Castor beans or Castor meal or Castor pomace or Castor flake
UN2977	Radioactive material, uranium hexafluoride, fissile
UN2978	Radioactive material, uranium hexafluoride
UN2983	Ethylene oxide and propylene oxide mixtures
UN2984	Hydrogen peroxide, aqueous solutions
UN2985	Chlorosilanes, flammable, corrosive, n.o.s.
UN2986	Chlorosilanes, corrosive, flammable, n.o.s.
UN2987	Chlorosilanes, corrosive, n.o.s.
UN2988	Chlorosilanes, water-reactive, flammable, corrosive, n.o.s.
UN2989	Lead phosphite, dibasic
UN2990	Life-saving appliances, self-inflating
UN2991	Carbamate pesticides, liquid, toxic, flammable
UN2992	Carbamate pesticides, liquid, toxic
UN2993	Arsenical pesticides, liquid, toxic, flammable
UN2994	Arsenical pesticides, liquid, toxic
UN2995	Organochlorine pesticides, liquid, toxic, flammable.
UN2996	Organochlorine pesticides, liquid, toxic
UN2997	Triazine pesticides, liquid, toxic, flammable
UN2998	Triazine pesticides, liquid, toxic
UN3002	Phenyl urea pesticides, liquid, toxic
UN3005	Thiocarbamate pesticide, liquid, toxic, flammable
UN3006	Thiocarbamate pesticide, liquid, toxic
UN3009	Copper based pesticides, liquid, toxic, flammable
UN3010	Copper based pesticides, liquid, toxic
UN3011	Mercury based pesticides, liquid, toxic, flammable
UN3012	Mercury based pesticides, liquid, toxic
UN3013	Substituted nitrophenol pesticides, liquid, toxic, flammable
UN3014	Substituted nitrophenol pesticides, liquid, toxic
UN3015	Bipyridilium pesticides, liquid, toxic, flammable
UN3016	Bipyridilium pesticides, liquid, toxic
UN3017	Organophosphorus pesticides, liquid, toxic, flammable
UN3018	Organophosphorus pesticides, liquid, toxic
UN3019	Organotin pesticides, liquid, toxic, flammable
UN3020	Organotin pesticides, liquid, toxic
UN3021	Pesticides, liquid, flammable, toxic

ID Number	Description
UN3022	1,2-Butylene oxide, stabilized
UN3023	2-Methly-2-heptanethiol
UN3024	Coumarin derivative pesticides, liquid, flammable, toxic
UN3025	Coumarin derivative pesticides, liquid, toxic, flammable
UN3026	Coumarin derivative pesticides, liquid, toxic
UN3027	Coumarin derivative pesticides, solid, toxic
UN3028	Batteries, dry, containing potassium hydroxide solid
UN3048	Aluminum phosphide pesticides
UN3054	Cyclohexyl mercaptan
UN3055	2-(2-Aminoethoxy) ethanol
UN3056	n-Heptaldehyde
UN3057	Trifluoroacetyl chloride
UN3064	Nitroglycerin, solution in alcohol
UN3065	Alcoholic beverages
UN3066	Paint or Paint related material
UN3070	Ethylene oxide and dichlorodifluoromethane mixture
UN3071	Mercaptans, liquid, toxic, flammable, n.o.s. or Mercaptan mixtures, liquid, toxic, flammable, n.o.s.
UN3072	Life-saving appliances, not self inflating
UN3073	Vinylpyridines, stabilized
NA3077	Hazardous waste, solid, n.o.s.
NA3077	Other regulated substances, solid, n.o.s.
UN3077	Environmentally hazardous substance, solid, n.o.s.
UN3078	Cerium
UN3079	Methacrylonitrile, stabilized
UN3080	Isocyanates, toxic, flammable, n.o.s. or Isocyanate solutions, toxic, flammable, n.o.s.
NA3082	Hazardous waste, liquid, n.o.s.
NA3082	Other regulated substances, liquid, n.o.s.
UN3082	Environmentally hazardous substance, liquid, n.o.s.
UN3083	Perchloryl fluoride
UN3084	Corrosive solids, oxidizing, n.o.s.
UN3085	Oxidizing solid, corrosive, n.o.s.
UN3086	Toxic solids, oxidizing, n.o.s.
UN3087	Oxidizing solid, toxic, n.o.s.
UN3088	Self-heating solid, organic, n.o.s.
UN3089	Metal powders, flammable, n.o.s.
UN3090	Lithium metal batteries
UN3091	Lithium metal batteries, contained in equipment
UN3091	Lithium metal batteries, packed with equipment
UN3092	1-Methoxy-2-proponal
UN3093	Corrosive liquids, oxidizing, n.o.s.
UN3094	Corrosive liquids, water-reactive, n.o.s.
UN3095	Corrosive solids, self-heating, n.o.s.
UN3096	Corrosive solids, water-reactive, n.o.s.
UN3097	Flammable solid, oxidizing, n.o.s.
UN3098	Oxidizing liquid, corrosive, n.o.s.
UN3099	Oxidizing liquid, toxic, n.o.s.
UN3100	Oxidizing solid, self-heating, n.o.s.
UN3101	Organic peroxide type B, liquid
UN3102	Organic peroxide type B, solid
UN3103	Organic peroxide type C, liquid
UN3104	Organic peroxide type C, solid
UN3105	Organic peroxide type D, liquid

ID Number	Description
UN3106	Organic peroxide type D, solid
UN3107	Organic peroxide type E, liquid
UN3108	Organic peroxide type E, solid
UN3109	Organic peroxide type F, liquid
UN3110	Organic peroxide type F, solid
UN3111	Organic peroxide type B, liquid, temperature controlled
UN3112	Organic peroxide type B, solid, temperature controlled
UN3113	Organic peroxide type C, liquid, temperature controlled
UN3114	Organic peroxide type C, solid, temperature controlled
UN3115	Organic peroxide type D, liquid, temperature controlled
UN3116	Organic peroxide type D, solid, temperature controlled
UN3117	Organic peroxide type E, liquid, temperature controlled
UN3118	Organic peroxide type E, solid, temperature controlled
UN3119	Organic peroxide type F, liquid, temperature controlled
UN3120	Organic peroxide type F, solid, temperature controlled
UN3121	Oxidizing solid, water-reactive, n.o.s.
UN3122	Toxic liquids, oxidizing, n.o.s.
UN3123	Toxic liquids, water-reactive, n.o.s.
UN3124	Toxic solids, self-heating, n.o.s.
UN3125	Toxic solids, water-reactive, n.o.s.
UN3126	Self-heating solid, corrosive, organic, n.o.s.
UN3127	Self-heating solid, oxidizing, n.o.s.
UN3128	Self-heating solid, toxic, organic, n.o.s.
UN3129	Water-reactive liquid, corrosive, n.o.s.
UN3130	Water-reactive liquid, toxic, n.o.s.
UN3131	Water-reactive solid, corrosive, n.o.s.
UN3132	Water-reactive solid, flammable, n.o.s.
UN3133	Water-reactive solid, oxidizing, n.o.s.
UN3134	Water-reactive solid, toxic, n.o.s.
UN3135	Water-reactive solid, self-heating, n.o.s.
UN3136	Trifluoromethane, refrigerated liquid
UN3137	Oxidizing, solid, flammable, n.o.s.
UN3138	Ethylene, acetylene and propylene in mixture, refrigerated liquid
UN3139	Oxidizing, liquid, n.o.s.
UN3140	Alkaloids, liquid, n.o.s. or Alkaloid salts, liquid, n.o.s.
UN3141	Antimony compounds, inorganic, liquid, n.o.s.
UN3142	Disinfectants, liquid, toxic, n.o.s
UN3143	Dyes, solid, toxic, n.o.s. or Dye intermediates, solid, toxic, n.o.s.
UN3144	Nicotine compounds, liquid, n.o.s. or Nicotine preparations, liquid, n.o.s.
UN3145	Alkylphenols, liquid, n.o.s.
UN3146	Organotin compounds, solid, n.o.s.
UN3147	Dyes, solid, corrosive, n.o.s. or Dye intermediates, solid, corrosive, n.o.s.
UN3148	Water-reactive, liquid, n.o.s.
UN3149	Hydrogen peroxide and peroxyacetic acid mixtures, stabilized
UN3150	Devices, small, hydrocarbon gas powered or Hydrocarbon gas refills for small devices
UN3151	Polyhalogenated biphenyls, liquid or Halogenated monomethyldiphenyl-methanes, liquid or Polyhalogenated terphenyls liquid
UN3152	Polyhalogenated biphenyls, solid or Halogenated monomethyldiphenyl-methanes, solid or Polyhalogenated terphenyls, solid
UN3153	Perfluoro(methyl vinyl ether)
UN3154	Perfluoro(ethyl vinyl ether)
UN3155	Pentachlorophenol
UN3156	Compressed gas, oxidizing, n.o.s.
UN3157	Liquefied gas, oxidizing, n.o.s.

ID Number	Description
UN3158	Gas, refrigerated liquid, n.o.s.
UN3159	1,1,1,2-Tetrafluoroethane or Refrigerant gas R 134a
UN3160	Liquefied gas, toxic, flammable, n.o.s.
UN3161	Liquefied gas, flammable, n.o.s.
UN3162	Liquefied gas, toxic, n.o.s.
UN3163	Liquefied gas, n.o.s.
UN3164	Articles, pressurized pneumatic or hydraulic
UN3165	Aircraft hydraulic power unit fuel tank
UN3166	Vehicle, flammable gas powered or Vehicle, fuel cell, flammable gas powered
UN3166	Vehicle, flammable liquid powered or Vehicle, fuel cell, flammable liquid powered
UN3167	Gas sample, non-pressurized, flammable, n.o.s.
UN3168	Gas sample, non-pressurized, toxic, flammable, n.o.s.
UN3169	Gas sample, non-pressurized, toxic, n.o.s.
UN3170	Aluminum smelting by-products or Aluminum remelting by-products
UN3171	Battery-powered vehicle or Battery-powered equipment
UN3172	Toxins, extracted from living sources, liquid, n.o.s.
UN3174	Titanium disulphide
UN3175	Solids containing flammable liquid, n.o.s.
UN3176	Flammable solid, organic, molten, n.o.s.
NA3178	Smokeless powder for small arms
UN3178	Flammable solid, inorganic, n.o.s.
UN3179	Flammable solid, toxic, inorganic, n.o.s.
UN3180	Flammable solid, corrosive, inorganic, n.o.s.
UN3181	Metal salts of organic compounds, flammable, n.o.s.
UN3182	Metal hydrides, flammable, n.o.s.
UN3183	Self-heating liquid, organic, n.o.s.
UN3184	Self-heating liquid, toxic, organic, n.o.s.
UN3185	Self-heating liquid, corrosive, organic, n.o.s.
UN3186	Self-heating liquid, inorganic, n.o.s.
UN3187	Self-heating liquid, toxic, inorganic, n.o.s.
UN3188	Self-heating liquid, corrosive, inorganic, n.o.s.
UN3189	Metal powder, self-heating, n.o.s.
UN3190	Self-heating solid, inorganic, n.o.s.
UN3191	Self-heating solid, toxic, inorganic, n.o.s.
UN3192	Self-heating solid, corrosive, inorganic, n.o.s.
UN3194	Pyrophoric liquid, inorganic, n.o.s.
UN3200	Pyrophoric solid, inorganic, n.o.s.
UN3205	Alkaline earth metal alcoholates, n.o.s.
UN3206	Alkali metal alcoholates, self-heating, corrosive, n.o.s.
UN3208	Metallic substance, water-reactive, n.o.s.
UN3209	Metallic substance, water-reactive, self-heating, n.o.s.
UN3210	Chlorates, inorganic, aqueous solution, n.o.s.
UN3211	Perchlorates, inorganic, aqueous solution, n.o.s.
UN3212	Hypochlorites, inorganic, n.o.s.
UN3213	Bromates, inorganic, aqueous solution, n.o.s.
UN3214	Permanganates, inorganic, aqueous solution, n.o.s.
UN3215	Persulfates, inorganic, n.o.s.
UN3216	Persulfates, inorganic, aqueous solution, n.o.s.
UN3218	Nitrates, inorganic, aqueous solution, n.o.s.
UN3219	Nitrites, inorganic, aqueous solution, n.o.s.
UN3220	Pentafluoroethane or Refrigerant gas R 125
UN3221	Self-reactive liquid type B
UN3222	Self-reactive solid type B

ID Number	Description
UN3223	Self-reactive liquid type C
UN3224	Self-reactive solid type C
UN3225	Self-reactive liquid type D
UN3226	Self-reactive solid type D
UN3227	Self-reactive liquid type E
UN3228	Self-reactive solid type E
UN3229	Self-reactive liquid type F
UN3230	Self-reactive solid type F
UN3231	Self-reactive liquid type B, temperature controlled
UN3232	Self-reactive solid type B, temperature controlled
UN3233	Self-reactive liquid type C, temperature controlled
UN3234	Self-reactive solid type C, temperature controlled
UN3235	Self-reactive liquid type D, temperature controlled
UN3236	Self-reactive solid type D, temperature controlled
UN3237	Self-reactive liquid type E, temperature controlled
UN3238	Self-reactive solid type E, temperature controlled
UN3239	Self-reactive liquid type F, temperature controlled
UN3240	Self-reactive solid type F, temperature controlled
UN3241	2-Bromo-2-nitropropane-1,3-diol
UN3242	Azodicarbonamide
UN3243	Solids containing toxic liquid, n.o.s.
UN3244	Solids containing corrosive liquid, n.o.s.
UN3246	Methanesulfonyl chloride
UN3247	Sodium peroxoborate, anhydrous
UN3248	Medicine, liquid, flammable, toxic, n.o.s.
UN3249	Medicine, solid, toxic, n.o.s.
UN3250	Chloroacetic acid, molten
UN3251	Isosorbide-5-mononitrate
UN3252	Difluoromethane or Refrigerant gas R 32
UN3253	Disodium trioxosilicate
UN3254	Tributylphosphane
UN3255	tert-Butyl hypochlorite
UN3256	Elevated temperature liquid, flammable, n.o.s.
UN3257	Elevated temperature liquid, n.o.s.
UN3258	Elevated temperature solid, n.o.s.
UN3259	Amines, solid, corrosive, n.o.s. or, Polyamines, solid, corrosive n.o.s.
UN3260	Corrosive solid, acidic, inorganic, n.o.s.
UN3261	Corrosive solid, acidic, organic, n.o.s.
UN3262	Corrosive solid, basic, inorganic, n.o.s.
UN3263	Corrosive solid, basic, organic, n.o.s.
UN3264	Corrosive liquid, acidic, inorganic, n.o.s.
UN3265	Corrosive liquid, acidic, organic, n.o.s.
UN3266	Corrosive liquid, basic, inorganic, n.o.s.
UN3267	Corrosive liquid, basic, organic, n.o.s.
UN3268	Safety devices
UN3269	Polyester resin kit, liquid
UN3270	Nitrocellulose membrane filters
UN3271	Ethers, n.o.s.
UN3272	Esters, n.o.s.
UN3273	Nitriles, flammable, toxic, n.o.s.
UN3274	Alcoholates solution, n.o.s.
UN3275	Nitriles, toxic, flammable, n.o.s.
UN3276	Nitriles, liquid, toxic, n.o.s.
UN3277	Chloroformates, toxic, corrosive, n.o.s.

ID Number	Description
UN3278	Organophosphorus compound, liquid, toxic, n.o.s.
UN3279	Organophosphorus compound, toxic, flammable, n.o.s.
UN3280	Organoarsenic compound, liquid, n.o.s.
UN3281	Metal carbonyls, liquid, n.o.s.
UN3282	Organometallic compound, liquid, toxic, n.o.s.
UN3283	Selenium compound, solid, n.o.s.
UN3284	Tellurium compound, n.o.s.
UN3285	Vanadium compound, n.o.s.
UN3286	Flammable liquid, toxic, corrosive, n.o.s.
UN3287	Toxic liquid, inorganic, n.o.s.
UN3288	Toxic solid, inorganic, n.o.s.
UN3289	Toxic liquid, corrosive, inorganic, n.o.s.
UN3290	Toxic solid, corrosive, inorganic, n.o.s.
UN3291	Regulated medical waste, n.o.s. or Clinical waste, unspecified, n.o.s. or (BIO) Medical waste, n.o.s or Biomedical waste, n.o.s. or Medical waste, n.o.s.
UN3292	Batteries, containing sodium
UN3292	Cells, containing sodium
UN3293	Hydrazine, aqueous solution
UN3294	Hydrogen cyanide, solution in alcohol
UN3295	Hydrocarbons, liquid, n.o.s.
UN3296	Heptafluoropropane or Refrigerant gas R 227
UN3297	Ethylene oxide and chlorotetra-fluoroethane mixture
UN3298	Ethylene oxide and pentafluoroethane mixture
UN3299	Ethylene oxide and tetrafluoroethane mixture
UN3300	Ethylene oxide and carbon dioxide mixture
UN3301	Corrosive liquid, self-heating, n.o.s.
UN3302	2-Dimethylaminoethyl acrylate, stabilized
UN3303	Compressed gas, toxic, oxidizing, n.o.s.
UN3304	Compressed gas, toxic, corrosive, n.o.s.
UN3305	Compressed gas, toxic, flammable, corrosive, n.o.s.
UN3306	Compressed gas, toxic, oxidizing, corrosive, n.o.s.
UN3307	Liquified gas, toxic, oxidizing, n.o.s.
UN3308	Liquified gas, toxic, corrosive, n.o.s.
UN3309	Liquified gas, toxic, flammable, corrosive, n.o.s.
UN3310	Liquified gas, toxic, oxidizing, corrosive, n.o.s.
UN3311	Gas, refrigerated liquid, oxidizing, n.o.s.
UN3312	Gas, refrigerated liquid, flammable, n.o.s.
UN3313	Organic pigments, self-heating
UN3314	Plastic molding compound
UN3316	Chemical kit
UN3316	First aid kit
UN3317	2-Amino-4,6-Dinitrophenol, wetted
UN3318	Ammonia solution
UN3319	Nitroglycerin mixture, desensitized, solid, n.o.s.
UN3320	Sodium borohydride and sodium hydroxide solution
UN3321	Radioactive material, low specific activity (LSA-II)
UN3322	Radioactive material, low specific activity (LSA-III)
UN3327	Radioactive material, Type A package, fissile
UN3328	Radioactive material, Type B(U) package, fissile
UN3329	Radioactive material, Type B(M) package, fissile
UN3331	Radioactive material, transported under special arrangement, fissile
UN3332	Radioactive material, Type A package, special form
UN3333	Radioactive material, Type A package, special form, fissile
NA3334	Self-defense spray, non-pressurized

ID Number	Description
UN3334	Aviation regulated liquid, n.o.s.
UN3335	Aviation regulated solid, n.o.s.
UN3336	Mercaptans, liquid, flammable, n.o.s. or Mercaptan mixture, liquid, flammable, n.o.s.
UN3337	Refrigerant gas R404A
UN3338	Refrigerant gas R407A
UN3339	Refrigerant gas R407B
UN3340	Refrigerant gas R407C
UN3341	Thiourea dioxide
UN3342	Xanthates
UN3343	Nitroglycerin mixture, desensitized, liquid, flammable, n.o.s.
UN3344	Pentaerythrite tetranitrate mixture, desensitized, solid, n.o.s. or Pentaerythritol tetranitrate mixture, desensitized, solid, n.o.s. or PETN mixture, desensitized, solid, n.o.s.
UN3345	Phenoxyacetic acid derivative pesticide, solid, toxic
UN3346	Phenoxyacetic acid derivative pesticide, liquid, flammable, toxic
UN3347	Phenoxyacetic acid derivative pesticide, liquid, toxic, flammable
UN3348	Phenoxyacetic acid derivative pesticide, liquid, toxic
UN3349	Pyrethroid pesticide, solid, toxic
UN3350	Pyrethroid pesticide, liquid, flammable, toxic
UN3351	Pyrethroid pesticide, liquid, toxic, flammable
UN3352	Pyrethroid pesticide, liquid, toxic
UN3354	Insecticide gases, flammable, n.o.s.
UN3355	Insecticide gases toxic, flammable, n.o.s.
NA3356	Oxygen generator, chemical, spent
UN3356	Oxygen generator, chemical
UN3357	Nitroglycerin mixture, desensitized, liquid, n.o.s.
UN3358	Refrigerating machines
UN3360	Fibers, vegetable, dry
UN3361	Chlorosilanes, toxic, corrosive, n.o.s.
UN3362	Chlorosilanes, toxic, corrosive, flammable, n.o.s.
UN3363	Dangerous goods in machinery or Dangerous goods in apparatus
UN3364	Trinitrophenol (picric acid), wetted
UN3365	Trinitrochlorobenzene (picryl chloride), wetted
UN3366	Trinitrotoluene (TNT), wetted
UN3367	Trinitrobenzene, wetted
UN3368	Trinitrobenzoic acid, wetted
UN3369	Sodium dinitro-o-cresolate, wetted
UN3370	Urea nitrate, wetted
UN3371	2-Methylbutanal
UN3373	Biological substance, Category B
UN3375	Ammonium nitrate emulsion or Ammonium nitrate suspension or Ammonium nitrate gel
UN3376	4-Nitrophenylhydrazine
UN3377	Sodium perborate monohydrate
UN3378	Sodium carbonate peroxyhydrate
UN3379	Desensitized explosive, liquid, n.o.s.
UN3380	Desensitized explosive, solid, n.o.s.
UN3381	Toxic by inhalation liquid, n.o.s.
UN3382	Toxic by inhalation liquid, n.o.s.
UN3383	Toxic by inhalation liquid, flammable, n.o.s.
UN3384	Toxic by inhalation liquid, flammable, n.o.s.
UN3385	Toxic by inhalation liquid, water-reactive, n.o.s.
UN3386	Toxic by inhalation liquid, water-reactive, n.o.s.
UN3387	Toxic by inhalation liquid, oxidizing, n.o.s.

ID Number	Description
UN3388	Toxic by inhalation liquid, oxidizing, n.o.s.
UN3389	Toxic by inhalation liquid, corrosive, n.o.s.
UN3390	Toxic by inhalation liquid, corrosive, n.o.s.
UN3391	Organometallic substance, solid, pyrophoric
UN3392	Organometallic substance, liquid, pyrophoric
UN3393	Organometallic substance, solid, pyrophoric, water-reactive
UN3394	Organometallic substance, liquid, pyrophoric, water-reactive
UN3395	Organometallic substance, solid, water-reactive
UN3396	Organometallic substance, solid, water-reactive, flammable
UN3397	Organometallic substance, solid, water-reactive, self-heating
UN3398	Organometallic substance, liquid, water-reactive
UN3399	Organometallic substance, liquid, water-reactive, flammable
UN3400	Organometallic substance, solid, self-heating
UN3401	Alkali metal amalgam, solid
UN3402	Alkaline earth metal amalgams, solid
UN3403	Potassium, metal alloys, solid
UN3404	Potassium sodium alloys, solid
UN3405	Barium chlorate, solution
UN3406	Barium perchlorate, solution
UN3407	Chlorate and magnesium chloride mixture solution
UN3408	Lead perchlorate, solution
UN3409	Chloronitrobenzenes, liquid
UN3410	4-Chloro-o-toluidine hydrochloride, solution
UN3411	beta-Naphthylamine solution
UN3412	Formic acid
UN3413	Potassium cyanide solution
UN3414	Sodium cyanide solution
UN3415	Sodium fluoride solution
UN3416	Chloroacetophenone, liquid
UN3417	Xylyl bromide, solid
UN3418	2,4-Toluylenediamine solution or 2,4-Toluenediamine solution
UN3419	Boron trifluoride acetic acid complex, solid
UN3420	Boron trifluoride propionic acid complex, solid
UN3421	Potassium hydrogendifluoride solution
UN3422	Potassium fluoride solution
UN3423	Tetramethylammonium hydroxide, solid
UN3424	Ammonium dinitro-o-cresolate solution
UN3425	Bromoacetic acid, solid
UN3426	Acrylamide solution
UN3427	Chlorobenzyl chlorides, solid
UN3428	3-Chloro-4-methylphenyl isocyanate, solid
UN3429	Chlorotoluidines, liquid
UN3430	Xylenols, liquid
UN3431	Nitrobenzotrifluorides, solid
UN3432	Polychlorinated biphenyls, solid
UN3434	Nitrocresols, liquid
UN3436	Hexafluoroacetone hydrate, solid
UN3437	Chlorocresols, solid
UN3438	alpha-Methylbenzyl alcohol, solid
UN3439	Nitriles, solid, toxic, n.o.s.
UN3440	Selenium compound, liquid, n.o.s.
UN3441	Chlorodinitrobenzenes, solid
UN3442	Dichloroanilines, solid
UN3443	Dinitrobenzenes, solid

ID Number	Description
UN3444	Nicotine hydrochloride, solid
UN3445	Nicotine sulphate, solid
UN3446	Nitrotoluenes, solid
UN3447	Nitroxylenes, solid
UN3448	Tear gas substance, solid, n.o.s.
UN3449	Bromobenzyl cyanides, solid
UN3450	Diphenylchloroarsine, solid
UN3451	Toluidines, solid
UN3452	Xylidines, solid
UN3453	Phosphoric acid, solid
UN3454	Dinitrotoluenes, solid
UN3455	Cresols, solid
UN3456	Nitrosylsulphuric acid, solid
UN3457	Chloronitrotoluenes, solid
UN3458	Nitroanisoles, solid
UN3459	Nitrobromobenzenes, solid
UN3460	N-Ethylbenzyltoluidines, solid
UN3462	Toxins, extracted from living sources, solid, n.o.s.
UN3463	Propionic acid
UN3464	Organophosphorus compound, solid, toxic, n.o.s.
UN3465	Organoarsenic compound, solid, n.o.s.
UN3466	Metal carbonyls, solid, n.o.s.
UN3467	Organometallic compound, solid, toxic, n.o.s.
UN3468	Hydrogen in a metal hydride storage system or Hydrogen in a metal hydride storage system contained in equipment or Hydrogen in a metal hydride storage system packed with equipment
UN3469	Paint, flammable, corrosive
UN3469	Paint related material, flammable, corrosive
UN3470	Paint, corrosive, flammable
UN3470	Paint related material corrosive, flammable
UN3471	Hydrogendifluoride solution, n.o.s
UN3472	Crotonic acid, liquid
UN3473	Fuel cell cartridges or Fuel cell cartridges contained in equipment or Fuel cell cartridges packed with equipment
UN3474	1-Hydroxybenzotriazole, monohydrate
UN3475	Ethanol and gasoline mixture or Ethanol and motor spirit mixture or Ethanol and petrol mixture
UN3476	Fuel cell cartridges or Fuel cell cartridges contained in equipment or Fuel cell cartridges packed with equipment
UN3477	Fuel cell cartridges or Fuel cell cartridges contained in equipment or Fuel cell cartridges packed with equipment
UN3478	Fuel cell cartridges or Fuel cell cartridges contained in equipment or Fuel cell cartridges packed with equipment
UN3479	Fuel cell cartridges or Fuel cell cartridges contained in equipment or Fuel cell cartridges packed with equipment
UN3480	Lithium ion batteries
UN3481	Lithium ion batteries contained in equipment
UN3481	Lithium ion batteries packed with equipment
UN3482	Alkali metal dispersions, flammable or Alkaline earth metal dispersions, flammable
UN3483	Motor fuel anti-knock mixture, flammable
UN3484	Hydrazine aqueous solution, flammable
UN3485	Calcium hypochlorite, dry, corrosive or Calcium hypochlorite mixtures, dry, corrosive
UN3486	Calcium hypochlorite mixture, dry, corrosive
UN3487	Calcium hypochlorite, hydrated, corrosive or Calcium hypochlorite, hydrated mixture, corrosive

ID Number	Description
UN3488	Toxic by inhalation, flammable, corrosive, n.o.s.
UN3489	Toxic by inhalation liquid, flammable, corrosive, n.o.s.
UN3490	Toxic by inhalation liquid, water-reactive, flammable, n.o.s.
UN3491	Toxic by inhalation liquid, water-reactive, flammable, n.o.s
UN3494	Petroleum sour crude oil, flammable, toxic
UN3495	Iodine
UN3496	Batteries, nickel-metal hydride
UN3497	Krill meal
UN3498	Iodine monochloride, liquid
UN3499	Capacitor, electric double layer
UN3500	Chemical under pressure, n.o.s.
UN3501	Chemical under pressure, flammable, n.o.s.
UN3502	Chemical under pressure, toxic, n.o.s.
UN3503	Chemical under pressure, corrosive, n.o.s.
UN3504	Chemical under pressure, flammable, toxic, n.o.s.
UN3505	Chemical under pressure, flammable, corrosive, n.o.s.
UN3506	Mercury contained in manufactured articles
UN3507	Uranium hexafluoride, radioactive material, excepted package
UN3508	Capacitor, asymmetric
UN3510	Adsorbed gas, flammable, n.o.s.
UN3511	Adsorbed gas, n.o.s.
UN3512	Adsorbed gas, toxic, n.o.s.
UN3513	Adsorbed gas, oxidizing, n.o.s.
UN3514	Adsorbed gas, toxic, flammable, n.o.s.
UN3515	Adsorbed gas, toxic, oxidizing, n.o.s.
UN3516	Adsorbed gas, toxic, corrosive, n.o.s.
UN3517	Adsorbed gas, toxic, flammable, corrosive, n.o.s.
UN3518	Adsorbed gas, toxic, oxidizing, corrosive, n.o.s.
UN3519	Boron trifluoride, adsorbed
UN3520	Chlorine, adsorbed
UN3521	Silicon tetrafluoride, adsorbed
UN3522	Arsine, adsorbed
UN3523	Germane, adsorbed
UN3524	Phosphorus pentafluoride, adsorbed
UN3525	Phosphine, adsorbed
UN3526	Hydrogen selenide, adsorbed
UN3527	Polyester resin kit, solid
UN3528	Engine, internal combustion, flammable liquid powered or Engine fuel cell, flammable liquid powered or Machinery, internal combustion, flammable liquid powered or Machinery, fuel cell, flammable liquid powered
UN3529	Engine, internal combustion, flammable gas powered or Engine fuel cell, flammable gas powered or Machinery, internal combustion, flammable gas powered or Machinery, fuel cell, flammable gas powered
UN3530	Engine, internal combustion or Machinery, internal combustion
UN3531	Polymerizing substance, solid, stabilized, n.o.s.
UN3532	Polymerizing substance, liquid, stabilized, n.o.s.
UN3533	Polymerizing substance, solid, temperature controlled, n.o.s.
UN3534	Polymerizing substance, liquid, temperature controlled, n.o.s.
UN3535	Toxic solid, flammable, inorganic, n.o.s.
UN3536	Lithium batteries installed in cargo transport unit
UN3537	Articles containing flammable gas, n.o.s.
UN3538	Articles containing non-flammable, non-toxic gas, n.o.s.
UN3539	Articles containing toxic gas, n.o.s.
UN3540	Articles containing flammable liquid, n.o.s.
UN3541	Articles containing flammable solid, n.o.s.

ID Number	Description
UN3542	Articles containing a substance liable to spontaneous combustion, n.o.s.
UN3543	Articles containing a substance which in contact with water emits flammable gases, n.o.s.
UN3544	Articles containing oxidizing substance, n.o.s.
UN3545	Articles containing organic peroxide, n.o.s.
UN3546	Articles containing toxic substance, n.o.s.
UN3547	Articles containing corrosive substance, n.o.s.
UN3548	Articles containing miscellaneous dangerous goods, n.o.s.
ID8000	Consumer commodity
NA9035	Gas identification set
NA9191	Chlorine dioxide, hydrate, frozen
NA9202	Carbon monoxide, refrigerated liquid
NA9206	Methyl phosphonic dichloride
NA9260	Aluminum, molten
NA9263	Chloropivaloyl chloride
NA9264	3,5-Dichloro-2,4,6-trifluoropyridine
NA9269	Trimethoxysilane

Hazardous Materials Table

PUBLISHER'S NOTE: Space limitations preclude our using the entire §172.101 Hazardous Materials Table. We are including the first seven columns of the table. We are also including a ERG Guide No. column and a placard column, which directly relate to drivers of vehicles transporting hazardous materials.

§172.101 Purpose and use of hazardous materials table.

(a) The Hazardous Materials Table (Table) in this section designates the materials listed therein as hazardous materials for the purpose of transportation of those materials. For each listed material, the Table identifies the hazard class or specifies that the material is forbidden in transportation, and gives the proper shipping name or directs the user to the preferred proper shipping name. In addition, the Table specifies or references requirements in this subchapter pertaining to labeling, packaging, quantity limits aboard aircraft and stowage of hazardous materials aboard vessels.

(b) **Column 1: Symbols**. Column 1 of the Table contains six symbols ("+", "A", "D", "G", "I", and "W"), as follows:

(1) The plus (+) sign fixes the proper shipping name, hazard class and packing group for that entry without regard to whether the material meets the definition of that class, packing group or any other hazard class definition. When the plus sign is assigned to a proper shipping name in Column (1) of the §172.101 Table, it means that the material is known to pose a risk to humans. When a plus sign is assigned to mixtures or solutions containing a material where the hazard to humans is significantly different from that of the pure material or where no hazard to humans is posed, the material may be described using an alternative shipping name that represents the hazards posed by the material. An appropriate alternate proper shipping name and hazard class may be authorized by the Associate Administrator.

(2) The letter "A" denotes a material that is subject to the requirements of this subchapter only when offered or intended for transportation by aircraft, unless the material is a hazardous substance or a hazardous waste. A shipping description entry preceded by an "A" may be used to describe a material for other modes of transportation provided all applicable requirements for the entry are met.

(3) The letter "D" identifies proper shipping names which are appropriate for describing materials for domestic transportation but may be inappropriate for international transportation under the provisions of international regulations (e.g., IMO, ICAO). An alternate proper shipping name may be selected when either domestic or international transportation is involved.

(4) The letter "G" identifies proper shipping names for which one or more technical names of the hazardous material must be entered in parentheses, in association with the basic description. (See §172.203(k).)

(5) The letter "I" identifies proper shipping names which are appropriate for describing materials in international transportation. An alternate proper shipping name may be selected when only domestic transportation is involved.

(6) The letter "W" denotes a material that is subject to the requirements of this subchapter only when offered or intended for transportation by vessel, unless the material is a hazardous substance or a hazardous waste. A shipping description entry preceded by a "W" may be used to describe a material for

other modes of transportation provided all applicable requirements for the entry are met.

(c) **Column 2: Hazardous materials descriptions and proper shipping names**. Column 2 lists the hazardous materials descriptions and proper shipping names of materials designated as hazardous materials. Modification of a proper shipping name may otherwise be required or authorized by this section. Proper shipping names are limited to those shown in Roman type (not italics).

(1) Proper shipping names may be used in the singular or plural and in either capital or lower case letters. Words may be alternatively spelled in the same manner as they appear in the ICAO Technical Instructions or the IMDG Code. For example "aluminum" may be spelled "aluminium" and "sulfur" may be spelled "sulphur". However, the word "inflammable" may not be used in place of the word "flammable".

(2) Punctuation marks and words in italics are not part of the proper shipping name, but may be used in addition to the proper shipping name. The word "or" in italics indicates that there is a choice of terms in the sequence that may alternately be used as the proper shipping name or as part of the proper shipping name, as appropriate. For example, for the hazardous materials description "Carbon dioxide, solid or Dry ice" either "Carbon dioxide, solid" or "Dry ice" may be used as the proper shipping name; and for the hazardous materials description "Articles, pressurized pneumatic or hydraulic," either "Articles, pressurized pneumatic" or "Articles, pressurized hydraulic" may be used as the proper shipping name.

(3) The word "poison" or "poisonous" may be used interchangeably with the word "toxic" when only domestic transportation is involved. The abbreviation "n.o.i." or "n.o.i.b.n." may be used interchangeably with "n.o.s.".

(4) Except for hazardous wastes, when qualifying words are used as part of the proper shipping name, their sequence in the package markings and shipping paper description is optional. However, the entry in the Table reflects the preferred sequence.

(5) When one entry references another entry by use of the word "see", if both names are in Roman type, either name may be used as the proper shipping name (e.g., Ethyl alcohol, *see* Ethanol).

(6) When a proper shipping name includes a concentration range as part of the shipping description, the actual concentration, if it is within the range stated, may be used in place of the concentration range. For example, an aqueous solution of hydrogen peroxide containing 30 percent peroxide may be described as "Hydrogen peroxide, aqueous solution *with not less than 20 percent but not more than 40 percent hydrogen peroxide*" or "Hydrogen peroxide, aqueous solution *with 30 percent hydrogen peroxide*." Also, the percent sign (%) may be used in place of the word "percent" when words in italics containing the word "percent" are used in addition to the proper shipping name.

(7) Use of the prefix "mono" is optional in any shipping name, when appropriate. Thus, Iodine monochloride may be used interchangeably with Iodine chloride. In "Glycerol alphamonochlorohydrin" the term "mono" is considered a prefix to the term "chlorohydrin" and may be deleted.

(8) Use of the word "liquid" or "solid". The word "liquid" or "solid" may be added to a proper shipping name when a hazardous material specifically listed by name may, due to differing physical states, be a liquid or solid. When the packaging specified in Column 8 is inappropriate for the physical state of the material, the table provided in paragraph (i)(4) of this section should be used to

determine the appropriate packaging section.

(9) *Hazardous wastes*. If the word "waste" is not included in the hazardous material description in Column 2 of the Table, the proper shipping name for a hazardous waste (as defined in §171.8 of this subchapter), shall include the word "Waste" preceding the proper shipping name of the material. For example: Waste acetone.

(10) *Mixtures and solutions*. (i) A mixture or solution meeting the definition of one or more hazard class that is not identified specifically by name, comprised of a single predominant hazardous material identified in the Table by technical name and one or more hazardous and/or non-hazardous material, must be described using the proper shipping name of the hazardous material and the qualifying word "mixture" or "solution", as appropriate, unless—

(A) Except as provided in §172.101(i)(4) the packaging specified in Column 8 is inappropriate to the physical state of the material;

(B) The shipping description indicates that the proper shipping name applies only to the pure or technically pure hazardous material;

(C) The hazard class, packing group, or subsidiary hazard of the mixture or solution is different from that specified for the entry;

(D) There is a significant change in the measures to be taken in emergencies;

(E) The material is identified by special provision in Column 7 of the §172.101 Table as a material poisonous by inhalation; however, it no longer meets the definition of poisonous by inhalation or it falls within a different hazard zone than that specified in the special provision; or

(F) The material can be appropriately described by a shipping name that describes its intended application, such as "Coating solution", "Extracts, flavoring" or "Compound, cleaning liquid."

(ii) If one or more of the conditions in paragraphs (c)(10)(i)(A) through (F) of this section is satisfied then the proper shipping name selection process in (c)(12)(ii) must be used.

(iii) A mixture or solution meeting the definition of one or more hazard class that is not identified in the Table specifically by name, comprised of two or more hazardous materials in the same hazard class, must be described using an appropriate shipping description (e.g., "Flammable liquid, n.o.s."). The name that most appropriately describes the material shall be used; e.g., an alcohol not listed by its technical name in the Table shall be described as "Alcohol, n.o.s." rather than "Flammable liquid, n.o.s.". Some mixtures may be more appropriately described according to their application, such as "Coating solution" or "Extracts, flavoring liquid" rather than by an n.o.s. entry. Under the provisions of subparts C and D of this part, the technical names of at least two components most predominately contributing to the hazards of the mixture or solution may be required in association with the proper shipping name.

(11) Except for a material subject to or prohibited by §§173.21, 173.54, 173.56(d), 173.56(e), 173.224(c) or 173.225(b) of this subchapter, a material that is considered to be a hazardous waste or a sample of a material for which the hazard class is uncertain and must be determined by testing may be assigned a tentative proper shipping name, hazard class, identification number and packing group, if applicable, based on the shipper's tentative determination according to:

(i) Defining criteria in this subchapter;

(ii) The hazard precedence prescribed in §173.2a of this subchapter;

(iii) The shippers knowledge of the material;

HAZMAT TABLE

(iv) In addition to paragraphs (c)(11)(i) through (iii) of this section, for a sample of a material other than a waste, the following must be met:

(A) Except when the word "Sample" already appears in the proper shipping name, the word "Sample" must appear as part of the proper shipping name or in association with the basic description on the shipping paper;

(B) When the proper shipping description for a sample is assigned a "G" in Column (1) of the §172.101 Table, and the primary constituent(s) for which the tentative classification is based are not known, the provisions requiring a technical name for the constituent(s) do not apply; and

(C) A sample must be transported in a combination packaging which conforms to the requirements of this subchapter that are applicable to the tentative packing group assigned, and may not exceed a net mass of 2.5 kg. (5.5 pounds) per package.

Note to Paragraph (c)(11): For the transportation of samples of self-reactive materials, organic peroxides, explosives or lighters, *see* §§173.224(c)(3), 173.225(c)(2), 173.56(d) or 173.308(b)(2) of this subchapter, respectively.

(12) Except when the proper shipping name in the Table is preceded by a plus (+)—

(i) If it is specifically determined that a material meets the definition of a hazard class, packing group or hazard zone, other than the class, packing group or hazard zone shown in association with the proper shipping name, or does not meet the defining criteria for a subsidiary hazard shown in Column 6 of the Table, the material shall be described by an appropriate proper shipping name listed in association with the correct hazard class, packing group, hazard zone, or subsidiary hazard for the material.

(ii) *Generic or n.o.s. descriptions.* If an appropriate technical name is not shown in the Table, selection of a proper shipping name shall be made from the generic or n.o.s. descriptions corresponding to the specific hazard class, packing group, hazard zone, or subsidiary hazard, if any, for the material. The name that most appropriately describes the material shall be used; e.g, an alcohol not listed by its technical name in the Table shall be described as "Alcohol, n.o.s." rather than "Flammable liquid, n.o.s.". Some mixtures may be more appropriately described according to their application, such as "Coating solution" or "Extracts, flavoring, liquid", rather than by an n.o.s. entry, such as "Flammable liquid, n.o.s." It should be noted, however, that an n.o.s. description as a proper shipping name may not provide sufficient information for shipping papers and package markings. Under the provisions of subparts C and D of this part, the technical name of one or more constituents which makes the product a hazardous material may be required in association with the proper shipping name.

(iii) *Multiple hazard materials.* If a material meets the definition of more than one hazard class, and is not identified in the Table specifically by name (e.g., acetyl chloride), the hazard class of the material shall be determined by using the precedence specified in §173.2a of this subchapter, and an appropriate shipping description (e.g., "Flammable liquid, corrosive n.o.s.") shall be selected as described in paragraph (c)(12)(ii) of this section.

(iv) If it is specifically determined that a material is not a forbidden material and does not meet the definition of any hazard class, the material is not a hazardous material.

(13) *Self-reactive materials and organic peroxides.* A generic proper shipping name for a self-reactive material or an organic peroxide, as listed in Column 2 of the Table, must be selected based on the material's technical

name and concentration, in accordance with the provisions of §§173.224 or 173.225 of this subchapter, respectively.

(14) A proper shipping name that describes all isomers of a material may be used to identify any isomer of that material if the isomer meets criteria for the same hazard class or division, subsidiary risk(s) and packing group, unless the isomer is specifically identified in the Table.

(15) Unless a hydrate is specifically listed in the Table, a proper shipping name for the equivalent anhydrous substance may be used, if the hydrate meets the same hazard class or division, subsidiary risk(s) and packing group.

(16) Unless it is already included in the proper shipping name in the §172.101 Table, the qualifying words "liquid" or "solid" may be added in association with the proper shipping name when a hazardous material specifically listed by name in the §172.101 Table may, due to the differing physical states of the various isomers of the material, be either a liquid or a solid (for example "Dinitrotoluenes, liquid" and "Dinitrotoluenes, solid"). Use of the words "liquid" or "solid" is subject to the limitations specified for the use of the words "mixture" or "solution" in paragraph (c)(10) of this section. The qualifying word "molten" may be added in association with the proper shipping name when a hazardous material, which is a solid in accordance with the definition in §171.8 of this subchapter, is offered for transportation in the molten state (for example, "Alkylphenols, solid, n.o.s., molten").

(d) **Column 3: Hazard class or Division**. Column 3 contains a designation of the hazard class or division corresponding to each proper shipping name, or the word "Forbidden".

(1) A material for which the entry in this column is "Forbidden" may not be offered for transportation or transported. This prohibition does not apply if the material is diluted, stabilized or incorporated in a device and it is classed in accordance with the definitions of hazardous materials contained in part 173 of this subchapter.

(2) When a reevaluation of test data or new data indicates a need to modify the "Forbidden" designation or the hazard class or packing group specified for a material specifically identified in the Table, this data should be submitted to the Associate Administrator.

(3) A basic description of each hazard class and the section reference for class definitions appear in §173.2 of this subchapter.

(4) Each reference to a Class 3 material is modified to read "Combustible liquid" when that material is reclassified in accordance with §173.150(e) or (f) of this subchapter or has a flash point above 60°C (140°F) but below 93°C (200°F).

(e) **Column 4: Identification number**. Column 4 lists the identification number assigned to each proper shipping name. Those preceded by the letters "UN" are associated with proper shipping names considered appropriate for international transportation as well as domestic transportation. Those preceded by the letters "NA" are associated with proper shipping names not recognized for transportation outside of the United States. Identification numbers in the "NA9000" series are associated with proper shipping names not appropriately covered by international hazardous materials (dangerous goods) transportation standards, or not appropriately addressed by international transportation standards for emergency response information purposes, except for transportation in the United States. Those preceded by the letters "ID" are associated with proper shipping names recognized by the ICAO Technical Instructions (see §171.7 of this subchapter for availability).

HAZMAT TABLE

(f) **Column 5: Packing group**. Column 5 specifies one or more packing groups assigned to a material corresponding to the proper shipping name and hazard class for that material. Class 2, Class 7, Division 6.2 (other than regulated medical wastes), and ORM-D materials, do not have packing groups. Articles in other than Class 1 are not assigned to packing groups. For packing purposes, any requirement for a specific packaging performance level is set out in the applicable packing authorizations of Part 173. Packing Groups I, II and III indicate the degree of danger presented by the material is great, medium or minor, respectively. If more than one packing group is indicated for an entry, the packing group for the hazardous material is determined using the criteria for assignment of packing groups specified in subpart D of part 173. When a reevaluation of test data or new data indicates a need to modify the specified packing group(s), the data should be submitted to the Associate Administrator. Each reference in this column to a material which is a hazardous waste or a hazardous substance, and whose proper shipping name is preceded in Column 1 of the Table by the letter "A" or "W", is modified to read "III" on those occasions when the material is offered for transportation or transported by a mode in which its transportation is not otherwise subject to requirements of this subchapter.

(g) **Column 6: Labels**. Column 6 specifies codes which represent the hazard warning labels required for a package filled with a material conforming to the associated hazard class and proper shipping name, unless the package is otherwise excepted from labeling by a provision in subpart E of this part, or part 173 of this subchapter. The first code is indicative of the primary hazard of the material. Additional label codes are indicative of subsidiary hazards. Provisions in §172.402 may require that a label other than that specified in Column 6 be affixed to the package in addition to that specified in Column 6. No label is required for a material classed as a combustible liquid or for a Class 3 material that is reclassed as a combustible liquid. For "Empty" label requirements, see §173.428 of this subchapter. The codes contained in Column 6 are defined according to the following table:

LABEL SUBSTITUTION TABLE

Label code	Label name
1	Explosive.
1.1[1]	Explosive 1.1.[1]
1.2[1]	Explosive 1.2.[1]
1.3[1]	Explosive 1.3.[1]
1.4[1]	Explosive 1.4.[1]
1.5[1]	Explosive 1.5.[1]
1.6[1]	Explosive 1.6.[1]
2.1	Flammable Gas.
2.2	Non-Flammable Gas.
2.3	Poison Gas.
3	Flammable Liquid.
4.1	Flammable Solid.
4.2	Spontaneously Combustible.
4.3	Dangerous When Wet.
5.1	Oxidizer.
5.2	Organic Peroxide.

LABEL SUBSTITUTION TABLE, Continued

Label code	Label name
6.1 (inhalation hazard, Zone A or B)	Poison Inhalation Hazard.
6.1 (other than inhalation hazard, Zone A or B)[2]	Poison.
6.2	Infectious Substance.
7	Radioactive.
8	Corrosive.
9	Class 9.

[1] Refers to the appropriate compatibility group letter.

[2] The packing group for a material is indicated in column 5 of the table.

(h) **Column 7: Special provisions**. Column 7 specifies codes for special provisions applicable to hazardous materials. When Column 7 refers to a special provision for a hazardous material, the meaning and requirements of that special provision are as set forth in §172.102 of this subpart.

ERG Guide No. The Emergency Response Guidebook (ERG) Guide Number column is not part of the §172.101 Table in the Hazardous Materials Regulations. This column has been added for your convenience. This column provides the three-digit emergency response guide number assigned to the name of the material in the 2016 Emergency Response Guidebook.

The letter "P" following some guide numbers indicates that the material may undergo violent polymerization if subjected to heat or contamination.

ERG Guide numbers that are shaded indicate that the Table of Initial Isolation and Protective Action Distances (the green pages of the ERG) should be consulted. These materials are either TIH (Toxic Inhalation Hazard) material, or a chemical warfare agent, or a Dangerous Water Reactive Material (produces toxic gas upon contact with water).

Placard Advisory. The placard advisory column is not part of the §172.101 Table in the Hazardous Materials Regulations. This column has been added for your convenience. It provides a quick indication of the placard(s) required for the shipping description, based only on the information in the other columns of the §172.101 Table. To determine the actual placards required for a specific shipment, consult the Hazardous Materials Regulations §172.504 and §172.505.

* An asterisk after the placard name indicates that placarding is required for any quantity of material being transported. If multiple placards are listed, all placards are required for any quantity.

HAZMAT TABLE

Symbols (1)	Hazardous materials descriptions and proper shipping names (2)	Hazard class or Division (3)	Identification Numbers (4)	PG (5)	Label Codes (6)	Special Provisions (§172.102) (7)	ERG Guide No.	Placard Advisory Consult §172.504 & §172.505 *Placard any quantity
	Accellerene, see p-Nitrosodimethylaniline							
	Accumulators, electric, see Batteries, wet etc.							
	Accumulators, pressurized, pneumatic or hydraulic (containing non-flammable gas) see Articles, pressurized pneumatic or hydraulic (containing non-flammable gas)							
	Acetal	3	UN1088	II	3	IB2, T4, TP1	127	FLAMMABLE
	Acetaldehyde	3	UN1089	I	3	B16, T11, TP2, TP7	129P	FLAMMABLE
A	Acetaldehyde ammonia	9	UN1841	III	9	IB8, IP3, IP7, T1, TP33	171	CLASS 9
	Acetaldehyde oxime	3	UN2332	III	3	B1, IB3, T4, TP1	129	FLAMMABLE
	Acetic acid, glacial or Acetic acid solution, with more than 80 percent acid, by mass	8	UN2789	II	8, 3	A3, A7, A10, B2, IB2, T7, TP2	132	CORROSIVE
	Acetic acid solution, not less than 50 percent but not more than 80 percent acid, by mass	8	UN2790	II	8	148, A3, A7, A10, B2, IB2, T7, TP2	153	CORROSIVE
	Acetic acid solution, with more than 10 percent and less than 50 percent acid, by mass.	8	UN2790	III	8	148, IB3, T4, TP1	153	CORROSIVE
	Acetic anhydride	8	UN1715	II	8, 3	A3, A7, A10, B2, IB2, T7, TP2	137	CORROSIVE
	Acetone	3	UN1090	II	3	IB2, T4, TP1	127	FLAMMABLE
	Acetone cyanohydrin, stabilized	6.1	UN1541	I	6.1	2, B9, B14, B32, B76, B77, N34, T20, TP2, TP13, TP38, TP45	155	INHALATION HAZARD CLASS 6*
	Acetone oils	3	UN1091	II	3	IB2, T4, TP1, TP8	127	FLAMMABLE
	Acetonitrile	3	UN1648	II	3	IB2, T7, TP2	127	FLAMMABLE
	Acetyl acetone peroxide with more than 9 percent by mass active oxygen	Forbidden						
	Acetyl benzoyl peroxide, solid, or with more than 40 percent in solution	Forbidden						
	Acetyl bromide	8	UN1716	II	8	B2, IB2, T8, TP2	156	CORROSIVE
	Acetyl chloride	3	UN1717	II	3, 8	A3, A7, IB1, N34, T8, TP2	155	FLAMMABLE

Symbol	Hazardous materials descriptions and proper shipping names	Hazard class or Division	Identification Numbers	PG	Label Codes	Special provisions	Guide No.	Description
	Acetyl cyclohexanesulfonyl peroxide, with more than 82 percent wetted with less than 12 percent water	Forbidden						
	Acetyl iodide	8	UN1898	II	8	B2, IB2, T7, TP2, TP13	156	CORROSIVE
	Acetyl methyl carbinol	3	UN2621	III	3	B1, IB3, T2, TP1	127	FLAMMABLE
	Acetyl peroxide, solid, or with more than 25 percent in solution	Forbidden						
	Acetylene, dissolved	2.1	UN1001		2.1	N86, N88	116	FLAMMABLE GAS
	Acetylene (liquefied)	Forbidden						
	Acetylene silver nitrate	Forbidden						
	Acetylene, solvent free	Forbidden						
	Acetylene tetrabromide, see **Tetrabromoethane**							
	Acid butyl phosphate, see **Butyl acid phosphate**							
	Acid, sludge, see **Sludge acid**							
	Acridine	6.1	UN2713	III	6.1	IB8, IP3, T1, TP33	153	POISON
	Acrolein dimer, stabilized	3	UN2607	III	3	387, B1, IB3, T2, TP1	129P	FLAMMABLE
	Acrolein, stabilized	6.1	UN1092	I	6.1, 3	1, 380, 387, B9, B14, B30, B42, B77, T22, TP2, TP7, TP13, TP38, TP44	131P	INHALATION HAZARD CLASS 3*
	Acrylamide, solid	6.1	UN2074	III	6.1	IB8, IP3, T1, TP33	153P	POISON
	Acrylamide solution	6.1	UN3426	III	6.1	IB3, T4, TP1	153P	POISON
	Acrylic acid, stabilized	8	UN2218	II	8, 3	387, B2, IB2, T7, TP2	132P	CORROSIVE
	Acrylonitrile, stabilized	3	UN1093	I	3, 6.1	387, B9, T14, TP2, TP13	131P	FLAMMABLE
	Actuating cartridge, explosive, see **Cartridges, power device**							
	Adhesives, *containing a flammable liquid*	3	UN1133	I	3	T11, TP1, TP8, TP27	128	FLAMMABLE
				II	3	149, B52, IB2, T4, TP1, TP8	128	FLAMMABLE
				III	3	B1, B52, IB3, T2, TP1	128	FLAMMABLE
	Adiponitrile	6.1	UN2205	III	6.1	IB3, T3, TP1	153	POISON
G	**Adsorbed gas, n.o.s.**	2.2	UN3511		2.2		174	NONFLAMMABLE GAS
G	**Adsorbed gas, flammable, n.o.s.**	2.1	UN3510		2.1		174	FLAMMABLE GAS
G	**Adsorbed gas, oxidizing, n.o.s.**	2.2	UN3513		2.2, 5.1		174	NONFLAMMABLE GAS

HAZMAT TABLE

Symbols (1)	Hazardous materials descriptions and proper shipping names (2)	Hazard class or Division (3)	Identification Numbers (4)	PG (5)	Label Codes (6)	Special Provisions (§172.102) (7)	ERG Guide No.	Placard Advisory Consult §172.504 & §172.505 *Placard any quantity
G	Adsorbed gas, toxic, n.o.s. *Inhalation hazard zone A*	2.3	UN3512		2.3	1	173	INHALATION HAZARD CLASS 2*
G	Adsorbed gas, toxic, n.o.s. *Inhalation hazard zone B*	2.3	UN3512		2.3	2, B9, B14	173	INHALATION HAZARD CLASS 2*
G	Adsorbed gas, toxic, n.o.s. *Inhalation hazard zone C*	2.3	UN3512		2.3	3, B14	173	INHALATION HAZARD CLASS 2*
G	Adsorbed gas, toxic, n.o.s. *Inhalation hazard zone D*	2.3	UN3512		2.3	4	173	INHALATION HAZARD CLASS 2*
G	Adsorbed gas, toxic, corrosive, n.o.s. *Inhalation hazard zone A*	2.3	UN3516		2.3, 8	1, 379	173	INHALATION HAZARD CLASS 2*
G	Adsorbed gas, toxic, corrosive, n.o.s. *Inhalation hazard zone B*	2.3	UN3516		2.3, 8	2, 379, B9, B14	173	INHALATION HAZARD CLASS 2*
G	Adsorbed gas, toxic, corrosive, n.o.s. *Inhalation hazard zone C*	2.3	UN3516		2.3, 8	3, 379, B14	173	INHALATION HAZARD CLASS 2*
G	Adsorbed gas, toxic, corrosive, n.o.s. *Inhalation hazard zone D*	2.3	UN3516		2.3, 8	4, 379	173	INHALATION HAZARD CLASS 2*
G	Adsorbed gas, toxic, flammable, n.o.s. *Inhalation hazard zone A*	2.3	UN3514		2.3, 2.1	1	173	INHALATION HAZARD CLASS 2*
G	Adsorbed gas, toxic, flammable, n.o.s. *Inhalation hazard zone B*	2.3	UN3514		2.3, 2.1	2, B9, B14	173	INHALATION HAZARD CLASS 2*
G	Adsorbed gas, toxic, flammable, n.o.s. *Inhalation hazard zone C*	2.3	UN3514		2.3, 2.1	3, B14	173	INHALATION HAZARD CLASS 2*
G	Adsorbed gas, toxic, flammable, n.o.s. *Inhalation hazard zone D*	2.3	UN3514		2.3, 2.1	4	173	INHALATION HAZARD CLASS 2*
G	Adsorbed gas, toxic, flammable, corrosive, n.o.s. *Inhalation hazard zone A*	2.3	UN3517		2.3, 2.1, 8	1	173	INHALATION HAZARD CLASS 2*
G	Adsorbed gas, toxic, flammable, corrosive, n.o.s. *Inhalation hazard zone B*	2.3	UN3517		2.3, 2.1, 8	2, B9, B14	173	INHALATION HAZARD CLASS 2*
G	Adsorbed gas, toxic, flammable, corrosive, n.o.s. *Inhalation hazard zone C*	2.3	UN3517		2.3, 2.1, 8	3, B14	173	INHALATION HAZARD CLASS 2*

Sym	Hazardous materials descriptions	Hazard class	ID No.	Label codes	Special provisions	Guide	Guide name
G	Adsorbed gas, toxic, flammable, corrosive, n.o.s. *Inhalation hazard zone D*	2.3	UN3517	2.3, 2.1, 8	4	173	INHALATION HAZARD CLASS 2*
G	Adsorbed gas, toxic, oxidizing, n.o.s. *Inhalation hazard zone A*	2.3	UN3515	2.3, 5.1	1	173	INHALATION HAZARD CLASS 2*
G	Adsorbed gas, toxic, oxidizing, n.o.s. *Inhalation hazard zone B*	2.3	UN3515	2.3, 5.1	2, B9, B14	173	INHALATION HAZARD CLASS 2*
G	Adsorbed gas, toxic, oxidizing, n.o.s. *Inhalation hazard zone C*	2.3	UN3515	2.3, 5.1	3, B14	173	INHALATION HAZARD CLASS 2*
G	Adsorbed gas, toxic, oxidizing, n.o.s. *Inhalation hazard zone D*	2.3	UN3515	2.3, 5.1	4	173	INHALATION HAZARD CLASS 2*
G	Adsorbed gas, toxic, oxidizing, corrosive, n.o.s. *Inhalation hazard zone A*	2.3	UN3518	2.3, 5.1, 8	1	173	INHALATION HAZARD CLASS 2*
G	Adsorbed gas, toxic, oxidizing, corrosive, n.o.s. *Inhalation hazard zone B*	2.3	UN3518	2.3, 5.1, 8	2, B9, B14	173	INHALATION HAZARD CLASS 2*
G	Adsorbed gas, toxic, oxidizing, corrosive, n.o.s. *Inhalation hazard zone C*	2.3	UN3518	2.3, 5.1, 8	3, B14	173	INHALATION HAZARD CLASS 2*
G	Adsorbed gas, toxic, oxidizing, corrosive, n.o.s. *Inhalation hazard zone D*	2.3	UN3518	2.3, 5.1, 8	4	173	INHALATION HAZARD CLASS 2*
	Aerosols, corrosive, Packing Group II or III, (each not exceeding 1 L capacity)	2.2	UN1950	2.2, 8	A34	126	NONFLAMMABLE GAS
	Aerosols, flammable, (each not exceeding 1 L capacity)	2.1	UN1950	2.1	N82	126	FLAMMABLE GAS
	Aerosols, flammable, n.o.s. (engine starting fluid) (each not exceeding 1 L capacity)	2.1	UN1950	2.1	N82	126	FLAMMABLE GAS
	Aerosols, non-flammable, (each not exceeding 1 L capacity)	2.2	UN1950	2.2		126	NONFLAMMABLE GAS
	Aerosols, poison, Packing Group III (each not exceeding 1 L capacity)	2.2	UN1950	2.2, 6.1		126	NONFLAMMABLE GAS
	Air bag inflators, or Air bag modules, or Seat-belt pretensioners, see **Safety devices**, electrically initiated or **Safety devices, pyrotechnic**						
	Air, compressed	2.2	UN1002	2.2	78	122	NONFLAMMABLE GAS
	Air, refrigerated liquid, *(cryogenic liquid)*	2.2	UN1003	2.2, 5.1	T75, TP5, TP22	122	NONFLAMMABLE GAS

Symbols (1)	Hazardous materials descriptions and proper shipping names (2)	Hazard class or Division (3)	Identification Numbers (4)	PG (5)	Label Codes (6)	Special Provisions (§172.102) (7)	ERG Guide No.	Placard Advisory Consult §172.504 & §172.505 *Placard any quantity
	Air, refrigerated liquid, *(cryogenic liquid) non-pressurized*	2.2	UN1003		2.2, 5.1	T75, TP5, TP22	122	NONFLAMMABLE GAS
	Aircraft engines (including turbines), see **Engines, internal combustion**							
	Aircraft evacuation slides, see **Lifesaving appliances etc.**							
	Aircraft hydraulic power unit fuel tank *(containing a mixture of anhydrous hydrazine and monomethyl hydrazine) (M86 fuel)*	3	UN3165	I	3, 6.1, 8		131	FLAMMABLE
	Aircraft survival kits, see **Life saving appliances etc.**							
G	**Alcoholates solution, n.o.s.,** *in alcohol*	3	UN3274	II	3, 8	IB2	132	FLAMMABLE
	Alcoholic beverages	3	UN3065	II	3	24, 149, B1, IB2, T4, TP1	127	FLAMMABLE
				III	3	24, B1, IB3, N11, T2, TP1	127	FLAMMABLE
	Alcohols, n.o.s.	3	UN1987	I	3	172, T11, TP1, TP8, TP27	127	FLAMMABLE
				II	3	172, IB2, T7, TP1, TP8, TP28	127	FLAMMABLE
				III	3	172, B1, IB3, T4, TP1, TP29	127	FLAMMABLE
G	**Alcohols, flammable, toxic, n.o.s.**	3	UN1986	I	3, 6.1	T14, TP2, TP13, TP27	131	FLAMMABLE
				II	3, 6.1	IB2, T11, TP2, TP27	131	FLAMMABLE
				III	3, 6.1	B1, IB3, T7, TP1, TP28	131	FLAMMABLE
	Aldehydes, n.o.s.	3	UN1989	I	3	T11, TP1, TP27	129P	FLAMMABLE
				II	3	IB2, T7, TP1, TP8, TP28	129P	FLAMMABLE
				III	3	B1, IB3, T4, TP1, TP29	129P	FLAMMABLE
G	**Aldehydes, flammable, toxic, n.o.s.**	3	UN1988	I	3, 6.1	T14, TP2, TP13, TP27	131P	FLAMMABLE
				II	3, 6.1	IB2, T11, TP2, TP27	131P	FLAMMABLE
				III	3, 6.1	B1, IB3, T7, TP1, TP28	131P	FLAMMABLE
	Aldol	6.1	UN2839	II	6.1	IB2, T7, TP2	153	POISON
G	**Alkali metal alcoholates, self-heating, corrosive, n.o.s.**	4.2	UN3206	II	4.2, 8	64, A7, IB5, IP2, T3, TP33, W31	136	SPONTANEOUSLY COMBUSTIBLE

Symbol	Hazardous materials descriptions and proper shipping names	Class	ID No.	PG	Label codes	Special provisions	Guide No.	Guide description
				III	4.2, 8	64, A7, IB8, IP3, T1, TP33, W31	136	SPONTANEOUSLY COMBUSTIBLE
	Alkali metal alloys, liquid, n.o.s.	4.3	UN1421	I	4.3	A2, A7, B48, N34, W31	138	DANGEROUS WHEN WET*
	Alkali metal amalgam, liquid	4.3	UN1389	I	4.3	A2, A7, N34, W31	138	DANGEROUS WHEN WET*
	Alkali metal amalgam, solid	4.3	UN3401	I	4.3	IB4, IP1, N40, T9, TP7, TP33, W31	138	DANGEROUS WHEN WET*
	Alkali metal amides	4.3	UN1390	II	4.3	A6, A7, A8, A19, A20, IB7, IP2, IP21, T3, TP33, W31, W40	139	DANGEROUS WHEN WET*
	Alkali metal dispersions, flammable or Alkaline earth metal dispersions, flammable	4.3	UN3482	I	4.3, 3	A2, A7, W31	138	DANGEROUS WHEN WET*
	Alkali metal dispersions, or Alkaline earth metal dispersions	4.3	UN1391	I	4.3	A2, A7, W31	138	DANGEROUS WHEN WET*
	Alkaline corrosive liquids, n.o.s., see Caustic alkali liquids, n.o.s.							
G	Alkaline earth metal alcoholates, n.o.s.	4.2	UN3205	II	4.2	65, A7, IB6, IP2, T3, TP33, W31	135	SPONTANEOUSLY COMBUSTIBLE
				III	4.2	65, A7, IB8, IP3, T1, TP33, W31	135	SPONTANEOUSLY COMBUSTIBLE
	Alkaline earth metal alloys, n.o.s.	4.3	UN1393	II	4.3	A19, IB7, IP2, IP4, T3, TP33, W31, W40	138	DANGEROUS WHEN WET*
	Alkaline earth metal amalgams, liquid	4.3	UN1392	I	4.3	A19, N34, N40, W31	138	DANGEROUS WHEN WET*
	Alkaline earth metal amalgams, solid	4.3	UN3402	I	4.3	A19, N34, N40, T9, TP7, TP33, W31	138	DANGEROUS WHEN WET*
G	Alkaloids, liquid, n.o.s., or Alkaloid salts, liquid, n.o.s.	6.1	UN3140	I	6.1	A4, T14, TP2, TP27	151	POISON
				II	6.1	IB2, T11, TP2, TP27	151	POISON
				III	6.1	IB3, T7, TP1, TP28	151	POISON
G	Alkaloids, solid, n.o.s. or Alkaloid salts, solid, n.o.s. poisonous	6.1	UN1544	I	6.1	IB7, IP1, T6, TP33	151	POISON
				II	6.1	IB8, IP2, IP4, T3, TP33	151	POISON
				III	6.1	IB8, IP3, T1, TP33	151	POISON

Symbols (1)	Hazardous materials descriptions and proper shipping names (2)	Hazard class or Division (3)	Identification Numbers (4)	PG (5)	Label Codes (6)	Special Provisions (§172.102) (7)	ERG Guide No.	Placard Advisory Consult §172.504 & §172.505 *Placard any quantity
	Alkyl sulfonic acids, liquid or Aryl sulfonic acids, liquid with more than 5 percent free sulfuric acid	8	UN2584	II	8	B2, IB2, T8, TP2, TP13	153	CORROSIVE
	Alkyl sulfonic acids, liquid or Aryl sulfonic acids, liquid with not more than 5 percent free sulfuric acid	8	UN2586	III	8	IB3, T4, TP1	153	CORROSIVE
	Alkyl sulfonic acids, solid or Aryl sulfonic acids, solid, with more than 5 percent free sulfuric acid	8	UN2583	II	8	IB8, IP2, IP4, T3, TP33	153	CORROSIVE
	Alkyl sulfonic acids, solid or Aryl sulfonic acids, solid with not more than 5 percent free sulfuric acid	8	UN2585	III	8	IB8, IP3, T1, TP33	153	CORROSIVE
	Alkylphenols, liquid, n.o.s. *(including C2-C12 homologues)*	8	UN3145	I	8	T14, TP2	153	CORROSIVE
				II	8	IB2, T11, TP2, TP27	153	CORROSIVE
				III	8	IB3, T7, TP1, TP28	153	CORROSIVE
	Alkylphenols, solid, n.o.s. *(including C2-C12 homologues)*	8	UN2430	I	8	IB7, IP1, T6, TP33	153	CORROSIVE
				II	8	IB8, IP2, IP4, T3, TP33	153	CORROSIVE
				III	8	IB8, IP3, T1, TP33	153	CORROSIVE
	Alkylsulfuric acids	8	UN2571	II	8	B2, IB2, T8, TP2, TP13, TP28	156	CORROSIVE
	Allethrin, see Pesticides, liquid, toxic, n.o.s.							
	Allyl acetate	3	UN2333	II	3, 6.1	IB2, T7, TP1, TP13	131	FLAMMABLE
	Allyl alcohol	6.1	UN1098	I	6.1, 3	2, B9, B14, B32, B77, T20, TP13, TP38, TP45	131	INHALATION HAZARD CLASS 6*
	Allyl bromide	3	UN1099	I	3, 6.1	T14, TP2, TP13	131P	FLAMMABLE
	Allyl chloride	3	UN1100	I	3, 6.1	T14, TP2, TP13	131P	FLAMMABLE
	Allyl chlorocarbonate, see Allyl chloroformate							
	Allyl chloroformate	6.1	UN1722	I	6.1, 3, 8	2, B9, B14, B32, N41, T20, TP2, TP13, TP38, TP45	155	INHALATION HAZARD CLASS 6*
	Allyl ethyl ether	3	UN2335	II	3, 6.1	IB2, T7, TP1, TP13	131	FLAMMABLE
	Allyl formate	3	UN2336	I	3, 6.1	T14, TP2, TP13	131	FLAMMABLE
	Allyl glycidyl ether	3	UN2219	III	3	B1, IB3, T2, TP1	129	FLAMMABLE

Name	Hazard class or Division	Identification Number	PG	Label Codes	Special Provisions	Guide No.	Guide Name
Allyl iodide	3	UN1723	II	3, 8	A3, IB1, N34, T7, TP2, TP13	132	FLAMMABLE
Allyl isothiocyanate, stabilized	6.1	UN1545	II	6.1, 3	387, A3, A7, IB2, T7, TP2	155	POISON
Allylamine	6.1	UN2334	I	6.1, 3	2, B9, B14, B32, T20, TP2, TP13, TP38, TP45	131	INHALATION HAZARD CLASS 6*
Allyltrichlorosilane, stabilized	8	UN1724	II	8, 3	387, A7, B2, E6, N34, T10, TP2, TP7, TP* 3	155	CORROSIVE
Aluminum borohydride or Aluminum borohydride in devices	4.2	UN2870	I	4.2, 4.3	B11, T21, TP7, TP33	135	SPONTANEOUSLY COMBUSTIBLE, DANGEROUS WHEN WET*
Aluminum bromide, anhydrous	8	UN1725	II	8	IB8, IP2, IP4, T3, TP33	137	CORROSIVE
Aluminum bromide, solution	8	UN2580	III	8	IB3, T4, TP1	154	CORROSIVE
Aluminum carbide	4.3	UN1394	II	4.3	A20, IB7, IP2, IP21, N41, T3, TP33, W31, W40	138	DANGEROUS WHEN WET*
Aluminum chloride, anhydrous	8	UN1726	II	8	IB8, IP2, IP4, ˝3, TP33	137	CORROSIVE
Aluminum chloride, solution	8	UN2581	III	8	IB3, T4, TP1	154	CORROSIVE
Aluminum dross, wet or hot	Forbidden						
Aluminum ferrosilicon powder	4.3	UN1395	II	4.3, 6.1	A19, IB5, IP2, T3, TP33, W31, W40	139	DANGEROUS WHEN WET*
			III		A19, A20, IB4	139	DANGEROUS WHEN WET*
Aluminum hydride	4.3	UN2463	I	4.3	A19, N40, W31	138	DANGEROUS WHEN WET*
D Aluminum, molten	9	NA9260	III	9	IB3, T1, TP3	169	CLASS 9
Aluminum nitrate	5.1	UN1438	III	5.1	A1, A29, IB8, IP3, T1, TP33	140	OXIDIZER
Aluminum phosphate solution, see Corrosive liquids, etc.							
Aluminum phosphide	4.3	UN1397	I	4.3, 6.1	A8, A19, N40, W31	139	DANGEROUS WHEN WET*
Aluminum phosphide pesticides	6.1	UN3048	I	6.1	A8, IB7, IP1, T6, TP33, W31	157	POISON

Symbols (1)	Hazardous materials descriptions and proper shipping names (2)	Hazard class or Division (3)	Identification Numbers (4)	PG (5)	Label Codes (6)	Special Provisions (§172.102) (7)	ERG Guide No.	Placard Advisory Consult §172.504 & §172.505 *Placard any quantity
	Aluminum powder, coated	4.1	UN1309	II	4.1	IB8, IP2, IP21, T3, TP33, W100	170	FLAMMABLE SOLID
				III	4.1	B134, IB8, IP21, T1, TP33, W100	170	FLAMMABLE SOLID
	Aluminum powder, uncoated	4.3	UN1396	II	4.3	A19, A20, IB7, IP2, IP21, T3, TP33, W31, W40	138	DANGEROUS WHEN WET*
				III	4.3	A19, A20, IB8, IP21, T1, TP33, W31	138	DANGEROUS WHEN WET*
	Aluminum resinate	4.1	UN2715	III	4.1	IB6, T1, TP33	133	FLAMMABLE SOLID
	Aluminum silicon powder, uncoated	4.3	UN1398	III	4.3	A1, A19, B136, IB8, IP4, T1, TP33, W31	138	DANGEROUS WHEN WET*
	Aluminum smelting by-products or Aluminum remelting by-products	4.3	UN3170	II	4.3	128, B115, IB7, IP2, IP21, T3, TP33, W31, W40	138	DANGEROUS WHEN WET*
				III	4.3	128, B115, IB8, IP21, T1, TP33, W31	138	DANGEROUS WHEN WET*
	Amatols, see Explosives, blasting, type B							
G	Amine, flammable, corrosive, n.o.s. or Polyamines, flammable, corrosive, n.o.s.	3	UN2733	I	3, 8	T14, TP1, TP27	132	FLAMMABLE
				II	3, 8	IB2, T11, TP1, TP27	132	FLAMMABLE
				III	3, 8	B1, IB3, T7, TP1, TP28	132	FLAMMABLE
G	Amine, liquid, corrosive, flammable, n.o.s. or Polyamines, liquid, corrosive, flammable, n.o.s.	8	UN2734	I	8, 3	N34, T14, TP2, TP27	132	CORROSIVE
				II	8, 3	IB2, T11, TP2, TP27	132	CORROSIVE
G	Amines, liquid, corrosive, n.o.s. or Polyamines, liquid, corrosive, n.o.s.	8	UN2735	I	8	B10, N34, T14, TP2, TP27	153	CORROSIVE
				II	8	B2, IB2, T11, TP1, TP27	153	CORROSIVE
				III	8	IB3, T7, TP1, TP28	153	CORROSIVE
G	Amines, solid, corrosive, n.o.s., or Polyamines, solid, corrosive n.o.s.	8	UN3259	I	8	IB7, IP1, T6, TP33	154	CORROSIVE

Sym	Hazardous materials descriptions and proper shipping names	Hazard class or Division	Identification Numbers	PG	Label Codes	Special Provisions	Guide No.	Placard
	2-Amino-4-chlorophenol	6.1	UN2673	II	6.1	IB8, IP2, IP4, T3, TP33	154	CORROSIVE
	2-Amino-5-diethylaminopentane	6.1	UN2946	III	6.1	IB8, IP3, T1, TP33	154	CORROSIVE
	2-Amino-4, 6-Dinitrophenol, wetted *with not less than 20 percent water by mass*	4.1	UN3317	I	4.1	23, A8, A19, A2J, N41, W31	151	POISON
	2-(2-Aminoethoxy) ethanol	8	UN3055	III	8	IB3, T4, TP1	153	POISON
	N-Aminoethylpiperazine	8	UN2815	III	8, 6.1	IB3, T4, TP1	113	FLAMMABLE SOLID
+	Aminophenols (*o-; m-; p-*)	6.1	UN2512	III	6.1	IB8, IP3, T1, TP33	154	CORROSIVE
	Aminopropyldiethanolamine, see Amines, etc.						153	CORROSIVE
	n-Aminopropylmorpholine, see Amines, etc.						152	POISON
I	Aminopyridines (*o-; m-; p-*)	6.1	UN2671	II	6.1	IB8, IP2, IP4, T3, TP33	153	POISON
	Ammonia, anhydrous	2.3	UN1005		2.3, 8	4, 379, N87, T50	125	INHALATION -HAZARD CLASS 2"
D	Ammonia, anhydrous	2.2	UN1005		2.2	13, 379, T50	125	NONFLAMMABLE GAS
D	Ammonia solution, *relative density less than 0.880 at 15 degrees C in water, with more than 50 percent ammonia.*	2.2	UN3318		2.2	13, T50	125	NONFLAMMABLE GAS
I	Ammonia solution, *relative density less than 0.880 at 15 degrees C in water, with more than 50 percent ammonia.*	2.3	UN3318		2.3, 8	4, N87, T50	125	INHALATION HAZARD CLASS 2"
	Ammonia solution, *relative density between 0.880 and 0.957 at 15 degrees C in water, with more than 10 percent but not more than 35 percent ammonia*	8	UN2672	III	8	336, IB3, IP8, T7, TP2	154	CORROSIVE
	Ammonia solution, *relative density less than 0.880 at 15 degrees C in water, with more than 35 percent but not more than 50 percent ammonia*	2.2	UN2073		2.2	N87	125	NONFLAMMABLE GAS
	Ammonium arsenate	6.1	UN1546	II	6.1	IB8, IP2, IP4, T3, TP33	151	POISON
	Ammonium azide	Forbidden						
	Ammonium bifluoride, solid, see Ammonium hydrogendifluoride, solid							
	Ammonium bifluoride solution, see Ammonium hydrogendifluoride, solution							
	Ammonium bromate	Forbidden						

Symbols (1)	Hazardous materials descriptions and proper shipping names (2)	Hazard class or Division (3)	Identification Numbers (4)	PG (5)	Label Codes (6)	Special Provisions (§172.102) (7)	ERG Guide No.	Placard Advisory Consult §172.504 & §172.505 *Placard any quantity
	Ammonium chlorate	Forbidden						
	Ammonium dichromate	5.1	UN1439	II	5.1	IB8, IP2, IP4, T3, TP33	141	OXIDIZER
	Ammonium dinitro-o-cresolate, solid	6.1	UN1843	II	6.1	IB8, IP2, IP4, T3, TP33	141	POISON
	Ammonium dinitro-o-cresolate solution	6.1	UN3424	II	6.1	IB2, T7, TP2	141	POISON
				III	6.1	IB2, T7, TP2	141	POISON
	Ammonium fluoride	6.1	UN2505	III	6.1	IB8, IP3, T1, TP33	154	POISON
	Ammonium fluorosilicate	6.1	UN2854	III	6.1	IB8, IP3, T1, TP33	151	POISON
	Ammonium fulminate	Forbidden						
	Ammonium hydrogen sulfate	8	UN2506	II	8	IB8, IP2, IP4, T3, TP33	154	CORROSIVE
	Ammonium hydrogendifluoride, solid	8	UN1727	II	8	IB8, IP2, IP4, N34, T3, TP33	154	CORROSIVE
	Ammonium hydrogendifluoride, solution	8	UN2817	II	8, 6.1	IB2, N34, T8, TP2, TP13	154	CORROSIVE
				III	8, 6.1	IB3, N3, T4, TP1, TP13	154	CORROSIVE
	Ammonium hydrosulfide, solution, see Ammonium sulfide solution							
D	Ammonium hydroxide, see Ammonia solutions, etc.							
	Ammonium metavanadate	6.1	UN2859	II	6.1	IB8, IP2, IP4, T3, TP33	154	POISON
	Ammonium nitrate based fertilizer	5.1	UN2067	III	5.1	52, 148, 150, B120, IB8, IP3, T1, TP33	140	OXIDIZER
A W	Ammonium nitrate based fertilizer	9	UN2071	III	9	132, B136, IB8, IP3	140	CLASS 9
	Ammonium nitrate emulsion or Ammonium nitrate suspension or Ammonium nitrate gel, intermediate for blasting explosives	5.1	UN3375	II	5.1	147, 148, 163, IB2, IP16	140	OXIDIZER
D	Ammonium nitrate–fuel oil mixture containing only prilled ammonium nitrate and fuel oil	1.5D	NA0331		1.5D	148	112	EXPLOSIVES 1.5
	Ammonium nitrate, liquid (hot concentrated solution)	5.1	UN2426		5.1	148, B5, T7	140	OXIDIZER
	Ammonium nitrate, with more than 0.2 percent combustible substances, including any organic substance calculated as carbon, to the exclusion of any other added substance	1.1D	UN0222		1.1D	370	112	EXPLOSIVES 1.1*

Name and description	Hazard class or Division	Identification Numbers	PG	Label Codes	Special Provisions	(page)	(label)
Ammonium nitrate, with not more than 0.2% combustible substances, including any organic substance, calculated as carbon to the exclusion of any other added substance	5.1	UN1942	III	5.1	148, A1, A29, B120, IB8, IP3, T1, TP33	140	OXIDIZER
Ammonium nitrite	Forbidden						
Ammonium perchlorate	1.1D	UN0402		1.1D	107	112	EXPLOSIVES 1.1*
Ammonium perchlorate	5.1	UN1442	II	5.1	107, A9, IB6, IP2, T3, TP33	143	OXIDIZER
Ammonium permanganate	Forbidden						
Ammonium persulfate	5.1	UN1444	III	5.1	A1, A29, IB8, IP3, T1, TP33	140	OXIDIZER
Ammonium picrate, *dry or wetted with less than 10 percent water, by mass*	1.1D	UN0004		1.1D		112	EXPLOSIVES 1.1*
Ammonium picrate, *wetted with not less than 10 percent water, by mass*	4.1	UN1310	I	4.1	23, A2, N41, W31	113	FLAMMABLE SOLID
Ammonium polysulfide, solution	8	UN2818	II	8, 6.1	IB2, T7, TP2, TP13	154	CORROSIVE
			III	8, 6.1	IB3, T4, TP1, TP13	154	CORROSIVE
Ammonium polyvanadate	6.1	UN2861	II	6.1	IB8, IP2, IP4, T3, TP33	151	POISON
Ammonium silicofluoride, see Ammonium fluorosilicate							
Ammonium sulfide solution	8	UN2683	II	8, 6.1, 3	IB1, T7, TP2, TP13	132	CORROSIVE
Ammunition, blank, see Cartridges for weapons, blank							
Ammunition, illuminating *with or without burster, expelling charge or propelling charge*	1.2G	UN0171		1.2G		112	EXPLOSIVES 1.2*
Ammunition, illuminating *with or without burster, expelling charge or propelling charge*	1.3G	UN0254		1.3G		112	EXPLOSIVES 1.3*
Ammunition, illuminating *with or without burster, expelling charge or propelling charge*	1.4G	UN0297		1.4G		114	EXPLOSIVES 1.4
Ammunition, incendiary *liquid or gel, with burster, expelling charge or propelling charge*	1.3J	UN0247		1.3J		112	EXPLOSIVES 1.3*
Ammunition, incendiary *(water-activated contrivances) with burster, expelling charge or propelling charge, see* **Contrivances, water-activated, etc.**							
Ammunition, incendiary, white phosphorus, *with burster, expelling charge or propelling charge*	1.2H	UN0243		1.2H		112	EXPLOSIVES 1.2*

Symbols (1)	Hazardous materials descriptions and proper shipping names (2)	Hazard class or Division (3)	Identification Numbers (4)	PG (5)	Label Codes (6)	Special Provisions (§172.102) (7)	ERG Guide No.	Placard Advisory Consult §172.504 & §172.505 *Placard any quantity
	Ammunition, incendiary, white phosphorus, with burster, *expelling charge or propelling charge*	1.3H	UN0244		1.3H		112	EXPLOSIVES 1.3*
	Ammunition, incendiary *with or without burster, expelling charge, or propelling charge*	1.2G	UN0009		1.2G		112	EXPLOSIVES 1.2*
	Ammunition, incendiary *with or without burster, expelling charge, or propelling charge*	1.3G	UN0010		1.3G		112	EXPLOSIVES 1.3*
	Ammunition, incendiary *with or without burster, expelling charge or propelling charge*	1.4G	UN0300		1.4G		114	EXPLOSIVES 1.4
	Ammunition, practice	1.4G	UN0362		1.4G		114	EXPLOSIVES 1.4
	Ammunition, practice	1.3G	UN0488		1.3G		112	EXPLOSIVES 1.3*
	Ammunition, proof	1.4G	UN0363		1.4G		114	EXPLOSIVES 1.4
	Ammunition, rocket, see **Warheads, rocket** *etc.*							
	Ammunition, SA (small arms), see **Cartridges for weapons,** *etc.*							
	Ammunition, smoke (water-activated contrivances), white phosphorus, with burster, expelling charge or propelling charge, see **Contrivances, water-activated,** *etc. (UN0248)*							
	Ammunition, smoke (water-activated contrivances), without white phosphorus or phosphides, with burster, expelling charge or propelling charge, see **Contrivances, water-activated,** *etc. (UN0249)*							
	Ammunition smoke, white phosphorus *with burster, expelling charge, or propelling charge*	1.2H	UN0245		1.2H		112	EXPLOSIVES 1.2*
	Ammunition, smoke, white phosphorus *with burster, expelling charge, or propelling charge*	1.3H	UN0246		1.3H		112	EXPLOSIVES 1.3*
	Ammunition, smoke *with or without burster, expelling charge or propelling charge*	1.2G	UN0015		1.2G		112	EXPLOSIVES 1.2*
	Ammunition, smoke *with or without burster, expelling charge or propelling charge*	1.3G	UN0016		1.3G		112	EXPLOSIVES 1.3*

Sym	Hazardous materials descriptions and proper shipping names	Hazard class or Division	Identification Numbers	PG	Label Codes	Special Provisions	Guide No.	Placard
	Ammunition, smoke with or without burster, expelling charge or propelling charge	1.4G	UN0303		1.4G		114	EXPLOSIVES 1.4
	Ammunition, sporting, see Cartridges for weapons, etc. (UN0328; UN0339)							
	Ammunition, tear-producing, non-explosive, without burster or expelling charge, non-fuzed	6.1	UN2017		6.1, 8		159	POISON
	Ammunition, tear-producing with burster, expelling charge or propelling charge	1.2G	UN0018		1.2G, 8, 6.1		112	EXPLOSIVES 1.2*
	Ammunition, tear-producing with burster, expelling charge or propelling charge	1.3G	UN0019		1.3G, 8, 6.1		112	EXPLOSIVES 1.3*
	Ammunition, tear-producing with burster, expelling charge or propelling charge	1.4G	UN0301		1.4G, 8, 6.1		114	EXPLOSIVES 1.4
	Ammunition, toxic, non-explosive, without burster or expelling charge, non-fuzed	6.1	UN2016		6.1		151	POISON
	Ammunition, toxic (water-activated contrivances), with burster, expelling charge or propelling charge, see Contrivances, water-activated, etc.							
G	Ammunition, toxic with burster, expelling charge or propelling charge	1.2K	UN0020		1.2K, 6.1		112	EXPLOSIVES 1.2*
G	Ammunition, toxic with burster, expelling charge or propelling charge	1.3K	UN0021		1.3K, 6.1		112	EXPLOSIVES 1.3*
	Amyl acetates	3	UN1104	III	3	B1, IB3, T2, TP1	129	FLAMMABLE
	Amyl acid phosphate	8	UN2819	III	8	IB3, T4, TP1	153	CORROSIVE
	Amyl butyrates	3	UN2620	III	3	B1, IB3, T2, TP1	130	FLAMMABLE
	Amyl chloride	3	UN1107	II	3	IB2, T4, TP1	129	FLAMMABLE
	Amyl formates	3	UN1109	III	3	B1, IB3, T2, TP1	129	FLAMMABLE
	Amyl mercaptan	3	UN1111	II	3	A3, IB2, T4, TP1	130	FLAMMABLE
	n-Amyl methyl ketone	3	UN1110	III	3	B1, IB3, T2, TP1	127	FLAMMABLE
	Amyl nitrate	3	UN1112	III	3	B1, IB3, T2, TP1	128	FLAMMABLE
	Amyl nitrite	3	UN1113	II	3	IB2, T4, TP1	129	FLAMMABLE
	Amylamines	3	UN1106	II	3, 8	IB2, T7, TP1	132	FLAMMABLE
				III	3, 8	B1, IB3, T4, TP1	132	FLAMMABLE

Symbols (1)	Hazardous materials descriptions and proper shipping names (2)	Hazard class or Division (3)	Identification Numbers (4)	PG (5)	Label Codes (6)	Special Provisions (§172.102) (7)	ERG Guide No.	Placard Advisory Consult §172.504 & §172.505 *Placard any quantity
	Amyltrichlorosilane	8	UN1728	II	8	A7, B2, B6, N34, T10, TP2, TP7, TP13	155	CORROSIVE
	Anhydrous ammonia, see Ammonia, anhydrous							
+	Anhydrous hydrofluoric acid, see Hydrogen fluoride, anhydrous							
	Aniline	6.1	UN1547	II	6.1	IB2, T7, TP2	153	POISON
	Aniline hydrochloride	6.1	UN1548	III	6.1	IB8, IP3, T1, TP33	153	POISON
	Aniline oil, see Aniline							
	Anisidines	6.1	UN2431	III	6.1	IB3, T4, TP1	153	POISON
	Anisole	3	UN2222	III	3	B1, IB3, T2, TP1	128	FLAMMABLE
	Anisoyl chloride	8	UN1729	II	8	B2, B4, IB8, IP2, IP4, T3, TP33	156	CORROSIVE
	Anti-freeze, liquid, see Flammable liquids, n.o.s.							
	Antimonous chloride, see Antimony trichloride							
G	Antimony compounds, inorganic, liquid, n.o.s.	6.1	UN3141	III	6.1	35, IB3, T7, TP1, TP28	157	POISON
G	Antimony compounds, inorganic, solid, n.o.s.	6.1	UN1549	III	6.1	35, IB8, IP3, T1, TP33	157	POISON
	Antimony lactate	6.1	UN1550	III	6.1	IB8, IP3, T1, TP33	151	POISON
	Antimony pentachloride, liquid	8	UN1730	II	8	B2, B2, T7, TP2	157	CORROSIVE
	Antimony pentachloride, solutions	8	UN1731	II	8	B2, B2, T7, TP2	157	CORROSIVE
				III	8	IB3, T4, TP1	157	CORROSIVE
	Antimony pentafluoride	8	UN1732	II	8, 6.1	A3, A7, A10, IB2, N3, N36, T7, TP2	157	CORROSIVE
	Antimony potassium tartrate	6.1	UN1551	III	6.1	IB8, IP3, T1, TP33	151	POISON
	Antimony powder	6.1	UN2871	III	6.1	IB8, IP3, T1, TP33	170	POISON
	Antimony sulfide and a chlorate, mixtures of	Forbidden						
	Antimony sulfide, solid, see Antimony compounds, inorganic, n.o.s.							
	Antimony trichloride, liquid	8	UN1733	II	8	B2, IB2	157	CORROSIVE

Symbol	Hazardous materials descriptions and proper shipping names	Hazard class or Division	Identification Numbers	PG	Label Codes	Special provisions	Guide	
	Antimony trichloride, solid	8	UN1733	II	8	IB8, IP2, IP4, T3, TP33	157	CORROSIVE
	Aqua ammonia, see Ammonia solution, etc.							
	Argon, compressed	2.2	UN1006		2.2		120	NONFLAMMABLE GAS
	Argon, refrigerated liquid (cryogenic liquid)	2.2	UN1951		2.2	T75, TP5	120	NONFLAMMABLE GAS
	Arsenic	6.1	UN1558	II	6.1	IB8, IP2, IP4, T3, TP33	152	POISON
	Arsenic acid, liquid	6.1	UN1553	I	6.1	T20, TP2, TP7 TP13, W31	154	POISON
	Arsenic acid, solid	6.1	UN1554	II	6.1	IB8, IP2, IP4, T3, TP33	154	POISON
	Arsenic bromide	6.1	UN1555	II	6.1	IB8, IP2, IP4, T3, TP33	151	POISON
	Arsenic chloride, see Arsenic trichloride							
G	Arsenic compounds, liquid, n.o.s. inorganic, including arsenates, n.o.s.; arsenites, n.o.s.; arsenic sulfides, n.o.s.; and organic compounds of arsenic, n.o.s.	6.1	UN1556	I	6.1	T14, TP2, TP13, TP27	152	POISON
				II	6.1	IB2, T11, TP2, TP13, TP27	152	POISON
				III	6.1	IB3, T7, TP2, TP28	152	POISON
G	Arsenic compounds, solid, n.o.s. inorganic, including arsenates, n.o.s.; arsenites, n.o.s.; arsenic sulfides, n.o.s.; and organic compounds of arsenic, n.o.s.	6.1	UN1557	I	6.1	IB7, IP1, T6, TP33	152	POISON
				II	6.1	IB8, IP2, IP4, T3, TP33	152	POISON
				III	6.1	IB8, IP3, T1, TP33	152	POISON
	Arsenic pentoxide	6.1	UN1559	II	6.1	IB8, IP2, IP4, T3, TP33	151	POISON
	Arsenic sulfide and a chlorate, mixtures of	Forbidden						
	Arsenic trichloride	6.1	UN1560	I	6.1	2, B9, B14, B32, B20, TP2, TP13, TP38, TP45	157	INHALATION HAZARD CLASS 6*
	Arsenic trioxide	6.1	UN1561	II	6.1	IB8, IP2, IP4, T3, TP33	151	POISON
	Arsenic, white, solid, see Arsenic trioxide							
	Arsenical dust	6.1	UN1562	II	6.1	IB8, IP2, IP4, T3, TP33	152	POISON
	Arsenical pesticides, liquid, flammable, toxic, flash point less than 23 degrees C	3	UN2760	I	3, 6.1	T14, TP2, TP13, TP27	131	FLAMMABLE
				II	3, 6.1	IB2, T11, TP2, TP13, TP27	131	FLAMMABLE
	Arsenical pesticides, liquid, toxic	6.1	UN2994	I	6.1	T14, TP2, TP13, TP27	151	POISON
				II	6.1	IB2, T11, TP2, TP13, TP27	151	POISON

Symbols (1)	Hazardous materials descriptions and proper shipping names (2)	Hazard class or Division (3)	Identification Numbers (4)	PG (5)	Label Codes (6)	Special Provisions (§172.102) (7)	ERG Guide No.	Placard Advisory Consult §172.504 & §172.505 *Placard any quantity
	Arsenical pesticides, liquid, toxic, flammable, *flash point not less than 23 degrees C*	6.1	UN2993	III	6.1	IB3, T7, TP2, TP28	151	POISON
				I	6.1, 3	T14, TP2, TP13, TP27	131	POISON
				II	6.1, 3	IB2, T11, TP2, TP13, TP27	131	POISON
	Arsenical pesticides, solid, toxic	6.1	UN2759	I	6.1	B1, IB3, T7, TP2, TP28	151	POISON
				II	6.1	IB7, IP1, T6, TP33	151	POISON
				III	6.1	IB8, IP2, IP4, T3, TP33	151	POISON
						IB8, IP3, T1, TP33		
	Arsenious acid, solid, see Arsenic trioxide							
	Arsenious and mercuric iodide solution, see Arsenic compounds, liquid, n.o.s.							
	Arsine	2.3	UN2188		2.3, 2.1	1	119	INHALATION HAZARD CLASS 2*
	Arsine, adsorbed	2.3	UN3522		2.3, 2.1	1	173	INHALATION HAZARD CLASS 2*
G	**Articles containing a substance liable to spontaneous combustion, n.o.s.**	4.2	UN3542			131, 391	135	SPONTANEOUSLY COMBUSTIBLE
G	**Articles containing a substance which in contact with water emits flammable gases, n.o.s.**	4.3	UN3543			131, 391	138	DANGEROUS WHEN WET*
G	**Articles containing corrosive substance, n.o.s**	8	UN3547			391	154	CORROSIVE
G	**Articles containing flammable gas, n.o.s.**	2.1	UN3537			391	115	FLAMMABLE GAS
G	**Articles containing flammable liquid, n.o.s.**	3	UN3540			391	127	FLAMMABLE
G	**Articles containing flammable solid, n.o.s.**	4.1	UN3541			391	133	FLAMMABLE SOLID
G	**Articles containing miscellaneous dangerous goods, n.o.s.**	9	UN3548			391	171	CLASS 9
G	**Articles containing non-flammable, non-toxic gas, n.o.s.**	2.2	UN3538			391	120	NONFLAMMABLE GAS
G	**Articles containing organic peroxide, n.o.s.**	5.2	UN3545			131, 391	145	ORGANIC PEROXIDE
G	**Articles containing oxidizing substance, n.o.s.**	5.1	UN3544			131, 391	140	OXIDIZER

Symbol	Hazardous materials descriptions and proper shipping names	Hazard class or Division	Identification Numbers	Label Codes	Special Provisions	123	INHALATION HAZARD CLASS 2*
G	Articles containing toxic gas, n.o.s.	2.3	UN3539	2.3	131, 391	123	INHALATION HAZARD CLASS 2*
G	Articles containing toxic substance, n.o.s.	6.1	UN3546	6.1	391	151	POISON
G	Articles, explosive, extremely insensitive or Articles, EEI	1.6N	UN0486	1.6N		114	EXPLOSIVES 1.6
G	Articles, explosive, n.o.s.	1.4S	UN0349	1.4S	101, 148, 347, 382	114	EXPLOSIVES 1.4
G	Articles, explosive, n.o.s.	1.4B	UN0350	1.4B	101	114	EXPLOSIVES 1.4
G	Articles, explosive, n.o.s.	1.4C	UN0351	1.4C	101	114	EXPLOSIVES 1.4
G	Articles, explosive, n.o.s.	1.4D	UN0352	1.4D	101	114	EXPLOSIVES 1.4
G	Articles, explosive, n.o.s.	1.4G	UN0353	1.4G	101	114	EXPLOSIVES 1.4
G	Articles, explosive, n.o.s.	1.1L	UN0354	1.1L	101	112	EXPLOSIVES 1.1*
G	Articles, explosive, n.o.s.	1.2L	UN0355	1.2L	101	112	EXPLOSIVES 1.2*
G	Articles, explosive, n.o.s.	1.3L	UN0356	1.3L	101	112	EXPLOSIVES 1.3*
G	Articles, explosive, n.o.s.	1.1C	UN0462	1.1C	101	112	EXPLOSIVES 1.1*
G	Articles, explosive, n.o.s.	1.1D	UN0463	1.1D	101	112	EXPLOSIVES 1.1*
G	Articles, explosive, n.o.s.	1.1E	UN0464	1.1E	101	112	EXPLOSIVES 1.1*
G	Articles, explosive, n.o.s.	1.1F	UN0465	1.1F	101	112	EXPLOSIVES 1.1*
G	Articles, explosive, n.o.s.	1.2C	UN0466	1.2C	101	112	EXPLOSIVES 1.2*
G	Articles, explosive, n.o.s.	1.2D	UN0467	1.2D	101	112	EXPLOSIVES 1.2*
G	Articles, explosive, n.o.s.	1.2E	UN0468	1.2E	101	112	EXPLOSIVES 1.2*
G	Articles, explosive, n.o.s.	1.2F	UN0469	1.2F	101	112	EXPLOSIVES 1.2*
G	Articles, explosive, n.o.s.	1.3C	UN0470	1.3C	101	112	EXPLOSIVES 1.3*
G	Articles, explosive, n.o.s.	1.4E	UN0471	1.4E	101	114	EXPLOSIVES 1.4
G	Articles, explosive, n.o.s.	1.4F	UN0472	1.4F	101	114	EXPLOSIVES 1.4
	Articles, pressurized pneumatic or hydraulic containing non-flammable gas	2.2	UN3164	2.2	371	126	NONFLAMMABLE GAS
	Articles, pyrophoric	1.2L	UN0380	1.2L		112	EXPLOSIVES 1.2*
	Articles, pyrotechnic for technical purposes	1.1G	UN0428	1.1G		112	EXPLOSIVES 1.1*
	Articles, pyrotechnic for technical purposes	1.2G	UN0429	1.2G		112	EXPLOSIVES 1.2*
	Articles, pyrotechnic for technical purposes	1.3G	UN0430	1.3G		112	EXPLOSIVES 1.3*
	Articles, pyrotechnic for technical purposes	1.4G	UN0431	1.4G	381	114	EXPLOSIVES 1.4

HAZMAT TABLE

Symbols (1)	Hazardous materials descriptions and proper shipping names (2)	Hazard class or Division (3)	Identification Numbers (4)	PG (5)	Label Codes (6)	Special Provisions (§172.102) (7)	ERG Guide No.	Placard Advisory Consult §172.504 & §172.505 *Placard any quantity
	Articles, pyrotechnic *for technical purposes*	1.4S	UN0432		1.4S		114	EXPLOSIVES 1.4
D	**Asbestos**	9	NA2212	III	9	156, IB8, IP2, IP4	171	CLASS 9
G I	**Asbestos, amphibole** *amosite, tremolite, actinolite, anthophyllite, or crocidolite*	9	UN2212	II	9	156, IB8, IP2, IP4, T3, TP33	171	CLASS 9
I	**Asbestos, chrysotile**	9	UN2590	III	9	156, IB8, IP2, IP3, T1, TP33	171	CLASS 9
	Ascaridole (organic peroxide)	Forbidden						
D	**Asphalt,** *at or above its flashpoint*	3	NA1999	III	3	IB3, T1, TP3	130	FLAMMABLE
D	**Asphalt, cut back, see Tars, liquid, etc.**							
	Automobile, motorcycle, tractor, other self-propelled vehicle, engine, or other mechanical apparatus, see **Vehicles** *or* **Battery** *etc.*							
A G	**Aviation regulated liquid, n.o.s.**	9	UN3334	II	9	A35, A189	171	CLASS 9
A G	**Aviation regulated solid, n.o.s.**	9	UN3335	II	9	A35	171	CLASS 9
	Azaurolic acid (salt of) (dry)	Forbidden						
	Azido guanidine picrate (dry)	Forbidden						
	5-Azido-1-hydroxy tetrazole	Forbidden						
	Azido hydroxy tetrazole (mercury and silver salts)	Forbidden						
	3-Azido-1,2-Propylene glycol dinitrate	Forbidden						
	Azidodithiocarbonic acid	Forbidden						
	Azidoethyl nitrate	Forbidden						
	1-Aziridinylphosphine oxide-(tris), see Tris-(1-aziridinyl)phosphine oxide, solution							
	Azodicarbonamide	4.1	UN3242	II	4.1	38, IB8, T3, TP33	149	FLAMMABLE SOLID
	Azotetrazole (dry)	Forbidden						
	Barium	4.3	UN1400	II	4.3	A19, IB7, IP2, IP21, T3, TP33, W31, W40	138	DANGEROUS WHEN WET
	Barium alloys, pyrophoric	4.2	UN1854	I	4.2	T21, TP7, TP33, W31	135	SPONTANEOUSLY COMBUSTIBLE

Sym	Hazardous materials descriptions and proper shipping names	Hazard class or division	Identification Numbers	PG	Label Codes	Special Provisions		
	Barium azide, *dry or wetted with less than 50 percent water, by mass*	1.1A	UN0224		1.1A, 6.1	111, 117	112	EXPLOSIVES 1.1*
	Barium azide, *wetted with not less than 50 percent water, by mass*	4.1	UN1571	I	4.1, 6.1	162, A2, W31	113	FLAMMABLE SOLID
	Barium bromate	5.1	UN2719	II	5.1, 6.1	IB8, IP2, IP4, T3, TP33	141	OXIDIZER
	Barium chlorate, solid	5.1	UN1445	II	5.1, 6.1	A9, IB6, IP2, N34, T3, TP33	141	OXIDIZER
	Barium chlorate, solution	5.1	UN3405	II	5.1, 6.1	A9, IB2, N34, T4, TP1	141	OXIDIZER
				III	5.1, 6.1	A9, IB2, N34, T4, TP1	141	OXIDIZER
G	Barium compounds, n.o.s.	6.1	UN1564	II	6.1	IB8, IP2, IP4, T3, TP33	154	POISON
				III	6.1	IB8, IP3, T1, TP33	154	POISON
	Barium cyanide	6.1	UN1565	I	6.1	IB7, IP1, N74, N75, T6, TP33, W31	157	POISON
	Barium hypochlorite *with more than 22 percent available chlorine*	5.1	UN2741	II	5.1, 6.1	A7, A9, IB8, IP2, IP4, N34, T3, TP33	141	OXIDIZER
	Barium nitrate	5.1	UN1446	II	5.1, 6.1	IB8, IP2, IP4, T3, TP33	141	OXIDIZER
	Barium oxide	6.1	UN1884	III	6.1	IB8, IP3, T1, TP33	157	POISON
	Barium perchlorate, solid	5.1	UN1447	II	5.1, 6.1	IB6, IP2, T3, TP33	141	OXIDIZER
	Barium perchlorate, solution	5.1	UN3406	II	5.1, 6.1	IB2, T4, TP1	141	OXIDIZER
				III	5.1, 6.1	IB2, T4, TP1	141	OXIDIZER
	Barium permanganate	5.1	UN1448	II	5.1, 6.1	IB6, IP2, T3, TP33	141	OXIDIZER
	Barium peroxide	5.1	UN1449	II	5.1, 6.1	A9, IB6, IP2, T3, TP33, W100	141	OXIDIZER
	Barium selenate, see Selenates *or* Selenites							
	Barium selenite, see Selenates *or* Selenites							

HAZMAT TABLE

Symbols (1)	Hazardous materials descriptions and proper shipping names (2)	Hazard class or Division (3)	Identification Numbers (4)	PG (5)	Label Codes (6)	Special Provisions (§172.102) (7)	ERG Guide No.	Placard Advisory Consult §172.504 & §172.505 *Placard any quantity
	Batteries, containing sodium	4.3	UN3292		4.3		138	DANGEROUS WHEN WET*
	Batteries, dry, containing potassium hydroxide solid, *electric storage*	8	UN3028		8	237	154	CORROSIVE
	Batteries, dry, sealed, n.o.s.					130	—	NONE
W	**Batteries, nickel-metal hydride** *see* **Batteries, dry, sealed, n.o.s.** *for nickel-metal hydride batteries transported by modes other than vessel*	9	UN3496		9	340	171	CLASS 9
	Batteries, wet, filled with acid, *electric storage*	8	UN2794		8	A51	154	CORROSIVE
	Batteries, wet, filled with alkali, *electric storage*	8	UN2795		8	A51	154	CORROSIVE
	Batteries, wet, non-spillable, *electric storage*	8	UN2800		8		154	CORROSIVE
	Battery fluid, acid	8	UN2796	II	8	A3, A7, B2, B15, IB2, N6, N34, T8, TP2	157	CORROSIVE
	Battery fluid, alkali	8	UN2797	II	8	B2, IB2, N6, T7, TP2, TP28	154	CORROSIVE
	Battery lithium type, see **Lithium batteries** *etc.*							
	The 2016 Emergency Response Guidebook (ERG) lists several different guide numbers for the shipping names **Battery-powered vehicle** or **Battery-powered equipment.** The type of battery determines the ERG guide number that should be used. For **Battery-powered vehicle** or **Battery-powered equipment** with a lithium ion battery the guide number is 147, with a lithium metal battery or a sodium battery the guide number is 138, and with a wet battery the guide number is 154.							
	Battery-powered vehicle or **Battery-powered equipment**	9	UN3171		9	134	—	CLASS 9
	Battery, wet, filled with acid or alkali with vehicle or mechanical equipment containing an internal combustion engine, see **Vehicle,** *etc. or* **Engines, Internal combustion,** *etc.*							
+	**Benzaldehyde**	9	UN1990	III	9	IB3, T2, TP1	171	CLASS 9
	Benzene	3	UN1114	II	3	IB2, T4, TP1	130	FLAMMABLE
	Benzene diazonium chloride (dry)	Forbidden						
	Benzene diazonium nitrate (dry)	Forbidden						

Sym	Hazardous materials descriptions and proper shipping names	Hazard class or Division	Identification Numbers	PG	Label Codes	Special Provisions	ERG Guide	Placard
	Benzene phosphorus dichloride, *see* **Phenyl phosphorus dichloride**							
	Benzene phosphorus thiodichloride, *see* **Phenyl phosphorus thiodichloride**							
	Benzene sulfonyl chloride	8	UN2225	III	8	IB3, T4, TP1	156	CORROSIVE
	Benzene triozonide	Forbidden						
	Benzenethiol, *see* Phenyl mercaptan							
	Benzidine	6.1	UN1885	II	6.1	IB8, IP2, IP4, T3, TP33	153	POISON
	1,3,2-Benzodioxaborole					A210		
	Benzol, see **Benzene**							
	Benzonitrile	6.1	UN2224	II	6.1	IB2, T7, TP2	152	POISON
	Benzoquinone	6.1	UN2587	II	6.1	IB8, IP2, IP4, T3, TP33	153	POISON
	Benzotrichloride	8	UN2226	II	8	B2, IB2, T7, TP2	156	CORROSIVE
	Benzotrifluoride	3	UN2338	II	3	IB2, T4, TP1	127	FLAMMABLE
	Benzoxidiazoles (dry)	Forbidden						
	Benzoyl azide	Forbidden						
	Benzoyl chloride	8	UN1736	II	8	B2, IB2, T8, TP2, TP13	137	CORROSIVE
	Benzyl bromide	6.1	UN1737	II	6.1, 8	A3, A7, IB2, N33, N34, T8, TP2, TP13	156	POISON
	Benzyl chloride	6.1	UN1738	II	6.1, 8	A3, A7, B70, IB2, N33, N42, T8, TP2, TP13	156	POISON
	Benzyl chloride unstabilized	6.1	UN1738	II	6.1, 8	A3, A7, B8, B11, IB2, N33, N34, N43, T8, TP2, TP13	156	POISON
	Benzyl chloroformate	8	UN1739	I	8	B4, N41, T10, TP2, TP13	137	CORROSIVE
	Benzyl iodide	6.1	UN2653	II	6.1	IB2, T7, TP2	156	POISON
	Benzyldimethylamine	8	UN2619	II	8, 3	B2, IB2, T7, TP2	132	CORROSIVE
	Benzylidene chloride	6.1	UN1886	II	6.1	IB2, T7, TP2	156	POISON
G	Beryllium compounds, n.o.s.	6.1	UN1566	II	6.1	IB8, IP2, IP4, T3, TP33	154	POISON
		6.1		III	6.1	IB8, IP3, T1, TP33	154	POISON
	Beryllium nitrate	5.1	UN2464	II	5.1, 6.1	IB8, IP2, IP4, T3, TP33	141	OXIDIZER

Sym-bols (1)	Hazardous materials descriptions and proper shipping names (2)	Hazard class or Division (3)	Identifica-tion Numbers (4)	PG (5)	Label Codes (6)	Special Provisions (§172.102) (7)	ERG Guide No.	Placard Advisory Consult §172.504 & §172.505 *Placard any quantity
	Beryllium, powder	6.1	UN1567	II	6.1, 4.1	IB8, IP2, IP4, T3, TP33, W100	134	POISON
	Bicyclo [2,2,1] hepta-2,5-diene, stabilized or 2,5-Norbornadiene, stabilized	3	UN2251	II	3	387, IB2, T7, TP2	128P	FLAMMABLE
	Biological substance, Category B	6.2	UN3373				A82	158	NONE
	Biphenyl triozonide	Forbidden						
	Bipyridilium pesticides, liquid, flammable, toxic, *flash point less than 23 degrees C*	3	UN2782	I	3, 6.1	T14, TP2, TP13, TP27	131	FLAMMABLE
				II	3, 6.1	IB2, T11, TP2, TP13, TP27	131	FLAMMABLE
	Bipyridilium pesticides, liquid, toxic	6.1	UN3016	I	6.1	T14, TP2, TP13, TP27	151	POISON
				II	6.1	IB2, T11, TP2, TP13, TP27	151	POISON
				III	6.1	IB3, T7, TP2, TP28	151	POISON
	Bipyridilium pesticides, liquid, toxic, flammable, *flash point nct less than 23 degrees C*	6.1	UN3015	I	6.1, 3	T14, TP2, TP13, TP27	131	POISON
				II	6.1, 3	IB2, T11, TP2, TP13, TP27	131	POISON
				III	6.1, 3	B1, IB3, T7, TP2, TP28	131	POISON
	Bipyridilium pesticides, solid, toxic	6.1	UN2781	I	6.1	IB7, IP1, T6, TP33	151	POISON
				II	6.1	IB8, IP2, IP4, T3, TP33	151	POISON
				III	6.1	IB8, IP3, T1, TP33	151	POISON
	Bis (Aminopropyl) piperazine, see Corrosive liquid, n.o.s.							
	Bisulfate, aqueous solution	8	UN2837	II	8	A7, B2, IB2, N34, T7, TP2	154	CORROSIVE
				III	8	A7, IB3, N34, T4, TP1	154	CORROSIVE
	Bisulfites, aqueous solutions, n.o.s.	8	UN2693	III	8	IB3, T7, TP1, TP28	154	CORROSIVE
	Black powder, compressed *or* **Gunpowder, compressed** *or* **Black powder, in pellets** *or* **Gunpowder, in pellets**	1.1D	UN0028	II	1.1D		112	EXPLOSIVES 1.1*
	Black powder *or* **Gunpowder,** *granular or as a meal*	1.1D	UN0027	II	1.1D		112	EXPLOSIVES 1.1*
D	**Black powder for small arms**	4.1	NA0027	I	4.1	70	—	FLAMMABLE SOLID

Symbols	Hazardous materials descriptions and proper shipping names	Hazard class or Division	Identification Numbers	PG	Label Codes	Special provisions	ERG Guide	Placard
	Blasting agent, n.o.s., see Explosives, blasting etc.							
	Blasting cap assemblies, see Detonator assemblies, non-electric, for blasting							
	Blasting caps, electric, see Detonators, electric for blasting							
	Blasting caps, non-electric, see Detonators, non-electric, for blasting							
	Bleaching powder, see Calcium hypochlorite mixtures, etc.							
	Bombs, photo-flash	1.1F	UN0037		1.1F		112	EXPLOSIVES 1.1*
	Bombs, photo-flash	1.1D	UN0038		1.1D		112	EXPLOSIVES 1.1*
	Bombs, photo-flash	1.2G	UN0039		1.2G		112	EXPLOSIVES 1.2*
	Bombs, photo-flash	1.3G	UN0299		1.3G		112	EXPLOSIVES 1.3*
	Bombs, smoke, non-explosive, with corrosive liquid, without initiating device	8	UN2028	II	8		153	CORROSIVE
	Bombs, with bursting charge	1.1F	UN0033		1.1F		112	EXPLOSIVES 1.1*
	Bombs, with bursting charge	1.1D	UN0034		1.1D		112	EXPLOSIVES 1.1*
	Bombs, with bursting charge	1.2D	UN0035		1.2D		112	EXPLOSIVES 1.2*
	Bombs, with bursting charge	1.2F	UN0291		1.2F		112	EXPLOSIVES 1.2*
	Bombs with flammable liquid, with bursting charge	1.1J	UN0399		1.1J		112	EXPLOSIVES 1.1*
	Bombs with flammable liquid, with bursting charge	1.2J	UN0400		1.2J		112	EXPLOSIVES 1.2*
	Boosters with detonator	1.1B	UN0225		1.1B		112	EXPLOSIVES 1.1*
	Boosters with detonator	1.2B	UN0268		1.2B		112	EXPLOSIVES 1.2*
	Boosters, without detonator	1.1D	UN0042		1.1D	148	112	EXPLOSIVES 1.1*
	Boosters, without detonator	1.2D	UN0283		1.2D		112	EXPLOSIVES 1.2*
	Borate and chlorate mixtures, see Chlorate and borate mixtures							
	Borneol	4.1	UN1312	III	4.1	A1, IB8, IP3, T1, TP33	133	FLAMMABLE SOLID
+	Boron tribromide	8	UN2692	I	8, 6.1	2, B9, B14, B32, N34, T20, TP2, TP13, TP38, TP45	157	CORROSIVE, INHALATION HAZARD CLASS 6*
	Boron trichloride	2.3	UN1741		2.3, 8	3, B9, B14	125	INHALATION HAZARD CLASS 2*

Symbols (1)	Hazardous materials descriptions and proper shipping names (2)	Hazard class or Division (3)	Identification Numbers (4)	PG (5)	Label Codes (6)	Special Provisions (§172.102) (7)	ERG Guide No.	Placard Advisory Consult §172.504 & §172.505 *Placard any quantity
	Boron trifluoride	2.3	UN1008		2.3, 8	2, 238, B9, B14	125	INHALATION HAZARD CLASS 2"
	Boron trifluoride acetic acid complex, liquid	8	UN1742	II	8	B2, B6, IB2, T8, TP2	157	CORROSIVE
	Boron trifluoride acetic acid complex, solid	8	UN3419	II	8	B2, B6, IB8, IP2, IP4, T3, TP33	157	CORROSIVE
	Boron trifluoride, adsorbed	2.3	UN3519		2.3, 8	2, B9, B14	173	INHALATION HAZARD CLASS 2"
	Boron trifluoride diethyl etherate	8	UN2604	I	8, 3	A19, T10, TP2, W31	132	CORROSIVE
	Boron trifluoride dihydrate	8	UN2851	II	8	IB2, T7, TP2	157	CORROSIVE
	Boron trifluoride dimethyl etherate	4.3	UN2965	I	4.3, 8, 3	A19, T10, TP2, TP7, TP13, W31	139	DANGEROUS WHEN WET*
	Boron trifluoride propionic acid complex, liquid	8	UN1743	II	8	B2, IB2, T8, TP2	157	CORROSIVE
	Boron trifluoride proponic acid complex, solid	8	UN3420	II	8	B2, IB8, IP2, IP4, T3, TP33	157	CORROSIVE
	Box toe gum, see Nitrocellulose etc.							
G	Bromates, inorganic, aqueous solution, n.o.s.	5.1	UN3213	II	5.1	350, IB2, T4, TP1	140	OXIDIZER
				III	5.1	350, IB2, T4, TP1	140	OXIDIZER
G	Bromates, inorganic, n.o.s.	5.1	UN1450	II	5.1	350, IB8, IP2, IP4, T3, TP33	140	OXIDIZER
+	Bromine	8	UN1744	I	8, 6.1	1, B9, B85, N34, N43, T22, TP2, TP10, TP13	154	CORROSIVE, INHALATION HAZARD CLASS 6"
	Bromine azide	Forbidden						
	Bromine chloride	2.3	UN2901		2.3, 8, 5.1	2, B9, B14, N86	124	INHALATION HAZARD CLASS 2"
+	Bromine pentafluoride	5.1	UN1745	I	5.1, 8, 6.1	1, B9, B14, B30, T22, TP2, TP13, TP38, TP44	144	OXIDIZER, INHALATION HAZARD CLASS 6"

Sym	Name	Class	ID No.	PG	Label Codes	Special Provisions	ERG	Placard
+	Bromine solutions	8	UN1744	I	8, 6.1	1, B9, B85, N34, N43, T22, TP2, TP10, TP13	154	CORROSIVE, INHALATION HAZARD CLASS 6*
+	Bromine solutions.	8	UN1744	I	8, 6.1	2, B9, B85, N34, N43, T22, TP2, TP10, TP13	154	CORROSIVE, INHALATION HAZARD CLASS 6*
+	Bromine trifluoride	5.1	UN1746	I	5.1, 6.1, 8	2, B9, B14, B32, T22, TP2, TP13, TP38, TP45	144	OXIDIZER, INHALATION HAZARD CLASS 6*
	4-Bromo-1,2-dinitrobenzene	Forbidden						
	4-Bromo-1,2-dinitrobenzene (unstable at 59 degrees C.)	Forbidden						
	1-Bromo-3-chloropropane	6.1	UN2688	III	6.1	IB3, T4, TP1	159	POISON
	1-Bromo-3-methylbutane	3	UN2341	III	3	B1, IB3, T2, TP1	130	FLAMMABLE
	1-Bromo-3-nitrobenzene (unstable at 56 degrees C)	Forbidden						
	2-Bromo-2-nitropropane-1,3-diol	4.1	UN3241	III	4.1	46, IB8, IP3	133	FLAMMABLE SOLID
	Bromoacetic acid, solid	8	UN3425	II	8	A7, IB8, IP2, IP4, N34, T3, TP33	156	CORROSIVE
	Bromoacetic acid solution	8	UN1938	II	8	A7, B2, IB2, T7, TP2	156	CORROSIVE
				III	8	B2, IB3, T7, TP2	156	CORROSIVE
+	Bromoacetone	6.1	UN1569	II	6.1, 3	2, T20, TP2, TP13	131	INHALATION HAZARD CLASS 6*
	Bromoacetyl bromide	8	UN2513	II	8	B2, IB2, T8, TP2	156	CORROSIVE
	Bromobenzene	3	UN2514	III	3	B1, IB3, T2, TP1	130	FLAMMABLE
	Bromobenzyl cyanides, liquid	6.1	UN1694	I	6.1	T14, TP2, TP13, W31	159	POISON
	Bromobenzyl cyanides, solid	6.1	UN3449	I	6.1	T6, TP33, W31	159	POISON
	1-Bromobutane	3	UN1126	II	3	IB2, T4, TP1	130	FLAMMABLE
	2-Bromobutane	3	UN2339	II	3	B1, IB2, T4, TP1	130	FLAMMABLE
	Bromochloromethane	6.1	UN1887	III	6.1	IB3, T4, TP1	160	POISON
	2-Bromoethyl ethyl ether	3	UN2340	III	3	IB2, T4, TP1	130	FLAMMABLE
	Bromoform	6.1	UN2515	III	6.1	IB3, T4, TP1	159	POISON
	Bromomethylpropanes	3	UN2342	II	3	IB2, T4, TP1	130	FLAMMABLE
	2-Bromopentane	3	UN2343	II	3	IB2, T4, TP1	130	FLAMMABLE

Symbols (1)	Hazardous materials descriptions and proper shipping names (2)	Hazard class or Division (3)	Identification Numbers (4)	PG (5)	Label Codes (6)	Special Provisions (§172.102) (7)	ERG Guide No.	Placard Advisory Consult §172.504 & §172.505 *Placard any quantity
	Bromopropanes	3	UN2344	II	3	IB2, T4, TP1	129	FLAMMABLE
				III	3	IB3, T2, TP1	129	FLAMMABLE
	3-Bromopropyne	3	UN2345	II	3	IB2, T4, TP1	130	FLAMMABLE
	Bromosilane	Forbidden						
	Bromotoluene-alpha, see Benzyl bromide							
	Bromotrifluoroethylene	2.1	UN2419		2.1		116	FLAMMABLE GAS
	Bromotrifluoromethane or **Refrigerant gas, R13B1**	2.2	UN1009		2.2	T50	126	NONFLAMMABLE GAS
	Brucine	6.1	UN1570	I	6.1	IB7, IP1, T6, TP33	152	POISON
	Bursters, explosive	1.1D	UN0043		1.1D		112	EXPLOSIVES 1.1*
	Butadienes, stabilized or **Butadienes and Hydrocarbon mixture, stabilized** containing more than 40% Butadienes	2.1	UN1010		2.1	387, T50	116P	FLAMMABLE GAS
	Butane see also **Petroleum gases, liquefied**	2.1	UN1011		2.1	19, T50	115	FLAMMABLE GAS
	Butane, butane mixtures and mixtures having similar properties in cartridges each not exceeding 500 grams, see Receptacles, etc.							
	Butanedione	3	UN2346	II	3	IB2, T4, TP1	127	FLAMMABLE
	1,2,4-Butanetriol trinitrate	Forbidden						
	Butanols	3	UN1120	II	3	IB2, T4, TP1, TP29	129	FLAMMABLE
				III	3	B1, IB3, T2, TP1	129	FLAMMABLE
	tert-Butoxycarbonyl azide	Forbidden						
	Butyl acetates	3	UN1123	II	3	IB2, T4, TP1	129	FLAMMABLE
				III	3	B1, IB3, T2, TP1	129	FLAMMABLE
	Butyl acid phosphate	8	UN1718	III	8	IB3, T4, TP1	153	CORROSIVE
	Butyl acrylates, stabilized	3	UN2348	III	3	387, B1, IB3, T2, TP1	129P	FLAMMABLE
	Butyl alcohols, see Butanols							
	Butyl benzenes	3	UN2709	III	3	B1, IB3, T2, TP2	128	FLAMMABLE
	n-Butyl bromide, see 1-Bromobutane							
	n-Butyl chloride, see Chlorobutanes							

Name	Hazard class or division	ID No.	PG	Label codes	Special provisions	Guide	Placard
n-Butyl chloroformate	6.1	UN2743	I	6.1, 8, 3	2, B9, B14, B32, T20, TP2, TP13, TP38, TP45	155	INHALATION HAZARD CLASS 6'
Butyl ethers, see Dibutyl ethers							
Butyl ethyl ether, see Ethyl butyl ether							
n-Butyl formate	3	UN1128	II	3	IB2, T4, TP1	129	FLAMMABLE
tert-Butyl hydroperoxide, with more than 90 percent with water	Forbidden						
tert-Butyl hypochlorite	4.2	UN3255	I	4.2, 8		135	SPONTANEOUSLY COMBUSTIBLE
N-n-Butyl imidazole	6.1	UN2690	II	6.1	IB2, T7, TP2	152	POISON
tert-Butyl isocyanate	6.1	UN2484	I	6.1, 3	1, B9, B14, B30, T20, TP2, TP13, TP38, TP44	155	INHALATION HAZARD CLASS 6'
n-Butyl isocyanate	6.1	UN2485	I	6.1, 3	2, B9, B14, B32, B77, T20, TP2, TP13, TP38, TP45	155P	INHALATION HAZARD CLASS 6'
Butyl mercaptan	3	UN2347	II	3	A3, IB2, T4, TP1	130	FLAMMABLE
n-Butyl methacrylate, stabilized	3	UN2227	III	3	387, B1, IB3, T2, TP1	130P	FLAMMABLE
Butyl methyl ether	3	UN2350	II	3	IB2, T4, TP1	127	FLAMMABLE
Butyl nitrites	3	UN2351	I	3	T11, TP1, TP8, TP27	129	FLAMMABLE
			II	3	IB2, T4, TP1	129	FLAMMABLE
			III	3	B1, IB3, T2, TP1	129	FLAMMABLE
tert-Butyl peroxyacetate, with more than 76 percent in solution	Forbidden						
n-Butyl peroxydicarbonate, with more than 52 percent in solution	Forbidden						
tert-Butyl peroxyisobutyrate, with more than 77 percent in solution	Forbidden						
Butyl phosphoric acid, see Butyl acid phosphate							
Butyl propionates	3	UN1914	III	3	B1, IB3, T2, TP1	130	FLAMMABLE
5-tert-Butyl-2,4,6-trinitro-m-xylene or Musk xylene	4.1	UN2956	III	4.1	159	149	FLAMMABLE SOLID
Butyl vinyl ether, stabilized	3	UN2352	II	3	387, IB2, T4, TP1	127P	FLAMMABLE
n-Butylamine	3	UN1125	II	3, 8	IB2, T7, TP1	132	FLAMMABLE
N-Butylaniline	6.1	UN2738	II	6.1	IB2, T7, TP2	153	POISON
tert-Butylcyclohexylchloroformate	6.1	UN2747	III	6.1	IB3, T4, TP1	156	POISON
Butylene see also Petroleum gases, liquefied	2.1	UN1012		2.1	19, T50	115	FLAMMABLE GAS
1,2-Butylene oxide, stabilized	3	UN3022	II	3	387, IB2, T4, TP1	127P	FLAMMABLE

Symbols (1)	Hazardous materials descriptions and proper shipping names (2)	Hazard class or Division (3)	Identification Numbers (4)	PG (5)	Label Codes (6)	Special Provisions (§172.102) (7)	ERG Guide No.	Placard Advisory Consult §172.504 & §172.505 *Placard any quantity
	Butyltoluenes	6.1	UN2667	III	6.1	IB3, T4, TP1	152	POISON
	Butyltrichlorosilane	8	UN1747	II	8, 3	A7, B2, B6, N34, T10, TP2, TP7, TP13	155	CORROSIVE
	1,4-Butynediol	6.1	UN2716	III	6.1	A1, IB8, IP3, T1, TP33	153	POISON
	Butyraldehyde	3	UN1129	II	3	IB2, T4, TP1	129P	FLAMMABLE
	Butyraldoxime	3	UN2840	III	3	B1, IB3, T2, TP1	129	FLAMMABLE
	Butyric acid	8	UN2820	III	8	IB3, T4, TP1	153	CORROSIVE
	Butyric anhydride	8	UN2739	III	8	IB3, T4, TP1	156	CORROSIVE
	Butyronitrile	3	UN2411	II	3, 6.1	IB2, T7, TP1, TP13	131	FLAMMABLE
	Butyryl chloride	3	UN2353	II	3, 8	IB2, T8, TP2, TP13	132	FLAMMABLE
	Cacodylic acid	6.1	UN1572	II	6.1	IB8, IP2, IP4, T3, TP33	151	POISON
G	Cadmium compounds	6.1	UN2570	I	6.1	IB7, IP1, T6, TP33	154	POISON
				II	6.1	IB8, IP2, IP4, T3, TP33	154	POISON
				III	6.1	IB8, IP3, T1, TP33	154	POISON
	Caesium hydroxide	8	UN2682	II	8	IB8, IP2, IP4, T3, TP33	157	CORROSIVE
	Caesium hydroxide solution	8	UN2681	II	8	B2, IB2, T7, TP2	154	CORROSIVE
				III	8	IB3, T4, TP1	154	CORROSIVE
	Calcium	4.3	UN1401	II	4.3	IB7, IP2, IP21, T3, TP33, W31, W40	138	DANGEROUS WHEN WET
	Calcium arsenate	6.1	UN1573	II	6.1	IB8, IP2, IP4, T3, TP33	151	POISON
	Calcium arsenate and calcium arsenite, mixtures, solid	6.1	UN1574	II	6.1	IB8, IP2, IP4, T3, TP33	151	POISON
	Calcium bisulfite solution, see Bisulfites, aqueous solutions, n.o.s.							
	Calcium carbide	4.3	UN1402	I	4.3	A1, A8, B55, B59, IB4, IP1, N34, T9, TP7, TP33, W31	138	DANGEROUS WHEN WET
				II	4.3	A1, A8, B55, B59, IB7, IP2, IP21, N34, T3, TP33, W31, W40	138	DANGEROUS WHEN WET

Hazardous materials descriptions and proper shipping names	Hazard class or Division	Identification Numbers	PG	Label Codes	Special Provisions	Guide No.	Placard
Calcium chlorate	5.1	UN1452	II	5.1	A9, IB8, IP2, IP4, N34, T3, TP33	140	OXIDIZER
Calcium chlorate aqueous solution	5.1	UN2429	II	5.1	A2, IB2, N41, T4, TP1	140	OXIDIZER
			III	5.1	A2, IB2, N41, T4, TP1	140	OXIDIZER
Calcium chlorite	5.1	UN1453	II	5.1	A9, IB8, IP2, IP4, N34, T3, TP33	140	OXIDIZER
Calcium cyanamide with more than 0.1 percent of calcium carbide	4.3	UN1403	III	4.3	A1, A19, IB8, IP4, T1, TP33, W31	138	DANGEROUS WHEN WET*
Calcium cyanide	6.1	UN1575	I	6.1	IB7, IP1, N79, N80, T6, TP33, W31	157	POISON
Calcium dithionite or Calcium hydrosulfite	4.2	UN1923	II	4.2	A19, A20, IB6, IP2, T3, TP33, W31	135	SPONTANEOUSLY COMBUSTIBLE
Calcium hydride	4.3	UN1404	I	4.3	A19, N40, W31	138	DANGEROUS WHEN WET*
Calcium hydrosulfite, see Calcium dithionite							
Calcium hypochlorite, dry, corrosive or Calcium hypochlorite mixtures, dry, corrosive with more than 39% available chlorine (8.8% available oxygen)	5.1	UN3485	II	5.1, 8	165, 166, A7, A9, IB8, IP2, IP4, IP13, N34, W9	140	OXIDIZER
Calcium hypochlorite, dry or Calcium hypochlorite mixture dry with more than 39% available chlorine (8.8% available oxygen)	5.1	UN1748	II	5.1	165, 166, A7, A9, IB8, IP2, IP4, IP13, N34, W9	140	OXIDIZER
			III	5.1	165, 171, A7, A9, IB8, IP4, IP13, N34, W9	140	OXIDIZER
Calcium hypochlorite, hydrated, corrosive or Calcium hypochlorite, hydrated mixture, corrosive with not less than 5.5% but not more than 16% water	5.1	UN3487	II	5.1, 8	165, IB8, IP2, IP4, IP13, W9	140	OXIDIZER
			III	5.1, 8	165, IB8, IP4, W9	140	OXIDIZER
Calcium hypochlorite, hydrated or Calcium hypochlorite, hydrated mixture, with not less than 5.5% but not more than 16% water	5.1	UN2880	II	5.1	165, IB8, IP2, IP4, IP13, W9	140	OXIDIZER
			III	5.1	165, 171, IB8, IP4, IP13, W9	140	OXIDIZER
Calcium hypochlorite mixture, dry, corrosive with more than 10% but not more than 39% available chlorine	5.1	UN3486	III	5.1, 8	165, A1, A29, IB8, IP3, IP13, N34, W9, W10	140	OXIDIZER

HAZMAT TABLE

Symbols (1)	Hazardous materials descriptions and proper shipping names (2)	Hazard class or Division (3)	Identification Numbers (4)	PG (5)	Label Codes (6)	Special Provisions (§172.102) (7)	ERG Guide No.	Placard Advisory Consult §172.504 & §172.505 *Placard any quantity
	Calcium hypochlorite mixture, dry, with more than 10% but not more than 39% available chlorine	5.1	UN2208	III	5.1	165, A1, A29, IB8, IP3, IP13, N34, W9, W10	140	OXIDIZER
	Calcium manganese silicon	4.3	UN2844	III	4.3	A1, A19, IB8, IP4, T1, TP33, W31	138	DANGEROUS WHEN WET*
	Calcium nitrate	5.1	UN1454		5.1	34, B120, IB8, IP3, T1, TP33	140	OXIDIZER
A	**Calcium oxide**	8	UN1910	III	8	IB8, IP3, T1, TP33	157	CORROSIVE
	Calcium perchlorate	5.1	UN1455	II	5.1	IB6, IP2, T3, TP33	140	OXIDIZER
	Calcium permanganate	5.1	UN1456	II	5.1	IB6, IP2, T3, TP33	140	OXIDIZER
	Calcium peroxide	5.1	UN1457	II	5.1	IB6, IP2, T3, TP33, W100	140	OXIDIZER
	Calcium phosphide	4.3	UN1360	I	4.3, 6.1	A8, A19, N40, W31	139	DANGEROUS WHEN WET*
	Calcium, pyrophoric or **Calcium alloys, pyrophoric**	4.2	UN1855	I	4.2	W31	135	SPONTANEOUSLY COMBUSTIBLE
	Calcium resinate	4.1	UN1313	III	4.1	A1, A19, IB6, T1, TP33	133	FLAMMABLE SOLID
	Calcium resinate, fused	4.1	UN1314	III	4.1	A1, A19, IB4, T1, TP33	133	FLAMMABLE SOLID
	Calcium selenate, see **Selenates** or **Selenites**							
	Calcium silicide	4.3	UN1405	II	4.3	A19, IB7, IP2, IP21, T3, TP33, W31	138	DANGEROUS WHEN WET*
				III	4.3	A1, A19, IB8, IP21, T1, TP33, W31	138	DANGEROUS WHEN WET*
	Camphor oil	3	UN1130	III	3	B1, IB3, T2, TP1	128	FLAMMABLE
	Camphor, synthetic	4.1	UN2717	III	4.1	A1, IB8, IP3, T1, TP33	133	FLAMMABLE SOLID
	Cannon primers, see **Primers, tubular**							
	Capacitor, asymmetric with an energy storage capacity greater than 0.3 Wh	9	UN3508		9	372	171	CLASS 9
	Capacitor, electric double layer with an energy storage capacity greater than 0.3 Wh	9	UN3499		9	361	171	CLASS 9

Symbol	Name and description	Hazard class or Division	Identification Numbers	PG	Label Codes	Special Provisions	Guide	Guide word
	Caproic acid	8	UN2829	III	8	IB3, T4, TP1	153	CORROSIVE
	Caps, blasting, see Detonators, etc.							
	Carbamate pesticides, liquid, flammable, toxic, *flash point less than 23 degrees C*	3	UN2758	I	3, 6.1	T14, TP2, TP13, TP27	131	FLAMMABLE
				II	3, 6.1	IB2, T11, TP2, TP13, TP27	131	FLAMMABLE
	Carbamate pesticides, liquid, toxic	6.1	UN2992	I	6.1	T14, TP2, TP13, TP27	151	POISON
				II	6.1	IB2, T11, TP2, TP13, TP27	151	POISON
				III	6.1	IB3, T7, TP2, TP28	151	POISON
	Carbamate pesticides, liquid, toxic, flammable, *flash point not less than 23 degrees C*	6.1	UN2991	I	6.1, 3	T14, TP2, TP13, TP27	131	POISON
				II	6.1, 3	IB2, T11, TP2, TP13, TP27	131	POISON
				III	6.1, 3	B1, IB3, T7, TP2, TP28	131	POISON
	Carbamate pesticides, solid, toxic	6.1	UN2757	I	6.1	IB7, IP1, T6, TP33	151	POISON
				II	6.1	IB8, IP2, IP4, T3, TP33	151	POISON
				III	6.1	IB8, IP3, T1, TP33	151	POISON
	Carbolic acid, see Phenol, solid *or* Phenol, molten							
	Carbolic acid solutions, see Phenol solutions							
I	Carbon, activated	4.2	UN1362	III	4.2	IB8, IP3, T1, TP33, W31	133	SPONTANEOUSLY COMBUSTIBLE
I	Carbon, *animal or vegetable origin*	4.2	UN1361	II	4.2	IB6, T3, TP33	133	SPONTANEOUSLY COMBUSTIBLE
				III	4.2	IB8, IP3, T1, TP33	133	SPONTANEOUSLY COMBUSTIBLE
	Carbon bisulfide, see Carbon disulfide							
	Carbon dioxide	2.2	UN1013		2.2		120	NONFLAMMABLE GAS
	Carbon dioxide, refrigerated liquid	2.2	UN2187		2.2	T75, TP5	120	NONFLAMMABLE GAS
A W	Carbon dioxide, solid *or* Dry ice	9	UN1845		None		120	CLASS 9
	Carbon disulfide	3	UN1131	I	3, 6.1	B16, T14, TP2 TP7, TP13, W31	131	FLAMMABLE
	Carbon monoxide, compressed	2.3	UN1016		2.3, 2.1	4	119	INHALATION HAZARD CLASS 2"

Symbols (1)	Hazardous materials descriptions and proper shipping names (2)	Hazard class or Division (3)	Identification Numbers (4)	PG (5)	Label Codes (6)	Special Provisions (§172.102) (7)	ERG Guide No.	Placard Advisory Consult §172.504 & §172.505 *Placard any quantity
D	Carbon monoxide, refrigerated liquid (cryogenic liquid)	2.3	NA9202		2.3, 2.1	4, T75, TP5	168	INHALATION HAZARD CLASS 2*
	Carbon tetrabromide	6.1	UN2516	III	6.1	IB8, IP3, T1, TP33	151	POISON
	Carbon tetrachloride	6.1	UN1846	II	6.1	IB2, N36, T7, TP2	151	POISON
	Carbonyl chloride, see Phosgene							
	Carbonyl fluoride	2.3	UN2417		2.3, 8	2	125	INHALATION HAZARD CLASS 2*
	Carbonyl sulfide	2.3	UN2204		2.3, 2.1	3, B14	119	INHALATION HAZARD CLASS 2*
	Cartridge cases, empty primed, see Cases, cartridge, empty, with primer							
	Cartridges, actuating, for aircraft ejector seat catapult, fire extinguisher, canopy removal or apparatus, see Cartridges, power device							
	Cartridges, explosive, see Charges, demolition							
	Cartridges, flash	1.1G	UN0049		1.1G		112	EXPLOSIVES 1.1*
	Cartridges, flash	1.3G	UN0050		1.3G		112	EXPLOSIVES 1.3*
	Cartridges for weapons, blank	1.1C	UN0326		1.1C		112	EXPLOSIVES 1.1*
	Cartridges for weapons, blank	1.2C	UN0413		1.2C		112	EXPLOSIVES 1.2*
	Cartridges for weapons, blank or Cartridges, small arms, blank	1.3C	UN0327		1.3C		112	EXPLOSIVES 1.3*
	Cartridges for weapons, blank or Cartridges, small arms, blank	1.4C	UN0338		1.4C		114	EXPLOSIVES 1.4
	Cartridges for weapons, blank or Cartridges, small arms, blank or Cartridges for tools, blank	1.4S	UN0014		None		114	EXPLOSIVES 1.4
	Cartridges for weapons, inert projectile	1.2C	UN0328		1.2C		112	EXPLOSIVES 1.2*
	Cartridges for weapons, inert projectile or Cartridges, small arms	1.4S	UN0012		None		114	EXPLOSIVES 1.4
	Cartridges for weapons, inert projectile or Cartridges, small arms	1.4C	UN0339		1.4C		114	EXPLOSIVES 1.4

Sym	Hazardous materials descriptions		ID No.			Guide	Label
	Cartridges for weapons, inert projectile or Cartridges, small arms	1.3C	UN0417	1.3C		112	EXPLOSIVES 1.3*
	Cartridges for weapons, with bursting charge	1.1F	UN0005	1.1F		112	EXPLOSIVES 1.1*
	Cartridges for weapons, with bursting charge	1.1E	UN0006	1.1E		112	EXPLOSIVES 1.1*
	Cartridges for weapons, with bursting charge	1.2F	UN0007	1.2F		112	EXPLOSIVES 1.2*
	Cartridges for weapons, with bursting charge	1.2E	UN0321	1.2E		112	EXPLOSIVES 1.2*
	Cartridges for weapons, with bursting charge	1.4F	UN0348	1.4F		114	EXPLOSIVES 1.4
	Cartridges for weapons, with bursting charge	1.4E	UN0412	1.4E		114	EXPLOSIVES 1.4
	Cartridges, oil well	1.3C	UN0277	1.3C		112	EXPLOSIVES 1.3*
	Cartridges, oil well	1.4C	UN0278	1.4C		114	EXPLOSIVES 1.4
	Cartridges, power device	1.3C	UN0275	1.3C		112	EXPLOSIVES 1.3*
	Cartridges, power device	1.4C	UN0276	1.4C	110	114	EXPLOSIVES 1.4
	Cartridges, power device	1.4S	UN0323	1.4S	110, 347	114	EXPLOSIVES 1.4
	Cartridges, power device	1.2C	UN0381	1.2C		112	EXPLOSIVES 1.2*
D	Cartridges power device (used to project fastening devices)	ORM-D		None	222	—	NONE
	Cartridges, safety, blank, see Cartridges for weapons, blank (UN 0014)						
	Cartridges, safety, see Cartridges for weapons, inert projectile, or Cartridges, small arms or Cartridges, power device (UN 0323)						
	Cartridges, signal	1.3G	UN0054	1.3G		112	EXPLOSIVES 1.3*
	Cartridges, signal	1.4G	UN0312	1.4G		114	EXPLOSIVES 1.4
	Cartridges, signal	1.4S	UN0405	1.4S		114	EXPLOSIVES 1.4
D	Cartridges, small arms	ORM-D		None	222	—	NONE
	Cartridges, sporting, see Cartridges for weapons, inert projectile, or Cartridges, small arms						
	Cartridges, starter, jet engine, see Cartridges, power device						
	Cases, cartridge, empty with primer	1.4S	UN0055	1.4S	50	114	EXPLOSIVES 1.4
	Cases, cartridges, empty with primer	1.4C	UN0379	1.4C	50	114	EXPLOSIVES 1.4
	Cases, combustible, empty, without primer	1.4C	UN0446	1.4C		114	EXPLOSIVES 1.4
	Cases, combustible, empty, without primer	1.3C	UN0447	1.3C		112	EXPLOSIVES 1.3*
	Casinghead gasoline see Gasoline						

HAZMAT TABLE

Symbols (1)	Hazardous materials descriptions and proper shipping names (2)	Hazard class or Division (3)	Identification Numbers (4)	PG (5)	Label Codes (6)	Special Provisions (§172.102) (7)	ERG Guide No.	Placard Advisory Consult §172.504 & §172.505 *Placard any quantity
A W	Castor beans or Castor meal or Castor pomace or Castor flake	9	UN2969	II	None	IB8, IP2, IP4, T3, TP33, A210	171	CLASS 9
	Catecholborane							
G	Caustic alkali liquids, n.o.s.	8	UN1719	II	8	B2, IB2, T11, TP2, TP27	154	CORROSIVE
				III	8	IB3, T7, TP1, TP28	154	CORROSIVE
	Caustic potash, (etc.), see Potassium hydroxide etc.							
	Caustic soda, (etc.), see Sodium hydroxide etc.							
	Cells, containing sodium	4.3	UN3292		4.3		138	DANGEROUS WHEN WET*
	Celluloid, in block, rods, rolls, sheets, tubes, etc., except scrap	4.1	UN2000	III	4.1	420	133	FLAMMABLE SOLID
	Celluloid, scrap	4.2	UN2002	III	4.2	IB8, IP3	135	SPONTANEOUSLY COMBUSTIBLE
	Cement, see Adhesives containing flammable liquid							
	Cerium, slabs, ingots, or rods	4.1	UN1333	II	4.1	IB8, IP2, IP4, N34, W100	170	FLAMMABLE SOLID
	Cerium, turnings or gritty powder	4.3	UN3078	II	4.3	A1, IB7, IP2, IP21, T3, TP33, W31, W40	138	DANGEROUS WHEN WET*
	Cesium or Caesium	4.3	UN1407	I	4.3	A7, A19, IB4, IP1, N34, N40, W31	138	DANGEROUS WHEN WET*
	Cesium nitrate or Caesium nitrate	5.1	UN1451	III	5.1	A1, A29, IB8, IP3, T1, TP33	140	OXIDIZER
D	Charcoal briquettes, shell, screenings, wood, etc.	4.2	NA1361	III	4.2	IB8, T1, TP33	133	SPONTANEOUSLY COMBUSTIBLE
	Charges, bursting, plastics bonded	1.1D	UN0457		1.1D		112	EXPLOSIVES 1.1*
	Charges, bursting, plastics bonded	1.2D	UN0458		1.2D		112	EXPLOSIVES 1.2*
	Charges, bursting, plastics bonded	1.4D	UN0459		1.4D		114	EXPLOSIVES 1.4
	Charges, bursting, plastics bonded	1.4S	UN0460		1.4S	347	114	EXPLOSIVES 1.4
	Charges, demolition	1.1D	UN0048		1.1D		112	EXPLOSIVES 1.1*
	Charges, depth	1.1D	UN0056		1.1D		112	EXPLOSIVES 1.1*

Symbol	Hazardous materials descriptions and proper shipping names	Hazard class or Division	Identification Numbers	PG	Label Codes	Special Provisions	Guide	Label
	Charges, expelling, explosive, for fire extinguishers, see Cartridges, power device							
	Charges, explosive, commercial without detonator	1.1D	UN0442		1.1D		112	EXPLOSIVES 1.1*
	Charges, explosive, commercial without detonator	1.2D	UN0443		1.2D		112	EXPLOSIVES 1.2*
	Charges, explosive, commercial without detonator	1.4D	UN0444		1.4D		114	EXPLOSIVES 1.4
	Charges, explosive, commercial without detonator	1.4S	UN0445		1.4S	347	114	EXPLOSIVES 1.4
	Charges, propelling	1.1C	UN0271		1.1C		112	EXPLOSIVES 1.1*
	Charges, propelling	1.3C	UN0272		1.3C		112	EXPLOSIVES 1.3*
	Charges, propelling	1.2C	UN0415		1.2C		112	EXPLOSIVES 1.2*
	Charges, propelling	1.4C	UN0491		1.4C		114	EXPLOSIVES 1.4
	Charges, propelling, for cannon	1.3C	UN0242		1.3C		112	EXPLOSIVES 1.3*
	Charges, propelling, for cannon	1.1C	UN0279		1.1C		112	EXPLOSIVES 1.1*
	Charges, propelling, for cannon	1.2C	UN0414		1.2C		112	EXPLOSIVES 1.2*
	Charges, shaped, flexible, linear	1.4D	UN0237		1.4D		114	EXPLOSIVES 1.4
	Charges, shaped, flexible, linear	1.1D	UN0288		1.1D		112	EXPLOSIVES 1.1*
	Charges, shaped, without detonator	1.1D	UN0059		1.1D		112	EXPLOSIVES 1.1*
	Charges, shaped, without detonator	1.2D	UN0439		1.2D		112	EXPLOSIVES 1.2*
	Charges, shaped, without detonator	1.4D	UN0440		1.4D		114	EXPLOSIVES 1.4
	Charges, shaped, without detonator	1.4S	UN0441		1.4S	347	114	EXPLOSIVES 1.4
	Charges, supplementary explosive	1.1D	UN0060		1.1D		112	EXPLOSIVES 1.1*
D	Chemical kit	8	NA1760	II	8		154	CORROSIVE
	Chemical kit	9	UN3316	II	9	15	171	CLASS 9
G	Chemical under pressure, corrosive, n.o.s.	2.2	UN3503		2.2, 8	362, T50, TP40	125	NONFLAMMABLE GAS
G	Chemical under pressure, flammable, corrosive, n.o.s.	2.1	UN3505		2.1, 8	362, T50, TP40	118	FLAMMABLE GAS
G	Chemical under pressure, flammable, n.o.s.	2.1	UN3501		2.1	362, T50, TP40	115	FLAMMABLE GAS
G	Chemical under pressure, flammable, toxic, n.o.s.	2.1	UN3504		2.1, 6.1	362, T50, TP40	119	FLAMMABLE GAS
G	Chemical under pressure, n.o.s.	2.2	UN3500		2.2	362, T50, TP40	126	NONFLAMMABLE GAS
G	Chemical under pressure, toxic, n.o.s.	2.2	UN3502		2.2, 6.1	362, T50, TP40	123	NONFLAMMABLE GAS
	Chloral, anhydrous, stabilized	6.1	UN2075	II	6.1	IB2, T7, TP2	153	POISON

Symbols (1)	Hazardous materials descriptions and proper shipping names (2)	Hazard class or Division (3)	Identification Numbers (4)	PG (5)	Label Codes (6)	Special Provisions (§172.102) (7)	ERG Guide No.	Placard Advisory Consult §172.504 & §172.505 *Placard any quantity
	Chlorate and borate mixtures	5.1	UN1458	II	5.1	A9, IB8, IP2, IP4, N34, T3, TP33	140	OXIDIZER
				III	5.1	A9, IB8, IP3, N34, T1, TP33	140	OXIDIZER
	Chlorate and magnesium chloride mixture solid	5.1	UN1459	II	5.1	A9, IB8, IP2, IP4, N34, T3, TP33	140	OXIDIZER
				III	5.1	A9, IB8, IP3, N34, T1, TP33	140	OXIDIZER
	Chlorate and magnesium chloride mixture solution	5.1	UN3407	II	5.1	A9, IB2, N34, T4, TP1	140	OXIDIZER
				III	5.1	A9, IB2, N34, T4, TP1	140	OXIDIZER
	Chlorate of potash, see Potassium chlorate							
	Chlorate of soda, see Sodium chlorate							
G	Chlorates, inorganic, aqueous solution, n.o.s.	5.1	UN3210	II	5.1	351, IB2, T4, TP1	140	OXIDIZER
				III	5.1	351, IB2, T4, TP1	140	OXIDIZER
G	Chlorates, inorganic, n.o.s.	5.1	UN1461	II	5.1	351, A9, IB6, IP2, N34, T3, TP33	140	OXIDIZER
	Chloric acid aqueous solution, *with not more than 10 percent chloric acid*	5.1	UN2626	II	5.1	IB2, T4, TP1, W31	140	OXIDIZER
	Chloride of phosphorus, see Phosphorus trichloride							
	Chloride of sulfur, see Sulfur chloride							
	Chlorinated lime, see Calcium hypochlorite mixtures, *etc.*							
	Chlorine	2.3	UN1017		2.3, 5.1, 8	2, B9, B14, N86, T50, TP19	124	INHALATION HAZARD CLASS 2*
	Chlorine, adsorbed	2.3	UN3520		2.3, 5.1, 8	2, B9, B14, N86	173	INHALATION HAZARD CLASS 2*
	Chlorine azide	Forbidden						
D	Chlorine dioxide, hydrate, frozen	5.1	NA9191	II	5.1, 6.1		143	OXIDIZER

	Chlorine dioxide (not hydrate)	Forbidden					
	Chlorine pentafluoride	2.3	UN2548		2.3, 5.1, 8	1, B7, B9, B14, N86	124	INHALATION HAZARD CLASS 2*
	Chlorine trifluoride	2.3	UN1749		2.3, 5.1, 8	2, B7, B9, B14, N86	124	INHALATION HAZARD CLASS 2*
	Chlorite solution	8	UN1908	II	8	A3, A7, B2, IB2, N34, T7, TP2, TP24	154	CORROSIVE
				III	8	A3, A7, B2, IB3, N34, T4, TP2, TP24	154	CORROSIVE
G	**Chlorites, inorganic, n.o.s.**	5.1	UN1462	II	5.1	352, A7, IB6, IF2, N34, T3, TP33	143	OXIDIZER
	1-Chloro-1,1-difluoroethane or Refrigerant gas R 142b	2.1	UN2517		2.1	T50	115	FLAMMABLE GAS
	3-Chloro-4-methylphenyl isocyanate, liquid	6.1	UN2236	II	6.1	IB2	156	POISON
	3-Chloro-4-methylphenyl isocyanate, solid	6.1	UN3428	II	6.1	IB8, IP2, IP4, T3, TP33	156	POISON
	1-Chloro-1,2,2,2-tetrafluoroethane or Refrigerant gas R 124	2.2	UN1021		2.2	T50	126	NONFLAMMABLE GAS
	4-Chloro-o-toluidine hydrochloride, solid	6.1	UN1579	III	6.1	IB8, IP3, T1, TP33	153	POISON
	4-Chloro-o-toluidine hydrochloride, solution	6.1	UN3410	III	6.1	IB3, T4, TP1	153	POISON
	1-Chloro-2,2,2-trifluoroethane or Refrigerant gas R 133a	2.2	UN1983		2.2	T50	126	NONFLAMMABLE GAS
	Chloroacetic acid, molten	6.1	UN3250	II	6.1, 8	IB1, T7, TP3, TP28	153	POISON
	Chloroacetic acid, solid	6.1	UN1751	II	6.1, 8	A3, A7, IB8, IP2, IP4, N34, T3, TP33	153	POISON
	Chloroacetic acid, solution	6.1	UN1750	II	6.1, 8	A7, IB2, N34, T7, TP2	153	POISON
	Chloroacetone, stabilized	6.1	UN1695	I	6.1, 3, 8	2, B9, B14, B32, N12, N32, N34, T20, TP2, TP13, TP38, TP45	131	INHALATION HAZARD CLASS 6*
+	*Chloroacetone (unstabilized)*	Forbidden					
	Chloroacetonitrile	6.1	UN2668	I	6.1, 3	2, B9, B14, B32, IB9, T20, TP2, TP13, TP38, TP45	131	INHALATION HAZARD CLASS 6*
	Chloroacetophenone, liquid, (CN)	6.1	UN3416	II	6.1	A3, IB2, N12, N32, N33, T7, TP2, TP13	153	POISON
	Chloroacetophenone, solid, (CN)	6.1	UN1697	II	6.1	A3, IB8, IP2, IP4, N12, N32, N33, N34, T3, TP2, TP13, TP33	153	POISON

Symbols (1)	Hazardous materials descriptions and proper shipping names (2)	Hazard class or Division (3)	Identification Numbers (4)	PG (5)	Label Codes (6)	Special Provisions (§172.102) (7)	ERG Guide No.	Placard Advisory Consult §172.504 & §172.505 *Placard any quantity
	Chloroacetyl chloride	6.1	UN1752	I	6.1, 8	2, B3, B8, B9, B14, B32, B77, N34, N43, T20, TP2, TP13, TP38, TP45	156	INHALATION HAZARD CLASS 6*
	Chloroanilines, liquid	6.1	UN2019	II	6.1	IB2, T7, TP2	152	POISON
	Chloroanilines, solid	6.1	UN2018	II	6.1	IB8, IP2, IP4, T3, TP33	152	POISON
	Chloroanisidines	6.1	UN2233	III	6.1	IB8, IP3, T1, TP33	152	POISON
	Chlorobenzene	3	UN1134	III	3	B1, IB3, T2, TP1	130	FLAMMABLE
	Chlorobenzol, see Chlorobenzene							
	Chlorobenzotrifluorides	3	UN2234	III	3	B1, IB3, T2, TP1	130	FLAMMABLE
	Chlorobenzyl chlorides, liquid	6.1	UN2235	III	6.1	IB3, T4, TP1	153	POISON
	Chlorobenzyl chlorides, solid	6.1	UN3427	III	6.1	IB8, IP3, T1, TP33	153	POISON
	Chlorobutanes	3	UN1127	II	3	IB2, T4, TP1	130	FLAMMABLE
	Chlorocresols solution	6.1	UN2669	II	6.1	IB2, T7, TP2	152	POISON
				III	6.1	IB3, T7, TP2	152	POISON
	Chlorocresols, solid	6.1	UN3437	II	6.1	IB8, IP2, IP4, T3, TP33	152	POISON
	Chlorodifluorobromomethane *or Refrigerant gas R 12B1*	2.2	UN1974		2.2	T50	126	NONFLAMMABLE GAS
	Chlorodifluoromethane and chloropentafluoroethane mixture *or Refrigerant gas R 502 with fixed boiling point, with approximately 49 percent chlorodifluoromethane*	2.2	UN1973		2.2	T50	126	NONFLAMMABLE GAS
+	Chlorodifluoromethane *or Refrigerant gas R 22*	2.2	UN1018		2.2	T50	126	NONFLAMMABLE GAS
+	Chlorodinitrobenzenes, liquid	6.1	UN1577	II	6.1	IB2, T7, TP2	153	POISON
+	Chlorodinitrobenzenes, solid	6.1	UN3441	II	6.1	IB8, IP2, IP4, T3, TP33	153	POISON
	2-Chloroethanal	6.1	UN2232	I	6.1	2, B9, B14, B32, T20, TP2, TP13, TP38, TP45	153	INHALATION HAZARD CLASS 6*
	Chloroform	6.1	UN1888	III	6.1	IB3, N36, T7, TP2	151	POISON
G	Chloroformates, toxic, corrosive, flammable, n.o.s.	6.1	UN2742	II	6.1, 8, 3	5, IB1, T7, TP2	155	POISON
G	Chloroformates, toxic, corrosive, n.o.s.	6.1	UN3277	II	6.1, 8	IB8, T8, TP2, TP13, TP28	154	POISON

Sym	Name of material	Class	ID No.	PG	Label codes	Special provisions	Guide	Placard
	Chloromethyl chloroformate	6.1	UN2745	II	6.1, 8	IB2, T7, TP2, TP13	157	POISON
	Chloromethyl ethyl ether	3	UN2354	II	3, 6.1	IB2, T7, TP1, TP13	131	FLAMMABLE
	Chloronitroanilines	6.1	UN2237	III	6.1	IB8, IP3, T1, TP33	153	POISON
+	Chloronitrobenzenes, liquid	6.1	UN3409	II	6.1	IB2, T7, TP2	152	POISON
+	Chloronitrobenzenes, solid	6.1	UN1578	II	6.1	IB8, IP2, IP4, T3, TP33	152	POISON
	Chloronitrotoluenes, liquid	6.1	UN2433	III	6.1	IB3, T4, TP1	152	POISON
	Chloronitrotoluenes, solid	6.1	UN3457	III	6.1	IB8, IP3, T1, TP33	152	POISON
	Chloropentafluoroethane or Refrigerant gas R 115	2.2	UN1020		2.2	T50	126	NONFLAMMABLE GAS
	Chlorophenolates, liquid or Phenolates, liquid	8	UN2904	III	8	IB3	154	CORROSIVE
	Chlorophenolates, solid or Phenolates, solid	8	UN2905	III	8	IB8, IP3, T1, TP33	154	CORROSIVE
	Chlorophenols, liquid	6.1	UN2021	III	6.1	IB3, T4, TP1	153	POISON
	Chlorophenols, solid	6.1	UN2020	III	6.1	IB8, IP3, T1, TP1, TP33	153	POISON
	Chlorophenyltrichlorosilane	8	UN1753	II	8	A7, B2, B6, N34, T10, TP2, TP7	156	CORROSIVE
+	Chloropicrin	6.1	UN1580	I	6.1	2, B7, B9, B14, B32, B46, T22, TP2, TP13, TP38, TP45	154	INHALATION HAZARD CLASS 6*
	Chloropicrin and methyl bromide mixtures	2.3	UN1581		2.3	2, B9, B14, N86, T50	123	INHALATION HAZARD CLASS 2*
	Chloropicrin and methyl chloride mixtures	2.3	UN1582		2.3	2, N86, T50	119	INHALATION HAZARD CLASS 2*
	Chloropicrin mixture, flammable (pressure not exceeding 14.7 psia at 115 degrees F flash point below 100 degrees F) see Toxic liquids, flammable, etc.							
G	Chloropicrin mixtures, n.o.s.	6.1	UN1583	I	6.1	5	154	INHALATION HAZARD CLASS 6*
				II	6.1	IB2	154	POISON
				III	6.1	IB3	154	POISON
D	Chloropivaloyl chloride	6.1	NA9263	I	6.1, 8	2, B9, B14, B32, T20, TP4, TP13, TP38, TP45	156	INHALATION HAZARD CLASS 6*
	Chloroplatinic acid, solid	8	UN2507	III	8	IB8, IP3, T1, TP33	154	CORROSIVE
	Chloroprene, stabilized	3	UN1991	I	3, 6.1	387, B57, T14, TP2, TP13	131P	FLAMMABLE

Symbols (1)	Hazardous materials descriptions and proper shipping names (2)	Hazard class or Division (3)	Identification Numbers (4)	PG (5)	Label Codes (6)	Special Provisions (§172.102) (7)	ERG Guide No.	Placard Advisory Consult §172.504 & §172.505 *Placard any quantity
	Chloroprene, uninhibited	Forbidden						
	1-Chloropropane	3	UN1278	II	3	IB2, IP8, N34, T7, TP2	129	FLAMMABLE
	2-Chloropropane	3	UN2356	II	3	N36, T11, TP2, TP13	129	FLAMMABLE
	3-Chloropropanol-1	6.1	UN2849	III	6.1	IB3, T4, TP1	153	POISON
	2-Chloropropene	3	UN2456	I	3	N36, T11, TP2	130P	FLAMMABLE
	2-Chloropropionic acid	8	UN2511	III	8	IB3, T4, TP2	153	CORROSIVE
	2-Chloropyridine	6.1	UN2822	II	6.1	IB2, T7, TP2	153	POISON
	Chlorosilanes, corrosive, flammable, n.o.s.	8	UN2986	II	8, 3	T14, TP2, TP7, TP13, TP27	155	CORROSIVE
	Chlorosilanes, corrosive, n.o.s.	8	UN2987	II	8	B2, T14, TP2, TP7, TP13, TP27	156	CORROSIVE
	Chlorosilanes, flammable, corrosive, n.o.s.	3	UN2985	II	3, 8	T14, TP2, TP7, TP13, TP27	155	FLAMMABLE
G	**Chlorosilanes, toxic, corrosive, flammable, n.o.s.**	6.1	UN3362	II	6.1, 8, 3	T14, TP2, TP7, TP13, TP27	155	POISON
G	**Chlorosilanes, toxic, corrosive, n.o.s.**	6.1	UN3361	II	6.1, 8	T14, TP2, TP7, TP13, TP27	156	POISON
	Chlorosilanes, water-reactive, flammable, corrosive, n.o.s.	4.3	UN2988	I	4.3, 3, 8	A2, T14, TP2, TP7, TP13, W31	139	DANGEROUS WHEN WET*
+	**Chlorosulfonic acid** *(with or without sulfur trioxide)*	8	UN1754	I	8, 6.1	2, B9, B10, B14, B32, T20, TP2, TP38, TP45	137	CORROSIVE, INHALATION HAZARD CLASS 6*
	Chlorotoluenes	3	UN2238	III	3	B1, IB3, T2, TP1	129	FLAMMABLE
	Chlorotoluidines, liquid	6.1	UN3429	III	6.1	IB3, T4, TP1	153	POISON
	Chlorotoluidines, solid	6.1	UN2239	III	6.1	IB8, IP3, T1, TP33	153	POISON
	Chlorotrifluoromethane and trifluoromethane azeotropic mixture *or* **Refrigerant gas R 503** *with approximately 60 percent chlorotrifluoromethane*	2.2	UN2599		2.2		126	NONFLAMMABLE GAS
	Chlorotrifluoromethane *or* **Refrigerant gas R 13**	2.2	UN1022		2.2		126	NONFLAMMABLE GAS

Hazardous material description	Class	ID No.	PG	Special provisions	Guide	Label
Chromic acid solution	8	UN1755	II	B2, IB2, T8, TF2	154	CORROSIVE
			III	IB3, T4, TP1	154	CORROSIVE
Chromic anhydride, see Chromium trioxide, anhydrous						
Chromic fluoride, solid	8	UN1756	II	IB8, IP2, IP4, T3, TP33	154	CORROSIVE
Chromic fluoride, solution	8	UN1757	II	B2, IB2, T7, TF2	154	CORROSIVE
			III	IB3, T4, TP1	154	CORROSIVE
Chromium nitrate	5.1	UN2720	III	A1, A29, IB8, IP3, T1, TP33	141	OXIDIZER
Chromium oxychloride	8	UN1758	I	A7, B10, N34, T10, TP2	137	CORROSIVE
Chromium trioxide, anhydrous	5.1	UN1463	II	IB8, IP2, IP4, T3, TP33, W31	141	OXIDIZER
	5.1, 6.1, 8					
Chromosulfuric acid	8	UN2240	I	A7, B4, B6, N34, T10, TP2, TP13	154	CORROSIVE
Chromyl chloride, see Chromium oxychloride						
Cigar and cigarette lighters, charged with fuel, see Lighters or Lighter refills containing flammable gas	Forbidden					
Coal briquettes, hot						
Coal gas, compressed	2.3	UN1023		3	2.3, 2.1	119	INHALATION HAZARD CLASS 2*
Coal tar distillates, flammable	3	UN1136	II	IB2, T4, TP1	128	FLAMMABLE
			III	B1, IB3, T4, TP1, TP29	128	FLAMMABLE
Coal tar dye, corrosive, liquid, n.o.s., see Dyes, liquid or solid, n.o.s. or Dye intermediates, liquid or solid, n.o.s., corrosive						
Coating solution (includes surface treatments or coatings used for industrial or other purposes such as vehicle undercoating, drum or barrel lining)	3	UN1139	I	T11, TP1, TP8, TP27	127	FLAMMABLE
			II	149, IB2, T4, TP1, TP8	127	FLAMMABLE
			III	B1, IB3, T2, TP1	127	FLAMMABLE
Cobalt naphthenates, powder	4.1	UN2001	III	A19, IB8, IP3, T1, TP33	133	FLAMMABLE SOLID
Cobalt resinate, precipitated	4.1	UN1318	III	A1, A19, IB6, T1, TP33	133	FLAMMABLE SOLID
Coke, hot	Forbidden					
Collodion, see Nitrocellulose etc.						

Symbols (1)	Hazardous materials descriptions and proper shipping names (2)	Hazard class or Division (3)	Identification Numbers (4)	PG (5)	Label Codes (6)	Special Provisions (§172.102) (7)	ERG Guide No.	Placard Advisory Consult §172.504 & §172.505 *Placard any quantity
D G	Combustible liquid, n.o.s.	Comb liq	NA1993	III	None	148, IB3, T1, TP1	128	COMBUSTIBLE (BULK ONLY)
G	Components, explosive train, n.o.s.	1.2B	UN0382	II	1.2B	101	112	EXPLOSIVES 1.2*
G	Components, explosive train, n.o.s.	1.4B	UN0383	II	1.4B	101	114	EXPLOSIVES 1.4
G	Components, explosive train, n.o.s.	1.4S	UN0384	II	1.4S	101, 347	114	EXPLOSIVES 1.4
G	Components, explosive train, n.o.s.	1.1B	UN0461	II	1.1B	101	112	EXPLOSIVES 1.1*
	Composition B, see Hexolite, etc.							
D G	Compounds, cleaning liquid	8	NA1760	I	8	A7, B10, T14, TP2, TP27	154	CORROSIVE
				II	8	386, B2, IB2, N37, T11, TP2, TP27	154	CORROSIVE
				III	8	386, IB3, N37, T7, TP1, TP28	154	CORROSIVE
D G	Compounds, cleaning liquid	3	NA1993	I	3	T11, TP1	128	FLAMMABLE
				II	3	IB2, T7, TP1, TP8, TP28	128	FLAMMABLE
				III	3	B1, B52, IB3, T4, TP1, TP29	128	FLAMMABLE
D G	Compounds, tree killing, liquid or Compounds, weed killing, liquid	8	NA1760	I	8	A7, B10, T14, TP2, TP27	154	CORROSIVE
				II	8	B2, IB2, N37, T11, TP2, TP27	154	CORROSIVE
				III	8	IB3, N37, T7, TP1, TP28	154	CORROSIVE
D G	Compounds, tree killing, liquid or Compounds, weed killing, liquid	3	NA1993	I	3	T11, TP1	128	FLAMMABLE
				II	3	IB2, T7, TP1, TP8, TP28	128	FLAMMABLE
				III	3	B1, B52, IB3, T4, TP1, TP29	128	FLAMMABLE
D G	Compounds, tree killing, liquid or Compounds, weed killing, liquid	6.1	NA2810	I	6.1	T14, TP2, TP13, TP27	153	POISON

Symbols	Hazardous materials descriptions and proper shipping names	Hazard class or Division	Identification Numbers	PG	Label Codes	Special Provisions	ERG Guide No.	
				II	6.1	IB2, T11, TP2, *TP27	153	POISON
				III	6.1	IB3, T7, TP1, T*28	153	POISON
G	Compressed gas, flammable, n.o.s.	2.1	UN1954		2.1		115	FLAMMABLE GAS
G	Compressed gas, n.o.s.	2.2	UN1956		2.2		126	NONFLAMMABLE GAS
G	Compressed gas, oxidizing, n.o.s.	2.2	UN3156		2.2, 5.1	A14	122	NONFLAMMABLE GAS
G I	Compressed gas, toxic, corrosive, n.o.s. *Inhalation Hazard Zone A*	2.3	UN3304		2.3, 8	1	125	INHALATION HAZARD CLASS 2*
G I	Compressed gas, toxic, corrosive, n.o.s. *Inhalation Hazard Zone B*	2.3	UN3304		2.3, 8	2, B9, B14	125	INHALATION HAZARD CLASS 2*
G I	Compressed gas, toxic, corrosive, n.o.s. *Inhalation Hazard Zone C*	2.3	UN3304		2.3, 8	3, B14	125	INHALATION HAZARD CLASS 2*
G I	Compressed gas, toxic, corrosive, n.o.s. *Inhalation Hazard Zone D*	2.3	UN3304		2.3, 8	4	125	INHALATION HAZARD CLASS 2*
G I	Compressed gas, toxic, flammable, corrosive, n.o.s. *Inhalation Hazard Zone A*	2.3	UN3305		2.3, 2.1, 8	1	119	INHALATION HAZARD CLASS 2*
G I	Compressed gas, toxic, flammable, corrosive, n.o.s. *Inhalation Hazard Zone B*	2.3	UN3305		2.3, 2.1, 8	2, B9, B14	119	INHALATION HAZARD CLASS 2*
G I	Compressed gas, toxic, flammable, corrosive, n.o.s. *Inhalation Hazard Zone C*	2.3	UN3305		2.3, 2.1, 8	3, B14	119	INHALATION HAZARD CLASS 2*
G I	Compressed gas, toxic, flammable, corrosive, n.o.s. *Inhalation Hazard Zone D*	2.3	UN3305		2.3, 2.1, 8	4	119	INHALATION HAZARD CLASS 2*
G	Compressed gas, toxic, flammable, n.o.s. *Inhalation hazard Zone A*	2.3	UN1953		2.3, 2.1	1	119	INHALATION HAZARD CLASS 2*
G	Compressed gas, toxic, flammable, n.o.s. *Inhalation hazard Zone B*	2.3	UN1953		2.3, 2.1	2, B9, B14	119	INHALATION HAZARD CLASS 2*
G	Compressed gas, toxic, flammable, n.o.s. *Inhalation Hazard Zone C*	2.3	UN1953		2.3, 2.1	3, B14	119	INHALATION HAZARD CLASS 2*
G	Compressed gas, toxic, flammable, n.o.s. *Inhalation Hazard Zone D*	2.3	UN1953		2.3, 2.1	4	119	INHALATION HAZARD CLASS 2*
G	Compressed gas, toxic, n.o.s. *Inhalation Hazard Zone A*	2.3	UN1955		2.3	1	123	INHALATION HAZARD CLASS 2*

Symbols (1)	Hazardous materials descriptions and proper shipping names (2)	Hazard class or Division (3)	Identification Numbers (4)	PG (5)	Label Codes (6)	Special Provisions (§172.102) (7)	ERG Guide No.	Placard Advisory Consult §172.504 & §172.505 *Placard any quantity
G	Compressed gas, toxic, n.o.s. Inhalation Hazard Zone B	2.3	UN1955		2.3	2, B9, B14	123	INHALATION HAZARD CLASS 2*
G	Compressed gas, toxic, n.o.s. Inhalation Hazard Zone C	2.3	UN1955		2.3	3, B14	123	INHALATION HAZARD CLASS 2*
G	Compressed gas, toxic, n.o.s. Inhalation Hazard Zone D	2.3	UN1955		2.3	4	123	INHALATION HAZARD CLASS 2*
G I	Compressed gas, toxic, oxidizing, corrosive, n.o.s Inhalation Hazard Zone A	2.3	UN3306		2.3, 5.1, 8	1	124	INHALATION HAZARD CLASS 2*
G I	Compressed gas, toxic, oxidizing, corrosive, n.o.s Inhalation Hazard Zone B	2.3	UN3306		2.3, 5.1, 8	2, B9, B14	124	INHALATION HAZARD CLASS 2*
G I	Compressed gas, toxic, oxidizing, corrosive, n.o.s Inhalation Hazard Zone C	2.3	UN3306		2.3, 5.1, 8	3, B14	124	INHALATION HAZARD CLASS 2*
G I	Compressed gas, toxic, oxidizing, corrosive, n.o.s Inhalation Hazard Zone D	2.3	UN3306		2.3, 5.1, 8	4	124	INHALATION HAZARD CLASS 2*
G	Compressed gas, toxic, oxidizing, n.o.s Inhalation Hazard Zone A	2.3	UN3303		2.3, 5.1	1	124	INHALATION HAZARD CLASS 2*
G	Compressed gas, toxic, oxidizing, n.o.s Inhalation Hazard Zone B	2.3	UN3303		2.3, 5.1	2, B9, B14	124	INHALATION HAZARD CLASS 2*
G	Compressed gas, toxic, oxidizing, n.o.s Inhalation Hazard Zone C	2.3	UN3303		2.3, 5.1	3, B14	124	INHALATION HAZARD CLASS 2*
G	Compressed gas, toxic, oxidizing, n.o.s Inhalation Hazard Zone D	2.3	UN3303		2.3, 5.1	4	124	INHALATION HAZARD CLASS 2*
D	Consumer commodity	ORM-D			None	222	—	NONE
D	Consumer commodity	9	ID8000		9		171	CLASS 9
G	Contrivances, water-activated, with burster, expelling charge or propelling charge	1.2L	UN0248		1.2L		112	EXPLOSIVES 1.2*
G	Contrivances, water-activated, with burster, expelling charge or propelling charge	1.3L	UN0249		1.3L		112	EXPLOSIVES 1.3*
	Copper acetoarsenite	6.1	UN1585	II	6.1	IB8, IP2, IP4, T3, TP33	151	POISON

Symbols	Hazardous materials descriptions and proper shipping names	Hazard class or Division	Identification Numbers	PG	Label Codes	Special Provisions	Guide	Label
	Copper acetylide	Forbidden						
	Copper amine azide	Forbidden						
	Copper arsenite	6.1	UN1586	II	6.1	IB8, IP2, IP4, T3, TP33	151	POISON
	Copper based pesticides, liquid, flammable, toxic, *flash point less than 23 degrees C*	3	UN2776	I	3, 6.1	T14, TP2, TP13, TP27	131	FLAMMABLE
				II	3, 6.1	IB2, T11, TP2, TP13, TP27	131	FLAMMABLE
	Copper based pesticides, liquid, toxic	6.1	UN3010	I	6.1	T14, TP2, TP13, TP27	151	POISON
				II	6.1	IB2, T11, TP2, TP13, TP27	151	POISON
				III	6.1	IB3, T7, TP2, TP28	151	POISON
	Copper based pesticides, liquid, toxic, flammable *flashpoint not less than 23 degrees C*	6.1	UN3009	I	6.1, 3	T14, TP2, TP13, TP27	131	POISON
				II	6.1, 3	IB2, T11, TP2, TP13, TP28	131	POISON
				III	6.1, 3	B1, IB3, T7, TP2, TP28	131	POISON
	Copper based pesticides, solid, toxic	6.1	UN2775	I	6.1	IB7, IP1, T6, TP33	151	POISON
				II	6.1	IB8, IP2, IP4, T3, TP33	151	POISON
				III	6.1	IB8, IP3, T1, TP33	151	POISON
	Copper chlorate	5.1	UN2721	II	5.1	A1, IB8, IP2, IP4, T3, TP33	140	OXIDIZER
	Copper chloride	8	UN2802	III	8	IB8, IP3, T1, TP33	154	CORROSIVE
	Copper cyanide	6.1	UN1587	II	6.1	IB8, IP2, IP4, T3, TP33	151	POISON
	Copper selenate, *see* Selenates *or* Selenites							
	Copper selenite, *see* Selenates *or* Selenites							
	Copper tetramine nitrate	Forbidden						
A W	Copra	4.2	UN1363	III	4.2	B136, IB8, IP3, IP7	135	SPONTANEOUSLY COMBUSTIBLE
	Cord, detonating, *flexible*	1.1D	UN0065	II	1.1D	102, 148	112	EXPLOSIVES 1.1*
	Cord, detonating, *flexible*	1.4D	UN0289	II	1.4D	148	114	EXPLOSIVES 1.4
	Cord, detonating *or* Fuze, detonating *metal clad*	1.2D	UN0102	II	1.2D		112	EXPLOSIVES 1.2*
	Cord, detonating *or* Fuze, detonating *metal clad*	1.1D	UN0290	II	1.1D		112	EXPLOSIVES 1.1*
	Cord, detonating, mild effect *or* Fuse, detonating, mild effect *metal clad*	1.4D	UN0104	II	1.4D		114	EXPLOSIVES 1.4
	Cord, igniter	1.4G	UN0066	II	1.4G		114	EXPLOSIVES 1.4

Symbols (1)	Hazardous materials descriptions and proper shipping names (2)	Hazard class or Division (3)	Identification Numbers (4)	PG (5)	Label Codes (6)	Special Provisions (§172.102) (7)	ERG Guide No.	Placard Advisory Consult §172.504 & §172.505 *Placard any quantity
	Cordeau detonant fuse, see Cord, detonating, etc; Cord, detonating, flexible							
	Cordite, see Powder, smokeless							
G	Corrosive liquid, acidic, inorganic, n.o.s.	8	UN3264	I	8	B10, T14, TP2, TP27	154	CORROSIVE
				II	8	386, B2, IB2, T11, TP2, TP27	154	CORROSIVE
				III	8	IB3, T7, TP1, TP28	154	CORROSIVE
G	Corrosive liquid, acidic, organic, n.o.s.	8	UN3265	I	8	B10, T14, TP2, TP27	153	CORROSIVE
				II	8	148, B2, IB2, T11, TP2, TP27	153	CORROSIVE
				III	8	386, IB3, T7, TP1, TP28	153	CORROSIVE
G	Corrosive liquid, basic, inorganic, n.o.s.	8	UN3266	I	8	T14, TP2, TP27	154	CORROSIVE
				II	8	386, B2, IB2, T11, TP2, TP27	154	CORROSIVE
				III	8	IB3, T7, TP1, TP28	154	CORROSIVE
G	Corrosive liquid, basic, organic, n.o.s.	8	UN3267	I	8	B10, T14, TP2, TP27	153	CORROSIVE
				II	8	B2, IB2, T11, TP2, TP27	153	CORROSIVE
				III	8	IB3, T7, TP1, TP28	153	CORROSIVE
G	Corrosive liquid, self-heating, n.o.s.	8	UN3301	I	8, 4.2	B10	136	CORROSIVE
				II	8, 4.2	B2, IB1	136	CORROSIVE
G	Corrosive liquids, flammable, n.o.s.	8	UN2920	I	8, 3	B10, T14, TP2, TP27	132	CORROSIVE
				II	8, 3	B2, IB2, T11, TP2, TP27	132	CORROSIVE
G	Corrosive liquids, n.o.s.	8	UN1760	I	8	A7, B10, T14, TP2, TP27	154	CORROSIVE
				II	8	B2, IB2, T11, TP2, TP27	154	CORROSIVE
				III	8	IB3, T7, TP1, TP28	154	CORROSIVE
G	Corrosive liquids, oxidizing, n.o.s.	8	UN3093	I	8, 5.1	A7	157	CORROSIVE
				II	8, 5.1	A7, IB2	157	CORROSIVE

Sym	Hazardous materials descriptions	Class	ID No.	PG	Label Codes	Special Provisions	ERG	
G	Corrosive liquids, toxic, n.o.s.	8	UN2922	I	8, 6.1	A7, B10, T14, TP2, TP13, TP27	154	CORROSIVE
				II	8, 6.1	B3, IB2, T7, TP2	154	CORROSIVE
				III	8, 6.1	IB3, T7, TP1, TP28	154	CORROSIVE
G	Corrosive liquids, water-reactive, n.o.s.	8	UN3094	I	8, 4.3	A7	138	CORROSIVE, DANGEROUS WHEN WET
				II	8, 4.3	A7	138	CORROSIVE, DANGEROUS WHEN WET
G	Corrosive solid, acidic, inorganic, n.o.s.	8	UN3260	I	8	IB7, IP1, T6, TP33	154	CORROSIVE
				II	8	IB8, IP2, IP4, T3, TP33	154	CORROSIVE
				III	8	IB8, IP3, T1, TP33	154	CORROSIVE
G	Corrosive solid, acidic, organic, n.o.s.	8	UN3261	I	8	IB7, IP1, T6, TP33	154	CORROSIVE
				II	8	IB8, IP2, IP4, T3, TP33	154	CORROSIVE
				III	8	IB8, IP3, T1, TP33	154	CORROSIVE
G	Corrosive solid, basic, inorganic, n.o.s.	8	UN3262	I	8	IB7, IP1, T6, TP33	154	CORROSIVE
				II	8	IB8, IP2, IP4, T3, TP33	154	CORROSIVE
				III	8	IB8, IP3, T1, TP33	154	CORROSIVE
G	Corrosive solid, basic, organic, n.o.s.	8	UN3263	I	8	IB7, IP1, T6, TP33	154	CORROSIVE
				II	8	IB8, IP2, IP4, T3, TP33	154	CORROSIVE
				III	8	IB8, IP3, T1, TP33	154	CORROSIVE
G	Corrosive solids, flammable, n.o.s.	8	UN2921	I	8, 4.1	IB6, T6, TP33	134	CORROSIVE
				II	8, 4.1	IB8, IP2, IP4, T3, TP33	134	CORROSIVE
G	Corrosive solids, n.o.s.	8	UN1759	I	8	IB7, IP1, T6, TP33	154	CORROSIVE
				II	8	128, IB8, IP2, IP4, T3, TP33	154	CORROSIVE
				III	8	128, IB8, IP3, T1, TP33	154	CORROSIVE
G	Corrosive solids, oxidizing, n.o.s.	8	UN3084	I	8, 5.1	T6, TP33	157	CORROSIVE
				II	8, 5.1	IB6, IP2, T3, TP33	157	CORROSIVE
G	Corrosive solids, self-heating, n.o.s.	8	UN3095	I	8, 4.2	T6, TP33	136	CORROSIVE

Symbols (1)	Hazardous materials descriptions and proper shipping names (2)	Hazard class or Division (3)	Identification Numbers (4)	PG (5)	Label Codes (6)	Special Provisions (§172.102) (7)	ERG Guide No.	Placard Advisory Consult §172.504 & §172.505 *Placard any quantity
				II	8, 4.2	IB6, IP2, T3, TP33	136	CORROSIVE
G	Corrosive solids, toxic, n.o.s.	8	UN2923	I	8, 6.1	IB7, T6, TP33	154	CORROSIVE
				II	8, 6.1	IB8, IP2, IP4, T3, TP33	154	CORROSIVE
				III	8, 6.1	IB8, IP3, T1, TP33	154	CORROSIVE
G	Corrosive solids, water-reactive, n.o.s.	8	UN3096	I	8, 4.3	IB4, IP1, T6, TP33	138	CORROSIVE, DANGEROUS WHEN WET*
				II	8, 4.3	IB6, IP2, T3, TP33, W100	138	CORROSIVE, DANGEROUS WHEN WET*
D W	Cotton	9	NA1365		9	137, IB8, IP2, IP4, W41	133	CLASS 9
A W	Cotton waste, oily	4.2	UN1364	III	4.2	IB8, IP3, IP7	133	SPONTANEOUSLY COMBUSTIBLE
A I W	Cotton, wet	4.2	UN1365	III	4.2	IB8, IP3, IP7	133	SPONTANEOUSLY COMBUSTIBLE
	Coumarin derivative pesticides, liquid, flammable, toxic, *flashpoint less than 23 degrees C*	3	UN3024	I	3, 6.1	T14, TP2, TP13, TP27	131	FLAMMABLE
				II	3, 6.1	IB2, T11, TP2, TP13, TP27	131	FLAMMABLE
	Coumarin derivative pesticides, liquid, toxic	6.1	UN3026	I	6.1	T14, TP2, TP13, TP27	151	POISON
				II	6.1	IB2, T11, TP2, TP27	151	POISON
				III	6.1	IB3, T7, TP1, TP28	151	POISON
	Coumarin derivative pesticides, liquid, toxic, flammable, *flash point not less than 23 degrees C*	6.1	UN3025	I	6.1, 3	T14, TP2, TP13, TP27	131	POISON
				II	6.1, 3	IB2, T11, TP2, TP13, TP27	131	POISON
				III	6.1, 3	B1, IB3, T7, TP1, TP28	131	POISON
	Coumarin derivative pesticides, solid, toxic	6.1	UN3027	I	6.1	IB7, IP1, T6, TP33	151	POISON
				II	6.1	IB8, IP2, IP4, T3, TP33	151	POISON
				III	6.1	IB8, IP3, T1, TP33	151	POISON

Sym	Hazardous materials descriptions and proper shipping names	Hazard class or division	Identification numbers	PG	Label codes	Special provisions	ERG	Placard
	Cresols, liquid	6.1	UN2076	II	6.1, 8	IB8, IP2, IP4, T7, TP2	153	POISON
	Cresols, solid	6.1	UN3455	II	6.1, 8	IB8, IP2, IP4, T3, TP33	153	POISON
	Cresylic acid	6.1	UN2022	II	6.1, 8	IB2, T7, TP2, TP13	153	POISON
	Crotonaldehyde or Crotonaldehyde, stabilized	6.1	UN1143	I	6.1, 3	2, 175, 387, B9, B14, B32, B77, T20, TP2, TP13, TP38, TP45	131P	INHALATION HAZARD CLASS 6*
	Crotonic acid, liquid	8	UN3472	III	8	IB8, T1	153	CORROSIVE
	Crotonic acid, solid	8	UN2823	III	8	IB8, IP3, T1, TP33	153	CORROSIVE
	Crotonylene	3	UN1144	I	3	T11, TP2	128	FLAMMABLE
	Cupriethylenediamine solution	8	UN1761	II	8, 6.1	IB2, T7, TP2	154	CORROSIVE
				III	8, 6.1	IB3, T7, TP1, TP28	154	CORROSIVE
	Cutters, cable, explosive	1.4S	UN0070		1.4S		114	EXPLOSIVES 1.4
	Cyanide or cyanide mixtures, dry, see Cyanides, inorganic, solid, n.o.s.							
G	Cyanide solutions, n.o.s.	6.1	UN1935	I	6.1	T14, TP2, TP13, TP27	157	POISON
				II	6.1	IB2, T11, TP2, TP13, TP27	157	POISON
				III	6.1	IB3, T7, TP2, TP13, TP28	157	POISON
	Cyanides, inorganic, solid, n.o.s.	6.1	UN1588	I	6.1	IB7, IP1, N74, N75, T6, TP33	157	POISON
				II	6.1	IB8, IP2, IP4, N74, N75, T3, TP33	157	POISON
				III	6.1	IB8, IP3, N74, N75, T1, TP33	157	POISON
	Cyanogen	2.3	UN1026		2.3, 2.1	2	119	INHALATION HAZARD CLASS 2*
	Cyanogen bromide	6.1	UN1889	I	6.1, 8	A6, A8, T6, TP33, W31	157	POISON
	Cyanogen chloride, stabilized	2.3	UN1589		2.3, 8	1, 387	125	INHALATION HAZARD CLASS 2*
	Cyanuric chloride	8	UN2670	II	8	IB8, IP2, IP4, T3, TP33	157	CORROSIVE
	Cyanuric triazide	Forbidden						
	Cyclobutane	2.1	UN2601		2.1		115	FLAMMABLE GAS

Symbols (1)	Hazardous materials descriptions and proper shipping names (2)	Hazard class or Division (3)	Identification Numbers (4)	PG (5)	Label Codes (6)	Special Provisions (§172.102) (7)	ERG Guide No.	Placard Advisory Consult §172.504 & §172.505 *Placard any quantity
	Cyclobutyl chloroformate	6.1	UN2744	II	6.1, 8, 3	IB1, T7, TP2, TP13	155	POISON
	1,5,9-Cyclododecatriene	6.1	UN2518	III	6.1	IB3, T4, TP1	153	POISON
	Cycloheptane	3	UN2241	II	3	IB2, T4, TP2	128	FLAMMABLE
	Cycloheptatriene	3	UN2603	II	3, 6.1	IB2, T7, TP1, TP13	131	FLAMMABLE
	Cycloheptene	3	UN2242	II	3	B1, IB2, T4, TP1	128	FLAMMABLE
	Cyclohexane	3	UN1145	II	3	IB2, T4, TP1	128	FLAMMABLE
	Cyclohexanone	3	UN1915	III	3	B1, IB3, T2, TP1	127	FLAMMABLE
	Cyclohexene	3	UN2256	II	3	IB2, T4, TP1	130	FLAMMABLE
	Cyclohexenyltrichlorosilane	8	UN1762	II	8	A7, B2, N34, T10, TP2, TP7, TP13	156	CORROSIVE
	Cyclohexyl acetate	3	UN2243	III	3	B1, IB3, T2, TP1	130	FLAMMABLE
	Cyclohexyl isocyanate	6.1	UN2488	I	6.1, 3	2, B9, B14, B32, B77, T20, TP2, TP13, TP38, TP45	155	INHALATION HAZARD CLASS 6*
	Cyclohexyl mercaptan	3	UN3054	III	3	B1, IB3, T2, TP1	129	FLAMMABLE
	Cyclohexylamine	8	UN2357	II	8, 3	IB2, T7, TP2	132	CORROSIVE
	Cyclohexyltrichlorosilane	8	UN1763	II	8	A7, B2, N34, T10, TP2, TP7, TP13	156	CORROSIVE
	Cyclonite and cyclotetramethylenetetranitramine mixtures, wetted or desensitized see RDX and HMX mixtures, wetted or desensitized etc.							
	Cyclonite and HMX mixtures, wetted or desensitized see RDX and HMX mixtures, wetted or desensitized etc.							
	Cyclonite and octogen mixtures, wetted or desensitized see RDX and HMX mixtures, wetted or desensitized etc.							
	Cyclonite, see Cyclotrimethylenetrinitramine, etc.							
	Cyclooctadiene phosphines, see 9-Phosphabicyclononanes							
	Cyclooctadienes	3	UN2520	III	3	B1, IB3, T2, TP1	130P	FLAMMABLE

Name	Class	ID No.	PG	Label codes	Special provisions	Packaging	Label
Cyclooctatetraene	3	UN2358	II	3	IB2, T4, TP1	128P	FLAMMABLE
Cyclopentane	3	UN1146	II	3	IB2, T7, TP1	128	FLAMMABLE
Cyclopentane, methyl, see Methylcyclopentane							
Cyclopentanol	3	UN2244	III	3	B1, IB3, T2, TP1	129	FLAMMABLE
Cyclopentanone	3	UN2245	III	3	B1, IB3, T2, TP1	128	FLAMMABLE
Cyclopentene	3	UN2246	II	3	IB2, IP8, T7, TP2	128	FLAMMABLE
Cyclopropane	2.1	UN1027		2.1	T50	115	FLAMMABLE GAS
Cyclotetramethylene tetranitramine (dry or unphlegmatized) (HMX)	Forbidden						
Cyclotetramethylenetetranitramine, desensitized or Octogen, desensitized or HMX, desensitized	1.1D	UN0484		1.1D		112	EXPLOSIVES 1.1*
Cyclotetramethylenetetranitramine, wetted or HMX, wetted or Octogen, wetted with not less than 15 percent water, by mass	1.1D	UN0226		1.1D		112	EXPLOSIVES 1.1*
Cyclotrimethylenenitramine and octogen, mixtures, wetted or desensitized see RDX and HMX mixtures, wetted or desensitized etc.							
Cyclotrimethylenetrinitramine and cyclotetramethylenetetranitramine mixtures, wetted or desensitized see RDX and HMX mixtures, wetted or desensitized etc.							
Cyclotrimethylenenitramine and HMX mixtures, wetted or desensitized see RDX and HMX mixtures, wetted or desensitized etc.							
Cyclotrimethylenetrinitramine, desensitized or Cyclonite, desensitized or Hexogen, desensitized or RDX, desensitized	1.1D	UN0483		1.1D		112	EXPLOSIVES 1.1*
Cyclotrimethylenetrinitramine, wetted or Cyclonite, wetted or Hexogen, wetted or RDX, wetted with not less than 15 percent water by mass	1.1D	UN0072		1.1D		112	EXPLOSIVES 1.1*
Cymenes	3	UN2046	III	3	B1, IB3, T2, TP1	130	FLAMMABLE
Dangerous Goods in Machinery or Dangerous Goods in Apparatus	9	UN3363			136, A105	171	CLASS 9
Decaborane	4.1	UN1868	II	4.1, 6.1	A19, A20, IB6 IP2, T3, TP33, W31	134	FLAMMABLE SOLID
Decahydronaphthalene	3	UN1147	III	3	B1, IB3, T2, TP1	130	FLAMMABLE

Symbols (1)	Hazardous materials descriptions and proper shipping names (2)	Hazard class or Division (3)	Identification Numbers (4)	PG (5)	Label Codes (6)	Special Provisions (§172.102) (7)	ERG Guide No.	Placard Advisory Consult §172.504 & §172.505 *Placard any quantity
	n-Decane	3	UN2247	III	3	B1, IB3, T2, TP1	128	FLAMMABLE
	Deflagrating metal salts of aromatic nitroderivatives, n.o.s	1.3C	UN0132		1.3C		112	EXPLOSIVES 1.3*
	Delay electric igniter, see Igniters							
D	Denatured alcohol	3	NA1987	II	3	172, T8	127	FLAMMABLE
				III	3	172, B1, T7	127	FLAMMABLE
	Depth charges, see Charges, depth							
G	**Desensitized explosive, liquid, n.o.s.**	3	UN3379	I	3	164	113	FLAMMABLE
G	**Desensitized explosive, solid, n.o.s.**	4.1	UN3380	I	4.1	164	113	FLAMMABLE SOLID
	Detonating relays, see Detonators, etc.							
	Detonator assemblies, non-electric, for blasting	1.1B	UN0360		1.1B		112	EXPLOSIVES 1.1*
	Detonator assemblies, non-electric, for blasting	1.4B	UN0361		1.4B	103, 148	114	EXPLOSIVES 1.4
	Detonator assemblies, non-electric, for blasting	1.4S	UN0500		1.4S	148, 347	114	EXPLOSIVES 1.4
	Detonators, electric, for blasting	1.1B	UN0030		1.1B	148	112	EXPLOSIVES 1.1*
	Detonators, electric, for blasting	1.4B	UN0255		1.4B	103, 148	114	EXPLOSIVES 1.4
	Detonators, electric, for blasting	1.4S	UN0456		1.4S	148, 347	114	EXPLOSIVES 1.4
	Detonators for ammunition	1.1B	UN0073		1.1B		112	EXPLOSIVES 1.1*
	Detonators for ammunition	1.2B	UN0364		1.2B		112	EXPLOSIVES 1.2*
	Detonators for ammunition	1.4B	UN0365		1.4B	103	114	EXPLOSIVES 1.4
	Detonators for ammunition	1.4S	UN0366		1.4S	347	114	EXPLOSIVES 1.4
	Detonators, non-electric, for blasting	1.1B	UN0029		1.1B		112	EXPLOSIVES 1.1*
	Detonators, non-electric, for blasting	1.4B	UN0267		1.4B	103	114	EXPLOSIVES 1.4
	Detonators, non-electric, for blasting	1.4S	UN0455		1.4S	148, 347	114	EXPLOSIVES 1.4
	Deuterium, compressed	2.1	UN1957		2.1	N89	115	FLAMMABLE GAS
	Devices, small, hydrocarbon gas powered or Hydrocarbon gas refills for small devices with release device	2.1	UN3150		2.1		115	FLAMMABLE GAS
	Di-n-amylamine	3	UN2841	III	3, 6.1	B1, IB3, T4, TP1	131	FLAMMABLE
	Di-n-butyl peroxydicarbonate, with more than 52 percent in solution	Forbidden						

Hazardous materials descriptions	Hazard class	ID No.	PG	Label Codes	Special provisions	Guide	Label
Di-n-butylamine	8	UN2248	II	8, 3	IB2, T7, TP2	132	CORROSIVE
2,2-Di-(tert-butylperoxy) butane, with more than 55 percent in solution	Forbidden						
Di-(tert-butylperoxy) phthalate, with more than 55 percent in solution	Forbidden						
2,2-Di-(4,4-di-tert-butylperoxycyclohexyl) propane, with more than 42 percent with inert solid	Forbidden						
Di-2, 4-dichlorobenzoyl peroxide, with more than 75 percent with water	Forbidden						
1,2-Di-(dimethylamino)ethane	3	UN2372	II	3	IB2, T4, TP1	129	FLAMMABLE
Di-(2-ethylhexyl) phosphoric acid, see **Diisooctyl acid phosphate**							
Di-(1-hydroxytetrazole) (dry)	Forbidden						
Di-(1-naphthoyl) peroxide	Forbidden						
a,a'-Di-(nitroxy) methylether	Forbidden						
Di-(beta-nitroxyethyl) ammonium nitrate	Forbidden						
Diacetone alcohol	3	UN1148	II	3	IB2, T4, TP1	129	FLAMMABLE
			III	3	B1, IB3, T2, TP1	129	FLAMMABLE
Diacetone alcohol peroxides, with more than 57 percent in solution with more than 9 percent hydrogen peroxide, less than 26 percent diacetone alcohol and less than 9 percent water; total active oxygen content more than 9 percent by mass	Forbidden						
Diacetyl, see **Butanedione**							
Diacetyl peroxide, solid, or with more than 25 percent in solution	Forbidden						
Diallylamine	3	UN2359	II	3, 6.1, 8	IB2, T7, TP1	132	FLAMMABLE
Diallylether	3	UN2360	II	3, 6.1	IB2, N12, T7, TP1, TP13	131P	FLAMMABLE
4,4'-Diaminodiphenyl methane	6.1	UN2651	III	6.1	IB8, IP3, T1, TP33	153	POISON
p-Diazidobenzene	Forbidden						
1,2-Diazidoethane	Forbidden						
1,1'-Diazoaminonaphthalene	Forbidden						
Diazoaminotetrazole (dry)	Forbidden						
Diazodinitrophenol (dry)	Forbidden						

Symbols (1)	Hazardous materials descriptions and proper shipping names (2)	Hazard class or Division (3)	Identification Numbers (4)	PG (5)	Label Codes (6)	Special Provisions (§172.102) (7)	ERG Guide No.	Placard Advisory Consult §172.504 & §172.505 *Placard any quantity
	Diazodinitrophenol, wetted *with not less than 40 percent water or mixture of alcohol and water, by mass*	1.1A	UN0074		1.1A	111, 117	112	EXPLOSIVES 1.1*
	Diazodiphenylmethane	Forbidden						
	Diazonium nitrates (dry)	Forbidden						
	Diazonium perchlorates (dry)	Forbidden						
	1,3-Diazopropane	Forbidden						
	Dibenzyl peroxydicarbonate, with more than 87 percent with water	Forbidden						
	Dibenzyldichlorosilane	8	UN2434	II	8	B2, T10, TP2, TP7, TP13	156	CORROSIVE
	Diborane	2.3	UN1911		2.3, 2.1	1, N89	119	INHALATION HAZARD CLASS 2*
D	Diborane mixtures	2.1	NA1911		2.1	5	119	FLAMMABLE GAS
	Dibromoacetylene	Forbidden						
	1,2-Dibromobutan-3-one	6.1	UN2648	II	6.1	IB2	154	POISON
	Dibromochloropropane	6.1	UN2872	II	6.1	IB2, T7, TP2	159	POISON
				III	6.1	IB3, T4, TP1	159	POISON
A	Dibromodifluoromethane, R12B2	9	UN1941	III	None	T11, TP2	171	CLASS 9
	1,2-Dibromoethane, see Ethylene dibromide							
	Dibromomethane	6.1	UN2664	III	6.1	IB3, T4, TP1	160	POISON
	Dibutyl ethers	3	UN1149	III	3	B1, IB3, T2, TP1	128	FLAMMABLE
	Dibutylaminoethanol	6.1	UN2873	III	6.1	IB3, T4, TP1	153	POISON
	N,N'-Dichlorazodicarbonamidine (salts of) (dry)	Forbidden						
	1,1-Dichloro-1-nitroethane	6.1	UN2650	II	6.1	IB2, T7, TP2	153	POISON
D	3,5-Dichloro-2,4,6-trifluoropyridine	6.1	NA9264	I	6.1	2, B9, B14, B32, T20, TP4, TP13, TP38, TP45	151	INHALATION HAZARD CLASS 6*
	Dichloroacetic acid	8	UN1764	II	8	A3, A7, B2, IB2, N34, T8, TP2	153	CORROSIVE
	1,3-Dichloroacetone	6.1	UN2649	II	6.1	IB8, IP2, IP4, T3, TP33	153	POISON

Symbol	Hazardous materials descriptions and proper shipping names	Hazard class or division	Identification numbers	PG	Special provisions	Guide	Label
	Dichloroacetyl chloride	8	UN1765	II	8	A3, A7, B2, B6, IB2, N34, T7, TP2	156	CORROSIVE
	Dichloroacetylene	Forbidden						
+	**Dichloroanilines, liquid**	6.1	UN1590	II	6.1	IB2, T7, TP2	153	POISON
	Dichloroanilines, solid	6.1	UN3442	II	6.1	IB8, IP2, IP4, T3, TP33	153	POISON
+	**o-Dichlorobenzene**	6.1	UN1591	III	6.1	IB3, T4, TP1	152	POISON
	2,2'-Dichlorodiethyl ether	6.1	UN1916	II	6.1, 3	IB2, N33, N34, T7, TP2	152	POISON
	Dichlorodifluoromethane and difluoroethane azeotropic mixture *or Refrigerant gas R 500 with approximately 74 percent dichlorodifluoromethane*	2.2	UN2602		2.2	T50	126	NONFLAMMABLE GAS
	Dichlorodifluoromethane *or Refrigerant gas R 12*	2.2	UN1028		2.2	T50	126	NONFLAMMABLE GAS
	Dichlorodimethyl ether, symmetrical	6.1	UN2249	I	6.1, 3		131	POISON
	1,1-Dichloroethane	3	UN2362	II	3	IB2, T4, TP1	130	FLAMMABLE
	1,2-Dichloroethane, see Ethylene dichloride							
	Dichloroethyl sulfide	Forbidden						
	1,2-Dichloroethylene	3	UN1150	II	3	IB2, T7, TP2	130P	FLAMMABLE
	Dichlorofluoromethane *or Refrigerant gas R 21*	2.2	UN1029		2.2	T50	126	NONFLAMMABLE GAS
	Dichloroisocyanuric acid, dry *or* **Dichloroisocyanuric acid salts**	5.1	UN2465	II	5.1	28, IB8, IP2, IP4, T3, TP33	140	OXIDIZER
	Dichloroisopropyl ether	6.1	UN2490	II	6.1	IB2, T7, TP2	153	POISON
	Dichloromethane	6.1	UN1593	III	6.1	IB3, IP8, N36, T7, TP2	160	POISON
	Dichloropentanes	3	UN1152	III	3	B1, IB3, T2, TP1	130	FLAMMABLE
	Dichlorophenyl isocyanates	6.1	UN2250	II	6.1	IB8, IP2, IP4, T3, TP33	156	POISON
	Dichlorophenyltrichlorosilane	8	UN1766	II	8	A7, B2, B6, N34, T10, TP2, TP7, TP13	156	CORROSIVE
	1,2-Dichloropropane	3	UN1279	II	3	IB2, N36, T4, TP1	130	FLAMMABLE
	1,3-Dichloropropanol-2	6.1	UN2750	II	6.1	IB2, T7, TP2	153	POISON
	Dichloropropene and propylene dichloride mixture, see 1,2-Dichloropropane							
	Dichloropropenes	3	UN2047	II	3	IB2, T4, TP1	129	FLAMMABLE
				III	3	B1, IB3, T2, TP1	129	FLAMMABLE

Symbols (1)	Hazardous materials descriptions and proper shipping names (2)	Hazard class or Division (3)	Identification Numbers (4)	PG (5)	Label Codes (6)	Special Provisions (§172.102) (7)	ERG Guide No.	Placard Advisory Consult §172.504 & §172.505 *Placard any quantity
	Dichlorosilane	2.3	UN2189		2.3, 2.1, 8	2, B9, B14	119	INHALATION HAZARD CLASS 2*
	1,2 Dichloro-1,1,2,2-tetrafluoroethane or Refrigerant gas R 114	2.2	UN1958		2.2	T50	126	NONFLAMMABLE GAS
	Dichlorovinylchloroarsine	Forbidden						
	Dicycloheptadiene, see Bicyclo [2,2,1] hepta-2,5-diene, stabilized							
	Dicyclohexylamine	8	UN2565	III	8	IB3, T4, TP1	153	CORROSIVE
	Dicyclohexylammonium nitrite	4.1	UN2687	III	4.1	IB8, IP3, T1, TP33	133	FLAMMABLE SOLID
	Dicyclopentadiene	3	UN2048	III	3	B1, IB3, T2, TP1	130P	FLAMMABLE
	Didymium nitrate	5.1	UN1465	III	5.1	A1, IB8, IP3, T1, TP33	140	OXIDIZER
D	Diesel fuel	3	NA1993	III	None	144, B1, IB3, T4, TP1, TP29	128	COMBUSTIBLE (BULK ONLY)
I	Diesel fuel	3	UN1202	III	3	144, B1, IB3, T2, TP1	128	FLAMMABLE
	Diethanol nitrosamine dinitrate (dry)	Forbidden						
	Diethoxymethane	3	UN2373	II	3	IB2, T4, TP1	127	FLAMMABLE
	3,3-Diethoxypropene	3	UN2374	II	3	IB2, T4, TP1	127	FLAMMABLE
	Diethyl carbonate	3	UN2366	III	3	B1, IB3, T2, TP1	128	FLAMMABLE
	Diethyl cellosolve, see Ethylene glycol diethyl ether							
	Diethyl ether or Ethyl ether	3	UN1155	I	3	T11, TP2	127	FLAMMABLE
	Diethyl ketone	3	UN1156	II	3	IB2, T4, TP1	127	FLAMMABLE
	Diethyl peroxydicarbonate, with more than 27 percent in solution	Forbidden						
	Diethyl sulfate	6.1	UN1594	II	6.1	IB2, T7, TP2	152	POISON
	Diethyl sulfide	3	UN2375	II	3	IB2, T7, TP1, TP13	129	FLAMMABLE
	Diethylamine	3	UN1154	II	3, 8	A3, IB2, N34, T7, TP1	132	FLAMMABLE
	2-Diethylaminoethanol	8	UN2686	III	8, 3	B2, B2, T7, TP2	132	CORROSIVE
	3-Diethylamino-propylamine	3	UN2684	III	3, 8	B1, IB3, T4, TP1	132	FLAMMABLE
+	N,N-Diethylaniline	6.1	UN2432	III	6.1	IB3, T4, TP1	153	POISON
	Diethylbenzene	3	UN2049	III	3	B1, IB3, T2, TP1	130	FLAMMABLE

Hazardous materials descriptions	Class/Division	ID number	PG	Label codes	Special provisions	Guide	Label
Diethyldichlorosilane	8	UN1767	II	8, 3	A7, B6, N34, T10, TP2, TP7, TP13	155	CORROSIVE
Diethylene glycol dinitrate	Forbidden						
Diethyleneglycol dinitrate, desensitized with not less than 25 percent non-volatile water-insoluble phlegmatizer, by mass	1.1D	UN0075		1.1D		112	EXPLOSIVES 1.1*
Diethylenetriamine	8	UN2079	II	8	B2, IB2, T7, TP2	154	CORROSIVE
N,N-Diethylethylenediamine	8	UN2685	II	8, 3	IB2, T7, TP2	132	CORROSIVE
Diethylgold bromide	Forbidden						
Diethylthiophosphoryl chloride	8	UN2751	II	8	B2, IB2, T7, TP2	155	CORROSIVE
Difluorochloroethanes, see 1-Chloro-1,1-difluoroethanes							
1,1-Difluoroethane or Refrigerant gas R 152a	2.1	UN1030		2.1	T50	115	FLAMMABLE GAS
1,1-Difluoroethylene or Refrigerant gas R 1132a	2.1	UN1959		2.1		116P	FLAMMABLE GAS
Difluoromethane or Refrigerant gas R 32	2.1	UN3252		2.1	T50	115	FLAMMABLE GAS
Difluorophosphoric acid, anhydrous	8	UN1768	II	8	A7, B2, IB2, N5, N34, T8, TP2	154	CORROSIVE
2,3-Dihydropyran	3	UN2376	II	3	IB2, T4, TP1	127	FLAMMABLE
1,8-Dihydroxy-2,4,5,7-tetranitroanthraquinone (chrysamminic acid)	Forbidden						
Diiodoacetylene	Forbidden						
Diisobutyl ketone	3	UN1157	III	3	B1, IB3, T2, TP1	128	FLAMMABLE
Diisobutylamine	3	UN2361	III	3, 8	B1, IB3, T4, TP1	132	FLAMMABLE
Diisobutylene, isomeric compounds	3	UN2050	II	3	IB2, T4, TP1	128	FLAMMABLE
Diisooctyl acid phosphate	8	UN1902	III	8	IB3, T4, TP1	153	CORROSIVE
Diisopropyl ether	3	UN1159	II	3	IB2, T4, TP1	127	FLAMMABLE
Diisopropylamine	3	UN1158	II	3, 8	IB2, T7, TP1	132	FLAMMABLE
Diisopropylbenzene hydroperoxide, with more than 72 percent in solution	Forbidden						
Diketene, stabilized	6.1	UN2521	I	6.1, 3	2, 387, B9, B14, B32, T20, TP2, TP13, TP38, TP45	131P	INHALATION HAZARD CLASS 6*
1,2-Dimethoxyethane	3	UN2252	II	3	IB2, T4, TP1	127	FLAMMABLE
1,1-Dimethoxyethane	3	UN2377	II	3	IB2, T7, TP1	127	FLAMMABLE
Dimethyl carbonate	3	UN1161	II	3	IB2, T4, TP1	129	FLAMMABLE

Symbols (1)	Hazardous materials descriptions and proper shipping names (2)	Hazard class or Division (3)	Identification Numbers (4)	PG (5)	Label Codes (6)	Special Provisions (§172.102) (7)	ERG Guide No.	Placard Advisory Consult §172.504 & §172.505 *Placard any quantity
	Dimethyl chlorothiophosphate, see Dimethyl thiophosphoryl chloride							
	2,5-Dimethyl-2,5-dihydroperoxy hexane, with more than 82 percent with water	Forbidden						
	Dimethyl disulfide	3	UN2381	II	3, 6.1	IB2, T7, TP2, TP13, TP39	131	FLAMMABLE
	Dimethyl ether	2.1	UN1033		2.1	T50	115	FLAMMABLE GAS
	Dimethyl-N-propylamine	3	UN2266	II	3, 8	IB2, T7, TP2, TP13	132	FLAMMABLE
	Dimethyl sulfate	6.1	UN1595	I	6.1, 8	2, B9, B14, B32, B77, T20, TP2, TP13, TP38, TP45	156	INHALATION HAZARD CLASS 6*
	Dimethyl sulfide	3	UN1164	II	3	IB2, IP8, T7, TP2	130	FLAMMABLE
	Dimethyl thiophosphoryl chloride	6.1	UN2267	II	6.1, 8	IB2, T7, TP2	156	POISON
	Dimethylamine, anhydrous	2.1	UN1032		2.1	N87, T50	118	FLAMMABLE GAS
	Dimethylamine solution	3	UN1160	II	3, 8	IB2, T7, TP1	132	FLAMMABLE
	2-Dimethylaminoacetonitrile	3	UN2378	II	3, 6.1	IB2, T7, TP1	131	FLAMMABLE
	2-Dimethylaminoethanol	8	UN2051	II	8, 3	B2, IB2, T7, TP2	132	CORROSIVE
	2-Dimethylaminoethyl acrylate, stabilized	6.1	UN3302	II	6.1	387, IB2, T7, TP2	152	POISON
	2-Dimethylaminoethyl methacrylate	6.1	UN2522	II	6.1	IB2, T7, TP2	153P	POISON
	N,N-Dimethylaniline	6.1	UN2253	II	6.1	IB1, T7, TP2	153	POISON
	2,3-Dimethylbutane	3	UN2457	II	3	IB2, T7, TP1	128	FLAMMABLE
	1,3-Dimethylbutylamine	3	UN2379	II	3, 8	IB2, T7, TP1	132	FLAMMABLE
	Dimethylcarbamoyl chloride	8	UN2262	II	8	B2, IB2, T7, TP2	156	CORROSIVE
	Dimethylcyclohexanes	3	UN2263	II	3	IB2, T4, TP1	128	FLAMMABLE
	N,N-Dimethylcyclohexylamine	8	UN2264	II	8, 3	B2, IB2, T7, TP2	132	CORROSIVE
	Dimethyldichlorosilane	3	UN1162	II	3, 8	B77, T10, TP2, TP7, TP13	155	FLAMMABLE
	Dimethyldiethoxysilane	3	UN2380	II	3	IB2, T4, TP1	127	FLAMMABLE
	Dimethyldioxanes	3	UN2707	II	3	IB2, T4, TP1	127	FLAMMABLE
				III	3	B1, IB3, T2, TP1	127	FLAMMABLE

Hazardous materials descriptions and proper shipping names	Hazard class or Division	Identification Numbers	PG	Label Codes	Special provisions	Guide	
N,N-Dimethylformamide	3	UN2265	III	3	B1, IB3, T2, TP2	129	FLAMMABLE
Dimethylhexane dihydroperoxide (dry)	Forbidden						
Dimethylhydrazine, symmetrical	6.1	UN2382	I	6.1, 3	2, B9, B14, B32, B77, T20, TP2, TP13, TP38, TP45	131	INHALATION HAZARD CLASS 6*
Dimethylhydrazine, unsymmetrical	6.1	UN1163	I	6.1, 3, 8	2, B7, B9, B14, B32, T20, TP2, TP13, TP38, TP45	131	INHALATION HAZARD CLASS 6*
2,2-Dimethylpropane	2.1	UN2044		2.1		115	FLAMMABLE GAS
Dinitro-o-cresol	6.1	UN1598	II	6.1	IB8, IP2, IP4, T3, TP33	153	POISON
1,3-Dinitro-5,5-dimethyl hydantoin	Forbidden						
Dinitro-7,8-dimethylglycoluril (dry)	Forbidden						
1,3-Dinitro-4,5-dinitrosobenzene	Forbidden						
1,4-Dinitro-1,1,4,4-tetramethylolbutanetetranitrate (dry)	Forbidden						
2,4-Dinitro-1,3,5-trimethylbenzene	Forbidden						
Dinitroanilines	6.1	UN1596	II	6.1	IB8, IP2, IP4, T3 TP33	153	POISON
Dinitrobenzenes, liquid	6.1	UN1597	II	6.1	11, IB2, T7, TP2	152	POISON
			III		11, IB3, T7, TP2	152	POISON
Dinitrobenzenes, solid	6.1	UN3443	II	6.1	IB8, IP2, IP4, T3, TP33	152	POISON
Dinitrochlorobenzene, see Chlorodinitrobenzene							
1,2-Dinitroethane (dry)	Forbidden						
1,1-Dinitroethane (dry)	Forbidden						
Dinitrogen tetroxide	2.3	UN1067		2.3, 5.1, 8	1, B7, B14, B45, B46, B61, B66, B67, B77, T50, TP21	124	INHALATION HAZARD CLASS 2*
Dinitroglycoluril or Dingu	1.1D	UN0489	II	1.1D		112	EXPLOSIVES 1.1*
Dinitromethane	Forbidden						
Dinitrophenol, dry or wetted with less than 15 percent water, by mass	1.1D	UN0076	II	1.1D, 6.1		112	EXPLOSIVES 1.1*
Dinitrophenol solutions	6.1	UN1599	II	6.1	IB2, T7, TP2	153	POISON
			III		IB2, T4, TP1	153	POISON
Dinitrophenol, wetted with not less than 15 percent water, by mass	4.1	UN1320	I	4.1, 6.1	23, A8, A19, A20, N41, W31	113	FLAMMABLE SOLID

Symbols (1)	Hazardous materials descriptions and proper shipping names (2)	Hazard class or Division (3)	Identification Numbers (4)	PG (5)	Label Codes (6)	Special Provisions (§172.102) (7)	ERG Guide No.	Placard Advisory Consult §172.504 & §172.505 *Placard any quantity
	Dinitrophenolates alkali metals, dry or wetted with less than 15 percent water, by mass	1.3C	UN0077		1.3C, 6.1		112	EXPLOSIVES 1.3*
	Dinitrophenolates, wetted with not less than 15 percent water, by mass	4.1	UN1321	I	4.1, 6.1	23, A8, A19, A20, N41, W31	113	FLAMMABLE SOLID
	Dinitropropylene glycol	Forbidden						
	Dinitroresorcinol, dry or wetted with less than 15 percent water, by mass	1.1D	UN0078		1.1D		112	EXPLOSIVES 1.1*
	2,4-Dinitroresorcinol (heavy metal salts of) (dry)	Forbidden						
	4,6-Dinitroresorcinol (heavy metal salts of) (dry)	Forbidden						
	Dinitroresorcinol, wetted with not less than 15 percent water, by mass	4.1	UN1322	I	4.1	23, A8, A19, A20, N41, W31	113	FLAMMABLE SOLID
	3,5-Dinitrosalicylic acid (lead salt) (dry)	Forbidden						
	Dinitrosobenzene	1.3C	UN0406		1.3C		112	EXPLOSIVES 1.3*
	Dinitrosobenzylamidine and salts of (dry)	Forbidden						
	2,2-Dinitrostilbene	Forbidden						
	Dinitrotoluenes, liquid	6.1	UN2038	II	6.1	IB2, T7, TP2	152	POISON
	Dinitrotoluenes, molten	6.1	UN1600	II	6.1	T7, TP3	152	POISON
	Dinitrotoluenes, solid	6.1	UN3454	II	6.1	IB8, IP2, IP4, T3, TP33	152	POISON
	1,9-Dinitroxy pentamethylene-2,4, 6,8-tetramine (dry)	Forbidden						
	Dioxane	3	UN1165	II	3	IB2, T4, TP1	127	FLAMMABLE
	Dioxolane	3	UN1166	II	3	IB2, T4, TP1	127	FLAMMABLE
	Dipentene	3	UN2052	III	3	B1, IB3, T2, TP1	128	FLAMMABLE
	Diphenylamine chloroarsine	6.1	UN1698	I	6.1	T6, TP33, W31	154	POISON
	Diphenylchloroarsine, liquid	6.1	UN1699	I	6.1	A8, B14, B32, N33, N34, T14, TP2, TP13, TP27, W31	151	POISON
	Diphenylchloroarsine, solid	6.1	UN3450	I	6.1	IB7, IP1, T6, TP33, W31	151	POISON

Sym	Name	Class	ID No.	PG	Div	Special Provisions	Guide	Label
	Diphenyldichlorosilane	8	UN1769	II	8	A7, B2, N34, T10, TP2, TP7, TP13	156	CORROSIVE
	Diphenylmethyl bromide	8	UN1770	II	8	IB8, IP2, IP4, T3, TP33	153	CORROSIVE
	Dipicryl sulfide, dry or wetted with less than 10 percent water, by mass	1.1D	UN0401		1.1D		112	EXPLOSIVES 1.1*
	Dipicryl sulfide, wetted with not less than 10 percent water, by mass	4.1	UN2852	I	4.1	162, A2, N41, N84, W31	113	FLAMMABLE SOLID
	Dipicrylamine, see Hexanitrodiphenylamine							
	Dipropionyl peroxide, with more than 28 percent in solution	Forbidden						
	Di-n-propyl ether	3	UN2384	II	3	IB2, T4, TP1	127	FLAMMABLE
	Dipropyl ketone	3	UN2710	III	3	B1, IB3, T2, TP1	128	FLAMMABLE
	Dipropylamine	3	UN2383	II	3, 8	IB2, T7, TP1	132	FLAMMABLE
G	Disinfectant, liquid, corrosive, n.o.s.	8	UN1903	I	8	A7, B10, T14, TP2, TP27	153	CORROSIVE
G	Disinfectants, liquid, corrosive, n.o.s.	8	UN1903	II	8	B2, IB2, T7, TP2	153	CORROSIVE
				III	8	IB3, T4, TP1	153	CORROSIVE
G	Disinfectants, liquid, toxic, n.o.s.	6.1	UN3142	I	6.1	A4, T14, TP2, TP27	151	POISON
				II	6.1	IB2, T11, TP2, TP27	151	POISON
				III	6.1	IB3, T7, TP1, TP28	151	POISON
G	Disinfectants, solid, toxic, n.o.s.	6.1	UN1601	I	6.1	IB7, IP1, T6, TF33	151	POISON
				II	6.1	IB8, IP2, IP4, T3, TP33	151	POISON
				III	6.1	IB8, IP3, T1, TP33	151	POISON
	Disodium trioxosilicate	8	UN3253	III	8	IB8, IP3, T1, TP33	154	CORROSIVE
G	Dispersant gases, n.o.s., see Refrigerant gases, n.o.s.							
	Divinyl ether, stabilized	3	UN1167	I	3	387, A7, T11, TP2	128P	FLAMMABLE
	Dodecyltrichlorosilane	8	UN1771	II	8	A7, B2, B6, N34, T10, TP2, TP7, TP13	156	CORROSIVE
	Dry ice, see Carbon dioxide, solid							
G	Dyes, liquid, corrosive n.o.s. or Dye intermediates, liquid, corrosive, n.o.s.	8	UN2801	I	8	11, B10, T14, TP2, TP27	154	CORROSIVE
				II	8	11, B2, IB2, T11, TP2, TP27	154	CORROSIVE

HAZMAT TABLE

Symbols (1)	Hazardous materials descriptions and proper shipping names (2)	Hazard class or Division (3)	Identification Numbers (4)	PG (5)	Label Codes (6)	Special Provisions (§172.102) (7)	ERG Guide No.	Placard Advisory Consult §172.504 & §172.505 *Placard any quantity
				III	8	11, IB3, T7, TP1, TP28	154	CORROSIVE
G	Dyes, liquid, toxic, n.o.s. or Dye intermediates, liquid, toxic, n.o.s.	6.1	UN1602	I	6.1		151	POISON
				II	6.1	IB2	151	POISON
				III	6.1	IB3	151	POISON
G	Dyes, solid, corrosive, n.o.s. or Dye intermediates, solid, corrosive, n.o.s.	8	UN3147	I	8	IB7, IP1, T6, TP33	154	CORROSIVE
				II	8	IB8, IP2, IP4, T3, TP33	154	CORROSIVE
				III	8	IB8, IP3, T1, TP33	154	CORROSIVE
G	Dyes, solid, toxic, n.o.s. or Dye intermediates, solid, toxic, n.o.s.	6.1	UN3143	I	6.1	A5, IB7, IP1, T6, TP33	151	POISON
				II	6.1	IB8, IP2, IP4, T3, TP33	151	POISON
				III	6.1	IB8, IP3, T1, TP33	151	POISON
	Dynamite, see Explosive, blasting, type A							
	Electrolyte (acid or alkali) for batteries, see Battery fluid, acid or Battery fluid, alkali							
G	Elevated temperature liquid, flammable, n.o.s., with flash point above 37.8 C, at or above its flash point	3	UN3256	III	3	IB1, T3, TP3, TP29	128	FLAMMABLE
G	Elevated temperature liquid, n.o.s., at or above 100 C and below its flash point (including molten metals, molten salts, etc.)	9	UN3257	III	9	IB1, T3, TP3, TP29	171	CLASS 9
G	Elevated temperature solid, n.o.s., at or above 240 C, see §173.247(h)(4)	9	UN3258	III	9		171	CLASS 9
	Engine, internal combustion, flammable gas powered or Engine, fuel cell, flammable gas powered or Machinery, internal combustion, flammable gas powered or Machinery, fuel cell, flammable gas powered	2.1	UN3529		2.1	135, A200	115	FLAMMABLE GAS

Symbols	Hazardous materials descriptions and proper shipping names	Hazard class or Division	Identification Numbers	PG	Label Codes	Special provisions	ERG Guide No.	Placard
	Engine, internal combustion, flammable liquid powered or Engine, fuel cell, flammable liquid powered or Machinery, internal combustion, flammable liquid powered or Machinery, fuel cell, flammable liquid powered	3	UN3528		3	135, A200	128	FLAMMABLE
G	Engine, internal combustion or Machinery, internal combustion	9	UN3530	III	9	135, A200	171	CLASS 9
G	Environmentally hazardous substance, liquid, n.o.s.	9	UN3082	III	9	8, 146, 173, 335, IB3, T4, TP1, TP29	171	CLASS 9
G	Environmentally hazardous substance, solid, n.o.s.	9	UN3077	III	9	8, 146, 335, 384, A112, B54, B120, IB8, IP3, N20, N91, T1, TP33	171	CLASS 9
	Epibromoyhydrin	6.1	UN2558	I	6.1, 3	T14, TP2, TP13	131	POISON
+	Epichlorohydrin	6.1	UN2023	II	6.1, 3	IB2, T7, TP2, TP13	131P	POISON
	1,2-Epoxy-3-ethoxypropane	3	UN2752	III	3	B1, IB3, T2, TP1	127	FLAMMABLE
	Esters, n.o.s.	3	UN3272	II	3	IB2, T7, TP1, TP8, TP28	127	FLAMMABLE
				III	3	B1, IB3, T4, TP1, TP29	127	FLAMMABLE
	Etching acid, liquid, n.o.s., see Hydrofluoric acid, etc.							
	Ethane	2.1	UN1035		2.1		115	FLAMMABLE GAS
D	Ethane-Propane mixture, refrigerated liquid	2.1	NA1961		2.1	T75, TP5	115	FLAMMABLE GAS
	Ethane, refrigerated liquid	2.1	UN1961		2.1	T75, TP5	115	FLAMMABLE GAS
	Ethanol amine dinitrate	Forbidden						
	Ethanol and gasoline mixture or Ethanol and motor spirit mixture or Ethanol and petrol mixture, *with more than 10% ethanol*	3	UN3475	II	3	144, 177, IB2, T4, TP1	127	FLAMMABLE
	Ethanol or Ethyl alcohol or Ethanol solutions or Ethyl alcohol solutions	3	UN1170	II	3	24, IB2, T4, TP1	127	FLAMMABLE
				III	3	24, B1, IB3, T2, TP1	127	FLAMMABLE
	Ethanolamine or Ethanolamine solutions	8	UN2491	III	8	IB3, T4, TP1	153	CORROSIVE
	Ether, see Diethyl ether							
	Ethers, n.o.s.	3	UN3271	II	3	IB2, T7, TP1, TP8, TP28	127	FLAMMABLE
				III	3	B1, IB3, T4, TP1	127	FLAMMABLE
	Ethyl acetate	3	UN1173	II	3	IB2, T4, TP1	129	FLAMMABLE
	Ethyl acrylate, stabilized	3	UN1917	II	3	387, IB2, T4, TP1, TP13	129P	FLAMMABLE

Symbols (1)	Hazardous materials descriptions and proper shipping names (2)	Hazard class or Division (3)	Identification Numbers (4)	PG (5)	Label Codes (6)	Special Provisions (§172.102) (7)	ERG Guide No.	Placard Advisory Consult §172.504 & §172.505 *Placard any quantity
	Ethyl alcohol, see Ethanol							
	Ethyl aldehyde, see Acetaldehyde							
	Ethyl amyl ketone	3	UN2271	III	3	B1, IB3, T2, TP1	128	FLAMMABLE
	N-Ethyl-N-benzylaniline	6.1	UN2274	III	6.1	IB3, T4, TP1	153	POISON
	Ethyl borate	3	UN1176	II	3	IB2, T4, TP1	129	FLAMMABLE
	Ethyl bromide	6.1	UN1891	II	6.1	IB2, IP8, T7, TP2, TP13	131	POISON
	Ethyl bromoacetate	6.1	UN1603	II	6.1, 3	IB2, T7, TP3	155	POISON
	Ethyl butyl ether	3	UN1179	II	3	B1, IB2, T4, TP1	127	FLAMMABLE
	Ethyl butyrate	3	UN1180	III	3	B1, IB3, T2, TP1	130	FLAMMABLE
	Ethyl chloride	2.1	UN1037		2.1	B77, N86, T50	115	FLAMMABLE GAS
	Ethyl chloroacetate	6.1	UN1181	II	6.1, 3	IB2, T7, TP2	155	POISON
	Ethyl chloroformate	6.1	UN1182	I	6.1, 3, 8	2, B9, B14, B32, N34, T20, TP2, TP13, TP38, TP45	155	INHALATION HAZARD CLASS 6*
	Ethyl 2-chloropropionate	3	UN2935	III	3	B1, IB3, T2, TP1	129	FLAMMABLE
+	Ethyl chlorothioformate	8	UN2826	II	8, 6.1, 3	2, B9, B14, B32, T20, TP2, TP38, TP45	155	CORROSIVE, INHALATION HAZARD CLASS 6*
	Ethyl crotonate	3	UN1862	II	3	IB2, T4, TP2	130	FLAMMABLE
	Ethyl ether, see Diethyl ether							
	Ethyl fluoride or Refrigerant gas R161	2.1	UN2453		2.1		115	FLAMMABLE GAS
	Ethyl formate	3	UN1190	II	3	IB2, T4, TP1	129	FLAMMABLE
	Ethyl hydroperoxide	Forbidden						
	Ethyl isobutyrate	3	UN2385	II	3	IB2, T4, TP1	129	FLAMMABLE
+	Ethyl isocyanate	6.1	UN2481	I	6.1, 3	1, B9, B14, B30, T20, TP2, TP13, TP38, TP44	155	INHALATION HAZARD CLASS 6*
	Ethyl lactate	3	UN1192	III	3	B1, IB3, T2, TP1	129	FLAMMABLE
	Ethyl mercaptan	3	UN2363	I	3	T11, TP2, TP13	129	FLAMMABLE

Symbol	Hazardous materials descriptions and proper shipping names	Hazard class	ID number	PG	Label codes	Special provisions	Guide	Placard
	Ethyl methacrylate, stabilized	3	UN2277	II	3	387, IB2, T4, TP1	130P	FLAMMABLE
	Ethyl methyl ether	2.1	UN1039	II	2.1		115	FLAMMABLE GAS
	Ethyl methyl ketone or Methyl ethyl ketone	3	UN1193	II	3	IB2, T4, TP1	127	FLAMMABLE
	Ethyl nitrite solutions	3	UN1194	I	3, 6.1		131	FLAMMABLE
	Ethyl orthoformate	3	UN2524	III	3	B1, IB3, T2, TP1	129	FLAMMABLE
	Ethyl oxalate	6.1	UN2525	III	6.1	IB3, T4, TP1	156	POISON
	Ethyl perchlorate	Forbidden						
D	Ethyl phosphonothioic dichloride, anhydrous	6.1	NA2927	I	6.1, 8	2, B9, B14, B32, T20, TP4, TP12, TP13, TP38, TP45	154	INHALATION HAZARD CLASS 6*
D	Ethyl phosphonous dichloride, anhydrous *pyrophoric liquid*	6.1	NA2845	I	6.1, 4.2	2, B9, B14, B32, T20, TP4, TP12, TP13, TP38, TP45	135	INHALATION HAZARD CLASS 6*
D	Ethyl phosphorodichloridate	6.1	NA2927	I	6.1, 8	2, B9, B14, B32, T20, TP4, TP12, TP13, TP38, TP45	154	INHALATION HAZARD CLASS 6*
	Ethyl propionate	3	UN1195	II	3	IB2, T4, TP1	129	FLAMMABLE
	Ethyl propyl ether	3	UN2615	II	3	IB2, T4, TP1	127	FLAMMABLE
	Ethyl silicate, see Tetraethyl silicate							
	Ethylacetylene, stabilized	2.1	UN2452		2.1	387, N88	116P	FLAMMABLE GAS
	Ethylamine	2.1	UN1036		2.1	B77, N87, T50	118	FLAMMABLE GAS
	Ethylamine, aqueous solution *with not less than 50 percent but not more than 70 percent ethylamine*	3	UN2270	II	3, 8	IB2, T7, TP1	132	FLAMMABLE
	N-Ethylaniline	6.1	UN2272	III	6.1	IB3, T4, TP1	153	POISON
	2-Ethylaniline	6.1	UN2273	III	6.1	IB3, T4, TP1	153	POISON
	Ethylbenzene	3	UN1175	II	3	IB2, T4, TP1	130	FLAMMABLE
	N-Ethylbenzyltoluidines liquid	6.1	UN2753	III	6.1	IB3, T7, TP1	153	POISON
	N-Ethylbenzyltoluidines, solid	6.1	UN3460	III	6.1	IB8, IP3, T1, TP33	153	POISON
	2-Ethylbutanol	3	UN2275	III	3	B1, IB3, T2, TP1	129	FLAMMABLE
	2-Ethylbutyl acetate	3	UN1177	III	3	B1, IB3, T2, TP1	130	FLAMMABLE
	2-Ethylbutyraldehyde	3	UN1178	II	3	B1, IB2, T4, TP1	130	FLAMMABLE
	Ethyldichloroarsine	6.1	UN1892	I	6.1	2, B9, B14, B32, T20, TP2, TP13, TP38, TP45	151	INHALATION HAZARD CLASS 6*

Symbols (1)	Hazardous materials descriptions and proper shipping names (2)	Hazard class or Division (3)	Identification Numbers (4)	PG (5)	Label Codes (6)	Special Provisions (§172.102) (7)	ERG Guide No.	Placard Advisory Consult §172.504 & §172.505 *Placard any quantity
	Ethyldichlorosilane	4.3	UN1183	I	4.3, 8, 3	A2, A7, N34, T14, TP2, TP7, TP13, W31	139	DANGEROUS WHEN WET*
	Ethylene, acetylene and propylene in mixture, refrigerated liquid with at least 71.5 percent ethylene with not more than 22.5 percent acetylene and not more than 6 percent propylene	2.1	UN3138		2.1	T75, TP5	115	FLAMMABLE GAS
	Ethylene chlorohydrin	6.1	UN1135	I	6.1, 3	2, B9, B14, B32, T20, TP2, TP13, TP38, TP45	131	INHALATION HAZARD CLASS 6*
	Ethylene	2.1	UN1962		2.1		116P	FLAMMABLE GAS
	Ethylene diamine diperchlorate	Forbidden						
	Ethylene dibromide	6.1	UN1605	I	6.1	2, B9, B14, B32, B77, T20, TP2, TP13, TP38, TP45	154	INHALATION HAZARD CLASS 6*
	Ethylene dibromide and methyl bromide liquid mixtures, see Methyl bromide and ethylene dibromide liquid mixtures							
	Ethylene dichloride	3	UN1184	II	3, 6.1	IB2, N36, T7, TP1	131	FLAMMABLE
	Ethylene glycol diethyl ether	3	UN1153	II	3	IB2, T4, TP1	127	FLAMMABLE
		3		III	3	B1, IB3, T2, TP1	127	FLAMMABLE
	Ethylene glycol dinitrate	Forbidden						
	Ethylene glycol monoethyl ether	3	UN1171	III	3	B1, IB3, T2, TP1	127	FLAMMABLE
	Ethylene glycol monoethyl ether acetate	3	UN1172	III	3	B1, IB3, T2, TP1	129	FLAMMABLE
	Ethylene glycol monomethyl ether	3	UN1188	III	3	B1, IB3, T2, TP1	127	FLAMMABLE
	Ethylene glycol monomethyl ether acetate	3	UN1189	III	3	B1, IB3, T2, TP1	129	FLAMMABLE
	Ethylene oxide and carbon dioxide mixture with more than 87 percent ethylene oxide	2.3	UN3300		2.3, 2.1	4	119P	INHALATION HAZARD CLASS 2*
	Ethylene oxide and carbon dioxide mixtures with more than 9 percent but not more than 87 percent ethylene oxide	2.1	UN1041		2.1	T50	115	FLAMMABLE GAS
	Ethylene oxide and carbon dioxide mixtures with not more than 9 percent ethylene oxide	2.2	UN1952		2.2		126	NONFLAMMABLE GAS
	Ethylene oxide and chlorotetrafluoroethane mixture with not more than 8.8 percent ethylene oxide	2.2	UN3297		2.2	T50	126	NONFLAMMABLE GAS

Hazardous material description	Hazard class	ID No.	PG	Special provisions	Label codes	Guide	Placard
Ethylene oxide and dichlorodifluoromethane mixture, with not more than 12.5 percent ethylene oxide	2.2	UN3070		T50	2.2	126	NONFLAMMABLE GAS
Ethylene oxide and pentafluoroethane mixture with not more than 7.9 percent ethylene oxide	2.2	UN3298		T50	2.2	126	NONFLAMMABLE GAS
Ethylene oxide and propylene oxide mixtures, with not more than 30 percent ethylene oxide	3	UN2983	I	5, A11, N4, N34, T14, TP2, TP7, TP13	3, 6.1	131P	FLAMMABLE
Ethylene oxide and tetrafluoroethane mixture with not more than 5.6 percent ethylene oxide	2.2	UN2299		T50	2.2	126	NONFLAMMABLE GAS
Ethylene oxide or Ethylene oxide with nitrogen up to a total pressure of 1 MPa (10 bar) at 50 degrees C	2.3	UN1040		4, 342, T50, TP21	2.3, 2.1	119P	INHALATION HAZARD CLASS 2*
Ethylene, refrigerated liquid (cryogenic liquid)	2.1	UN1038		T75, T5	2.1	115	FLAMMABLE GAS
Ethylenediamine	8	UN1604	II	IB2, T7, TP2	8, 3	132	CORROSIVE
Ethyleneimine, stabilized	6.1	UN1185	I	1, 387, B9, B14, B30, B77, N25, N32, T22, TP2, TP13, TP38, TP44	6.1, 3	131P	INHALATION HAZARD CLASS 6*
Ethylhexaldehyde, see Octyl aldehydes etc.							
2-Ethylhexyl chloroformate	6.1	UN2748	II	IB2, T7, TP2, TP13	6.1, 8	156	POISON
2-Ethylhexylamine	3	UN2276	III	B1, IB3, T4, TP1	3, 8	132	FLAMMABLE
Ethylphenyldichlorosilane	8	UN2435	II	A7, B2, N34, T10, TP2, TP7, TP13	8	156	CORROSIVE
1-Ethylpiperidine	3	UN2386	II	IB2, T7, TP1	3, 8	132	FLAMMABLE
N-Ethyltoluidines	6.1	UN2754	II	IB2, T7, TP2	6.1	153	POISON
Ethyltrichlorosilane	3	UN1196	II	A7, N34, T10, TP2, TP7, TP13	3, 8	155	FLAMMABLE
Etiologic agent, see Infectious substances, etc.							
Explosive articles, see Articles, explosive, n.o.s. etc.							
Explosive, blasting, type A	1.1D	UN0081	1.1D	148	1.1D	112	EXPLOSIVES 1.1*
Explosive, blasting, type B	1.1D	UN0082	1.1D		1.1D	112	EXPLOSIVES 1.1*
Explosive, blasting, type B or Agent blasting, Type B	1.5D	UN0331	1.5D	105, 106, 148	1.5D	112	EXPLOSIVES 1.5
Explosive, blasting, type C	1.1D	UN0083	1.1D	123	1.1D	112	EXPLOSIVES 1.1*
Explosive, blasting, type D	1.1D	UN0084	1.1D		1.1D	112	EXPLOSIVES 1.1*
Explosive, blasting, type E	1.1D	UN0241	1.1D	148	1.1D	112	EXPLOSIVES 1.1*

Symbols (1)	Hazardous materials descriptions and proper shipping names (2)	Hazard class or Division (3)	Identification Numbers (4)	PG (5)	Label Codes (6)	Special Provisions (§172.102) (7)	ERG Guide No.	Placard Advisory Consult §172.504 & §172.505 *Placard any quantity
	Explosive, blasting, type E or Agent blasting, Type E	1.5D	UN0332		1.5D	105, 106, 148	112	EXPLOSIVES 1.5
	Explosive, forbidden. See §173.54	Forbidden						
	Explosive substances, see Substances, explosive, n.o.s. etc.							
	Explosives, slurry, see Explosive, blasting, type E							
	Explosives, water gels, see Explosive, blasting, type E							
	Extracts, aromatic, liquid	3	UN1169	II	3	149, IB2, T4, TP1, TP8	127	FLAMMABLE
				III	3	B1, IB3, T2, TP1	127	FLAMMABLE
	Extracts, flavoring, liquid	3	UN1197	II	3	149, IB2, T4, TP1, TP8	127	FLAMMABLE
				III	3	B1, IB3, T2, TP1	127	FLAMMABLE
	Fabric with animal or vegetable oil, see Fibers or Fabrics, etc.							
	Ferric arsenate	6.1	UN1606	II	6.1	IB8, IP2, IP4, T3, TP33	151	POISON
	Ferric arsenite	6.1	UN1607	II	6.1	IB8, IP2, IP4, T3, TP33	151	POISON
	Ferric chloride, anhydrous	8	UN1773	III	8	IB8, IP3, T1, TP33	157	CORROSIVE
	Ferric chloride, solution	8	UN2582	III	8	B15, IB3, T4, TP1	154	CORROSIVE
	Ferric nitrate	5.1	UN1466	III	5.1	A1, A29, IB8, IP3, T1, TP33	140	OXIDIZER
	Ferrocerium	4.1	UN1323	II	4.1	59, A19, IB8, IP2, IP4, T3, TP33, W100	170	FLAMMABLE SOLID
	Ferrosilicon, with 30 percent or more but less than 90 percent silicon	4.3	UN1408	III	4.3, 6.1	A1, A19, B6, IB8, IB8, IP4, IP7, T1, TP33, W100	139	DANGEROUS WHEN WET*
	Ferrous arsenate	6.1	UN1608	II	6.1	IB8, IP2, IP4, T3, TP33	151	POISON
D	Ferrous chloride, solid	8	NA1759	II	8	IB8, IP2, IP4, T3, TP33	154	CORROSIVE
D	Ferrous chloride, solution	8	NA1760	II	8	B3, IB2, T11, TP2, TP27	154	CORROSIVE
	Ferrous metal borings or Ferrous metal shavings or Ferrous metal turnings or Ferrous metal cuttings in a form liable to self-heating	4.2	UN2793	III	4.2	A1, A19, B134, B136, IB8, IP3, IP7, IP21, W100	170	SPONTANEOUSLY COMBUSTIBLE
	Fertilizer ammoniating solution with free ammonia	2.2	UN1043		2.2	N87	125	NONFLAMMABLE GAS

Symbols	Hazardous materials descriptions and proper shipping names	Hazard class or division	Identification Numbers	PG	Label codes	Special provisions	Guide No.	Placard
A I W	Fibers, animal or Fibers, vegetable burnt, wet or damp	4.2	UN1372	III	4.2		133	SPONTANEOUSLY COMBUSTIBLE
I W	Fibers, vegetable, dry	4.1	UN3360	III	4.1	137	133	FLAMMABLE SOLID
A W	Fibers or Fabrics, animal or vegetable or Synthentic, n.o.s. with animal or vegetable oil	4.2	UN1373	III	4.2	137, IB8, IP3, T1, TP33, W31	133	SPONTANEOUSLY COMBUSTIBLE
	Fibers or Fabrics impregnated with weakly nitrated nitrocellulose, n.o.s.	4.1	UN1353	III	4.1	A1, IB8, IP3	133	FLAMMABLE SOLID
	Films, nitrocellulose base, from which gelatine has been removed; film scrap, see Celluloid, scrap							
	Films, nitrocellulose base, gelatine coated (except scrap)	4.1	UN1324	III	4.1		133	FLAMMABLE SOLID
	Fire extinguisher charges, corrosive liquid	8	UN1774	II	8	N41	154	CORROSIVE
	Fire extinguisher charges, expelling, explosive, see Cartridges, power device							
	Fire extinguishers containing compressed or liquefied gas	2.2	UN1044		2.2	110	126	NONFLAMMABLE GAS
	Firelighters, solid with flammable liquid	4.1	UN2623	III	4.1	A1, A19	133	FLAMMABLE SOLID
	Fireworks	1.1G	UN0333		1.1G	108	112	EXPLOSIVES 1.1*
	Fireworks	1.2G	UN0334		1.2G	108	112	EXPLOSIVES 1.2*
	Fireworks	1.3G	UN0335		1.3G	108	112	EXPLOSIVES 1.3*
	Fireworks	1.4G	UN0336		1.4G	108, 200	114	EXPLOSIVES 1.4
	Fireworks	1.4S	UN0337		1.4S	108	114	EXPLOSIVES 1.4
	First aid kit	9	UN3316	III	9	15	171	CLASS 9
A W	Fish meal, stabilized or Fish scrap, stabilized	9	UN2216	III	None	155, B136, IB8, IP3, T1, TP33	171	CLASS 9
	Fish meal, unstabilized or Fish scrap, unstabilized	4.2	UN1374	II	4.2	155, A1, A19, B8, IP2, IP4, T3, TP33, W31, W40	133	SPONTANEOUSLY COMBUSTIBLE
	Flammable compressed gas, see Compressed or Liquefied gas, flammable, etc.							
	Flammable compressed gas (small receptacles not fitted with a dispersion device, not refillable), see Receptacles, etc.							
	Flammable gas in lighters, see Lighters or lighter refills, cigarettes, containing flammable gas							

Symbols (1)	Hazardous materials descriptions and proper shipping names (2)	Hazard class or Division (3)	Identification Numbers (4)	PG (5)	Label Codes (6)	Special Provisions (§172.102) (7)	ERG Guide No.	Placard Advisory Consult §172.504 & §172.505 *Placard any quantity
G	Flammable liquid, toxic, corrosive, n.o.s.	3	UN3286	I	3, 6.1, 8	T14, TP2, TP13, TP27	131	FLAMMABLE
				II	3, 6.1, 8	IB2, T11, TP2, TP13, TP27	131	FLAMMABLE
G	Flammable liquids, corrosive, n.o.s.	3	UN2924	I	3, 8	T14, TP2	132	FLAMMABLE
				II	3, 8	IB2, T11, TP2, TP27	132	FLAMMABLE
				III	3, 8	B1, IB3, T7, TP1, TP28	132	FLAMMABLE
G	Flammable liquids, n.o.s.	3	UN1993	I	3	T11, TP1, TP27	128	FLAMMABLE
				II	3	IB2, T7, TP1, TP8, TP28	128	FLAMMABLE
				III	3	B1, B52, IB3, T4, TP1, TP29	128	FLAMMABLE
G	Flammable liquids, toxic, n.o.s.	3	UN1992	I	3, 6.1	T14, TP2, TP13, TP27	131	FLAMMABLE
				II	3, 6.1	IB2, T7, TP2, TP13	131	FLAMMABLE
				III	3, 6.1	B1, IB3, T7, TP1, TP28	131	FLAMMABLE
G	Flammable solid, corrosive, inorganic, n.o.s.	4.1	UN3180	II	4.1, 8	A1, IB6, IP2, T3, TP33	134	FLAMMABLE SOLID
				III	4.1, 8	A1, IB6, T1, TP33	134	FLAMMABLE SOLID
G	Flammable solid, inorganic, n.o.s.	4.1	UN3178	II	4.1	A1, IB8, IP2, IP4, T3, TP33	133	FLAMMABLE SOLID
				III	4.1	A1, IB8, IP3, T1, TP33	133	FLAMMABLE SOLID
G	Flammable solid, organic, molten, n.o.s.	4.1	UN3176	II	4.1	IB1, T3, TP3, TP26	133	FLAMMABLE SOLID
				III	4.1	IB1, T1, TP3, TP26	133	FLAMMABLE SOLID
G	Flammable solid, oxidizing, n.o.s.	4.1	UN3097	II	4.1, 5.1	131	140	FLAMMABLE SOLID
				III	4.1, 5.1	131, T1, TP33	140	FLAMMABLE SOLID
G	Flammable solid, toxic, inorganic, n.o.s.	4.1	UN3179	II	4.1, 6.1	A1, IB6, IP2, T3, TP33	134	FLAMMABLE SOLID
				III	4.1, 6.1	A1, IB6, T1, TP33	134	FLAMMABLE SOLID

Sym	Hazardous materials descriptions and proper shipping names	Hazard class	ID No.	PG	Label codes	Special provisions	Guide	Hazard
G	Flammable solids, corrosive, organic, n.o.s.	4.1	UN2925	II	4.1, 8	A1, IB6, IP2, T3, TP33	134	FLAMMABLE SOLID
				III	4.1, 8	A1, IB6, T1, TP33	134	FLAMMABLE SOLID
G	Flammable solids, organic, n.o.s.	4.1	UN1325	II	4.1	A1, IB8, IP2, IP4, T3, TP33	133	FLAMMABLE SOLID
				III	4.1	A1, IB8, IP3, T1, TP33	133	FLAMMABLE SOLID
G	Flammable solids, toxic, organic, n.o.s.	4.1	UN2926	II	4.1, 6.1	A1, IB6, IP2, T3, TP33	134	FLAMMABLE SOLID
				III	4.1, 6.1	A1, IB6, T1, TP33	134	FLAMMABLE SOLID
	Flares, aerial	1.3G	UN0093	1.3G			112	EXPLOSIVES 1.3*
	Flares, aerial	1.4G	UN0403	1.4G			114	EXPLOSIVES 1.4
	Flares, aerial	1.4S	UN0404	1.4S			114	EXPLOSIVES 1.4
	Flares, aerial	1.1G	UN0420	1.1G			112	EXPLOSIVES 1.1*
	Flares, aerial	1.2G	UN0421	1.2G			112	EXPLOSIVES 1.2*
	Flares, airplane, see Flares, aerial							
	Flares, signal, see Cartridges, signal							
	Flares, surface	1.3G	UN0092	1.3G			112	EXPLOSIVES 1.3*
	Flares, surface	1.1G	UN0418	1.1G			112	EXPLOSIVES 1.1*
	Flares, surface	1.2G	UN0419	1.2G			112	EXPLOSIVES 1.2*
	Flares, water-activated, see Contrivances, water-activated, etc.							
	Flash powder	1.1G	UN0094	1.1G			112	EXPLOSIVES 1.1*
	Flash powder	1.3G	UN0305	1.3G			112	EXPLOSIVES 1.3*
	Flue dusts, poisonous, see Arsenical dust							
	Fluoric acid, see Hydrofluoric acid, etc.							
	Fluorine, compressed	2.3	UN1045		2.3, 5.1, 8	1, N86	124	INHALATION HAZARD CLASS 2*
	Fluoroacetic acid	6.1	UN2642	I	6.1	IB7, IP1, T6, TP33	154	POISON
	Fluoroanilines	6.1	UN2941	III	6.1	IB3, T4, TP1	153	POISON
	Fluorobenzene	3	UN2387	II	3	IB2, T4, TP1	130	FLAMMABLE
	Fluoroboric acid	8	UN1775	II	8	A7, B2, B15, IB2, N3, N34, T7, TP2	154	CORROSIVE

Symbols (1)	Hazardous materials descriptions and proper shipping names (2)	Hazard class or Division (3)	Identification Numbers (4)	PG (5)	Label Codes (6)	Special Provisions (§172.102) (7)	ERG Guide No.	Placard Advisory Consult §172.504 & §172.505 *Placard any quantity
	Fluorophosphoric acid anhydrous	8	UN1776	II	8	A7, B2, IB2, N3, N34, T8, TP2	154	CORROSIVE
G	Fluorosilicates, n.o.s.	6.1	UN2856	III	6.1	IB8, IP3, T1, TP33	151	POISON
	Fluorosilicic acid	8	UN1778	II	8	A7, B2, B15, IB2, N3, N34, T8, TP2	154	CORROSIVE
	Fluorosulfonic acid	8	UN1777	I	8	A7, A10, B6, B10, N3, N36, T10, TP2	137	CORROSIVE
	Fluorotoluenes	3	UN2388	II	3	IB2, T4, TP1	130	FLAMMABLE
	Forbidden materials. See §173.21	Forbidden						
	Formaldehyde solutions, flammable	3	UN1198	III	3, 8	176, B1, IB3, T4, TP1	132	FLAMMABLE
	Formaldehyde solutions, with not less than 25 percent formaldehyde	8	UN2209	III	8	IB3, T4, TP1	153	CORROSIVE
	Formaldehyde solutions (with not less than 10% and less than 25% formaldehyde), see Aviation regulated liquid, n.o.s. or Other regulated substances, liquid, n.o.s.							
	Formalin, see Formaldehyde solutions							
	Formic acid with not less than 10% but not more than 85% acid by mass	8	UN3412	II	8	IB2, T7, TP2	153	CORROSIVE
	Formic acid with not less than 5% but less than 10% acid by mass	8	UN3412	III	8	IB3, T4, TP1	153	CORROSIVE
	Formic acid with more than 85% acid by mass	8	UN1779	II	8, 3	B2, B28, IB2, T7, TP2	153	CORROSIVE
	Fracturing devices, explosive, without detonators for oil wells	1.1D	UN0099		1.1D		112	EXPLOSIVES 1.1*
	Fuel, aviation, turbine engine	3	UN1863	I	3	144, T11, TP1, TP8, TP28	128	FLAMMABLE
				II	3	144, IB2, T4, TP1, TP8	128	FLAMMABLE
				III	3	144, B1, IB3, T2, TP1	128	FLAMMABLE
	Fuel cell cartridges or Fuel cell cartridges contained in equipment or Fuel cell cartridges packed with equipment, containing corrosive substances	8	UN3477		8	328	153	CORROSIVE

Symbols	Hazardous materials descriptions and proper shipping names	Hazard class or Division	Identification Numbers	PG	Label Codes	Special provisions	ERG Guide No.	Placard
	Fuel cell cartridges or Fuel cell cartridges contained in equipment or Fuel cell cartridges packed with equipment, containing flammable liquids	3	UN3473		3	328	128	FLAMMABLE
	Fuel cell cartridges or Fuel cell cartridges contained in equipment or Fuel cell cartridges packed with equipment, containing hydrogen in metal hydride	2.1	UN3479		2.1	328	115	FLAMMABLE GAS
	Fuel cell cartridges or Fuel cell cartridges contained in equipment or Fuel cell cartridges packed with equipment, containing liquefied flammable gas	2.1	UN3478		2.1	328	115	FLAMMABLE GAS
	Fuel cell cartridges or Fuel cell cartridges contained in equipment or Fuel cell cartridges packed with equipment, containing water-reactive substances	4.3	UN3476		4.3	328	138	DANGEROUS WHEN WET
D	Fuel oil (No. 1, 2, 4, 5, or 6)	3	NA1993	III	3	144, B1, IB3, T4, TP1, TP29	128	FLAMMABLE
	Fuel system components (including fuel control units (FCU), carburetors, fuel lines, fuel pumps) see Dangerous Goods in Apparatus or Dangerous Goods in Machinery							
	Fulminate of mercury (dry)	Forbidden						
	Fulminate of mercury, wet, see Mercury fulminate, etc.							
	Fulminating gold	Forbidden						
	Fulminating mercury	Forbidden						
	Fulminating platinum	Forbidden						
	Fulminating silver	Forbidden						
	Fulminic acid	Forbidden						
	Fumaryl chloride	8	UN1780	II	8	B2, IB2, T7, TP2	156	CORROSIVE
	Fumigated lading, see §§172.302(g), 173.9 and 176.76(h)							
	Fumigated transport vehicle or freight container see §173.9							
	Furaldehydes	6.1	UN1199	II	6.1, 3	IB2, T7, TP2	153P	POISON
	Furan	3	UN2389	I	3	T12, TP2, TP13	128	FLAMMABLE
	Furfuryl alcohol	6.1	UN2874	III	6.1	IB3, T4, TP1	153	POISON
	Furfurylamine	3	UN2526	III	3, 8	B1, IB3, T4, TP1	132	FLAMMABLE
	Fuse, detonating, metal clad, see Cord, detonating, metal clad							·

Symbols (1)	Hazardous materials descriptions and proper shipping names (2)	Hazard class or Division (3)	Identification Numbers (4)	PG (5)	Label Codes (6)	Special Provisions (§172.102) (7)	ERG Guide No.	Placard Advisory Consult §172.504 & §172.505 *Placard any quantity
	Fuse, detonating, mild effect, metal clad, see Cord, detonating, mild effect, metal clad							
	Fuse, igniter tubular metal clad	1.4G	UN0103		1.4G		114	EXPLOSIVES 1.4
	Fuse, non-detonating instantaneous or quickmatch	1.3G	UN0101		1.3G		112	EXPLOSIVES 1.3*
	Fuse, safety	1.4S	UN0105		1.4S		114	EXPLOSIVES 1.4
D	Fusee (railway or highway)	4.1	NA1325	II	4.1	381	133	FLAMMABLE SOLID
	Fusel oil	3	UN1201	II	3	IB2, T4, TP1	127	FLAMMABLE
				III	3	B1, IB3, T2, TP1	127	FLAMMABLE
	Fuses, tracer, see Tracers for ammunition							
	Fuzes, combination, percussion and time, see Fuzes, detonating (UN0257, UN0367); Fuzes, igniting (UN0317, UN0368)							
	Fuzes, detonating	1.1B	UN0106		1.1B		112	EXPLOSIVES 1.1*
	Fuzes, detonating	1.2B	UN0107		1.2B		112	EXPLOSIVES 1.2*
	Fuzes, detonating	1.4B	UN0257		1.4B	116	114	EXPLOSIVES 1.4
	Fuzes, detonating	1.4S	UN0367		1.4S	116, 347	114	EXPLOSIVES 1.4
	Fuzes, detonating, with protective features	1.1D	UN0408		1.1D		112	EXPLOSIVES 1.1*
	Fuzes, detonating, with protective features	1.2D	UN0409		1.2D		112	EXPLOSIVES 1.2*
	Fuzes, detonating, with protective features	1.4D	UN0410		1.4D	116	114	EXPLOSIVES 1.4
	Fuzes, igniting	1.3G	UN0316		1.3G		112	EXPLOSIVES 1.3*
	Fuzes, igniting	1.4G	UN0317		1.4G		114	EXPLOSIVES 1.4
	Fuzes, igniting	1.4S	UN0368		1.4S		114	EXPLOSIVES 1.4
	Galactsan trinitrate	Forbidden						
	Gallium	8	UN2803	III	8	T1, TP33	172	CORROSIVE
	Gas cartridges, (flammable) without a release device, non-refillable	2.1	UN2037		2.1		115	FLAMMABLE GAS
D	Gas identification set	2.3	NA9035		2.3	6	123	INHALATION HAZARD CLASS 2*
	Gas oil	3	UN1202	III	3	144, B1, IB3, T2, TP1	128	FLAMMABLE

Sym.	Hazardous materials description	Class/Div.	ID No.	PG	Label codes	Special provisions	Guide
G	Gas, refrigerated liquid, flammable, n.o.s. (cryogenic liquid)	2.1	UN3312		2.1	T75, TP5	115 FLAMMABLE GAS
G	Gas, refrigerated liquid, n.o.s. (cryogenic liquid)	2.2	UN3158		2.2	T75, TP5	120 NONFLAMMABLE GAS
G	Gas, refrigerated liquid, oxidizing, n.o.s. (cryogenic liquid)	2.2	UN3311		2.2, 5.1	T75, TP5, TP22	122 NONFLAMMABLE GAS
	Gas sample, non-pressurized, flammable, n.o.s., not refrigerated liquid	2.1	UN3167		2.1		115 FLAMMABLE GAS
	Gas sample, non-pressurized, toxic, flammable, n.o.s., not refrigerated liquid	2.3	UN3168		2.3, 2.1	6	119 INHALATION HAZARD CLASS 2*
	Gas sample, non-pressurized, toxic, n.o.s., not refrigerated liquid	2.3	UN3169		2.3	6	123 INHALATION HAZARD CLASS 2*
	Gasoline, casinghead, see Gasoline						
	Gasoline includes gasoline mixed with ethyl alcohol, with not more than 10% alcohol	3	UN1203	II	3	144, 177, B1, B33, IB2, T4	128 FLAMMABLE
	Gelatine, blasting, see **Explosive, blasting, type A**						
	Gelatine dynamites, see **Explosive, blasting, type A**						
	Germane	2.3	UN2192		2.3, 2.1	2	119 INHALATION HAZARD CLASS 2*
	Germane, adsorbed	2.3	UN3523		2.3, 2.1	2	173 INHALATION HAZARD CLASS 2*
	Glycerol-1,3-dinitrate	Forbidden					
	Glycerol gluconate trinitrate	Forbidden					
	Glycerol lactate trinitrate	Forbidden					
	Glycerol alpha-monochlorohydrin	6.1	UN2689	III	6.1	IB3, T4, TP1	153 POISON
	Glyceryl trinitrate, see **Nitroglycerin**, etc.						
	Glycidaldehyde	3	UN2622	II	3, 6.1	IB2, IP8, T7, TP1	131P FLAMMABLE
	Grenades, hand or rifle, with bursting charge	1.1D	UN0284		1.1D		112 EXPLOSIVES 1.1*
	Grenades, hand or rifle, with bursting charge	1.2D	UN0285		1.2D		112 EXPLOSIVES 1.2*
	Grenades, hand or rifle, with bursting charge	1.1F	UN0292		1.1F		112 EXPLOSIVES 1.1*
	Grenades, hand or rifle, with bursting charge	1.2F	UN0293		1.2F		112 EXPLOSIVES 1.2*
	Grenades, illuminating, see **Ammunition, Illuminating**, etc.						
	Grenades, practice, hand or rifle	1.4S	UN0110		1.4S		114 EXPLOSIVES 1.4

Symbols (1)	Hazardous materials descriptions and proper shipping names (2)	Hazard class or Division (3)	Identification Numbers (4)	PG (5)	Label Codes (6)	Special Provisions (§172.102) (7)	ERG Guide No.	Placard Advisory Consult §172.504 & §172.505 *Placard any quantity
	Grenades, practice, *hand or rifle*	1.3G	UN0318		1.3G		112	EXPLOSIVES 1.3*
	Grenades, practice, *hand or rifle*	1.2G	UN0372		1.2G		112	EXPLOSIVES 1.2*
	Grenades practice, *hand or rifle*	1.4G	UN0452		1.4G		114	EXPLOSIVES 1.4
	Grenades, smoke, see **Ammunition, smoke** *, etc.*							
	Guanidine nitrate	5.1	UN1467	III	5.1	A1, IB8, IP3, T1, TP33	143	OXIDIZER
	Guanyl nitrosaminoguanylidene hydrazine (dry)	Forbidden						
	Guanyl nitrosaminoguanylidene hydrazine, wetted *with not less than 30 percent water, by mass*	1.1A	UN0113		1.1A	111, 117	112	EXPLOSIVES 1.1*
	Guanyl nitrosaminoguanyltetrazene (dry)	Forbidden						
	Guanyl nitrosaminoguanyltetrazene, wetted *or* **Tetrazene, wetted** *with not less than 30 percent water or mixture of alcohol and water, by mass*	1.1A	UN0114		1.1A	111, 117	112	EXPLOSIVES 1.1*
	Gunpowder, compressed *or* **Gunpowder in pellets,** *see* **Black powder** *(UN0028)*							
	Gunpowder, granular or as a meal, see **Black powder** *(UN0027)*							
	Hafnium powder, dry	4.2	UN2545	I	4.2	W31	135	SPONTANEOUSLY COMBUSTIBLE
				II	4.2	A19, A20, IB6, IP2, N34, T3, TP33, W31	135	SPONTANEOUSLY COMBUSTIBLE
				III	4.2	B135, IB8, IP21, T1, TP33, W31	135	SPONTANEOUSLY COMBUSTIBLE
	Hafnium powder, wetted *with not less than 25 percent water (a visible excess of water must be present) (a) mechanically produced, particle size less than 53 microns; (b) chemically produced, particle size less than 840 microns*	4.1	UN1326	II	4.1	A6, A19, A20, IB6, IP2, N34, T3, TP33, W31, W40	170	FLAMMABLE SOLID
	Hand signal device, see **Signal devices, hand**							
	Hazardous substances, liquid or solid, n.o.s., see **Environmentally hazardous substances,** *etc.*							
D G	**Hazardous waste, liquid, n.o.s.**	9	NA3082	III	9	IB3, T2, TP1	171	CLASS 9

Sym	Hazardous materials descriptions	Class	ID No.	PG	Label	Special provisions	Guide	Placard
D G	Hazardous waste, solid, n.o.s.	9	NA3077	III	9	B54, IB8, IP2, T1, TP33	171	CLASS 9
	Heating oil, light	3	UN1202	III	3	B1, IB3, T2, TP1	128	FLAMMABLE
	Helium, compressed	2.2	UN1046		2.2		120	NONFLAMMABLE GAS
	Helium, refrigerated liquid (cryogenic liquid)	2.2	UN1963		2.2	T75, TP5	120	NONFLAMMABLE GAS
	Heptafluoropropane or Refrigerant gas R 227	2.2	UN3296		2.2	T50	126	NONFLAMMABLE GAS
	n-Heptaldehyde	3	UN3056	III	3	B1, IB3, T2, TP1	129	FLAMMABLE
	Heptanes	3	UN1206	II	3	IB2, T4, TP2	128	FLAMMABLE
	n-Heptene	3	UN2278	II	3	IB2, T4, TP1	128	FLAMMABLE
	Hexachloroacetone	6.1	UN2661	III	6.1	IB3, T4, TP1	153	POISON
	Hexachlorobenzene	6.1	UN2729	III	6.1	B3, IB8, IP3, T⁻, TP33	152	POISON
	Hexachlorobutadiene	6.1	UN2279	III	6.1	IB3, T4, TP1	151	POISON
	Hexachlorocyclopentadiene	6.1	UN2646	I	6.1	2, B9, B14, B32, B77, T20, TP2, TP13, TP38, TP45	151	INHALATION HAZARD CLASS 6*
	Hexachlorophene	6.1	UN2875	III	6.1	IB8, IP3, T1, TP33	151	POISON
	Hexadecyltrichlorosilane	8	UN1781	II	8	A7, B2, B6, N34, T10, TP2, TP7, TP13	156	CORROSIVE
	Hexadienes	3	UN2458	II	3	IB2, T4, TP1	130	FLAMMABLE
	Hexaethyl tetraphosphate and compressed gas mixtures	2.3	UN1612		2.3	3	123	INHALATION HAZARD CLASS 2*
	Hexaethyl tetraphosphate, liquid	6.1	UN1611	II	6.1	IB2, N76, T7, TP2	151	POISON
	Hexaethyl tetraphosphate, solid	6.1	UN1611	II	6.1	IB8, IP2, IP4, N76	151	POISON
	Hexafluoroacetone	2.3	UN2420		2.3, 8	2, B9, B14	125	INHALATION HAZARD CLASS 2*
	Hexafluoroacetone hydrate, liquid	6.1	UN2552	II	6.1	IB2, T7, TP2	151	POISON
	Hexafluoroacetone hydrate, solid	6.1	UN3436	II	6.1	IB8, IP2, IP4, ⁻3, TP33	151	POISON
	Hexafluoroethane, or Refrigerant gas R 116	2.2	UN2193		2.2		126	NONFLAMMABLE GAS
	Hexafluorophosphoric acid	8	UN1782	II	8	A7, B2, IB2, N3, N34, T8, TP2	154	CORROSIVE
	Hexafluoropropylene, compressed or Refrigerant gas R 1216	2.2	UN1858		2.2	T50	126	NONFLAMMABLE GAS
	Hexaldehyde	3	UN1207	III	3	B1, IB3, T2, TP1	130	FLAMMABLE
	Hexamethylene diisocyanate	6.4	UN2281	II	6.1	IB2, T7, TP2, TP13	156	POISON

Symbols (1)	Hazardous materials descriptions and proper shipping names (2)	Hazard class or Division (3)	Identification Numbers (4)	PG (5)	Label Codes (6)	Special Provisions (§172.102) (7)	ERG Guide No.	Placard Advisory Consult §172.504 & §172.505 *Placard any quantity
	Hexamethylene triperoxide diamine (dry)	Forbidden						
	Hexamethylenediamine, solid	8	UN2280	III	8	IB8, IP3, T1, TP33	153	CORROSIVE
	Hexamethylenediamine solution	8	UN1783	II	8	IB2, T7, TP2	153	CORROSIVE
				III	8	IB3, T4, TP1	153	CORROSIVE
	Hexamethyleneimine	3	UN2493	II	3, 8	IB2, T7, TP1	132	FLAMMABLE
	Hexamethylenetetramine	4.1	UN1328	III	4.1	A1, IB8, IP3, T1, TP33	133	FLAMMABLE SOLID
	Hexamethylol benzene hexanitrate	Forbidden						
	Hexanes	3	UN1208	II	3	IB2, T4, TP2	128	FLAMMABLE
	2,2',4,4',6,6'-Hexanitro-3,3'-dihydroxyazobenzene (dry)	Forbidden						
	Hexanitroazoxy benzene	Forbidden						
	N,N'-(hexanitrodiphenyl) ethylene dinitramine (dry)	Forbidden						
	Hexanitrodiphenyl urea	Forbidden						
	2,2',3,4,4',6-Hexanitrodiphenylamine	Forbidden						
	Hexanitrodiphenylamine or Dipicrylamine or Hexyl	1.1D	UN0079		1.1D		112	EXPLOSIVES 1.1*
	2,3',4,4',6,6'-Hexanitrodiphenylether	Forbidden						
	Hexanitroethane	Forbidden						
	Hexanitrooxanilide	Forbidden						
	Hexanitrostilbene	1.1D	UN0392		1.1D		112	EXPLOSIVES 1.1*
	Hexanoic acid, see Corrosive liquids, n.o.s.							
	Hexanols	3	UN2282	III	3	B1, IB3, T2, TP1	129	FLAMMABLE
	1-Hexene	3	UN2370	II	3	IB2, T4, TP1	128	FLAMMABLE
	Hexogen and cyclotetramethylenetetranitramine mixtures, wetted or desensitized see RDX and HMX mixtures, wetted or desensitized etc.							
	Hexogen and HMX mixtures, wetted or desensitized see RDX and HMX mixtures, wetted or desensitized etc.							

Hazardous materials descriptions and proper shipping names	Hazard class or Division	Identification Numbers	PG	Label Codes	Special provisions	Guide No.	Symbol
Hexogen and octogen mixtures, wetted or desensitized see RDX and HMX mixtures, wetted or desensitized etc.							
Hexogen, see Cyclotrimethylenetrinitramine, etc.							
Hexolite, or Hexotol dry or wetted with less than 15 percent water, by mass	1.1D	UN0118		1.1D		112	EXPLOSIVES 1.1*
Hexotonal	1.1D	UN0393		1.1D		112	EXPLOSIVES 1.1*
Hexyl, see Hexanitrodiphenylamine							
Hexyltrichlorosilane	8	UN1784	II	8	A7, B2, B6, N34, T10, TP2, TP7, TP13	156	CORROSIVE
High explosives, see individual explosives' entries							
HMX, see Cyclotetramethylenete tranitramine, etc.							
Hydrazine, anhydrous	8	UN2029	I	8, 3, 6.1	A7, A10, B7, B16, B53	132	CORROSIVE
Hydrazine aqueous solution, flammable with more than 37% hydrazine, by mass	8	UN3484	I	8, 3, 6.1	B16, B53, T10, TP2, TP13	132	CORROSIVE
Hydrazine aqueous solution, with more than 37% hydrazine, by mass	8	UN2030	I	8, 6.1	B16, B53, T10, TP2, TP13	153	CORROSIVE
			II	8, 6.1	B16, B53, IB2, T7, TP2, TP13	153	CORROSIVE
			III	8, 6.1	B16, B53, IB3, T4, TP1	153	CORROSIVE
Hydrazine, aqueous solution, with not more than 37 percent hydrazine, by mass	6.1	UN3293	III	6.1	IB3, T4, TP1	152	POISON
Hydrazine azide	Forbidden						
Hydrazine chlorate	Forbidden						
Hydrazine dicarbonic acid diazide	Forbidden						
Hydrazine perchlorate	Forbidden						
Hydrazine selenate	Forbidden						
Hydriodic acid, anhydrous, see Hydrogen iodide, anhydrous							
Hydriodic acid	8	UN1787	II	8	A3, B2, IB2, N41, T7, TP2	154	CORROSIVE
			III	8	IB3, T4, TP1	154	CORROSIVE
Hydrobromic acid, anhydrous, see Hydrogen bromide, anhydrous							
Hydrobromic acid, with more than 49-percent hydrobromic acid	8	UN1788	II	8	B2, B15, IB2, N41, T7, TP2	154	CORROSIVE

Symbols (1)	Hazardous materials descriptions and proper shipping names (2)	Hazard class or Division (3)	Identification Numbers (4)	PG (5)	Label Codes (6)	Special Provisions (§172.102) (7)	ERG Guide No.	Placard Advisory Consult §172.504 & §172.505 *Placard any quantity
				III	8	IB3, T4, TP1	154	CORROSIVE
	Hydrobromic acid, with not more than 49 percent hydrobromic acid	8	UN1788	II	8	A3, B2, B15, IB2, N41, T7, TP2	154	CORROSIVE
				III	8	A3, IB3, T4, TP1	154	CORROSIVE
	Hydrocarbon gas mixture, compressed, n.o.s.	2.1	UN1964		2.1		115	FLAMMABLE GAS
	Hydrocarbon gas mixture, liquefied, n.o.s.	2.1	UN1965		2.1	T50	115	FLAMMABLE GAS
	Hydrocarbons, liquid, n.o.s.	3	UN3295	I	3	144, T11, TP1, TP8, TP28	128	FLAMMABLE
				II	3	144, IB2, T7, TP1, TP8, TP28	128	FLAMMABLE
				III	3	144, B1, IB3, T4, TP1, TP29	128	FLAMMABLE
	Hydrochloric acid, anhydrous, see Hydrogen chloride, anhydrous							
	Hydrochloric acid	8	UN1789	II	8	386, A3, B3, B15, B133, IB2, N41, T8, TP2	157	CORROSIVE
				III	8	A3, IB3, T4, TP1	157	CORROSIVE
	Hydrocyanic acid, anhydrous, see Hydrogen cyanide etc.							
	Hydrocyanic acid, aqueous solutions or Hydrogen cyanide, aqueous solutions with not more than 20 percent hydrogen cyanide	6.1	UN1613	I	6.1	2, B61, B65, B77, B82, T20, TP2, TP13	154	INHALATION HAZARD CLASS 6*
D	Hydrocyanic acid, aqueous solutions with less than 5 percent hydrogen cyanide	6.1	NA1613	II	6.1	IB1, T14, TP2, TP13, TP27	154	POISON
	Hydrocyanic acid, liquefied, see Hydrogen cyanide, etc.							
	Hydrocyanic acid (prussic), unstabilized	Forbidden						
	Hydrofluoric acid and Sulfuric acid mixtures	8	UN1786	I	8, 6.1	A7, B15, B23, N5, N34, T10, TP2, TP13	157	CORROSIVE
	Hydrofluoric acid, anhydrous, see Hydrogen fluoride, anhydrous							
	Hydrofluoric acid, with more than 60 percent strength	8	UN1790	I	8, 6.1	A7, B4, B15, B23, N5, N34, T10, TP2, TP13	157	CORROSIVE

Name and description	Class	ID No.	PG	Label codes	Special provisions	ERG	Placard
Hydrofluoric acid, with not more than 60 percent strength	8	UN1790	II	8, 6.1	A7, B15, IB2, N5, N34, T8, TP2	157	CORROSIVE
Hydrofluoroboric acid, see Fluoroboric acid							
Hydrofluorosilicic acid, see Fluorosilicic acid							
Hydrogen and Methane mixtures, compressed	2.1	UN2034		2.1	N89	115	FLAMMABLE GAS
Hydrogen bromide, anhydrous	2.3	UN1048		2.3, 8	3, B14, N86, N89	125	INHALATION HAZARD CLASS 2*
Hydrogen chloride, anhydrous	2.3	UN1050		2.3, 8	3, N86, N89	125	INHALATION HAZARD CLASS 2*
Hydrogen chloride, refrigerated liquid	2.3	UN2186		2.3, 8	3, B6	125	INHALATION HAZARD CLASS 2*
Hydrogen, compressed	2.1	UN1049		2.1	N89	115	FLAMMABLE GAS
Hydrogen cyanide, solution in alcohol with not more than 45 percent hydrogen cyanide	6.1	UN3294	I	6.1, 3	2, B9, B14, B32, T20, TP2, TP13, TP38, TP44	131	INHALATION HAZARD CLASS 6*
Hydrogen cyanide, stabilized with less than 3 percent water	6.1	UN1051	I	6.1, 3	1, 387, B35, B61, B65, B77, B82	117P	INHALATION HAZARD CLASS 6*
Hydrogen cyanide, stabilized, with less than 3 percent water and absorbed in a porous inert material	6.1	UN1614	I	6.1	5, 387	152	POISON
Hydrogen fluoride, anhydrous	8	UN1052	I	8, 6.1	3, B7, B46, B77, N86, T10, TP2	125	CORROSIVE, INHALATION HAZARD CLASS 6*
Hydrogen in a metal hydride storage system or **Hydrogen in a metal hydride storage system contained in equipment** or **Hydrogen in a metal hydride storage system packed with equipment**	2.1	UN3468		2.1	167	115	FLAMMABLE GAS
Hydrogen iodide, anhydrous	2.3	UN2197		2.3, 8	3, B14, N86, N89	125	INHALATION HAZARD CLASS 2*
Hydrogen iodide solution, see Hydriodic acid							
Hydrogen peroxide and peroxyacetic acid mixtures, stabilized with acids, water, and not more than 5 percent peroxyacetic acid	5.1	UN3149	II	5.1, 8	145, A2, A3, B53, IB2, IP5, IT7, TP2, TP6, TP24	140	OXIDIZER
Hydrogen peroxide, aqueous solutions with more than 40 percent but not more than 60 percent hydrogen peroxide (stabilized as necessary)	5.1	UN2014	II	5.1, 8	12, A60, B53, B80, B81, B85, IB2, IP5, T7, TP2, TP6, TP24, TP37	140	OXIDIZER

Symbols (1)	Hazardous materials descriptions and proper shipping names (2)	Hazard class or Division (3)	Identification Numbers (4)	PG (5)	Label Codes (6)	Special Provisions (§172.102) (7)	ERG Guide No.	Placard Advisory Consult §172.504 & §172.505 *Placard any quantity
	Hydrogen peroxide, aqueous solutions with not less than 20 percent but not more than 40 percent hydrogen peroxide (stabilized as necessary)	5.1	UN2014	II	5.1, 8	A2, A3, B53, IB2, IP5, T7, TP2, TP6, TP24, TP37	140	OXIDIZER
	Hydrogen peroxide, aqueous solutions with not less than 8 percent but less than 20 percent hydrogen peroxide (stabilized as necessary)	5.1	UN2984	III	5.1	A1, IB2, IP5, T4, TP1, TP6, TP24, TP37	140	OXIDIZER
	Hydrogen peroxide, stabilized or Hydrogen peroxide aqueous solutions, stabilized with more than 60 percent hydrogen peroxide	5.1	UN2015	I	5.1, 8	12, B53, B80, B81, B85, T9, TP2, TP6, TP24, TP37	143	OXIDIZER
	Hydrogen, refrigerated liquid *(cryogenic liquid)*	2.1	UN1966		2.1	T75, TP5	115	FLAMMABLE GAS
	Hydrogen selenide, adsorbed	2.3	UN3526		2.3, 2.1	1	173	INHALATION HAZARD CLASS 2*
	Hydrogen selenide, anhydrous	2.3	UN2202		2.3, 2.1	1	117	INHALATION HAZARD CLASS 2*
	Hydrogen sulfate, see Sulfuric acid							
	Hydrogen sulfide	2.3	UN1053		2.3, 2.1	2, B9, B14, N89	117	INHALATION HAZARD CLASS 2*
	Hydrogendifluoride, solid, n.o.s.	8	UN1740	II	8	IB8, IP2, IP4, N3, N34, T3, TP33	154	CORROSIVE
				III	8	IB8, IP3, N3, N34, T1, TP33	154	CORROSIVE
	Hydrogendifluorides, solution, n.o.s.	8	UN3471	II	8, 6.1	IB2, T7, TP2	154	CORROSIVE
				III	8, 6.1	IB3, T4, TP1	154	CORROSIVE
	Hydrosilicofluoric acid, see Fluorosilicic acid							
	1-Hydroxybenzotriazole, anhydrous, *dry or wetted with less than 20 percent water, by mass*	1.3C	UN0508		1.3C		112	EXPLOSIVES 1.3*
	1-Hydroxybenzotriazole, monohydrate	4.1	UN3474	I	4.1	N90	113	FLAMMABLE SOLID
	Hydroxyl amine iodide	Forbidden						
	Hydroxylamine sulfate	8	UN2865	III	8	IB8, IP3, T1, TP33	154	CORROSIVE

Symbol	Hazardous materials descriptions and proper shipping names	Hazard class or Division	Identification Numbers	PG	Label Codes	Special provisions	Guide No.	Placard
	Hypochlorite solutions	8	UN1791	II	8	148, A7, B2, B15, IB2, IP5, N34, T7, TP2, TP24	154	CORROSIVE
		8		III	8	386, IB3, N34, T4, TP2, TP24	154	CORROSIVE
G	Hypochlorites, Inorganic, n.o.s.	5.1	UN3212	II	5.1	349, A9, IB8, IP2, IP4, T3, TP33	140	OXIDIZER
	Hyponitrous acid	Forbidden						
	Igniter fuse, metal clad, see Fuse, igniter, tubular, metal clad							
	Igniters	1.1G	UN0121		1.1G		112	EXPLOSIVES 1.1*
	Igniters	1.2G	UN0314		1.2G		112	EXPLOSIVES 1.2*
	Igniters	1.3G	UN0315		1.3G		112	EXPLOSIVES 1.3*
	Igniters	1.4G	UN0325		1.4G		114	EXPLOSIVES 1.4
	Igniters	1.4S	UN0454		1.4S		114	EXPLOSIVES 1.4
	3,3'-Iminodipropylamine	8	UN2269	III	8	IB3, T4, TP2	153	CORROSIVE
G	Infectious substances, affecting animals only	6.2	UN2900		6.2	A82	158	NONE
G	Infectious substances, affecting humans	6.2	UN2814		6.2	A82	158	NONE
	Inflammable, see Flammable							
	Initiating explosives (dry)	Forbidden						
	Inositol hexanitrate (dry)	Forbidden						
G	Insecticide gases, n.o.s.	2.2	UN1968		2.2	T50	126	NONFLAMMABLE GAS
G	Insecticide gases, flammable, n.o.s.	2.1	UN3354		2.1	1	115	FLAMMABLE GAS
G	Insecticide gases, toxic, flammable, n.o.s. *Inhalation hazard Zone A*	2.3	UN3355		2.3, 2.1	2, B9, B14	119	INHALATION HAZARD CLASS 2*
G	Insecticide gases, toxic, flammable, n.o.s. *Inhalation hazard Zone B*	2.3	UN3355		2.3, 2.1	3, B14	119	INHALATION HAZARD CLASS 2*
G	Insecticide gases, toxic, flammable, n.o.s. *Inhalation hazard Zone C*	2.3	UN3355		2.3, 2.1	4	119	INHALATION HAZARD CLASS 2*
G	Insecticide gases, toxic, flammable, n.o.s. *Inhalation hazard Zone D*	2.3	UN3355		2.3, 2.1	3	119	INHALATION HAZARD CLASS 2*
G	Insecticide gases, toxic, n.o.s.	2.3	UN1967		2.3		123	INHALATION HAZARD CLASS 2*
	Inulin trinitrate (dry)	Forbidden						

Symbols (1)	Hazardous materials descriptions and proper shipping names (2)	Hazard class or Division (3)	Identification Numbers (4)	PG (5)	Label Codes (6)	Special Provisions (§172.102) (7)	ERG Guide No.	Placard Advisory Consult §172.504 & §172.505 *Placard any quantity
+	**Iodine**	8	UN3495	III	8, 6.1	IB8, IP3, T1, TP33	154	CORROSIVE
	Iodine azide (dry)	Forbidden						
	Iodine monochloride, liquid	8	UN3498	II	8	IB2, T7, TP2	157	CORROSIVE
	Iodine monochloride, solid	8	UN1792	II	8	B6, IB8, IP2, IP4, N41, T7, TP2	157	CORROSIVE
	Iodine pentafluoride	5.1	UN2495	I	5.1, 6.1, 8		144	OXIDIZER
	2-Iodobutane	3	UN2390	II	3	IB2, T4, TP1	129	FLAMMABLE
	Iodomethylpropanes	3	UN2391	II	3	IB2, T4, TP1	129	FLAMMABLE
	Iodopropanes	3	UN2392	III	3	B1, IB3, T2, TP1	129	FLAMMABLE
	Iodoxy compounds (dry)	Forbidden						
	Iridium nitratopentamine iridium nitrate	Forbidden						
	Iron chloride, see Ferric chloride							
	Iron oxide, spent, or **Iron sponge, spent** *obtained from coal gas purification*	4.2	UN1376	III	4.2	B18, B134, IB8, IP21, T1, TP33, W100	135	SPONTANEOUSLY COMBUSTIBLE
	Iron pentacarbonyl	6.1	UN1994	I	6.1, 3	1, B9, B14, B30, B77, T22, TP2, TP13, TP38, TP44	136	INHALATION HAZARD CLASS 6*
	Iron sesquichloride, see Ferric chloride							
	Irritating material, see Tear gas substances, etc.							
	Isobutane, *see also* **Petroleum gases, liquefied**	2.1	UN1969		2.1	19, T50	115	FLAMMABLE GAS
	Isobutanol or **Isobutyl alcohol**	3	UN1212	III	3	B1, IB3, T2, TP1	129	FLAMMABLE
	Isobutyl acetate	3	UN1213	II	3	IB2, T4, TP1	129	FLAMMABLE
	Isobutyl acrylate, stabilized	3	UN2527	III	3	387, B1, IB3, T2, TP1	129P	FLAMMABLE
	Isobutyl alcohol, see Isobutanol							
	Isobutyl aldehyde, see Isobutyraldehyde							
	Isobutyl formate	3	UN2393	II	3	IB2, T4, TP1	129	FLAMMABLE
	Isobutyl isobutyrate	3	UN2528	III	3	B1, IB3, T2, TP1	130	FLAMMABLE

Symbol	Hazardous materials descriptions and proper shipping names	Hazard class	ID No.	PG	Label codes	Special provisions	ERG	
+	Isobutyl isocyanate	6.1	UN2486	I	6.1, 3	1, B9, B14, E30, T20, TP2, TP13, TP27	155P	INHALATION HAZARD CLASS 6*
	Isobutyl methacrylate, stabilized	3	UN2283	III	3	387, B1, IB3, T2, TP1	130P	FLAMMABLE
	Isobutyl propionate	3	UN2394	III	3	B1, IB3, T2, TP1	129	FLAMMABLE
	Isobutylamine	3	UN1214	II	3, 8	IB2, T7, TP1	132	FLAMMABLE
	Isobutylene, see also Petroleum gases, liquefied	2.1	UN1055		2.1	19, T50	115	FLAMMABLE GAS
	Isobutyraldehyde or Isobutyl aldehyde	3	UN2045	II	3	IB2, T4, TP1	130	FLAMMABLE
	Isobutyric acid	3	UN2529	III	3, 8	B1, IB3, T4, TP1	132	FLAMMABLE
	Isobutyronitrile	3	UN2284	II	3, 6.1	IB2, T7, TP2, TP13	131	FLAMMABLE
	Isobutyryl chloride	3	UN2395	II	3, 8	IB1, T7, TP2	132	FLAMMABLE
G	Isocyanates, flammable, toxic, n.o.s. or Isocyanate solutions, flammable, toxic, n.o.s. *flash point less than 23 degrees C*	3	UN2478	II	3, 6.1	5, A3, A7, IB2, T11, TP2, TP13, TP27, W31	155	FLAMMABLE, INHALATION HAZARD CLASS 6*
				III		5, A3, A7, IB3, T7, TP1, TP13, TP28, W31	155	FLAMMABLE, INHALATION HAZARD CLASS 6*
G	Isocyanates, toxic, flammable, n.o.s. or Isocyanate solutions, toxic, flammable, n.o.s., *flash point not less than 23 degrees C but not more than 61 degrees C and boiling point less than 300 degrees C*	6.1	UN3080	II	6.1, 3	IB2, T11, TP2, TP13, TP27	155	POISON
G	Isocyanates, toxic, n.o.s. or Isocyanate solutions, toxic, n.o.s., *flash point more than 61 degrees C and boiling point less than 300 degrees C*	6.1	UN2206	II	6.1	IB2, T11, TP2, TP13, TP27	155	POISON
				III	6.1	IB3, T7, TP1, TP13, TP28	155	POISON
	Isocyanatobenzotrifluorides	6.1	UN2285	II	6.1, 3	5, IB2, T7, TP2	156	INHALATION HAZARD CLASS 6*
	Isoheptenes	3	UN2287	II	3	IB2, T4, TP1	128	FLAMMABLE
	Isohexenes	3	UN2288	II	3	IB2, IP8, T11, TP1	128	FLAMMABLE
	Isooctane, see Octanes							
	Isooctenes	3	UN1216	II	3	IB2, T4, TP1	128	FLAMMABLE
	Isopentane, see Pentane							
	Isopentanoic acid, see Corrosive liquids, n.o.s.							

Symbols (1)	Hazardous materials descriptions and proper shipping names (2)	Hazard class or Division (3)	Identification Numbers (4)	PG (5)	Label Codes (6)	Special Provisions (§172.102) (7)	ERG Guide No.	Placard Advisory Consult §172.504 & §172.505 *Placard any quantity
	Isopentenes	3	UN2371	I	3	T11, TP2	128	FLAMMABLE
	Isophorone diisocyanate	6.1	UN2290	III	6.1	IB3, T4, TP2	156	POISON
	Isophoronediamine	8	UN2289	III	8	IB3, T4, TP1	153	CORROSIVE
	Isoprene, stabilized	3	UN1218	I	3	387, T11, TP2	130P	FLAMMABLE
	Isopropanol or Isopropyl alcohol	3	UN1219	II	3	IB2, T4, TP1	129	FLAMMABLE
	Isopropenyl acetate	3	UN2403	II	3	IB2, T4, TP1	129P	FLAMMABLE
	Isopropenylbenzene	3	UN2303	III	3	B1, IB3, T2, TP1	128	FLAMMABLE
	Isopropyl acetate	3	UN1220	II	3	IB2, T4, TP1	129	FLAMMABLE
	Isopropyl acid phosphate	8	UN1793	III	8	IB2, T4, TP1	153	CORROSIVE
	Isopropyl alcohol, see Isopropanol							
	Isopropyl butyrate	3	UN2405	III	3	B1, IB3, T2, TP1	129	FLAMMABLE
	Isopropyl chloroacetate	3	UN2947	III	3	B1, IB3, T2, TP1	155	FLAMMABLE
	Isopropyl chloroformate	6.1	UN2407	I	6.1, 3, 8	2, B9, B14, B32, B77, T20, TP2, TP13, TP38, TP44	155	INHALATION HAZARD CLASS 6*
	Isopropyl 2-chloropropionate	3	UN2934	III	3	B1, IB3, T2, TP1	129	FLAMMABLE
	Isopropyl isobutyrate	3	UN2406	II	3	IB2, T4, TP1	127	FLAMMABLE
+	Isopropyl isocyanate	6.1	UN2483	I	6.1, 3	1, B9, B14, B30, T20, TP2, TP13, TP38, TP44	155P	INHALATION HAZARD CLASS 6*
	Isopropyl mercaptan, see Propanethiols							
	Isopropyl nitrate	3	UN1222	II	3	IB9	130	FLAMMABLE
	Isopropyl phosphoric acid, see Isopropyl acid phosphate							
	Isopropyl propionate	3	UN2409	II	3	IB2, T4, TP1	129	FLAMMABLE
	Isopropylamine	3	UN1221	I	3, 8	T11, TP2	132	FLAMMABLE
	Isopropylbenzene	3	UN1918	III	3	B1, IB3, T2, TP1	130	FLAMMABLE
	Isopropylcumyl hydroperoxide, with more than 72 percent in solution	Forbidden						

Sym	Hazardous materials descriptions and proper shipping names	Hazard class or Division	ID Numbers	PG	Label Codes	Special provisions	Guide	Hazard name
	Isosorbide dinitrate mixture with not less than 60 percent lactose, mannose, starch or calcium hydrogen phosphate	4.1	UN2907	II	4.1	IB6, IP2, N85	133	FLAMMABLE SOLID
	Isosorbide-5-mononitrate	4.1	UN3251	III	4.1	66, 159, IB8	133	FLAMMABLE SOLID
	Isothiocyanic acid	Forbidden						
	Jet fuel, see Fuel aviation, turbine engine							
D	Jet perforating guns, charged oil well, with detonator	1.1D	NA0124		1.1D	55, 56	112	EXPLOSIVES 1.1*
D	Jet perforating guns, charged oil well, with detonator	1.4D	NA0494		1.4D	55, 56	114	EXPLOSIVES 1.4
	Jet perforating guns, charged, oil well, without detonator	1.4D	UN0494		1.4D	55, 114	114	EXPLOSIVES 1.4
	Jet perforating guns, charged oil well, without detonator	1.1D	UN0124		1.1D	55	112	EXPLOSIVES 1.1*
	Jet perforators, see Charges, shaped, etc.							
	Jet tappers, without detonator, see Charges, shaped, etc.							
	Jet thrust igniters, for rocket motors or Jato, see Igniters							
	Jet thrust unit (Jato), see Rocket motors							
	Kerosene	3	UN1223	III	3	144, B1, IB3, T2, TP2	128	FLAMMABLE
G	Ketones, liquid, n.o.s.	3	UN1224	I	3	T11, TP1, TP6, TP27	127	FLAMMABLE
				II	3	IB2, T7, TP1, TP8, TP28	127	FLAMMABLE
				III	3	B1, IB3, T4, TP1, TP29	127	FLAMMABLE
	Krill meal	4.2	UN3497	II	4.2	155, IB6, IP2, T3, TP33	133	SPONTANEOUSLY COMBUSTIBLE
				III	4.2	155, IB8, IP3, T1, TP33	133	SPONTANEOUSLY COMBUSTIBLE
	Krypton, compressed	2.2	UN1056		2.2		120	NONFLAMMABLE GAS
	Krypton, refrigerated liquid (cryogenic liquid)	2.2	UN1970		2.2	T75, TP5	120	NONFLAMMABLE GAS
	Lacquer base or lacquer chips, nitrocellulose, dry, see Nitrocellulose, etc. (UN2557)							
	Lacquer base or lacquer chips, plastic, wet with alcohol or solvent, see Nitrocellulose (UN2059, UN2555, UN2556, UN2557) or Paint etc. (UN1263)							
	Lead acetate	6.1	UN1616	III	6.1	IB8, IP3, T1, T33	151	POISON
	Lead arsenates	6.1	UN1617	II	6.1	IB8, IP2, IP4, T3, TP33	151	POISON
	Lead arsenites	6.1	UN1618	II	6.1	IB8, IP2, IP4, T3, TP33	151	POISON

Symbols (1)	Hazardous materials descriptions and proper shipping names (2)	Hazard class or Division (3)	Identification Numbers (4)	PG (5)	Label Codes (6)	Special Provisions (§172.102) (7)	ERG Guide No.	Placard Advisory Consult §172.504 & §172.505 *Placard any quantity
	Lead azide (dry)	Forbidden						
	Lead azide, wetted with not less than 20 percent water or mixture of alcohol and water, by mass	1.1A	UN0129		1.1A	111, 117	112	EXPLOSIVES 1.1*
G	Lead compounds, soluble, n.o.s.	6.1	UN2291	III	6.1	138, IB8, IP3, T1, TP33	151	POISON
	Lead cyanide	6.1	UN1620	II	6.1	IB8, IP2, IP4, T3, TP33	151	POISON
	Lead dioxide	5.1	UN1872	III	5.1	A1, IB8, IP3, T1, TP33	140	OXIDIZER
	Lead dross, see Lead sulfate, with more than 3 percent free acid							
	Lead nitrate	5.1	UN1469	II	5.1, 6.1	IB8, IP2, IP4, T3, TP33	141	OXIDIZER
	Lead nitroresorcinate (dry)	Forbidden						
	Lead perchlorate, solid	5.1	UN1470	II	5.1, 6.1	IB6, IP2, T3, TP33	141	OXIDIZER
	Lead perchlorate, solution	5.1	UN3408	II	5.1, 6.1	IB2, T4, TP1	141	OXIDIZER
				III	5.1, 6.1	IB2, T4, TP1	141	OXIDIZER
	Lead peroxide, see Lead dioxide							
	Lead phosphite, dibasic	4.1	UN2989	II	4.1	IB8, IP2, IP4, T3, TP33	133	FLAMMABLE SOLID
				III	4.1	IB8, IP3, T1, TP33	133	FLAMMABLE SOLID
	Lead picrate (dry)	Forbidden						
	Lead styphnate (dry)	Forbidden						
	Lead styphnate, wetted or Lead trinitroresorcinate, wetted with not less than 20 percent water or mixture of alcohol and water, by mass	1.1A	UN0130		1.1A	111, 117	112	EXPLOSIVES 1.1*
	Lead sulfate with more than 3 percent free acid	8	UN1794	II	8	IB8, IP2, IP4, T3, TP33	154	CORROSIVE
	Lead trinitroresorcinate, see Lead styphnate, etc.							
	Life-saving appliances, not self inflating containing dangerous goods as equipment	9	UN3072		None	182	171	CLASS 9

Symbol	Hazardous materials descriptions and proper shipping names	Hazard class	ID No.	PG	Label Codes	Special Provisions	Guide	Placard
	Life-saving appliances, self-inflating	9	UN2990	9	None	338	171	CLASS 9
	Lighter refills containing flammable gas not exceeding 4 fluid ounces (7.22 cubic inches) and 65 grams of flammable gas	2.1	UN1057	2.1		169	115	FLAMMABLE GAS
	Lighter replacement cartridges containing liquefied petroleum gases see **Lighter refills** containing flammable gas, Etc.							
	Lighters *containing flammable gas*	2.1	UN1057	2.1		168	115	FLAMMABLE GAS
	Lighters, fuse	1.4S	UN0131	1.4S		115	114	EXPLOSIVES 1.4
	Lighters, new or empty, purged of all residual fuel and vapors					168		
	Lighters, non-pressurized, containing flammable liquid	3	NA1057	II	3	168	128	FLAMMABLE
	Lime, unslaked, see Calcium oxide							
G	**Liquefied gas, flammable, n.o.s.**	2.1	UN3161	2.1		T50	115	FLAMMABLE GAS
G	**Liquefied gas, n.o.s.**	2.2	UN3163	2.2		T50	126	NONFLAMMABLE GAS
G	**Liquefied gas, oxidizing, n.o.s.**	2.2	UN3157	2.2, 5.1		A14	122	NONFLAMMABLE GAS
G I	**Liquefied gas, toxic, corrosive, n.o.s.** *Inhalation Hazard Zone A*	2.3	UN3308	2.3, 8		1	125	INHALATION HAZARD CLASS 2*
G I	**Liquefied gas, toxic, corrosive, n.o.s.** *Inhalation Hazard Zone B*	2.3	UN3308	2.3, 8		2, B9, B14	125	INHALATION HAZARD CLASS 2*
G I	**Liquefied gas, toxic, corrosive, n.o.s.** *Inhalation Hazard Zone C*	2.3	UN3308	2.3, 8		3, B14	125	INHALATION HAZARD CLASS 2*
G I	**Liquefied gas, toxic, corrosive, n.o.s.** *Inhalation Hazard Zone D*	2.3	UN3308	2.3, 8		4	125	INHALATION HAZARD CLASS 2*
G I	**Liquefied gas, toxic, flammable, corrosive, n.o.s.** *Inhalation Hazard Zone A*	2.3	UN3309	2.3, 2.1, 8		1	119	INHALATION HAZARD CLASS 2*
G I	**Liquefied gas, toxic, flammable, corrosive, n.o.s.** *Inhalation Hazard Zone B*	2.3	UN3309	2.3, 2.1, 8		2, B9, B14	119	INHALATION HAZARD CLASS 2*
G I	**Liquefied gas, toxic, flammable, corrosive, n.o.s.** *Inhalation Hazard Zone C*	2.3	UN3309	2.3, 2.1, 8		3, B14	119	INHALATION HAZARD CLASS 2*
G I	**Liquefied gas, toxic, flammable, corrosive, n.o.s.** *Inhalation Hazard Zone D*	2.3	UN3309	2.3, 2.1, 8		4	119	INHALATION HAZARD CLASS 2*
G	**Liquefied gas, toxic, flammable, n.o.s.** *Inhalation Hazard Zone A*	2.3	UN3160	2.3, 2.1		1	119	INHALATION HAZARD CLASS 2*

Sym-bols (1)	Hazardous materials descriptions and proper shipping names (2)	Hazard class or Division (3)	Identifica-tion Numbers (4)	PG (5)	Label Codes (6)	Special Provisions (§172.102) (7)	ERG Guide No.	Placard Advisory Consult §172.504 & §172.505 *Placard any quantity
G	Liquefied gas, toxic, flammable, n.o.s. *Inhalation Hazard Zone B*	2.3	UN3150		2.3, 2.1	2, B9, B14	119	INHALATION HAZARD CLASS 2*
G	Liquefied gas, toxic, flammable, n.o.s. *Inhalation Hazard Zone C*	2.3	UN3160		2.3, 2.1	3, B14	119	INHALATION HAZARD CLASS 2*
G	Liquefied gas, toxic, flammable, n.o.s. *Inhalation Hazard Zone D*	2.3	UN3160		2.3, 2.1	4	119	INHALATION HAZARD CLASS 2*
G	Liquefied gas, toxic, n.o.s. *Inhalation Hazard Zone A*	2.3	UN3162		2.3	1	123	INHALATION HAZARD CLASS 2*
G	Liquefied gas, toxic, n.o.s. *Inhalation Hazard Zone B*	2.3	UN3162		2.3	2, B9, B14	123	INHALATION HAZARD CLASS 2*
G	Liquefied gas, toxic, n.o.s. *Inhalation Hazard Zone C*	2.3	UN3162		2.3	3, B14	123	INHALATION HAZARD CLASS 2*
G	Liquefied gas, toxic, n.o.s. *Inhalation Hazard Zone D*	2.3	UN3162		2.3	4	123	INHALATION HAZARD CLASS 2*
G I	Liquefied gas, toxic, oxidizing, corrosive, n.o.s. *Inhalation Hazard Zone A*	2.3	UN3310		2.3, 5.1, 8	1	124	INHALATION HAZARD CLASS 2*
G I	Liquefied gas, toxic, oxidizing, corrosive, n.o.s. *Inhalation Hazard Zone B*	2.3	UN3310		2.3, 5.1, 8	2, B9, B14	124	INHALATION HAZARD CLASS 2*
G I	Liquefied gas, toxic, oxidizing, corrosive, n.o.s. *Inhalation Hazard Zone C*	2.3	UN3310		2.3, 5.1, 8	3, B14	124	INHALATION HAZARD CLASS 2*
G I	Liquefied gas, toxic, oxidizing, corrosive, n.o.s. *Inhalation Hazard Zone D*	2.3	UN3310		2.3, 5.1, 8	4	124	INHALATION HAZARD CLASS 2*
G	Liquefied gas, toxic, oxidizing, n.o.s. *Inhalation Hazard Zone A*	2.3	UN3307		2.3, 5.1	1	124	INHALATION HAZARD CLASS 2*
G	Liquefied gas, toxic, oxidizing, n.o.s. *Inhalation Hazard Zone B*	2.3	UN3307		2.3, 5.1	2, B9, B14	124	INHALATION HAZARD CLASS 2*
G	Liquefied gas, toxic, oxidizing, n.o.s. *Inhalation Hazard Zone C*	2.3	UN3307		2.3, 5.1	3, B14	124	INHALATION HAZARD CLASS 2*
G	Liquefied gas, toxic, oxidizing, n.o.s. *Inhalation Hazard Zone D*	2.3	UN3307		2.3, 5.1	4	124	INHALATION HAZARD CLASS 2*

Hazardous materials descriptions	Hazard class	ID number	PG	Label codes	Special provisions	Guide No.	Label
Liquefied gases, non-flammable charged with nitrogen, carbon dioxide or air	2.2	UN1058		2.2		120	NONFLAMMABLE GAS
Liquefied hydrocarbon gas, see Hydrocarbon gas mixture, liquefied, n.o.s.							
Liquefied natural gas, see Methane, etc. (UN1972)							
Liquefied petroleum gas, see Petroleum gases, liquefied							
Lithium	4.3	UN1415	I	4.3	A7, A19, IB4, IP1, N45, T9, TP7, TP33, W31	138	DANGEROUS WHEN WET*
Lithium acetylide ethylenediamine complex, see Water reactive solid, etc.							
Lithium aluminum hydride	4.3	UN1410	I	4.3	A19, W31	138	DANGEROUS WHEN WET*
Lithium aluminum hydride, ethereal	4.3	UN1411	I	4.3, 3	A2, A11, N34	138	DANGEROUS WHEN WET*
Lithium batteries installed in cargo transport unit *lithium ion batteries*	9	UN3536		9	389	147	CLASS 9
Lithium batteries installed in cargo transport unit *lithium metal batteries*	9	UN3536		9	389	138	CLASS 9
Lithium borohydride	4.3	UN1413	I	4.3	A19, N40, W31	138	DANGEROUS WHEN WET*
Lithium ferrosilicon	4.3	UN2830	II	4.3	A19, IB7, IP2, IP21, T3, TP33, W31, W40	139	DANGEROUS WHEN WET*
Lithium hydride	4.3	UN1414	I	4.3	A19, N40, W31	138	DANGEROUS WHEN WET*
Lithium hydride, fused solid	4.3	UN2805	II	4.3	A8, A19, A20, IB4, T3, TP33, W31, W40	138	DANGEROUS WHEN WET*
Lithium hydroxide	8	UN2680	II	8	IB8, IP2, IP4, T3, TP33	154	CORROSIVE
Lithium hydroxide, solution	8	UN2679	II	8	B2, IB2, T7, TP2	154	CORROSIVE
	8		III	8	IB3, T4, TP2	154	CORROSIVE
Lithium hypochlorite, dry or Lithium hypochlorite mixture	5.1	UN1471	II	5.1	A9, IB8, IP2, IF4, N34, T3, TP33	140	OXIDIZER
	5.1		III	5.1	IB8, IP3, N34, T1, TP33	140	OXIDIZER
Lithium in cartridges, see Lithium							

Symbols (1)	Hazardous materials descriptions and proper shipping names (2)	Hazard class or Division (3)	Identification Numbers (4)	PG (5)	Label Codes (6)	Special Provisions (§172.102) (7)	ERG Guide No.	Placard Advisory Consult §172.504 & §172.505 *Placard any quantity
	Lithium ion batteries including lithium ion polymer batteries	9	UN3480	III	9	388, 422, A54, A100	147	CLASS 9
	Lithium ion batteries contained in equipment including lithium ion polymer batteries	9	UN3481		9	181, 388, 422, A54	147	CLASS 9
	Lithium ion batteries packed with equipment including lithium ion polymer batteries	9	UN3481		9	181, 388, 422, A54	147	CLASS 9
	Lithium metal batteries including lithium alloy batteries	9	UN3090		9	388, 422, A54	138	CLASS 9
	Lithium metal batteries contained in equipment including lithium alloy batteries	9	UN3091		9	181, 388, 422, A54, A101	138	CLASS 9
	Lithium metal batteries packed with equipment including lithium alloy batteries	9	UN3091		9	181, 388, 422, A54	138	CLASS 9
	Lithium nitrate	5.1	UN2722	III	5.1	A1, IB8, IP3, T1, TP33	140	OXIDIZER
	Lithium nitride	4.3	UN2806	I	4.3	A19, IB4, IP1, N40, W31	139	DANGEROUS WHEN WET*
	Lithium peroxide	5.1	UN1472	II	5.1	A9, IB6, IP2, N34, T3, TP33, W100	143	OXIDIZER
	Lithium silicon	4.3	UN1417	II	4.3	A19, A20, IB7, IP2, IP21, T3, TP33, W31, W40	138	DANGEROUS WHEN WET*
	LNG, see Methane etc. (UN1972)							
	London purple	6.1	UN1621	II	6.1	IB8, IP2, IP4, T3, TP33	151	POISON
	LPG, see Petroleum gases, liquefied							
	Lye, see Sodium hydroxide solutions							
	Magnesium aluminum phosphide	4.3	UN1419	I	4.3, 6.1	A19, N34, N40, W31	139	DANGEROUS WHEN WET*
+	Magnesium arsenate	6.1	UN1622	II	6.1	IB8, IP2, IP4, T3, TP33	151	POISON
	Magnesium bisulfite solution, see Bisulfites, aqueous solutions, n.o.s.							
	Magnesium bromate	5.1	UN1473	II	5.1	A1, IB8, IP2, IP4, T3, TP33	140	OXIDIZER
	Magnesium chlorate	5.1	UN2723	II	5.1	IB8, IP2, IP4, T3, TP33	140	OXIDIZER

Hazardous materials descriptions	Hazard class	ID Number	PG	Label codes	Special provisions	Guide	Placard
Magnesium diamide	4.2	UN2004	II	4.2	A8, A19, A20, B6, T3, TP33, W31	135	SPONTANEOUSLY COMBUSTIBLE
Magnesium dross, wet or hot	Forbidden						
Magnesium fluorosilicate	6.1	UN2853	III	6.1	IB8, IP3, T1, TP33	151	POISON
Magnesium granules, coated, particle size not less than 149 microns	4.3	UN2950	III	4.3	A1, A19, IB8, IP4, T1, TP33, W100	138	DANGEROUS WHEN WET*
Magnesium hydride	4.3	UN2010	I	4.3	A19, N40, W3*	138	DANGEROUS WHEN WET*
Magnesium or Magnesium alloys with more than 50 percent magnesium in pellets, turnings or ribbons	4.1	UN1869	III	4.1	A1, B134, IB8, IP21, T1, TP33, W100	138	FLAMMABLE SOLID
Magnesium nitrate	5.1	UN1474	III	5.1	332, A1, B120, IB8, IP3, T1, TP33	140	OXIDIZER
Magnesium perchlorate	5.1	UN1475	II	5.1	IB6, IP2, T3, TP33	140	OXIDIZER
Magnesium peroxide	5.1	UN1476	II	5.1	IB6, IP2, T3, TP33, W100	140	OXIDIZER
Magnesium phosphide	4.3	UN2011	I	4.3, 6.1	A19, N40, W31	139	DANGEROUS WHEN WET*
Magnesium, powder or Magnesium alloys, powder	4.3	UN1418	I	4.3, 4.2	A19, B56, W31	138	DANGEROUS WHEN WET*
			II	4.3, 4.2	A19, B56, IB5, IP2, T3, TP33, W31, W40	138	DANGEROUS WHEN WET*
			III	4.3, 4.2	A19, B56, IB8, IP4, T1, TP33, W31	138	DANGEROUS WHEN WET*
Magnesium scrap, see Magnesium, etc. (UN 1869)							
Magnesium silicide	4.3	UN2624	II	4.3	A19, A20, IB7, IP2, IP21, T3, TP33, W31, W40	138	DANGEROUS WHEN WET*
Magnetized material, see §173.21							
Maleic anhydride	8	UN2215	III	8	IB8, IP3, T1, TP33	156	CORROSIVE
Maleic anhydride, molten	8	UN2215	III	8	T4, TP3	156	CORROSIVE
Malononitrile	6.1	UN2647	II	6.1	IB8, IP2, IP4, T3, TP33	153	POISON
Mancozeb (manganese ethylenebisdithiocarbamate complex with zinc), see Maneb							

Symbols (1)	Hazardous materials descriptions and proper shipping names (2)	Hazard class or Division (3)	Identification Numbers (4)	PG (5)	Label Codes (6)	Special Provisions (§172.102) (7)	ERG Guide No.	Placard Advisory Consult §172.504 & §172.505 *Placard any quantity
	Maneb or Maneb preparations *with not less than 60 percent maneb*	4.2	UN2210	III	4.2, 4.3	57, A1, A19, IB6, T1, TP33, W100	135	SPONTANEOUSLY COMBUSTIBLE, DANGEROUS WHEN WET*
	Maneb stabilized *or* **Maneb preparations, stabilized** *against self-heating*	4.3	UN2968	III	4.3	54, A1, A19, IB8, IP4, T1, TP33, W100	135	DANGEROUS WHEN WET*
	Manganese nitrate	5.1	UN2724	III	5.1	A1, IB8, IP3, T1, TP33	140	OXIDIZER
	Manganese resinate	4.1	UN1330	III	4.1	A1, IB6, T1, TP33	133	FLAMMABLE SOLID
	Mannitan tetranitrate	Forbidden						
	Mannitol hexanitrate (dry)	Forbidden						
	Mannitol hexanitrate, wetted *or* **Nitromannite, wetted** *with not less than 40 percent water, or mixture of alcohol and water, by mass*	1.1D	UN0133			1.1D 121	112	EXPLOSIVES 1.1*
	Marine pollutants, liquid or solid, n.o.s., see Environmentally hazardous substances, liquid or solid, n.o.s.							
	Matches, block, see Matches, 'strike anywhere'							
	Matches, fusee	4.1	UN2254	III	4.1		133	FLAMMABLE SOLID
	Matches, safety *(book, card or strike on box)*	4.1	UN1944	III	4.1		133	FLAMMABLE SOLID
	Matches, strike anywhere	4.1	UN1331	III	4.1		133	FLAMMABLE SOLID
	Matches, wax, Vesta	4.1	UN1945	III	4.1		133	FLAMMABLE SOLID
	Matting acid, see Sulfuric acid							
	Medicine, liquid, flammable, toxic, n.o.s.	3	UN3248	II	3, 6.1	IB2	131	FLAMMABLE
				III	3, 6.1	IB3	131	FLAMMABLE
	Medicine, liquid, toxic, n.o.s.	6.1	UN1851	II	6.1		151	POISON
				III	6.1		151	POISON
	Medicine, solid, toxic, n.o.s.	6.1	UN3249	II	6.1	T3, TP33	151	POISON
				III	6.1	T3, TP33	151	POISON
	Memtetrahydrophthalic anhydride, see **Corrosive liquids, n.o.s.**							

Symbols	Hazardous materials descriptions and proper shipping names	Hazard class or Division	Identification Numbers	PG	Label Codes	Special Provisions		
	Mercaptans, liquid, flammable, n.o.s. or Mercaptan mixture, liquid, flammable, n.o.s.	3	UN3336	I	3	T11, TP2	130	FLAMMABLE
				II	3	IB2, T7, TP1, TP8, TP28	130	FLAMMABLE
				III	3	B1, B52, IB3, T4, TP1, TP29	130	FLAMMABLE
	Mercaptans, liquid, flammable, toxic, n.o.s or Mercaptan mixtures, liquid, flammable, toxic, n.o.s.	3	UN1228	II	3, 6.1	IB2, T11, TP2, TP27	131	FLAMMABLE
				III	3, 6.1	B1, IB3, T7, TP1, TP28	131	FLAMMABLE
	Mercaptans, liquid, toxic, flammable, n.o.s. or Mercaptan mixtures, liquid, toxic, flammable, n.o.s., *flash point not less than 23 degrees C*	6.1	UN3071	II	6.1, 3	IB2, T11, TP2, TP13, TP27	131	POISON
	5-Mercaptotetrazol-1-acetic acid	1.4C	UN0448	1.4C	1.4C		114	EXPLOSIVES 1.4
	Mercuric arsenate	6.1	UN1623	II	6.1	IB8, IP2, IP4, T3, TP33	151	POISON
	Mercuric chloride	6.1	UN1624	II	6.1	IB8, IP2, IP4, T3, TP33	154	POISON
	Mercuric compounds, see Mercury compounds, etc.							
	Mercuric nitrate	6.1	UN1625	II	6.1	IB8, IP2, IP4, N73, T3, TP33	141	POISON
+	Mercuric potassium cyanide	6.1	UN1626	I	6.1	IB7, IP1, N74, N75, T6, TP33, W31	157	POISON
	Mercuric sulfocyanate, see Mercury thiocyanate							
	Mercurol, see Mercury nucleate							
	Mercurous azide	Forbidden						
	Mercurous compounds, see Mercury compounds, etc.							
	Mercurous nitrate	6.1	UN1627	II	6.1	IB8, IP2, IP4, T3, TP33	141	POISON
A W	Mercury	8	UN2809	III	8, 6.1	365	172	CORROSIVE
	Mercury acetate	6.1	UN1629	II	6.1	IB8, IP2, IP4, T3, TP33	151	POISON
	Mercury acetylide	Forbidden						
	Mercury ammonium chloride	6.1	UN1630	II	6.1	IB8, IP2, IP4, T3, TP33	151	POISON
	Mercury based pesticides, liquid, flammable, toxic, *flash point less than 23 degrees C*	3	UN2778	I	3, 6.1	T14, TP2, TP13, TP27	131	FLAMMABLE
				II	3, 6.1	IB2, T11, TP2, TP13, TP27	131	FLAMMABLE
	Mercury based pesticides, liquid, toxic	6.1	UN3012	I	6.1	T14, TP2, TP13, TP27	151	POISON

Symbols (1)	Hazardous materials descriptions and proper shipping names (2)	Hazard class or Division (3)	Identification Numbers (4)	PG (5)	Label Codes (6)	Special Provisions (§172.102) (7)	ERG Guide No.	Placard Advisory Consult §172.504 & §172.505 *Placard any quantity
				II	6.1	IB2, T11, TP2, TP13, TP27	151	POISON
				III	6.1	IB3, T7, TP2, TP28	151	POISON
	Mercury based pesticides, liquid, toxic, flammable, *flash point not less than 23 degrees C*	6.1	UN3011	I	6.1, 3	T14, TP2, TP13, TP27	131	POISON
				II	6.1, 3	IB2, T11, TP2, TP13, TP27	131	POISON
				III	6.1, 3	IB3, T7, TP2, TP28	131	POISON
	Mercury based pesticides, solid, toxic	6.1	UN2777	I	6.1	IB7, IP1, T6, TP33	151	POISON
				II	6.1	IB8, IP2, IP4, T3, TP33	151	POISON
				III	6.1	IB8, IP3, T1, TP33	151	POISON
	Mercury benzoate	6.1	UN1631	II	6.1	IB8, IP2, IP4, T3, TP33	154	POISON
	Mercury bromides	6.1	UN1634	II	6.1	IB8, IP2, IP4, T3, TP33	154	POISON
G	Mercury compound, liquid, n.o.s.	6.1	UN2024	I	6.1		151	POISON
				II	6.1	IB2	151	POISON
				III	6.1	IB3	151	POISON
G	Mercury compound, solid, n.o.s.	6.1	UN2025	I	6.1	IB7, IP1, T6, TP33	151	POISON
				II	6.1	IB8, IP2, IP4, T3, TP33	151	POISON
				III	6.1	IB8, IP3, T1, TP33	151	POISON
A W	Mercury contained in manufactured articles	8	UN3506		8, 6.1	A191	172	CORROSIVE
	Mercury cyanide	6.1	UN1636	II	6.1	IB8, IP2, IP4, N74, N75, T3, TP33	154	POISON
	Mercury fulminate, wetted with not less than 20 percent water, or mixture of alcohol and water, by mass	1.1A	UN0135		1.1A	111, 117	112	EXPLOSIVES 1.1*
	Mercury gluconate	6.1	UN1637	II	6.1	IB8, IP2, IP4, T3, TP33	151	POISON
	Mercury iodide	6.1	UN1638	II	6.1	IB8, IP2, IP4, T3, TP33	151	POISON
	Mercury iodide aquabasic ammonobasic (Iodide of Millon's base)	Forbidden						
	Mercury nitride	Forbidden						
	Mercury nucleate	6.1	UN1639	II	6.1	IB8, IP2, IP4, T3, TP33	151	POISON

Sym	Name	Class	ID No.	PG	Label	Special Provisions	Guide	Placard
	Mercury oleate	6.1	UN1640	II	6.1	IB8, IP2, IP4, T3, TP33	151	POISON
	Mercury oxide	6.1	UN1641	II	6.1	IB8, IP2, IP4, T3, TP33	151	POISON
	Mercury oxycyanide	Forbidden						
	Mercury oxycyanide, desensitized	6.1	UN1642	II	6.1	IB8, IP2, IP4, T3, TP33	151	POISON
	Mercury potassium iodide	6.1	UN1643	II	6.1	IB8, IP2, IP4, T3, TP33	151	POISON
	Mercury salicylate	6.1	UN1644	II	6.1	IB8, IP2, IP4, T3, TP33	151	POISON
+	Mercury sulfates	6.1	UN1645	II	6.1	IB8, IP2, IP4, T3, TP33	151	POISON
	Mercury thiocyanate	6.1	UN1646	II	6.1	IB8, IP2, IP4, T3, TP33	151	POISON
	Mesityl oxide	3	UN1229	III	3	B1, IB3, T2, TP1	129	FLAMMABLE
G	Metal carbonyls, liquid, n.o.s.	6.1	UN3281	I	6.1	5, T14, TP2, TF13, TP27	151	POISON
				II	6.1	IB2, T11, TP2, TP27	151	POISON
				III	6.1	IB3, T7, TP1, TP28	151	POISON
G	Metal carbonyls, solid, n.o.s.	6.1	UN3466	I	6.1	IB7, IP1, T6, TF33	151	POISON
				II	6.1	IB8, IP2, IP4, T3, TP33	151	POISON
				III	6.1	IB8, IP3, T1, TF33	151	POISON
G	Metal catalyst, dry	4.2	UN2881	I	4.2	N34, T21, TP7, TP33, W31	135	SPONTANEOUSLY COMBUSTIBLE
				II	4.2	IB6, IP2, N34, T3, TP33, W31	135	SPONTANEOUSLY COMBUSTIBLE
				III	4.2	B135, IB8, IP21, N34, T1, TP33, W31	135	SPONTANEOUSLY COMBUSTIBLE
G	Metal catalyst, wetted *with a visible excess of liquid*	4.2	UN1378	II	4.2	A2, A8, IB1, N34, T3, TP33, W31, W40	170	SPONTANEOUSLY COMBUSTIBLE
	Metal hydrides, flammable, n.o.s.	4.1	UN3182	II	4.1	A1, IB4, T3, TP33, W31, W40	170	FLAMMABLE SOLID
				III	4.1	A1, IB4, T1, TP33, W31	170	FLAMMABLE SOLID
	Metal hydrides, water reactive n.o.s.	4.3	UN1409	I	4.3	A19, N34, N40, W31	138	DANGEROUS WHEN WET*
				II	4.3	A19, IB4, N34, N40, T3, TP33, W31, W40	138	DANGEROUS WHEN WET*
	Metal powder, self-heating, n.o.s.	4.2	UN3189	II	4.2	IB6, IP2, T3, TP33, W31	135	SPONTANEOUSLY COMBUSTIBLE

Sym-bols (1)	Hazardous materials descriptions and proper shipping names (2)	Hazard class or Division (3)	Identifica-tion Numbers (4)	PG (5)	Label Codes (6)	Special Provisions (§172.102) (7)	ERG Guide No.	Placard Advisory Consult §172.504 & §172.505 *Placard any quantity
				III	4.2	B135, IB8, IP4, T1, TP33, W31	135	SPONTANEOUSLY COMBUSTIBLE
	Metal powders, flammable, n.o.s.	4.1	UN3089	II	4.1	IB8, IP2, IP4, T3, TP33, W100	170	FLAMMABLE SOLID
				III	4.1	IB8, IP2, IP4, T1, TP33, W100	170	FLAMMABLE SOLID
	Metal salts of methyl nitramine (dry)	Forbidden						
G	Metal salts of organic compounds, flammable, n.o.s.	4.1	UN3181	II	4.1	A1, IB8, IP2, IP4, T3, TP33, W31	133	FLAMMABLE SOLID
				III	4.1	A1, IB8, IP3, T1, TP33, W31	133	FLAMMABLE SOLID
	Metaldehyde	4.1	UN1332	III	4.1	A1, IB8, IP3, T1, TP33	133	FLAMMABLE SOLID
G	Metallic substance, water-reactive, n.o.s.	4.3	UN3208	I	4.3	A7, IB4, W31	138	DANGEROUS WHEN WET*
				II	4.3	A7, IB7, IP2, IP21, T3, TP33, W31, W40	138	DANGEROUS WHEN WET*
				III	4.3	A7, IB8, IP21, T1, TP33, W31	138	DANGEROUS WHEN WET*
G	Metallic substance, water-reactive, self-heating, n.o.s.	4.3	UN3209	I	4.3, 4.2	A7, W31	138	DANGEROUS WHEN WET*
				II	4.3, 4.2	A7, IB5, IP2, T3, TP33, W31, W40	138	DANGEROUS WHEN WET*
				III	4.3, 4.2	A7, IB8, IP4, T1, TP33, W31	138	DANGEROUS WHEN WET*
	Methacrylaldehyde, stabilized	3	UN2396	II	3, 6.1	45, 387, IB2, T7, TP1, TP13	131P	FLAMMABLE
	Methacrylic acid, stabilized	8	UN2531	II	8	41, 387, IB2, T7, TP1, TP18, TP30	153P	CORROSIVE

Symbol	Hazardous materials descriptions and proper shipping names	Hazard class or division	ID No.	PG	Label codes	Special provisions	ERG	Placard
+	Methacrylonitrile, stabilized	6.1	UN3079	I	6.1, 3	2, 387, B9, B14, B32, T20, TP2, TP13, TP38, TP45	131P	INHALATION HAZARD CLASS 6*
	Methallyl alcohol	3	UN2614	III	3	B1, IB3, T2, TF1	129	FLAMMABLE
	Methane and hydrogen, mixtures, see Hydrogen and Methane mixtures, etc.							
	Methane, compressed or Natural gas, compressed (with high methane content)	2.1	UN1971		2.1		115	FLAMMABLE GAS
	Methane, refrigerated liquid (cryogenic liquid) or Natural gas, refrigerated liquid (cryogenic liquid), with high methane content)	2.1	UN1972		2.1	T75, TP5, 440	115	FLAMMABLE GAS
	Methanesulfonyl chloride	6.1	UN3246	I	6.1, 8	2, B9, B14, B32, T20, TP2, TP13, TP38, TP45	156	INHALATION HAZARD CLASS 6*
+I	Methanol	3	UN1230	II	3, 6.1	IB2, T7, TP2	131	FLAMMABLE
D	Methanol	3	UN1230	II	3	IB2, T7, TP2	131	FLAMMABLE
	Methazoic acid	Forbidden						
	4-Methoxy-4-methylpentan-2-one	3	UN2293	III	3	B1, IB3, T2, TP1	128	FLAMMABLE
	1-Methoxy-2-propanol	3	UN3092	III	3	B1, IB3, T2, TP1	129	FLAMMABLE
+	Methoxymethyl isocyanate	6.1	UN2605	I	6.1, 3	1, B9, B14, B30, T20, TP2, TP13, TP38, TP44	155	INHALATION HAZARD CLASS 6*
	Methyl acetate	3	UN1231	II	3	IB2, T4, TP1	129	FLAMMABLE
	Methyl acetylene and propadiene mixtures, stabilized	2.1	UN1060		2.1	387, N88, T50	116P	FLAMMABLE GAS
	Methyl acrylate, stabilized	3	UN1919	II	3	387, IB2, T4, TP1, TP13	129P	FLAMMABLE
	Methyl alcohol, see Methanol							
	Methyl allyl chloride	3	UN2554	II	3	IB2, T4, TP1, TP13	130P	FLAMMABLE
	Methyl amyl ketone, see Amyl methyl ketone							
	Methyl bromide	2.3	UN1062		2.3	3, B14, N86, T50	123	INHALATION HAZARD CLASS 2*
	Methyl bromide and chloropicrin mixtures with more than 2 percent chloropicrin, see Chloropicrin and methyl bromide mixtures							
	Methyl bromide and chloropicrin mixtures with not more than 2 percent chloropicrin, see Methyl bromide							
	Methyl bromide and ethylene dibromide mixtures, liquid	6.1	UN1647	I	6.1	2, B9, B14, B32, N65, T20, TP2, TP13, TP38, TP44	151	INHALATION HAZARD CLASS 6*

Symbols (1)	Hazardous materials descriptions and proper shipping names (2)	Hazard class or Division (3)	Identification Numbers (4)	PG (5)	Label Codes (6)	Special Provisions (§172.102) (7)	ERG Guide No.	Placard Advisory Consult §172.504 & §172.505 *Placard any quantity
	Methyl bromoacetate	6.1	UN2643	II	6.1	IB2, T7, TP2	155	POISON
	2-Methyl-1-butene	3	UN2459	I	3	T11, TP2	128	FLAMMABLE
	2-Methyl-2-butene	3	UN2460	II	3	IB2, IP8, T7, TP1	128	FLAMMABLE
	3-Methyl-1-butene	3	UN2561	I	3	T11, TP2	128	FLAMMABLE
	Methyl tert-butyl ether	3	UN2398	II	3	IB2, T7, TP1	127	FLAMMABLE
	Methyl butyrate	3	UN1237	II	3	IB2, T4, TP1	129	FLAMMABLE
	Methyl chloride or Refrigerant gas R 40	2.1	UN1063		2.1	N86, T50	115	FLAMMABLE GAS
	Methyl chloride and chloropicrin mixtures, see Chloropicrin and methyl chloride mixtures							
	Methyl chloride and methylene chloride mixtures	2.1	UN1912		2.1	N86, T50	115	FLAMMABLE GAS
	Methyl chloroacetate	6.1	UN2295	I	6.1, 3	T14, TP2, TP13	155	POISON
	Methyl chlorocarbonate, see Methyl chloroformate							
	Methyl chloroform, see 1,1,1-Trichloroethane							
	Methyl chloroformate	6.1	UN1238	I	6.1, 3, 8	1, B9, B14, B30, N34, T22, TP2, TP13, TP38, TP44	155	INHALATION HAZARD CLASS 6*
	Methyl chloromethyl ether	6.1	UN1239	I	6.1, 3	1, B9, B14, B30, T22, TP2, TP13, TP38, TP44	131	INHALATION HAZARD CLASS 6*
	Methyl 2-chloropropionate	3	UN2933	III	3	B1, IB3, T2, TP1	129	FLAMMABLE
	Methyl dichloroacetate	6.1	UN2299	III	6.1	IB3, T4, TP1	155	POISON
	Methyl ethyl ether, see Ethyl methyl ether							
	Methyl ethyl ketone, see Ethyl methyl ketone							
	Methyl ethyl ketone peroxide, in solution with more than 9 percent by mass active oxygen	Forbidden						
	2-Methyl-5-ethylpyridine	6.1	UN2300	III	6.1	IB3, T4, TP1	153	POISON
	Methyl fluoride or Refrigerant gas R 41	2.1	UN2454		2.1	T11, TP2	115	FLAMMABLE GAS
	Methyl formate	3	UN1243	I	3	T11, TP2	129	FLAMMABLE

Sym	Hazardous materials descriptions and proper shipping names	Hazard class or division	Identification numbers	PG	Label codes	Special provisions	Guide No.
	2-Methyl-2-heptanethiol	6.1	UN3023	I	6.1, 3	2, B9, B14, B32, TP2, TP13, TP38, TP45	131 INHALATION HAZARD CLASS 6*
	Methyl iodide	6.1	UN2644	I	6.1	2, B9, B14, B32, T20, TP2, TP13, TP38, TP45	151 INHALATION HAZARD CLASS 6*
	Methyl isobutyl carbinol	3	UN2053	III	3	B1, IB3, T2, TP1	129 FLAMMABLE
	Methyl isobutyl ketone	3	UN1245	II	3	IB2, T4, TP1	127 FLAMMABLE
	Methyl isobutyl ketone peroxide, *in solution with more than 9 percent by mass active oxygen*	Forbidden					
	Methyl isocyanate	6.1	UN2480	I	6.1, 3	1, B9, B14, B30, T22, TP2, TP13, TP38, TP44	155P INHALATION HAZARD CLASS 6*
	Methyl isopropenyl ketone, stabilized	3	UN1246	II	3	387, IB2, T4, TP1	127P FLAMMABLE
	Methyl isothiocyanate	6.1	UN2477	I	6.1, 3	2, B9, B14, B32, T20, TP2, TP13, TP38, TP45	131 INHALATION HAZARD CLASS 6*
	Methyl isovalerate	3	UN2400	II	3	IB2, T4, TP1	130 FLAMMABLE
	Methyl magnesium bromide, in ethyl ether	4.3	UN1928	I	4.3, 3		138 DANGEROUS WHEN WET*
	Methyl mercaptan	2.3	UN1064		2.3, 2.1	3, B7, B9, B14, N89, T50	117 INHALATION HAZARD CLASS 2*
	Methyl mercaptopropionaldehyde, see 4-Thiapentanal						
	Methyl methacrylate monomer, stabilized	3	UN1247	II	3	387, IB2, T4, TP1	129P FLAMMABLE
	Methyl nitramine (dry)	Forbidden					
	Methyl nitrate	Forbidden					
	Methyl nitrite	Forbidden					
	Methyl norbornene dicarboxylic anhydride, see Corrosive liquids, n.o.s.						
	Methyl orthosilicate	6.1	UN2606	I	6.1, 3	2, B9, B14, B32, T20, TP2, TP13, TP38, TP45	155 INHALATION HAZARD CLASS 6*
D	Methyl phosphonic dichloride	6.1	NA9206	I	6.1, 8	2, B9, B14, B32, N34, T20, TP4, TP13, TP38, TP45	137 INHALATION HAZARD CLASS 6*
	Methyl phosphonothioic dichloride, anhydrous, see Corrosive liquids, n.o.s.						

Sym-bols (1)	Hazardous materials descriptions and proper shipping names (2)	Hazard class or Division (3)	Identification Numbers (4)	PG (5)	Label Codes (6)	Special Provisions (§172.102) (7)	ERG Guide No.	Placard Advisory Consult §172.504 & §172.505 *Placard any quantity
D	**Methyl phosphonous dichloride,** *pyrophoric liquid*	6.1	NA2845	I	6.1, 4.2	2, B9, B14, B16, B32, T20, TP4, TP12, TP13, TP38, TP45	135	INHALATION HAZARD CLASS 6*
	Methyl picric acid (heavy metal salts of)	Forbidden						
	Methyl propionate	3	UN1248	II	3	IB2, T4, TP1	129	FLAMMABLE
	Methyl propyl ether	3	UN2612	II	3	IB2, IP8, T7, TP2	127	FLAMMABLE
	Methyl propyl ketone	3	UN1249	II	3	IB2, T4, TP1	127	FLAMMABLE
	Methyl sulfate, see **Dimethyl sulfate**							
	Methyl sulfide, see **Dimethyl sulfide**							
	Methyl trichloroacetate	6.1	UN2533	III	6.1	IB3, T4, TP1	156	POISON
	Methyl trimethylol methane trinitrate	Forbidden						
	Methyl vinyl ketone, stabilized	6.1	UN1251	I	6.1, 3, 8	1, 387, B9, B14, B30, T22, TP2, TP13, TP38, TP44	131P	INHALATION HAZARD CLASS 6*
	Methylal	3	UN1234	II	3	IB2, IP8, T7, TP2	127	FLAMMABLE
	Methylamine, anhydrous	2.1	UN1061		2.1	N87, T50	118	FLAMMABLE GAS
	Methylamine, aqueous solution	3	UN1235	II	3, 8	B1, IB2, T7, TP1	132	FLAMMABLE
	Methylamine dinitramine and dry salts thereof	Forbidden						
	Methylamine nitroform	Forbidden						
	Methylamine perchlorate (dry)	Forbidden						
	Methylamyl acetate	3	UN1233	III	3	B1, IB3, T2, TP1	130	FLAMMABLE
	N-Methylaniline	6.1	UN2294	III	6.1	IB3, T4, TP2	153	POISON
	alpha-Methylbenzyl alcohol, liquid	6.1	UN2937	III	6.1	IB3, T4, TP1	153	POISON
	alpha-Methylbenzyl alcohol, solid	6.1	UN3438	III	6.1	IB8, IP3, T1, TP33	153	POISON
	3-Methylbutan-2-one	3	UN2397	II	3	IB2, T4, TP1	127	FLAMMABLE
	2-Methylbutanal	3	UN3371	II	3	IB2, T4, TP1	129	FLAMMABLE
	N-Methylbutylamine	3	UN2945	II	3, 8	IB2, T7, TP1	132	FLAMMABLE

Symbol	Hazardous materials descriptions and proper shipping names	Hazard class or Division	ID Numbers	PG	Label Codes	Special provisions	ERG Guide	
	Methylchlorosilane	2.3	UN2534		2.3, 2.1, 8	2, B9, B14, N34	119	INHALATION HAZARD CLASS 2*
	Methylcyclohexane	3	UN2296	II	3	B1, IB2, T4, TP2	128	FLAMMABLE
	Methylcyclohexanols, flammable	3	UN2617	III	3	B1, IB3, T2, TP-	129	FLAMMABLE
	Methylcyclohexanone	3	UN2297	III	3	B1, IB3, T2, TP-	128	FLAMMABLE
	Methylcyclopentane	3	UN2298	II	3	IB2, T4, TP1	128	FLAMMABLE
D	Methyldichloroarsine	6.1	NA1556	I	6.1	2, T20, TP4, TP13, TP38, TP45	152	INHALATION HAZARD CLASS 6*
	Methyldichlorosilane	4.3	UN1242	I	4.3, 8, 3	A2, A7, B6, B77, N34, T14, TP2, TP7, TP13, W31	139	DANGEROUS WHEN WET*
	Methylene chloride, see Dichloromethane							
	Methylene glycol dinitrate	Forbidden						
	2-Methylfuran	3	UN2301	II	3	IB2, T4, TP1	128	FLAMMABLE
	a-Methylglucoside tetranitrate	Forbidden						
	a-Methylglycerol trinitrate	Forbidden						
	5-Methylhexan-2-one	3	UN2302	III	3	B1, IB3, T2, TP1	127	FLAMMABLE
	Methylhydrazine	6.1	UN1244	I	6.1, 3, 8	1, B7, B9, B14, B30, B77, N34, T22, TP2, TP13, TP38, TP44	131	INHALATION HAZARD CLASS 6*
	4-Methylmorpholine or n-methylmorpholine	3	UN2535	II	3, 8	B6, IB2, T7, TP1	132	FLAMMABLE
	Methylpentadienes	3	UN2461	II	3	IB2, T4, TP1	128	FLAMMABLE
	2-Methylpentan-2-ol	3	UN2560	III	3	B1, IB3, T2, TP1	129	FLAMMABLE
	Methylpentanes, see Hexanes							
	Methylphenyldichlorosilane	8	UN2437	II	8	T10, TP2, TP7, TP13	156	CORROSIVE
	1-Methylpiperidine	3	UN2399	II	3, 8	IB2, T7, TP1	132	FLAMMABLE
	Methyltetrahydrofuran	3	UN2536	II	3	IB2, T4, TP1	127	FLAMMABLE
	Methyltrichlorosilane	3	UN1250	II	3, 8	A7, B6, B77, N34, T10, TP2, TP7, TP13	155	FLAMMABLE
	alpha-Methylvaleraldehyde	3	UN2367	II	3	B1, IB2, T4, TP1	130	FLAMMABLE
	Mine rescue equipment containing carbon dioxide, see Carbon dioxide							

Sym-bols (1)	Hazardous materials descriptions and proper shipping names (2)	Hazard class or Division (3)	Identifica-tion Numbers (4)	PG (5)	Label Codes (6)	Special Provisions (§172.102) (7)	ERG Guide No.	Placard Advisory Consult §172.504 & §172.505 *Placard any quantity
	Mines with bursting charge	1.1F	UN0136		1.1F		112	EXPLOSIVES 1.1*
	Mines with bursting charge	1.1D	UN0137		1.1D		112	EXPLOSIVES 1.1*
	Mines with bursting charge	1.2D	UN0138		1.2D		112	EXPLOSIVES 1.2*
	Mines with bursting charge	1.2F	UN0294		1.2F		112	EXPLOSIVES 1.2*
	Mixed acid, see Nitrating acid mixtures etc.							
	Mobility aids, see Battery powered equipment or Battery powered vehicle							
D	**Model rocket motor**	1.4C	NA0276		1.4C	51	114	EXPLOSIVES 1.4*
D	**Model rocket motor**	1.4S	NA0323		1.4S	51	114	EXPLOSIVES 1.4*
	Molybdenum pentachloride	8	UN2508	III	8	IB8, IP3, T1, TP33	156	CORROSIVE
	Monochloroacetone (unstabilized)	Forbidden						
	Monochloroethylene, see Vinyl chloride, stabilized							
	Monoethanolamine, see Ethanolamine, solutions							
	Monoethylamine, see Ethylamine							
	Morpholine	8	UN2054	I	8, 3	T10, TP2	132	CORROSIVE
	Morpholine, aqueous, mixture, see Corrosive liquids, n.o.s.							
	Motor fuel anti-knock compounds, see Motor fuel anti-knock mixtures							
+	**Motor fuel anti-knock mixture, flammable**	6.1	UN3483	I	6.1, 3	14, T14, TP2, TP13	131	POISON
+	**Motor fuel anti-knock mixtures**	6.1	UN1649	I	6.1	14, B9, B90, T14, TP2, TP13	152	POISON
	Motor spirit, see Gasoline							
	Muriatic acid, see Hydrochloric acid							
	Musk xylene, see 5-tert-Butyl-2,4,6-trinitro-m-Xylene							
	Naphtha see Petroleum distillate n.o.s.							
	Naphthalene, crude or **Naphthalene, refined**	4.1	UN1334	III	4.1	A1, B120, IB8, IP3, T1, TP33	133	FLAMMABLE SOLID

	Name		Class	ID No.	PG	Label	Special Provisions	Guide	
	Naphthalene diozonide	Forbidden							
	beta-Naphthylamine, solid		6.1	UN1650	II	6.1	IB8, IP2, IP4, T3, TP33	153	POISON
	beta-Naphthylamine solution		6.1	UN3411	II	6.1	IB2, T7, TP2	153	POISON
					III	6.1	IB2, T7, TP2	153	POISON
	alpha-Naphthylamine		6.1	UN2077	III	6.1	IB8, IP3, T1, TP33	153	POISON
	Naphthalene, molten		4.1	UN2304	III	4.1	IB1, T1, TP3	133	FLAMMABLE SOLID
	Naphthylamineperchlorate	Forbidden							
	Naphthylthiourea		6.1	UN1651	II	6.1	IB8, IP2, IP4, T3, TP33	153	POISON
	Naphthylurea		6.1	UN1652	II	6.1	IB8, IP2, IP4, T3, TP33	153	POISON
	Natural gases (with high methane content), see Methane ,etc. (UN 1971, UN 1972)								
	Neohexane, see Hexanes								
	Neon, compressed		2.2	UN1065		2.2		120	NONFLAMMABLE GAS
	Neon, refrigerated liquid *(cryogenic liquid)*		2.2	UN1913		2.2	T75, TP5	120	NONFLAMMABLE GAS
	New explosive or explosive device, see §§ 173.51 and 173.56								
	Nickel carbonyl		6.1	UN1259	I	6.1, 3	1	131	INHALATION HAZARD CLASS 6"
	Nickel cyanide		6.1	UN1653	II	6.1	IB8, IP2, IP4, N74, N75, T3, TP33	151	POISON
	Nickel nitrate		5.1	UN2725	III	5.1	A1, IB8, IP3, T-, TP33	140	OXIDIZER
	Nickel nitrite		5.1	UN2726	III	5.1	A1, IB8, IP3, T-, TP33	140	OXIDIZER
	Nickel picrate	Forbidden							
	Nicotine		6.1	UN1654	II	6.1	IB2	151	POISON
G	Nicotine compounds, liquid, n.o.s. or Nicotine preparations, liquid, n.o.s.		6.1	UN3144	I	6.1	A4	151	POISON
					II	6.1	IB2, T11, TP2, TP27	151	POISON
					III	6.1	IB3, T7, TP1, TP28	151	POISON
G	Nicotine compounds, solid, n.o.s. or Nicotine preparations, solid, n.o.s.		6.1	UN1655	I	6.1	IB7, IP1, T6, TP33	151	POISON
					II.	6.1	IB8, IP2, IP4, T3, TP33	151	POISON
					III	6.1	IB3, T1, TP33	151	POISON

Symbols (1)	Hazardous materials descriptions and proper shipping names (2)	Hazard class or Division (3)	Identification Numbers (4)	PG (5)	Label Codes (6)	Special Provisions (§172.102) (7)	ERG Guide No.	Placard Advisory Consult §172.504 & §172.505 *Placard any quantity
	Nicotine hydrochloride liquid or solution	6.1	UN1656	II	6.1	IB2	151	POISON
				III	6.1	IB3	151	POISON
	Nicotine hydrochloride, solid	6.1	UN3444	II	6.1	IB8, IP2, IP4, T3, TP33	151	POISON
	Nicotine salicylate	6.1	UN1657	II	6.1	IB8, IP2, IP4, T3, TP33	151	POISON
	Nicotine sulfate solution	6.1	UN1658	II	6.1	IB2, T7, TP2	151	POISON
				III	6.1	IB3, T7, TP2	151	POISON
	Nicotine sulphate, solid	6.1	UN3445	II	6.1	IB8, IP2, IP4, T3, TP33	151	POISON
	Nicotine tartrate	6.1	UN1659	II	6.1	IB8, IP2, IP4, T3, TP33	151	POISON
	Nitrated paper (unstable)	Forbidden						
	Nitrates, inorganic, aqueous solution, n.o.s.	5.1	UN3218	II	5.1	58, IB2, T4, TP1	140	OXIDIZER
				III	5.1	58, IB2, T4, TP1	140	OXIDIZER
	Nitrates, inorganic, n.o.s.	5.1	UN1477	II	5.1	IB8, IP2, IP4, T3, TP33	140	OXIDIZER
				III	5.1	IB8, IP3, T1, TP33	140	OXIDIZER
	Nitrates of diazonium compounds	Forbidden						
	Nitrating acid mixtures, spent with more than 50 percent nitric acid	8	UN1826	I	8, 5.1	A7, T10, TP2, TP13	157	CORROSIVE
	Nitrating acid mixtures spent with not more than 50 percent nitric acid	8	UN1826	II	8	A7, B2, IB2, T8, TP2	157	CORROSIVE
	Nitrating acid mixtures with more than 50 percent nitric acid	8	UN1796	I	8, 5.1	A7, T10, TP2, TP13	157	CORROSIVE
	Nitrating acid mixtures with not more than 50 percent nitric acid	8	UN1796	II	8	A7, B2, IB2, T8, TP2, TP13	157	CORROSIVE
	Nitric acid other than red fuming, with at least 65 percent, but not more than 70 percent nitric acid	8	UN2031	II	8, 5.1	B2, B47, B53, IB2, IP15, T8, TP2	157	CORROSIVE
	Nitric acid other than red fuming, with more than 20 percent and less than 65 percent nitric acid	8	UN2031	II	8	A212, B2, B47, B53, IB2, IP15, T8, TP2	157	CORROSIVE
	Nitric acid other than red fuming with not more than 20 percent nitric acid	8	UN2031	II	8	B2, B47, B53, IB2, T8, TP2	157	CORROSIVE

Sym	Hazardous materials descriptions and proper shipping names	Hazard class or Division	Identification Numbers	PG	Special provisions	Guide	Label codes
+	Nitric acid, red fuming	8	UN2032	I	8, 5.1, 6.1	2, B9, B32, T20, TP2, TP13, TP38, TP45	157	CORROSIVE, INHALATION HAZARD CLASS 6*
	Nitric acid other than red fuming, with more than 70 percent nitric acid	8	UN2031	I	8, 5.1	B47, B53, T10, TP2, TP12, TP13	157	CORROSIVE
	Nitric oxide, compressed	2.3	UN1660		2.3, 5.1, 8	1, B77	124	INHALATION HAZARD CLASS 2*
	Nitric oxide and dinitrogen tetroxide mixtures or Nitric oxide and nitrogen dioxide mixtures	2.3	UN1975		2.3, 5.1, 8	1, B77	124	INHALATION HAZARD CLASS 2*
G	Nitriles, flammable, toxic, n.o.s.	3	UN3273	I	3, 6.1	T14, TP2, TP13, TP27	131	FLAMMABLE
				II	3, 6.1	IB2, T11, TP2, TP13, TP27	131	FLAMMABLE
G	Nitriles, toxic, flammable, n.o.s.	6.1	UN3275	I	6.1, 3	5, T14, TP2, TP-3, TP27	131	POISON
				II	6.1, 3	IB2, T11, TP2, TP13, TP27	131	POISON
G	Nitriles, liquid, toxic, n.o.s.	6.1	UN3276	I	6.1	5, T14, TP2, TP13, TP27	151	POISON
				II	6.1	IB2, T11, TP2, TP27	151	POISON
				III	6.1	IB3, T7, TP1, TP28	151	POISON
G	Nitriles, solid, toxic, n.o.s.	6.1	UN3439	I	6.1	IB7, IP1, T6, TP33	151	POISON
				II	6.1	IB8, IP2, IP4, T3, TP33	151	POISON
				III	6.1	IB8, IP3, T1, TP33	151	POISON
G	Nitrites, inorganic, aqueous solution, n.o.s.	5.1	UN3219	II	5.1	148, IB1, T4, TP1	140	OXIDIZER
				III	5.1	IB2, T4, TP1	140	OXIDIZER
G	Nitrites, inorganic, n.o.s.	5.1	UN2627	II	5.1	33, IB8, IP2, IP4, T3, TP33	140	OXIDIZER
G	3-Nitro-4-chlorobenzotrifluoride	6.1	UN2307	II	6.1	IB2, T7, TP2	152	POISON
	6-Nitro-4-diazotoluene-3-sulfonic acid (dry)	Forbidden						
	Nitro isobutane triol trinitrate	Forbidden						
	N-Nitro-N-methylglycolamide nitrate	Forbidden						
	2-Nitro-2-methylpropanol nitrate	Forbidden						
	Nitro urea	1.1D	UN0147	1.1D			112	EXPLOSIVE 1.1*
	N-Nitroaniline	Forbidden						
+	Nitroanilines (o-; m-; p-;)	6.1	UN1661	II	6.1	IB8, IP2, IP4, T3, TP33	153	POISON
	Nitroanisole, liquid	6.1	UN2730	III	6.1	IB3, T4, TP1	152	POISON

Symbols (1)	Hazardous materials descriptions and proper shipping names (2)	Hazard class or Division (3)	Identification Numbers (4)	PG (5)	Label Codes (6)	Special Provisions (§172.102) (7)	ERG Guide No.	Placard Advisory Consult §172.504 & §172.505 *Placard any quantity
	Nitroanisoles, solid	6.1	UN3458	III	6.1	IB8, IP3, T1, TP33	152	POISON
+	**Nitrobenzene**	6.1	UN1662	II	6.1	IB2, T7, TP2	152	POISON
	m-Nitrobenzene diazonium perchlorate	Forbidden						
	Nitrobenzenesulfonic acid	8	UN2305	II	8	B2, B4, IB8, IP2, IP4, T3, TP33	153	CORROSIVE
	Nitrobenzol, see Nitrobenzene							
	5-Nitrobenzotriazol	1.1D	UN0385		1.1D		112	EXPLOSIVES 1.1*
	Nitrobenzotrifluorides, liquid	6.1	UN2306	II	6.1	IB2, T7, TP2	152	POISON
	Nitrobenzotrifluorides, solid	6.1	UN3431	II	6.1	IB8, IP2, IP4, T3, TP33	152	POISON
	Nitrobromobenzenes, liquid	6.1	UN2732	III	6.1	IB3, T4, TP1	152	POISON
	Nitrobromobenzenes, solid	6.1	UN3459	III	6.1	IB8, IP3, T1, TP33	152	POISON
	Nitrocellulose, *dry or wetted with less than 25 percent water (or alcohol), by mass*	1.1D	UN0340		1.1D		112	EXPLOSIVES 1.1*
	Nitrocellulose membrane filters, *with not more than 12.6% nitrogen, by dry mass*	4.1	UN3270	II	4.1	43, A1	133	FLAMMABLE SOLID
	Nitrocellulose, plasticized *with not less than 18 percent plasticizing substance, by mass*	1.3C	UN0343		1.3C		112	EXPLOSIVES 1.3*
	Nitrocellulose, solution, flammable *with not more than 12.5 percent nitrogen, by mass, and not more than 55 percent nitrocellulose*	3	UN2059	I	3	198, T11, TP1, TP8, TP27	127	FLAMMABLE
				II	3	198, IB2, T4, TP1, TP8	127	FLAMMABLE
				III	3	198, B1, IB3, T2, TP1	127	FLAMMABLE
	Nitrocellulose, *unmodified or plasticized with less than 18 percent plasticizing substance, by mass*	1.1D	UN0341		1.1D		112	EXPLOSIVES 1.1*
	Nitrocellulose, wetted *with not less than 25 percent alcohol, by mass*	1.3C	UN0342		1.3C		112	EXPLOSIVES 1.3*
	Nitrocellulose with alcohol *with not less than 25 percent alcohol by mass, and with not more than 12.6 percent nitrogen, by dry mass*	4.1	UN2556	II	4.1	W31	113	FLAMMABLE SOLID

Hazardous materials descriptions and proper shipping names	Hazard class	ID No.	PG	Label codes	Special provisions	Guide	Response
Nitrocellulose, with not more than 12.6 percent nitrogen, by dry mass mixture with or without plasticizer, with or without pigment	4.1	UN2557	II	4.1	44, W31	133	FLAMMABLE SOLID
Nitrocellulose with water *with not less than 25 percent water by mass*	4.1	UN2555	II	4.1	W31	113	FLAMMABLE SOLID
Nitrochlorobenzene, see Chloronitrobenzenes etc.							
Nitrocresols, liquid	6.1	UN3434	III	6.1	IB3, T4, TP1	153	POISON
Nitrocresols, solid	6.1	UN2446	III	6.1	IB8, TP3, T1, TP33	153	POISON
Nitroethane	3	UN2842	III	3	B1, IB3, T2, TP1	129	FLAMMABLE
Nitroethyl nitrate	Forbidden						
Nitroethylene polymer	Forbidden						
Nitrogen, compressed	2.2	UN1066		2.2		120	NONFLAMMABLE GAS
Nitrogen dioxide, see Dinitrogen tetroxide							
Nitrogen fertilizer solution, see Fertilizer ammoniating solution etc.							
Nitrogen peroxide, see Dinitrogen tetroxide							
Nitrogen, refrigerated liquid *cryogenic liquid*	2.2	UN1977		2.2	345, 346, T75, TP5	120	NONFLAMMABLE GAS
Nitrogen tetroxide and nitric oxide mixtures, see Nitric oxide and nitrogen tetroxide mixtures							
Nitrogen tetroxide, see Dinitrogen tetroxide							
Nitrogen trichloride	Forbidden						
Nitrogen trifluoride	2.2	UN2451		2.2, 5.1		122	NONFLAMMABLE GAS
Nitrogen triiodide	Forbidden						
Nitrogen triiodide monoamine	Forbidden						
Nitrogen trioxide	2.3	UN2421		2.3, 5.1, 8	1	124	INHALATION HAZARD CLASS 2*
Nitroglycerin, desensitized *with not less than 40 percent non-volatile water insoluble phlegmatizer, by mass*	1.1D	UN0143		1.1D, 6.1	125	112	EXPLOSIVES 1.1*
Nitroglycerin, liquid, not desensitized	Forbidden						
Nitroglycerin mixture, desensitized, liquid, flammable, n.o.s. *with not more than 30 percent nitroglycerin, by mass*	3	UN3343	III	3	129	113	FLAMMABLE

Symbols (1)	Hazardous materials descriptions and proper shipping names (2)	Hazard class or Division (3)	Identification Numbers (4)	PG (5)	Label Codes (6)	Special Provisions (§172.102) (7)	ERG Guide No.	Placard Advisory Consult §172.504 & §172.505 *Placard any quantity
	Nitroglycerin mixture, desensitized, liquid, n.o.s. with not more than 30% nitroglycerin, by mass	3	UN3357	II	3	142	113	FLAMMABLE
	Nitroglycerin mixture, desensitized, solid, n.o.s. with more than 2 percent but not more than 10 percent nitroglycerin, by mass	4.1	UN3319	II	4.1	118	113	FLAMMABLE SOLID
	Nitroglycerin, solution in alcohol, with more than 1 percent but not more than 5 percent nitroglycerin	3	UN3064	II	3	N8	127	FLAMMABLE
	Nitroglycerin, solution in alcohol, with more than 1 percent but not more than 10 percent nitroglycerin	1.1D	UN0144		1.1D		112	EXPLOSIVES 1.1*
	Nitroglycerin solution in alcohol with not more than 1 percent nitroglycerin	3	UN1204	II	3	IB2, N34	127	FLAMMABLE
	Nitroguanidine nitrate	Forbidden						
	Nitroguanidine or Picrite, dry or wetted with less than 20 percent water, by mass	1.1D	UN0282		1.1D		112	EXPLOSIVES 1.1*
	Nitroguanidine, wetted or Picrite, wetted with not less than 20 percent water, by mass	4.1	UN1336	I	4.1	23, A8, A19, A20, N41, W31	113	FLAMMABLE SOLID
	1-Nitrohydantoin	Forbidden						
	Nitrohydrochloric acid	8	UN1798	I	8	B10, N41, T10, TP2, TP13	157	CORROSIVE
	Nitromannite (dry)	Forbidden						
	Nitromannite, wetted, see Mannitol hexanitrate, etc.							
	Nitromethane	3	UN1261	II	3		129	FLAMMABLE
	Nitromuriatic acid, see **Nitrohydrochloric acid**							
	Nitronaphthalene	4.1	UN2538	III	4.1	A1, IB8, IP3, T1, TP33	133	FLAMMABLE SOLID
+	**Nitrophenols (o-; m-; p-;)**	6.1	UN1663	III	6.1	IB8, IP3, T1, TP33	153	POISON
	m-Nitrophenyldinitro methane	Forbidden						
	4-Nitrophenylhydrazine, with not less than 30 percent water, by mass	4.1	UN3376	I	4.1	162, A8, A19, A20, N41, W31	113	FLAMMABLE SOLID
	Nitropropanes	3	UN2608	III	3	B1, IB3, T2, TP1	129	FLAMMABLE

Name	Hazard Class	PG	ID No.	Label Codes	Special Provisions	Guide No.	Placard
p-Nitrosodimethylaniline	4.2	II	UN1369	4.2	A19, A20, IB6, IP2, N34, T3, TP33	135	SPONTANEOUSLY COMBUSTIBLE
Nitrostarch, dry or wetted with less than 20 percent water, by mass	1.1D	II	UN0146	1.1D		112	EXPLOSIVES 1.1*
Nitrostarch, wetted with not less than 20 percent water, by mass	4.1	I	UN1337	4.1	23, A8, A19, A20, N41, W31	113	FLAMMABLE SOLID
Nitrosugars (dry)	Forbidden						
Nitrosyl chloride	2.3		UN1069	2.3, 8	3, B14	125	INHALATION HAZARD CLASS 2*
Nitrosylsulfuric acid, liquid	8	II	UN2308	8	A3, A7, B2, IB2, N34, T8, TP2	157	CORROSIVE
Nitrosylsulphuric acid, solid	8	II	UN3456	8	IB8, IP2, IP4, T3, TP33	157	CORROSIVE
Nitrotoluenes, liquid	6.1	II	UN1664	6.1	IB2, T7, TP2	152	POISON
Nitrotoluenes, solid	6.1	II	UN3446	6.1	IB8, IP2, IP4, T3, TP33	152	POISON
Nitrotoluidines (mono)	6.1	III	UN2660	6.1	IB8, IP3, T1, TP33	153	POISON
Nitrotriazolone or NTO	1.1D		UN0490	1.1D		112	EXPLOSIVES 1.1*
Nitrous oxide	2.2		UN1070	2.2, 5.1	A14	122	NONFLAMMABLE GAS
Nitrous oxide, refrigerated liquid	2.2		UN2201	2.2, 5.1	B6, T75, TP5, TP22	122	NONFLAMMABLE GAS
Nitroxylenes, liquid	6.1	II	UN1665	6.1	IB2, T7, TP2	152	POISON
Nitroxylenes, solid	6.1	II	UN3447	6.1	IB8, IP2, IP4, T3, TP33	152	POISON
Nitroxylol, see Nitroxylenes							
Nonanes	3	III	UN1920	3	B1, IB3, T2, TP2	128	FLAMMABLE
Nonflammable gas, n.o.s., see **Compressed gas**, etc. or **Liquefied gas** etc.							
Nonliquefied gases, see **Compressed gases**, etc.							
Nonliquefied hydrocarbon gas, see **Hydrocarbon gas mixture, compressed, n.o.s.**							
Nonyltrichlorosilane	8	II	UN1799	8	A7, B2, B6, N34, T10, TP2, TP7, TP13	156	CORROSIVE
2,5-Norbornadiene, stabilized, see **Bicyclo [2,2,1] hepta-2,5-diene, stabilized**							

Symbols (1)	Hazardous materials descriptions and proper shipping names (2)	Hazard class or Division (3)	Identification Numbers (4)	PG (5)	Label Codes (6)	Special Provisions (§172.102) (7)	ERG Guide No.	Placard Advisory Consult §172.504 & §172.505 *Placard any quantity
	Nordhausen acid, see Sulfuric acid, fuming etc.							
	Octadecyltrichlorosilane	8	UN1800	II	8	A7, B2, B6, N34, T10, TP2, TP7, TP13	156	CORROSIVE
	Octadiene	3	UN2309	II	3	B1, IB2, T4, TP1	128P	FLAMMABLE
	1,7-Octadine-3,5-diyne-1,8-dimethoxy-9-octadecynoic acid	Forbidden						
	Octafluorobut-2-ene or Refrigerant gas R 1318	2.2	UN2422		2.2		126	NONFLAMMABLE GAS
	Octafluorocyclobutane or Refrigerant gas RC 318	2.2	UN1976		2.2	T50	126	NONFLAMMABLE GAS
	Octafluoropropane, or Refrigerant gas, R 218	2.2	UN2424		2.2	T50	126	NONFLAMMABLE GAS
	Octanes	3	UN1262	II	3	IB2, T4, TP2	128	FLAMMABLE
	Octogen, etc. see Cyclotetramethylene tetranitramine, etc.							
	Octolite or Octol, *dry or wetted with less than 15 percent water, by mass*	1.1D	UN0266		1.1D		112	EXPLOSIVES 1.1*
	Octonal	1.1D	UN0496		1.1D		112	EXPLOSIVES 1.1*
	Octyl aldehydes	3	UN1191	III	3	B1, IB3, T2, TP1	129	FLAMMABLE
	Octyltrichlorosilane	8	UN1801	II	8	A7, B2, B6, N34, T10, TP2, TP7, TP13	156	CORROSIVE
	Oil gas, compressed	2.3	UN1071		2.3, 2.1	6	119	INHALATION HAZARD CLASS 2*
	Oleum, see Sulfuric acid, fuming							
	Organic peroxide type A, liquid or solid	Forbidden						
G	**Organic peroxide type B, liquid**	5.2	UN3101		5.2, 1	53	146	ORGANIC PEROXIDE
G	**Organic peroxide type B, liquid, temperature controlled**	5.2	UN3111		5.2, 1	53	148	ORGANIC PEROXIDE*
G	**Organic peroxide type B, solid**	5.2	UN3102		5.2, 1	53	146	ORGANIC PEROXIDE
G	**Organic peroxide type B, solid, temperature controlled**	5.2	UN3112		5.2, 1	53	148	ORGANIC PEROXIDE*
G	**Organic peroxide type C, liquid**	5.2	UN3103		5.2		146	ORGANIC PEROXIDE
G	**Organic peroxide type C, liquid, temperature controlled**	5.2	UN3113		5.2		148	ORGANIC PEROXIDE
G	**Organic peroxide type C, solid**	5.2	UN3104		5.2		146	ORGANIC PEROXIDE

Sym	Hazardous materials descriptions	Class	ID No.	PG	Special provisions	Guide	Label
G	Organic peroxide type C, solid, temperature controlled	5.2	UN3114			148	ORGANIC PEROXIDE
G	Organic peroxide type D, liquid	5.2	UN3105			145	ORGANIC PEROXIDE
G	Organic peroxide type D, liquid, temperature controlled	5.2	UN3115			148	ORGANIC PEROXIDE
G	Organic peroxide type D, solid	5.2	UN3106			145	ORGANIC PEROXIDE
G	Organic peroxide type D, solid, temperature controlled	5.2	UN3116			148	ORGANIC PEROXIDE
G	Organic peroxide type E, liquid	5.2	UN3107		A61	145	ORGANIC PEROXIDE
G	Organic peroxide type E, liquid, temperature controlled	5.2	UN3117			148	ORGANIC PEROXIDE
G	Organic peroxide type E, solid	5.2	UN3108			145	ORGANIC PEROXIDE
G	Organic peroxide type E, solid, temperature controlled	5.2	UN3118			148	ORGANIC PEROXIDE
G	Organic peroxide type F, liquid	5.2	UN3109		A61, IP5	145	ORGANIC PEROXIDE
G	Organic peroxide type F, liquid, temperature controlled	5.2	UN3119		IP5	148	ORGANIC PEROXIDE
G	Organic peroxide type F, solid	5.2	UN3110		TP33	145	ORGANIC PEROXIDE
G	Organic peroxide type F, solid, temperature controlled	5.2	UN3120		TP33	148	ORGANIC PEROXIDE
D	Organic phosphate, mixed with compressed gas or Organic phosphate compound, mixed with compressed gas or Organic phosphorus compound, mixed with compressed gas	2.3	NA1955		3	123	INHALATION HAZARD CLASS 2*
	Organic pigments, self-heating	4.2	UN3313	II	IB8, IP2, IP4, T3, TP33	135	SPONTANECUSLY COMBUSTIBLE
		4.2		III	IB8, IP3, T1, TF33	135	SPONTANECUSLY COMBUSTIBLE
G	Organoarsenic compound, liquid, n.o.s.	6.1	UN3280	I	5, T14, TP2, TF13, TP27	151	POISON
		6.1		II	IB2, T11, TP2, "TP27	151	POISON
		6.1		III	IB3, T7, TP1, TP28	151	POISON
G	Organoarsenic compound, solid, n.o.s.	6.1	UN3465	I	IB7, IP1, T6, TP33	151	POISON
		6.1		II	IB8, IP2, IP4, T3, TP33	151	POISON
		6.1		III	IB8, IP3, T1, TP33	151	POISON
	Organochlorine pesticides liquid, flammable, toxic, *flash point* less than 23 degrees C	3	UN2762	I	T14, TP2, TP13, TP27	131	FLAMMABLE
		3, 6.1		II	IB2, T11, TP2, TP13, TP27	131	FLAMMABLE
	Organochlorine pesticides, liquid, toxic	6.1	UN2996	I	T14, TP2, TP13, TP27	151	POISON
		6.1		II	IB2, T11, TP2, TP13, TP27	151	POISON

Symbols (1)	Hazardous materials descriptions and proper shipping names (2)	Hazard class or Division (3)	Identification Numbers (4)	PG (5)	Label Codes (6)	Special Provisions (§172.102) (7)	ERG Guide No.	Placard Advisory Consult §172.504 & §172.505 *Placard any quantity
	Organochlorine pesticides, liquid, toxic, flammable, *flash point not less than 23 degrees C*	6.1		III	6.1	IB3, T7, TP2, TP28	151	POISON
			UN2995	I	6.1, 3	T14, TP2, TP13, TP27	131	POISON
				II	6.1, 3	IB2, T11, TP2, TP13, TP27	131	POISON
				III	6.1, 3	B1, IB3, T7, TP2, TP28	131	POISON
	Organochlorine, pesticides, solid, toxic	6.1	UN2761	I	6.1	IB7, IP1, T6, TP33	151	POISON
				II	6.1	IB8, IP2, IP4, T3, TP33	151	POISON
				III	6.1	IB8, IP3, T1, TP33	151	POISON
G	Organometallic compound, liquid, toxic, n.o.s.	6.1	UN3282	I	6.1	T14, TP2, TP13, TP27	151	POISON
				II	6.1	IB2, T11, TP2, TP27	151	POISON
				III	6.1	IB3, T7, TP1, TP28	151	POISON
G	Organometallic compound, solid, toxic, n.o.s.	6.1	UN3467	I	6.1	IB7, IP1, T6, TP33	151	POISON
				II	6.1	IB8, IP2, IP4, T3, TP33	151	POISON
				III	6.1	IB8, IP3, T1, TP33	151	POISON
G	Organometallic substance, liquid, pyrophoric	4.2	UN3392	I	4.2	B11, T21, TP2, TP7, TP36	135	SPONTANEOUSLY COMBUSTIBLE
G	Organometallic substance, liquid, pyrophoric, water-reactive	4.2	UN3394	I	4.2, 4.3	B11, T21, TP2, TP7, TP36, TP47	135	SPONTANEOUSLY COMBUSTIBLE, DANGEROUS WHEN WET*
G	Organometallic substance, liquid, water-reactive	4.3	UN3398	I	4.3	T13, TP2, TP7, TP36, TP47, W31	135	DANGEROUS WHEN WET*
				II	4.3	IB1, IP2, T7, TP2, TP7, TP36, TP47, W31	135	DANGEROUS WHEN WET*
				III	4.3	IB2, IP4, T7, TP2, TP7, TP36, TP47, W31	135	DANGEROUS WHEN WET*
G	Organometallic substance, liquid, water-reactive, flammable	4.3	UN3399	I	4.3, 3	T13, TP2, TP7, TP36, TP47, W31	138	DANGEROUS WHEN WET*

Symbol	Hazardous materials descriptions and proper shipping names	Hazard class or Division	Identification Numbers	PG	Label Codes	Special Provisions	ERG No.	Placard
				II	4.3, 3	IB1, IP2, T7, TP2, TP36, TP47, WS1	138	DANGEROUS WHEN WET*
				III	4.3, 3	IB2, IP4, T7, TP2, TP7, TP36, TP47, WS1	138	DANGEROUS WHEN WET*
G	Organometallic substance, solid, pyrophoric	4.2	UN3391	I	4.2	T21, TP7, TP33, TP36	135	SPONTANEOUSLY COMBUSTIBLE
G	Organometallic substance, solid, pyrophoric, water-reactive	4.2	UN3393	I	4.2, 4.3	B11, T21, TP7, TP33, TP36, TP47	135	SPONTANEOUSLY COMBUSTIBLE, DANGEROUS WHEN WET*
G	Organometallic substance, solid, self-heating	4.2	UN3400	II	4.2	IB6, T3, TP33, TP36	138	SPONTANEOUSLY COMBUSTIBLE
				III	4.2	IB8, T1, TP33, TP36	138	SPONTANEOUSLY COMBUSTIBLE
G	Organometallic substance, solid, water-reactive	4.3	UN3395	I	4.3	N40, T9, TP7, TP33, TP36, TP47, W31	135	DANGEROUS WHEN WET*
				II	4.3	IB4, T3, TP33, TP36, TP47, W31	135	DANGEROUS WHEN WET*
				III	4.3	IB6, T1, TP33, TP36, TP47, W31	135	DANGEROUS WHEN WET*
G	Organometallic substance, solid, water-reactive, flammable	4.3	UN3396	I	4.3, 4.1	N40, T9, TP7, TP33, TP36, TP47, W31	138	DANGEROUS WHEN WET*
				II	4.3, 4.1	IB4, T3, TP33, TP36, TP47, W31	138	DANGEROUS WHEN WET*
				III	4.3, 4.1	IB6, T1, TP33, TP36, TP47, W31	138	DANGEROUS WHEN WET*
G	Organometallic substance, solid, water-reactive, self-heating	4.3	UN3397	I	4.3, 4.2	N40, T9, TP7, TP33, TP36, TP47, W31	138	DANGEROUS WHEN WET*
				II	4.3, 4.2	IB4, T3, TP33, TP36, TP47, W31	138	DANGEROUS WHEN WET*
				III	4.3, 4.2	IB6, T1, TP33, TP36, TP47, W31	138	DANGEROUS WHEN WET*
	Organophosphorus compound, toxic, flammable, n.o.s.	6.1	UN3279	I	6.1, 3	5, T14, TP2, TP13, TP27	131	POISON
				II	6.1, 3	IB2, T11, TP2, TP13, TP27	131	POISON

Symbols (1)	Hazardous materials descriptions and proper shipping names (2)	Hazard class or Division (3)	Identification Numbers (4)	PG (5)	Label Codes (6)	Special Provisions (§172.102) (7)	ERG Guide No.	Placard Advisory Consult §172.504 & §172.505 *Placard any quantity
G	Organophosphorus compound, liquid, toxic, n.o.s.	6.1	UN3278	I	6.1	5, T14, TP2, TP13, TP27	151	POISON
				II	6.1	IB2, T11, TP2, TP27	151	POISON
				III	6.1	IB3, T7, TP1, TP28	151	POISON
G	Organophosphorus compound, solid, toxic, n.o.s.	6.1	UN3464	I	6.1	IB7, IP1, T6, TP33	151	POISON
				II	6.1	IB8, IP2, IP4, T3, TP33	151	POISON
				III	6.1	IB8, IP3, T1, TP33	151	POISON
	Organophosphorus pesticides, liquid, flammable, toxic, *flash point less than 23 degrees C*	3	UN2784	I	3, 6.1	T14, TP2, TP13, TP27	131	FLAMMABLE
				II	3, 6.1	IB2, T11, TP2, TP13, TP27	131	FLAMMABLE
	Organophosphorus pesticides, liquid, toxic	6.1	UN3018	I	6.1	N76, T14, TP2, TP13, TP27	152	POISON
				II	6.1	IB2, N76, T11, TP2, TP13, TP27	152	POISON
				III	6.1	IB3, N76, T7, TP2, TP28	152	POISON
	Organophosphorus pesticides, liquid, toxic, flammable, *flashpoint not less than 23 degrees C*	6.1	UN3017	I	6.1, 3	N76, T14, TP2, TP13, TP27	131	POISON
				II	6.1, 3	IB2, N76, T11, TP2, TP13, TP27	131	POISON
				III	6.1, 3	B1, IB3, N76, T7, TP2, TP28	131	POISON
	Organophosphorus pesticides, solid, toxic	6.1	UN2783	I	6.1	IB7, IP1, N77, T6, TP33	152	POISON
				II	6.1	IB8, IP2, IP4, N77, T3, TP33	152	POISON
				III	6.1	IB8, IP3, N77, T1, TP33	152	POISON
	Organotin compounds, liquid, n.o.s.	6.1	UN2788	I	6.1	N33, N34, T14, TP2, TP13, TP27	153	POISON
				II	6.1	A3, IB2, N33, N34, T11, TP2, TP13, TP27	153	POISON

Symbols	Hazardous materials descriptions	Hazard class	ID No.	PG	Label Codes	Special provisions	ERG	Placard
	Organotin compounds, solid, n.o.s.	6.1	UN3146	III	6.1	IB3, T7, TP2, TP28	153	POISON
				I	6.1	A5, IB7, IP1, T6, TP33	153	POISON
				II	6.1	IB8, IP2, IP4, T3, TP33	153	POISON
				III	6.1	IB8, IP3, T1, TP33	153	POISON
	Organotin pesticides, liquid, flammable, toxic, *flash point less than 23 degrees C*	3	UN2787	I	3, 6.1	T14, TP2, TP13, TP27	131	FLAMMABLE
				II	3, 6.1	IB2, T11, TP2, TP13, TP27	131	FLAMMABLE
	Organotin pesticides, liquid, toxic	6.1	UN3020	I	6.1	T14, TP2, TP13, TP27	153	POISON
				II	6.1	IB2, T11, TP2, TP13, TP27	153	POISON
				III	6.1	IB3, T7, TP2, TP28	153	POISON
	Organotin pesticides, liquid, toxic, flammable, *flashpoint not less than 23 degrees C*	6.1	UN3019	I	6.1, 3	T14, TP2, TP13, TP27	131	POISON
				II	6.1, 3	IB2, T11, TP2, TP13, TP27	131	POISON
				III	6.1, 3	B1, IB3, T7, TF2, TP28	131	POISON
	Organotin pesticides, solid, toxic	6.1	UN2786	I	6.1	IB7, IP1, T6, TP33	153	POISON
				II	6.1	IB8, IP2, IP4, T3, TP33	153	POISON
				III	6.1	IB8, IP3, T1, TP33	153	POISON
	Orthonitroaniline, see Nitroanilines etc.							
	Osmium tetroxide	6.1	UN2471	I	6.1	A8, IB7, IP1, N33, N34, T6, TP33, W31	154	POISON
D G	**Other regulated substances, liquid, n.o.s.**	9	NA3082	III	9	A189, IB3, T2, TP1	171	CLASS 9
D G	**Other regulated substances, solid, n.o.s.**	9	NA3077	III	9	384, B54, IB8, IP2, T1, TP33	171	CLASS 9
G	**Oxidizing liquid, corrosive, n.o.s.**	5.1	UN3098	I	5.1, 8	62	140	OXIDIZER
				II	5.1, 8	62, IB1	140	OXIDIZER
				III	5.1, 8	62, IB2	140	OXIDIZER
G	**Oxidizing liquid, n.o.s.**	5.1	UN3139	I	5.1	62, 127, A2	140	OXIDIZER
				II	5.1	62, 127, 148, A2, IB2	140	OXIDIZER
				III	5.1	62, 127, 148, A2, IB2	140	OXIDIZER
G	**Oxidizing liquid, toxic, n.o.s.**	5.1	UN3099	I	5.1, 6.1	62	142	OXIDIZER

Symbols (1)	Hazardous materials descriptions and proper shipping names (2)	Hazard class or Division (3)	Identification Numbers (4)	PG (5)	Label Codes (6)	Special Provisions (§172.102) (7)	ERG Guide No.	Placard Advisory Consult §172.504 & §172.505 *Placard any quantity
				II	5.1, 6.1	62, IB1	142	OXIDIZER
				III	5.1, 6.1	62, IB2	142	OXIDIZER
G	Oxidizing solid, corrosive, n.o.s.	5.1	UN3085	I	5.1, 8	62	140	OXIDIZER
				II	5.1, 8	62, IB6, IP2, T3, TP33	140	OXIDIZER
				III	5.1, 8	62, IB8, IP3, T1, TP33	140	OXIDIZER
G	Oxidizing solid, flammable, n.o.s.	5.1	UN3137	I	5.1, 4.1	62	140	OXIDIZER
G	Oxidizing solid, n.o.s.	5.1	UN1479	I	5.1	62, IB5, IP1	140	OXIDIZER
				II	5.1	62, IB8, IP2, IP4, T3, TP33	140	OXIDIZER
				III	5.1	62, 148, IB8, IP3, T1, TP33	140	OXIDIZER
G	Oxidizing solid, self-heating, n.o.s.	5.1	UN3100	I	5.1, 4.2	62	135	OXIDIZER
				II	5.1, 4.2	62	135	OXIDIZER
G	Oxidizing solid, toxic, n.o.s.	5.1	UN3087	I	5.1, 6.1	62	141	OXIDIZER
				II	5.1, 6.1	62, IB6, IP2, T3, TP33	141	OXIDIZER
				III	5.1, 6.1	62, IB8, IP3, T1, TP33	141	OXIDIZER
G	Oxidizing solid, water-reactive, n.o.s.	5.1	UN3121	I	5.1, 4.3	62	144	OXIDIZER, DANGEROUS WHEN WET*
	Oxygen, compressed	2.2	UN1072		2.2, 5.1	110, A14	122	NONFLAMMABLE GAS
	Oxygen difluoride, compressed	2.3	UN2190		2.3, 5.1, 8	1, N86	124	INHALATION HAZARD CLASS 2*

Symbols	Hazardous materials descriptions and proper shipping names	Hazard class or Division	Identification Numbers	PG	Label Codes	Special Provisions	Guide No.	Response
	Oxygen generator, chemical (including when contained in associated equipment, e.g., passenger service units (PSUs), portable breathing equipment (PBE), etc.)	5.1	UN3356	III	5.1	61	140	OXIDIZER
+	Oxygen generator, chemical, spent	9	NA3356		9		140	CLASS 9
	Oxygen, refrigerated liquid (cryogenic liquid)	2.2	UN1073		2.2, 5.1	T75, TP5, TP22	122	NONFLAMMABLE GAS
	Paint, corrosive, flammable (including paint, lacquer, enamel, stain, shellac, varnish, polish, liquid filler, and liquid lacquer base)	8	UN3470	II	8, 3	367, IB2, T7, TP2, TP8, TP28	132	CORROSIVE
	Paint, flammable, corrosive (including paint, lacquer, enamel, stain, shellac, varnish, polish, liquid filler and liquid lacquer base)	3	UN3469	I	3, 8	367, T11, TP2, TP27	132	FLAMMABLE
				II	3, 8	367, IB2, T7, TP2, TP8, TP28	132	FLAMMABLE
				III	3, 8	367, IB3, T4, TP1, TP29	132	FLAMMABLE
	Paint including paint, lacquer, enamel, stain, shellac solutions, varnish, polish, liquid filler, and liquid lacquer base	3	UN1263	I	3	367, T11, TP1, TP8, TP27	128	FLAMMABLE
				II	3	149, 367, B52, B131, IB2, T4, TP1, TP8, TP28	128	FLAMMABLE
				III	3	367, B1, B52, B131, IB3, T2, TP1, TP29	128	FLAMMABLE
	Paint or Paint related material	8	UN3066	II	8	367, B2, IB2, T7, TP2, TP28	153	CORROSIVE
				III	8	367, B52, IB3, T4, TP1, TP29	153	CORROSIVE
	Paint related material corrosive, flammable (including paint thinning or reducing compound)	8	UN3470	II	8, 3	367, IB2, T7, TP2, TP8, TP28	132	CORROSIVE
	Paint related material, flammable, corrosive (including paint thinning or reducing compound)	3	UN3469	I	3, 8	367, T11, TP2, TP27	132	FLAMMABLE
				II	3, 8	367, IB2, T7, TP2, TP8, TP28	132	FLAMMABLE
				III	3, 8	367, IB3, T4, TP1, TP29	132	FLAMMABLE
	Paint related material including paint thinning, drying, removing, or reducing compound	3	UN1263	I	3	367, T11, TP1, TP8, TP27	128	FLAMMABLE

Symbols (1)	Hazardous materials descriptions and proper shipping names (2)	Hazard class or Division (3)	Identification Numbers (4)	PG (5)	Label Codes (6)	Special Provisions (§172.102) (7)	ERG Guide No.	Placard Advisory Consult §172.504 & §172.505 *Placard any quantity
				II	3	149, 367, B52, B131, IB2, T4, TP1, TP8, TP28	128	FLAMMABLE
				III	3	367, B1, B52, B131, IB3, T2, TP1, TP29	128	FLAMMABLE
	Paper, unsaturated oil treated incompletely dried (including carbon paper)	4.2	UN1379	III	4.2	IB8, IP3, W31	133	SPONTANEOUSLY COMBUSTIBLE
	Paraformaldehyde	4.1	UN2213	III	4.1	A1, B120, IB8, IP3, T1, TP33	133	FLAMMABLE SOLID
	Paraldehyde	3	UN1264	III	3	B1, IB3, T2, TP1	129	FLAMMABLE
	Paranitroaniline, solid, see Nitroanilines etc.							
D	Parathion and compressed gas mixture	2.3	NA1967		2.3	3	123	INHALATION HAZARD CLASS 2*
	Paris green, solid, see Copper acetoarsenite							
	PCB, see Polychlorinated biphenyls							
+	Pentaborane	4.2	UN1380	I	4.2, 6.1	1	135	SPONTANEOUSLY COMBUSTIBLE, INHALATION HAZARD CLASS 6*
	Pentachloroethane	6.1	UN1669	II	6.1	IB2, T7, TP2	151	POISON
	Pentachlorophenol	6.1	UN3155	II	6.1	IB8, IP2, IP4, T3, TP33	154	POISON
	Pentaerythrite tetranitrate (dry)	Forbidden						
	Pentaerythrite tetranitrate mixture, desensitized, solid, n.o.s. or Pentaerythritol tetranitrate mixture, desensitized, solid, n.o.s., with more than 10 percent but not more than 20 percent PETN, by mass	4.1	UN3344	II	4.1	118, N85	113	FLAMMABLE SOLID
	Pentaerythrite tetranitrate or Pentaerythritol tetranitrate or PETN, with not less than 7 percent wax by mass	1.1D	UN0411		1.1D	120	112	EXPLOSIVES 1.1*

Hazardous materials descriptions and proper shipping names	Hazard class or Division	Identification Numbers	PG	Label Codes	Special provisions	Guide No.	Placard
Pentaerythrite tetranitrate, wetted or Pentaerythritol tetranitrate, wetted with not less than 25 percent water, by mass, or PETN, wetted with not less than 25 percent water, by mass, or Pentaerythrite tetranitrate, or Pentaerythritol tetranitrate or PETN, desensitized with not less than 15 percent phlegmatizer by mass	1.1D	UN0150		1.1D	121	112	EXPLOSIVES 1.1*
Pentaerythritol tetranitrate, see Pentaerythrite tetranitrate, etc.							
Pentafluoroethane or Refrigerant gas R 125	2.2	UN3220		2.2	T50	126	NONFLAMMABLE GAS
Pentamethylheptane	3	UN2286	III	3	B1, IB3, T2, TP1	128	FLAMMABLE
Pentane-2,4-dione	3	UN2310	III	3, 6.1	B1, IB3, T4, TP1	131	FLAMMABLE
Pentanes	3	UN1265	I	3	T11, TP2	128	FLAMMABLE
			II	3	IB2, IP8, T4, TP1	128	FLAMMABLE
Pentanitroaniline (dry)	Forbidden						
Pentanols	3	UN1105	II	3	IB2, T4, TP1, TP29	129	FLAMMABLE
			III	3	B1, B3, IB3, T2, TP1	129	FLAMMABLE
1-Pentene (n-amylene)	3	UN1108	I	3	T11, TP2	128	FLAMMABLE
1-Pentol	8	UN2705	II	8	B2, IB2, T7, TP2	153P	CORROSIVE
Pentolite, dry or wetted with less than 15 percent water, by mass	1.1D	UN0151		1.1D		112	EXPLOSIVES 1.1*
Pepper spray, see Aerosols , etc. or Self-defense spray, non-pressurized							
Perchlorates, inorganic, aqueous solution, n.o.s.	5.1	UN3211	II	5.1	IB2, T4, TP1	140	OXIDIZER
			III	5.1	IB2, T4, TP1	140	OXIDIZER
Perchlorates, inorganic, n.o.s.	5.1	UN1481	II	5.1	IB6, IP2, T3, TP33	140	OXIDIZER
			III	5.1	IB8, IP3, T1, TP33	140	OXIDIZER
Perchloric acid, with more than 72 percent acid by mass	Forbidden						
Perchloric acid, with more than 50 percent but not more than 72 percent acid, by mass	5.1	UN1873	I	5.1, 8	A2, N41, T10, TP1	143	OXIDIZER
Perchloric acid with not more than 50 percent acid by mass	8	UN1802	II	8, 5.1	IB2, N41, T7, TP2	157	CORROSIVE
Perchloroethylene, see Tetrachloroethylene							
Perchloromethyl mercaptan	6.1	UN1670	I	6.1	2, B9, B14, B32, N34, T20, TP2, TP13, TP38, TP45	157	INHALATION HAZARD CLASS 6*
Perchloryl fluoride	2.3	UN3083		2.3, 5.1	2, B9, B14	124	INHALATION HAZARD CLASS 2*

Symbols (1)	Hazardous materials descriptions and proper shipping names (2)	Hazard class or Division (3)	Identification Numbers (4)	PG (5)	Label Codes (6)	Special Provisions (§172.102) (7)	ERG Guide No.	Placard Advisory Consult §172.504 & §172.505 *Placard any quantity
	Percussion caps, see Primers, cap type							
	Perfluoro-2-butene, see Octafluorobut-2-ene							
	Perfluoro(ethyl vinyl ether)	2.1	UN3154		2.1		115	FLAMMABLE GAS
	Perfluorom(ethyl vinyl ether)	2.1	UN3153		2.1		115	FLAMMABLE GAS
	Perfumery products with flammable solvents	3	UN1266	II	3	T50	127	FLAMMABLE
				III	3	149, IB2, T4, TP1, TP8	127	FLAMMABLE
						B1, IB3, T2, TP1		
G	**Permanganates, inorganic, aqueous solution, n.o.s.**	5.1	UN3214	II	5.1	26, 353, IB2, T4, TP1	140	OXIDIZER
G	**Permanganates, inorganic, n.o.s.**	5.1	UN1482	II	5.1	26, 353, A30, IB6, IP2, T3, TP33	140	OXIDIZER
				III	5.1	26, 353, A30, IB8, IP3, T1, TP33	140	OXIDIZER
	Permeation devices for calibrating air quality monitoring equipment See §173.175							
	Peroxides, inorganic, n.o.s.	5.1	UN1483	II	5.1	A7, A20, IB6, IP2, N34, T3, TP33, W100	140	OXIDIZER
				III	5.1	A7, A20, B134, IB8, IP21, N34, T1, TP33, W100	140	OXIDIZER
	Peroxyacetic acid, with more than 43 percent and with more than 6 percent hydrogen peroxide	Forbidden						
	Persulfates, inorganic, aqueous solution, n.o.s.	5.1	UN3216	III	5.1	IB2, T4, TP1, TP29	140	OXIDIZER
	Persulfates, inorganic, n.o.s.	5.1	UN3215	III	5.1	IB8, IP3, T1, TP33	140	OXIDIZER
G	*Pesticides, liquid, flammable, toxic, flash point less than 23 degrees C*	3	UN3021	I	3, 6.1	B5, T14, TP2, TP13, TP27	131	FLAMMABLE
				II	3, 6.1	IB2, T11, TP2, TP13, TP27	131	FLAMMABLE
G	*Pesticides, liquid, toxic, flammable, n.o.s. flash point not less than 23 degrees C*	6.1	UN2903	I	6.1, 3	T14, TP2, TP13, TP27	131	POISON
				II	6.1, 3	IB2, T11, TP2, TP13, TP27	131	POISON
				III	6.1, 3	B1, IB3, T7, TP2	131	POISON

Sym	Hazardous materials descriptions	Class	ID No.	PG	Label codes	Special provisions	ERG	
G	Pesticides, liquid, toxic, n.o.s.	6.1	UN2902	I	6.1	T14, TP2, TP13, TP27	151	POISON
				II	6.1	IB2, T11, TP2, TP13, TP27	151	POISON
				III	6.1	IB3, T7, TP2, TP28	151	POISON
G	Pesticides, solid, toxic, n.o.s.	6.1	UN2588	I	6.1	IB7, T6, TP33	151	POISON
				II	6.1	IB8, IP2, IP4, T3, TP33	151	POISON
				III	6.1	IB8, IP3, T1, TP33	151	POISON
	PETN, see Pentaerythrite tetranitrate							
	PETN/TNT, see Pentolite etc.							
	Petrol, see Gasoline							
	Petroleum crude oil	3	UN1267	I	3	144, 357, T11, TP1, TP8	128	FLAMMABLE
				II	3	144, 357, IB2, T4, TP1, TP8	128	FLAMMABLE
				III	3	144, 357, B1, IB3, T2, TP1	128	FLAMMABLE
	Petroleum distillates, n.o.s. or Petroleum products, n.o.s.	3	UN1268	I	3	144, T11, TP1, TP8	128	FLAMMABLE
				II	3	144, IB2, T7, TP1, TP8, TP28	128	FLAMMABLE
				III	3	144, B1, IB3, T4, TP1, TP29	128	FLAMMABLE
	Petroleum gases, liquefied or Liquefied petroleum gas	2.1	UN1075		2.1	T50, N95	115	FLAMMABLE GAS
D	Petroleum oil	3	NA1270	I	3	144, T11, TP1	128	FLAMMABLE
				II	3	144, IB2, T7, TP1, TP8, TP28	128	FLAMMABLE
				III	3	144, B1, IB3, T4, TP1, TP29	128	FLAMMABLE
I	Petroleum sour crude oil, flammable, toxic	3	UN3494	I	3, 6.1	343, T14, TP2, TP13	131	FLAMMABLE
				II	3, 6.1	343, IB2, T7, TP2	131	FLAMMABLE
				III	3, 6.1	343, IB3, T4, TP1	131	FLAMMABLE
	Phenacyl bromide	6.1	UN2645	II	6.1	IB8, IP2, IP4, T3, TP33	153	POISON
+	Phenetidines	6.1	UN2311	III	6.1	IB3, T4, TP1	153	POISON
	Phenol, molten	6.1	UN2312	II	6.1	B14, T7, TP3	153	POISON

Symbols (1)	Hazardous materials descriptions and proper shipping names (2)	Hazard class or Division (3)	Identification Numbers (4)	PG (5)	Label Codes (6)	Special Provisions (§172.102) (7)	ERG Guide No.	Placard Advisory Consult §172.504 & §172.505 *Placard any quantity
+	Phenol, solid	6.1	UN1671	II	6.1	IB8, IP2, IP4, N78, T3, TP33	153	POISON
	Phenol solutions	6.1	UN2821	II	6.1	IB2, T7, TP2	153	POISON
				III	6.1	IB3, T4, TP1	153	POISON
	Phenolsulfonic acid, liquid	8	UN1803	II	8	B2, IB2, N41, T7, TP2	153	CORROSIVE
	Phenoxyacetic acid derivative pesticide, liquid, flammable, toxic, *flash point less than 23 degrees C*	3	UN3346	I	3, 6.1	T14, TP2, TP13, TP27	131	FLAMMABLE
				II	3, 6.1	IB2, T11, TP2, TP13, TP27	131	FLAMMABLE
	Phenoxyacetic acid derivative pesticide, liquid, toxic	6.1	UN3348	I	6.1	T14, TP2, TP13, TP27	153	POISON
				II	6.1	IB2, T11, TP2, TP27	153	POISON
				III	6.1	IB3, T7, TP2, TP28	153	POISON
	Phenoxyacetic acid derivative pesticide, liquid, toxic, flammable, *flash point not less than 23 degrees C*	6.1	UN3347	I	6.1, 3	T14, TP2, TP13, TP27	131	POISON
				II	6.1, 3	IB2, T11, TP2, TP13, TP27	131	POISON
				III	6.1, 3	IB3, T7, TP2, TP28	131	POISON
	Phenoxyacetic acid derivative pesticide, solid, toxic	6.1	UN3345	I	6.1	IB7, IP1, T6, TP33	153	POISON
				II	6.1	IB8, IP2, IP4, T3, TP33	153	POISON
				III	6.1	IB8, IP3, T1, TP33	153	POISON
	Phenyl chloroformate	6.1	UN2746	II	6.1, 8	IB2, T7, TP2, TP13	156	POISON
	Phenyl isocyanate	6.1	UN2487	I	6.1, 3	2, B9, B14, B32, B77, N33, N34, T20, TP2, TP13, TP38, TP45	155	INHALATION HAZARD CLASS 6"
	Phenyl mercaptan	6.1	UN2337	I	6.1, 3	2, B9, B14, B32, B77, T20, TP2, TP13, TP38, TP45	131	INHALATION HAZARD CLASS 6"
	Phenyl phosphorus dichloride	8	UN2798	II	8	B2, B15, IB2, T7, TP2	137	CORROSIVE
	Phenyl phosphorus thiodichloride	8	UN2799	II	8	B2, B15, IB2, T7, TP2	137	CORROSIVE
	Phenyl urea pesticides, liquid, toxic	6.1	UN3002	I	6.1	T14, TP2, TP27	151	POISON
				II	6.1	T7, TP2	151	POISON

Symbols	Hazardous materials descriptions and proper shipping names	Hazard class or Division	Identification Numbers	PG	Label Codes	Special provisions	Guide No.	Hazard notes
	Phenylacetonitrile, liquid	6.1	UN2470	III	6.1	IB3, T4, TP1	151	POISON
	Phenylacetyl chloride	8	UN2577	II	8	B2, IB2, T7, TP2	152	POISON
	Phenylcarbylamine chloride	6.1	UN1672	I	6.1	2, B9, B14, B32, T20, TP2, TP13, TP38, TP45	156	CORROSIVE
							151	INHALATION HAZARD CLASS 6*
	m-Phenylene diaminediperchlorate (dry)	Forbidden						
+	Phenylenediamines (o-; m-; p-;)	6.1	UN1673	III	6.1	IB8, IP3, T1, TP33	153	POISON
	Phenylhydrazine	6.1	UN2572	II	6.1	IB2, T7, TP2	153	POISON
	Phenylmercuric acetate	6.1	UN1674	II	6.1	IB8, IP2, IP4, T3, TP33	151	POISON
G	Phenylmercuric compounds, n.o.s.	6.1	UN2026	I	6.1	IB7, IP1, T6, TP33	151	POISON
				II	6.1	IB8, IP2, IP4, T3, TP33	151	POISON
				III	6.1	IB8, IP3, T1, TP33	151	POISON
	Phenylmercuric hydroxide	6.1	UN1894	II	6.1	IB8, IP2, IP4, T3, TP33	151	POISON
	Phenylmercuric nitrate	6.1	UN1895	II	6.1	IB8, IP2, IP4, T3, TP33	151	POISON
	Phenyltrichlorosilane	8	UN1804	II	8	A7, B6, N34, T10, TP2, TP7, TP13	156	CORROSIVE
	Phosgene	2.3	UN1076		2.3, 8	1, B7, B46, N86	125	INHALATION HAZARD CLASS 2*
	9-Phosphabicyclononanes or Cyclooctadiene phosphines	4.2	UN2940	II	4.2	A19, IB6, IP2, T3, TP33, W31	135	SPONTANEOUSLY COMBUSTIBLE
	Phosphine	2.3	UN2199		2.3, 2.1	1	119	INHALATION HAZARD CLASS 2*
	Phosphine, adsorbed	2.3	UN3525		2.3, 2.1	1	173	INHALATION HAZARD CLASS 2*
	Phosphoric acid solution	8	UN1805	III	8	A7, IB3, N34, T4, TP1	154	CORROSIVE
	Phosphoric acid, solid	8	UN3453	III	8	IB8, IP3, T1, TP33	154	CORROSIVE
	Phosphoric acid triethyleneimine, see Tris-(1-aziridinyl)phosphine oxide, solution							
	Phosphoric anhydride, see Phosphorus pentoxide							
	Phosphorous acid	8	UN2834	III	8	IB8, IP3, T1, TP33	154	CORROSIVE
	Phosphorus, amorphous	4.1	UN1338	III	4.1	A1, A19, B1, B9, B26, IB8, IP3, T1, TP33	133	FLAMMABLE SOLID

Symbols (1)	Hazardous materials descriptions and proper shipping names (2)	Hazard class or Division (3)	Identification Numbers (4)	PG (5)	Label Codes (6)	Special Provisions (§172.102) (7)	ERG Guide No.	Placard Advisory Consult §172.504 & §172.505 *Placard any quantity
	Phosphorus bromide, see Phosphorus tribromide							
	Phosphorus chloride, see Phosphorus trichloride							
	Phosphorus heptasulfide, *free from yellow or white phosphorus*	4.1	UN1339	II	4.1	A20, IB4, N34, T3, TP33, W31	139	FLAMMABLE SOLID
	Phosphorus oxybromide	8	UN1939	II	8	B8, IB8, IP2, IP4, N41, N43, T3, TP33	137	CORROSIVE
	Phosphorus oxybromide, molten	8	UN2576	II	8	B2, B8, IB1, N41, N43, T7, TP3, TP13	137	CORROSIVE
+	Phosphorus oxychloride	6.1	UN1810	I	6.1, 8	2, B9, B14, B32, B77, N34, T20, TP2, TP13, TP38, TP45	137	INHALATION HAZARD CLASS 6*
	Phosphorus pentabromide	8	UN2691	II	8	A7, IB8, IP2, IP4, N34, T3, TP33	137	CORROSIVE
	Phosphorus pentachloride	8	UN1806	II	8	A7, IB8, IP2, IP4, N34, T3, TP33	137	CORROSIVE
	Phosphorus Pentafluoride	2.3	UN2198		2.3, 8	2, B9, B14	125	INHALATION HAZARD CLASS 2*
	Phosphorus pentafluoride, adsorbed	2.3	UN3524		2.3, 8	2, B9, B14	173	INHALATION HAZARD CLASS 2*
	Phosphorus pentasulfide, *free from yellow or white phosphorus*	4.3	UN1340	II	4.3, 4.1	A20, B59, IB4, T3, TP33, W31, W40	139	DANGEROUS WHEN WET*
	Phosphorus pentoxide	8	UN1807	II	8	A7, IB8, IP2, IP4, N34, T3, TP33	137	CORROSIVE
	Phosphorus sesquisulfide, *free from yellow or white phosphorus*	4.1	UN1341	II	4.1	A20, IB4, N34, T3, TP33, W31	139	FLAMMABLE SOLID
	Phosphorus tribromide	8	UN1808	II	8	A3, A7, B2, B25, IB2, N34, N43, T7, TP2	137	CORROSIVE
	Phosphorus trichloride	6.1	UN1809	I	6.1, 8	2, B9, B14, B15, B32, B77, N34, T20, TP2, TP13, TP38, TP45	137	INHALATION HAZARD CLASS 6*

Name	Class/Div.	ID No.	PG	Special Provisions	Label	Guide	Hazard
Phosphorus trioxide	8	UN2578	III	IB8, IP3, T1, TP33	8	157	CORROSIVE
Phosphorus trisulfide, *free from yellow or white phosphorus*	4.1	UN1343	II	A20, IB4, N34, T3, TP33, W31	4.1	139	FLAMMABLE SOLID
Phosphorus, white dry or Phosphorus, white, under water or Phosphorus, white, in solution or Phosphorus, yellow dry or Phosphorus, yellow, under water or Phosphorus, yellow, in solution	4.2	UN1381	I	B9, B26, N34, T9, TP3, TP31, W31	4.2, 6.1	136	SPONTANEOUSLY COMBUSTIBLE
Phosphorus white, molten	4.2	UN2447	I	B9, B26, N34, T21, TP3, TP7, TP26	4.2, 6.1	136	SPONTANEOUSLY COMBUSTIBLE
Phosphorus (white or red) and a chlorate, mixtures of	Forbidden						
Phosphoryl chloride, see Phosphorus oxychloride							
Phthalic anhydride with more than .05 percent maleic anhydride	8	UN2214	III	IB8, IP3, T1, TP33	8	156	CORROSIVE
Picolines	3	UN2313	III	B1, IB3, T4, TP1	3	129	FLAMMABLE
Picric acid, see Trinitrophenol, *etc.*							
Picrite, see Nitroguanidine, *etc.*							
Picryl chloride, see Trinitrochlorobenzene							
Pine oil	3	UN1272	III	B1, IB3, T2, TF2	3	129	FLAMMABLE
alpha-Pinene	3	UN2368	III	B1, IB3, T2, TF2	3	128	FLAMMABLE
Piperazine	8	UN2579	III	IB8, IP3, T1, TP33	8	153	CORROSIVE
Piperidine	8	UN2401	I	A10, T10, TP2	8, 3	132	CORROSIVE
Pivaloyl chloride, see Trimethylacetyl chloride							
Plastic molding compound *in dough, sheet or extruded rope form evolving flammable vapor*	9	UN3314	III	32, IB8, IP3, IP7	9	171	CLASS 9
Plastic solvent, n.o.s., see Flammable liquids, n.o.s.							
Plastics, nitrocellulose-based, self-heating, n.o.s.	4.2	UN2006	III		4.2	135	SPONTANEOUSLY COMBUSTIBLE
Poisonous gases, n.o.s., see Compressed or liquefied gases, flammable or toxic, n.o.s.							
Polyalkylamines, n.o.s., see Amines, *etc.*							
Polyamines, flammable, corrosive, n.o.s. see Amines, flammable, corrosive, n.o.s.							

Symbols (1)	Hazardous materials descriptions and proper shipping names (2)	Hazard class or Division (3)	Identification Numbers (4)	PG (5)	Label Codes (6)	Special Provisions (§172.102) (7)	ERG Guide No.	Placard Advisory Consult §172.504 & §172.505 *Placard any quantity
	Polyamines, liquid, corrosive, n.o.s. see Amines, liquid, corrosive, n.o.s.							
	Polyamines, liquid, corrosive, flammable, n.o.s. see Amines, liquid, corrosive, flammable, n.o.s.							
	Polychlorinated biphenyls, liquid	9	UN2315	II	9	9, 81, 140, IB3, T4, TP1	171	CLASS 9
	Polychlorinated biphenyls, solid	9	UN3432	II	9	9, 81, 140, IB8, IP2, IP4, T3, TP33	171	CLASS 9
	Polyester resin kit, *liquid base material*	3	UN3269	II	3	40, 149	128	FLAMMABLE
	Polyester resin kit, *solid base material*	4.1	UN3527	II	4.1	40, 157	128P	FLAMMABLE SOLID
	Polyhalogenated biphenyls, liquid *or* Halogenated monomethyldiphenyl-methanes, liquid *or* Polyhalogenated terphenyls liquid	9	UN3151	II	9	IB2	171	CLASS 9
	Polyhalogenated biphenyls, solid *or* Halogenated monomethyldiphenyl-methanes, solid *or* Polyhalogenated terphenyls, solid	9	UN3152	II	9	IB8, IP2, IP4, T3, TP33	171	CLASS 9
	Polymeric beads expandable, *evolving flammable vapor*	9	UN2211	III	9	32, IB8, IP3, IP7, T1, T33	171	CLASS 9
G	Polymerizing substance, liquid, stabilized, n.o.s	4.1	UN3532	III	4.1	387, 421, IB3, IP19, N92, T7, TP4, TP6	149P	FLAMMABLE SOLID
G	Polymerizing substance, liquid, temperature controlled, n.o.s.	4.1	UN3534	III	4.1	387, 421, IB3, IP19, N92, T7, TP4, TP6	150P	FLAMMABLE SOLID
G	Polymerizing substance, solid, stabilized, n.o.s.	4.1	UN3531	III	4.1	387, 421, IB7, IP19, N92, T7, TP4, TP6, TP33	149P	FLAMMABLE SOLID
G	Polymerizing substance, solid, temperature controlled, n.o.s.	4.1	UN3533	III	4.1	387, 421, IB7, IP19, N92, T7, TP4, TP6, TP33	150P	FLAMMABLE SOLID
	Potassium	4.3	UN2257	I	4.3	A7, A19, A20, B27, IB4, IP1, N6, N34, T9, TP7, TP33, W31	138	DANGEROUS WHEN WET*
	Potassium arsenate	6.1	UN1677	II	6.1	IB8, IP2, IP4, T3, TP33	151	POISON
	Potassium arsenite	6.1	UN1678	II	6.1	IB8, IP2, IP4, T3, TP33	154	POISON

Hazardous materials descriptions and proper shipping names	Hazard class or Division	Identification Numbers	PG	Label Codes	Special provisions	Guide	
Potassium bisulfite solution, see Bisulfites, aqueous solutions, n.o.s.							
Potassium borohydride	4.3	UN1870	I	4.3	A19, N40, W31	138	DANGEROUS WHEN WET
Potassium bromate	5.1	UN1484	II	5.1	IB8, IP2, IP4, T3, TP33	140	OXIDIZER
Potassium carbonyl	Forbidden						
Potassium chlorate	5.1	UN1485	II	5.1	A9, IB8, IP2, IP4, N34, T3, TP33	140	OXIDIZER
Potassium chlorate, aqueous solution	5.1	UN2427	II	5.1	A2, IB2, T4, TP1	140	OXIDIZER
			III	5.1	A2, IB2, T4, TP1	140	OXIDIZER
Potassium chlorate mixed with mineral oil, see **Explosive, blasting, type C**							
Potassium cuprocyanide	6.1	UN1679	II	6.1	IB8, IP2, IP4, T3, TP33	157	POISON
Potassium cyanide, solid	6.1	UN1680	I	6.1	B69, B77, IB7, IP1, N74, N75, T6, TP33, W31	157	POISON
Potassium cyanide solution	6.1	UN3413	I	6.1	B69, B77, N74, N75, T14, TP2, TP13, W31	157	POISON
			II	6.1	B69, B77, IB2, N74, N75, T11, TP2, TP13, TP27, W31		
			III	6.1	B69, B77, IB3, N74, N75, T7, TP2, TP13, TP28, W31		
Potassium dichloro isocyanurate or Potassium dichloro-s-triazinetrione, see **Dichloroisocyanuric acid, dry** or **Dichloroisocyanuric acid salts** etc.							
Potassium dithionite or **Potassium hydrosulfite**	4.2	UN1929	II	4.2	A8, A19, A20, IB6, IP2, T3, TP33, W31	135	SPONTANEOUSLY COMBUSTIBLE
Potassium fluoride, solid	6.1	UN1812	III	6.1	IB8, IP3, T1, TP33	154	POISON
Potassium fluoride solution	6.1	UN3422	III	6.1	IB3, T4, TP1	154	POISON
Potassium fluoroacetate	6.1	UN2628	I	6.1	IB7, IP1, T6, TP33	151	POISON
Potassium fluorosilicate	6.1	UN2655	III	6.1	IB8, IP3, T1, TP33	151	POISON
Potassium hydrate, see **Potassium hydroxide, solid**							
Potassium hydrogen fluoride, see **Potassium hydrogen difluoride**							

Symbols (1)	Hazardous materials descriptions and proper shipping names (2)	Hazard class or Division (3)	Identification Numbers (4)	PG (5)	Label Codes (6)	Special Provisions (§172.102) (7)	ERG Guide No.	Placard Advisory Consult §172.504 & §172.505 *Placard any quantity
	Potassium hydrogen fluoride solution, see Corrosive liquids, n.o.s.							
	Potassium hydrogen sulfate	8	UN2509	II	8	A7, IB8, IP2, IP4, N34, T3, TP33	154	CORROSIVE
	Potassium hydrogendifluoride solid	8	UN1811	II	8, 6.1	IB8, IP2, IP4, N3, N34, T3, TP33	154	CORROSIVE
	Potassium hydrogendifluoride solution	8	UN3421	II	8, 6.1	IB2, N3, N34, T7, TP2	154	CORROSIVE
				III	8, 6.1	IB3, N3, N34, T4, TP1	154	CORROSIVE
	Potassium hydrosulfite, see Potassium dithionite							
	Potassium hydroxide, liquid, see Potassium hydroxide, solution							
	Potassium hydroxide, solid	8	UN1813	II	8	IB8, IP2, IP4, T3, TP33	154	CORROSIVE
	Potassium hydroxide, solution	8	UN1814	II	8	B2, IB2, T7, TP2	154	CORROSIVE
				III	8	IB3, T4, TP1	154	CORROSIVE
	Potassium hypochlorite, solution, see Hypochlorite solutions, etc.							
	Potassium, metal alloys, liquid	4.3	UN1420	I	4.3	A7, A19, A20, B27, W31	138	DANGEROUS WHEN WET*
	Potassium, metal alloys, solid	4.3	UN3403	I	4.3	A19, A20, B27, IB4, IP1, T9, TP7, TP33, W31	138	DANGEROUS WHEN WET*
	Potassium metavanadate	6.1	UN2864	II	6.1	IB8, IP2, IP4, T3, TP33	151	POISON
	Potassium monoxide	8	UN2033	II	8	IB8, IP2, IP4, T3, TP33	154	CORROSIVE
	Potassium nitrate	5.1	UN1486	III	5.1	A1, A29, B120, IB8, IP3, T1, TP33, W1	140	OXIDIZER
	Potassium nitrate and sodium nitrite mixtures	5.1	UN1487	II	5.1	B78, IB8, IP2, IP4, T3, TP33	140	OXIDIZER
	Potassium nitrite	5.1	UN1488	II	5.1	IB8, IP2, IP4, T3, TP33	140	OXIDIZER
	Potassium perchlorate	5.1	UN1489	II	5.1	IB6, IP2, T3, TP33	140	OXIDIZER
	Potassium permanganate	5.1	UN1490	II	5.1	IB8, IP2, IP4, T3, TP33	140	OXIDIZER
	Potassium peroxide	5.1	UN1491	I	5.1	A20, IB6, IP1, N34	144	OXIDIZER

Name	Class	ID No.	PG	Label Codes	Special Provisions		
Potassium persulfate	5.1	UN1492	III	5.1	A1, A29, IB8, IP3, T1, TP33	140	OXIDIZER
Potassium phosphide	4.3	UN2012	I	4.3, 6.1	A19, N40, W31	139	DANGEROUS WHEN WET*
Potassium selenate, see Selenates or Selenites							
Potassium selenite, see Selenates or Selenites							
Potassium sodium alloys, liquid	4.3	UN1422	I	4.3	A7, A19, B27, N34, N40, T9, TP3, TP7, TP31, W31	138	DANGEROUS WHEN WET*
Potassium sodium alloys, solid	4.3	UN3404	I	4.3	A19, B27, N34, N40, T9, TP7, TP33, W31	138	DANGEROUS WHEN WET*
Potassium sulfide, anhydrous or Potassium sulfide with less than 30 percent water of crystallization	4.2	UN1382	II	4.2	A19, A20, B16, IB6, IP2, N34, T3, TP33, W31, W40	135	SPONTANEOUSLY COMBUSTIBLE
Potassium sulfide, hydrated with not less than 30 percent water of crystallization	8	UN1847	II	8	IB8, IP2, IP4, T3, TP33	153	CORROSIVE
Potassium superoxide	5.1	UN2466	I	5.1	A20, IB6, IP1	143	OXIDIZER
Powder cake, wetted or Powder paste, wetted *with not less than 17 percent alcohol by mass*	1.1C	UN0433		1.1C		112	EXPLOSIVES 1.1*
Powder cake, wetted or Powder paste, wetted *with not less than 25 percent water, by mass*	1.3C	UN0159		1.3C		112	EXPLOSIVES 1.3*
Powder paste, see Powder cake, etc.							
Powder, smokeless	1.1C	UN0160		1.1C		112	EXPLOSIVES 1.1*
Powder, smokeless	1.3C	UN0161		1.3C		112	EXPLOSIVES 1.3*
Powder, smokeless	1.4C	UN0509		1.4C	16	114	EXPLOSIVES 1.4
Power device, explosive, see Cartridges, power device							
Primers, cap type	1.4S	UN0044		None		114	NONE
Primers, cap type	1.1B	UN0377		1.1B		112	EXPLOSIVES 1.1*
Primers, cap type	1.4B	UN0378		1.4B		114	EXPLOSIVES 1.4
Primers, small arms, see Primers, cap type							
Primers, tubular	1.3G	UN0319		1.3G		112	EXPLOSIVES 1.3*
Primers, tubular	1.4G	UN0320		1.4G		114	EXPLOSIVES 1.4
Primers, tubular	1.4S	UN0376		None		114	NONE

HAZMAT TABLE

Symbols (1)	Hazardous materials descriptions and proper shipping names (2)	Hazard class or Division (3)	Identification Numbers (4)	PG (5)	Label Codes (6)	Special Provisions (§172.102) (7)	ERG Guide No.	Placard Advisory Consult §172.504 & §172.505 *Placard any quantity
	Printing ink, *flammable* or **Printing ink related material** *(including printing ink thinning or reducing compound), flammable*	3	UN1210	I	3	367, T11, TP1, TP8	129	FLAMMABLE
				II	3	149, 367, IB2, T4, TP1, TP8	129	FLAMMABLE
				III	3	367, B1, IB3, T2, TP1	129	FLAMMABLE
	Projectiles, illuminating, see Ammunition, illuminating, etc.							
	Projectiles, *inert, with tracer*	1.4S	UN0345		1.4S		114	EXPLOSIVES 1.4
	Projectiles, *inert, with tracer*	1.3G	UN0424		1.3G		112	EXPLOSIVES 1.3*
	Projectiles, *inert, with tracer*	1.4G	UN0425		1.4G		114	EXPLOSIVES 1.4
	Projectiles, *with burster or expelling charge*	1.2D	UN0346		1.2D		112	EXPLOSIVES 1.2*
	Projectiles, *with burster or expelling charge*	1.4D	UN0347		1.4D		114	EXPLOSIVES 1.4
	Projectiles, *with burster or expelling charge*	1.2F	UN0426		1.2F		112	EXPLOSIVES 1.2*
	Projectiles, *with burster or expelling charge*	1.4F	UN0427		1.4F		114	EXPLOSIVES 1.4
	Projectiles, *with burster or expelling charge*	1.2G	UN0434		1.2G		112	EXPLOSIVES 1.2*
	Projectiles, *with burster or expelling charge*	1.4G	UN0435		1.4G		114	EXPLOSIVES 1.4
	Projectiles, *with bursting charge*	1.1F	UN0167		1.1F		112	EXPLOSIVES 1.1*
	Projectiles, *with bursting charge*	1.1D	UN0168		1.1D		112	EXPLOSIVES 1.1*
	Projectiles, *with bursting charge*	1.2D	UN0169		1.2D		112	EXPLOSIVES 1.2*
	Projectiles, *with bursting charge*	1.2F	UN0324		1.2F		112	EXPLOSIVES 1.2*
	Projectiles, *with bursting charge*	1.4D	UN0344		1.4D		114	EXPLOSIVES 1.4
	Propadiene, stabilized	2.1	UN2200		2.1	387	116P	FLAMMABLE GAS
	*Propadiene mixed with methyl acetylene, see **Methyl acetylene** and propadiene mixtures, stabilized*							
	Propane, *see also* **Petroleum gases, liquefied**	2.1	UN1978		2.1	19, T50, N95	115	FLAMMABLE GAS
	Propanethiols	3	UN2402	II	3	IB2, T4, TP1, TP13	130	FLAMMABLE
	n-Propanol or **Propyl alcohol, normal**	3	UN1274	II	3	B1, IB2, T4, TP1	129	FLAMMABLE
				III	3	B1, IB3, T2, TP1	129	FLAMMABLE

Name	Class	ID No.	PG	Label Codes	Special Provisions	Guide	Description
Propellant, liquid	1.3C	UN0495		1.3C	37	112	EXPLOSIVES 1.3*
Propellant, liquid	1.1C	UN0497		1.1C	37	112	EXPLOSIVES 1.1*
Propellant, solid	1.1C	UN0498		1.1C		112	EXPLOSIVES 1.1*
Propellant, solid	1.3C	UN0499		1.3C		112	EXPLOSIVES 1.3*
Propellant, solid	1.4C	UN0501		1.4C		114	EXPLOSIVES 1.4
Propionaldehyde	3	UN1275	II	3	IB2, T7, TP1	129P	FLAMMABLE
Propionic acid with not less than 90% acid by mass	8	UN3463	II	8, 3	IB2, T7, TP2	153	CORROSIVE
Propionic acid with not less than 10% and less than 90% acid by mass	8	UN1848	III	8	IB3, T4, TP1	153	CORROSIVE
Propionic anhydride	8	UN2496	III	8	IB3, T4, TP1	156	CORROSIVE
Propionitrile	3	UN2404	II	3, 6.1	IB2, T7, TP1, TP13	131	FLAMMABLE
Propionyl chloride	3	UN1815	II	3, 8	IB1, T7, TP1	132	FLAMMABLE
n-Propyl acetate	3	UN1276	II	3	IB2, T4, TP1	129	FLAMMABLE
Propyl alcohol, see Propanol							
n-Propyl benzene	3	UN2364	III	3	B1, IB3, T2, TP1	128	FLAMMABLE
Propyl chloride see, 1-Chloropropane							
n-Propyl chloroformate	6.1	UN2740	I	6.1, 3, 8	2, B9, B14, B32, B77, N34, T20, TP2, TP13, TP38, TP44	155	INHALATION HAZARD CLASS 6*
Propyl formates	3	UN1281	II	3	IB2, T4, TP1	129	FLAMMABLE
n-Propyl isocyanate	6.1	UN2482	I	6.1, 3	1, B9, B14, B30, T20, TP2, TP13, TP38, TP44	155P	INHALATION HAZARD CLASS 6*
Propyl mercaptan, see Propanethiols							
n-Propyl nitrate	3	UN1865	II	3	IB9	128	FLAMMABLE
Propylamine	3	UN1277	II	3, 8	A7, IB2, N34, T7, TP1	132	FLAMMABLE
Propylene, see Petroleum gases, liquefied	2.1	UN1077		2.1	19, T50	115	FLAMMABLE GAS
Propylene chlorohydrin	6.1	UN2611	II	6.1, 3	IB2, T7, TP2, TP13	131	POISON
Propylene oxide	3	UN1280	I	3	N34, T11, TP2, TP7	127P	FLAMMABLE
Propylene tetramer	3	UN2850	III	3	B1, IB3, T2, TP2	128	FLAMMABLE
1,2-Propylenediamine	8	UN2258	II	8, 3	A3, IB2, N34, T7, TP2	132	CORROSIVE
Propyleneimine, stabilized	3	UN1921	I	3, 6.1	387, N34, T14, TP2, TP13	131P	FLAMMABLE

Symbols (1)	Hazardous materials descriptions and proper shipping names (2)	Hazard class or Division (3)	Identification Numbers (4)	PG (5)	Label Codes (6)	Special Provisions (§172.102) (7)	ERG Guide No.	Placard Advisory Consult §172.504 & §172.505 *Placard any quantity
	Propyltrichlorosilane	8	UN1816	II	8, 3	A7, B2, B6, N34, T10, TP2, TP7, TP13	155	CORROSIVE
	Prussic acid, see Hydrogen cyanide							
	Pyrethroid pesticide, liquid, flammable, toxic, *flash point less than 23 degrees C*	3	UN3350	I	3, 6.1	T14, TP2, TP13, TP27	131	FLAMMABLE
				II		T11, TP2, TP13, TP27	131	FLAMMABLE
	Pyrethroid pesticide, liquid, toxic	6.1	UN3352	I	6.1	T14, TP2, TP13, TP27	151	POISON
				II	6.1	IB2, T11, TP2, TP27	151	POISON
				III	6.1	IB3, T7, TP2, TP28	151	POISON
	Pyrethroid pesticide, liquid, toxic, flammable, *flash point not less than 23 degrees C*	6.1	UN3351	I	6.1, 3	T14, TP2, TP13, TP27	131	POISON
				II	6.1, 3	IB2, T11, TP2, TP13, TP27	131	POISON
				III	6.1, 3	IB3, T7, TP2, TP28	131	POISON
	Pyrethroid pesticide, solid, toxic	6.1	UN3349	I	6.1	IB7, IP1, T6, TP33	151	POISON
				II	6.1	IB8, IP2, IP4, T3, TP33	151	POISON
				III	6.1	IB8, IP3, T1, TP33	151	POISON
	Pyridine	3	UN1282	II	3	IB2, T4, TP2	129	FLAMMABLE
	Pyridine perchlorate	Forbidden						
G	Pyrophoric liquid, inorganic, n.o.s.	4.2	UN3194	I	4.2		135	SPONTANEOUSLY COMBUSTIBLE
G	Pyrophoric liquids, organic, n.o.s.	4.2	UN2845	I	4.2	B11, T22, TP2, TP7, W31	135	SPONTANEOUSLY COMBUSTIBLE
G	Pyrophoric metals, n.o.s., or Pyrophoric alloys, n.o.s.	4.2	UN1383	I	4.2	B11, T21, TP7, TP33, W31	135	SPONTANEOUSLY COMBUSTIBLE
G	Pyrophoric solid, inorganic, n.o.s.	4.2	UN3200	I	4.2	T21, TP7, TP33, W31	135	SPONTANEOUSLY COMBUSTIBLE
G	Pyrophoric solids, organic, n.o.s.	4.2	UN2846	I	4.2	W31	135	SPONTANEOUSLY COMBUSTIBLE

Hazardous materials descriptions and proper shipping names	Hazard class	ID No.	PG	Label codes	Special provisions	Guide	Placard
Pyrosulfuryl chloride	8	UN1817	II	8	B2, IB2, T8, TP2	137	CORROSIVE
Pyroxylin solution or solvent, see Nitrocellulose							
Pyrrolidine	3	UN1922	II	3, 8	IB2, T7, TP1	132	FLAMMABLE
Quebrachitol pentanitrate	Forbidden						
Quicklime, see Calcium oxide							
Quinoline	6.1	UN2656	III	6.1	IB3, T4, TP1	154	POISON
R 12, see Dichlorodifluoromethane							
R 12B1, see Chlorodifluorobromomethane							
R 13, see Chlorotrifluoromethane							
R 13B1, see Bromotrifluoromethane							
R 14, see Tetrafluoromethane							
R 21, see Dichlorofluoromethane							
R 22, see Chlorodifluoromethane							
R 114, see Dichlorotetrafluoroethane							
R 115, see Chloropentafluoroethane							
R 116, see Hexafluoroethane							
R 124, see Chlorotetrafluoroethane							
R 133a, see Chlorotrifluoroethane							
R 152a, see Difluoroethane							
R 500, see Dichlorodifluoromethane and difluoroethane, etc.							
R 502, see Chlorodifluoromethane and chloropentafluoroethane mixture, etc.							
R 503, see Chlorotrifluoromethane and trifluoromethane, etc.							
Radioactive material, excepted package-articles manufactured from natural uranium or depleted uranium or natural thorium	7	UN2909		None		161	NONE
Radioactive material, excepted package-empty packaging	7	UN2908		Empty 368		161	NONE
Radioactive material, excepted package-instruments or articles	7	UN2911		None		161	NONE
Radioactive material, excepted package-limited quantity of material	7	UN2910		None 368		161	NONE

Symbols (1)	Hazardous materials descriptions and proper shipping names (2)	Hazard class or Division (3)	Identification Numbers (4)	PG (5)	Label Codes (6)	Special Provisions (§172.102) (7)	ERG Guide No.	Placard Advisory Consult §172.504 & §172.505 *Placard any quantity
	Radioactive material, low specific activity (LSA-I) non fissile or fissile-excepted	7	UN2912		7	325, A56, T5, TP4, W7	162	RADIOACTIVE* (YELLOW III LABEL OR EXCLUSIVE USE SHIPMENTS)
	Radioactive material, low specific activity (LSA-II) non fissile or fissile-excepted	7	UN3321		7	325, A56, T5, TP4, W7	162	RADIOACTIVE* (YELLOW III LABEL OR EXCLUSIVE USE SHIPMENTS)
	Radioactive material, low specific activity (LSA-III) non fissile or fissile excepted	7	UN3322		7	325, A56, T5, TP4, W7	162	RADIOACTIVE* (YELLOW III LABEL OR EXCLUSIVE USE SHIPMENTS)
	Radioactive material, surface contaminated objects (SCO-I or SCO-II) non fissile or fissile-excepted	7	UN2913		7	325, A56	162	RADIOACTIVE* (YELLOW III LABEL OR EXCLUSIVE USE SHIPMENTS)
	Radioactive material, transported under special arrangement, non fissile or fissile excepted	7	UN2919		7	325, A56, 139	163	RADIOACTIVE* (YELLOW III LABEL OR EXCLUSIVE USE SHIPMENTS)
	Radioactive material, transported under special arrangement, fissile	7	UN3331		7	A56, 139	165	RADIOACTIVE* (YELLOW III LABEL OR EXCLUSIVE USE SHIPMENTS)
	Radioactive material, Type A package, fissile non-special form	7	UN3327		7	A56, W7, W8	165	RADIOACTIVE* (YELLOW III LABEL OR EXCLUSIVE USE SHIPMENTS)
	Radioactive material, Type A package non-special form, non fissile or fissile-excepted	7	UN2915		7	325, A56, W7, W8	163	RADIOACTIVE* (YELLOW III LABEL OR EXCLUSIVE USE SHIPMENTS)

Symbols	Hazardous materials descriptions and proper shipping names	Hazard class or Division	Identification Numbers	PG	Label Codes	Special provisions	Guide No.	Label/Description
	Radioactive material, Type A package, special form *non fissile or fissile-excepted*	7	UN3332		7	A56, W7, W8	164	RADIOACTIVE* (YELLOW III LABEL OR EXCLUSIVE USE SHIPMENTS)
	Radioactive material, Type A package, special form, fissile	7	UN3333		7	A56, W7, W8	165	RADIOACTIVE* (YELLOW III LABEL OR EXCLUSIVE USE SHIPMENTS)
	Radioactive material, Type B(M) package, fissile	7	UN3329		7	A56	165	RADIOACTIVE* (YELLOW III LABEL OR EXCLUSIVE USE SHIPMENTS)
	Radioactive material, Type B(M) package *non fissile or fissile-excepted*	7	UN2917		7	325, A56	163	RADIOACTIVE* (YELLOW III LABEL OR EXCLUSIVE USE SHIPMENTS)
	Radioactive material, Type B(U) package, fissile	7	UN3328		7	A56	165	RADIOACTIVE* (YELLOW III LABEL OR EXCLUSIVE USE SHIPMENTS)
	Radioactive material, Type B(U) package *non fissile or fissile-excepted*	7	UN2916		7	325, A56	163	RADIOACTIVE* (YELLOW III LABEL OR EXCLUSIVE USE SHIPMENTS)
	Radioactive material, uranium hexafluoride *non fissile or fissile-excepted*	7	UN2978		7, 6.1, 8		166	RADIOACTIVE* (YELLOW III LABEL OR EXCLUSIVE USE SHIPMENTS)
	Radioactive material, uranium hexafluoride, fissile	7	UN2977		7, 6.1, 8		166	RADIOACTIVE* (YELLOW III LABEL OR EXCLUSIVE USE SHIPMENTS)
A W	**Rags, oily**	4.2	UN1856	III	4.2		133	SPONTANEOUSLY COMBUSTIBLE
	Railway torpedo, see Signals, railway track, explosive							

Symbols (1)	Hazardous materials descriptions and proper shipping names (2)	Hazard class or Division (3)	Identification Numbers (4)	PG (5)	Label Codes (6)	Special Provisions (§172.102) (7)	ERG Guide No.	Placard Advisory Consult §172.504 & §172.505 *Placard any quantity
	RC 318, see Octafluorocyclobutane							
	RDX and cyclotetramethylenetetranitramine, wetted or desensitized see RDX and HMX mixtures, wetted or desensitized							
	RDX and HMX mixtures, wetted with not less than 15 percent water by mass or RDX and HMX mixtures, desensitized with not less than 10 percent phlegmatizer by mass	1.1D	UN0391		1.1D		112	EXPLOSIVES 1.1*
	RDX and Octogen mixtures, wetted or desensitized see RDX and HMX mixtures, wetted or desensitized etc.							
	RDX, see Cyclotrimethylenetrinitramine, etc.							
	RDX, see Cyclotrimethylenetrinitramine, etc.							
	Receptacles, small, containing gas or gas cartridges (flammable) without release device, not refillable and not exceeding 1 L capacity	2.1	UN2037		2.1		115	FLAMMABLE GAS
	Receptacles, small, containing gas or gas cartridges (non-flammable) without release device, not refillable and not exceeding 1 L capacity	2.2	UN2037		2.2		115	NONFLAMMABLE GAS
	Receptacles, small, containing gas or gas cartridges (oxidizing) without release device, not refillable and not exceeding 1 L capacity	2.2	UN2037		2.2, 5.1	A14	115	NONFLAMMABLE GAS
	Red phosphorus, see Phosphorus, amorphous							
	Refrigerant gas R 404A	2.2	UN3337		2.2	T50	126	NONFLAMMABLE GAS
	Refrigerant gas R 407A	2.2	UN3338		2.2	T50	126	NONFLAMMABLE GAS
	Refrigerant gas R 407B	2.2	UN3339		2.2	T50	126	NONFLAMMABLE GAS
	Refrigerant gas R 407C	2.2	UN3340		2.2	T50	126	NONFLAMMABLE GAS
G	Refrigerant gases, n.o.s.	2.2	UN1078		2.2	T50	126	NONFLAMMABLE GAS
D	Refrigerant gases, n.o.s. or Dispersant gases, n.o.s.	2.1	NA1954		2.1		115	FLAMMABLE GAS
	Refrigerating machines, containing flammable, non-toxic, liquefied gas	2.1	UN3358		2.1		115	FLAMMABLE GAS

Hazardous materials description and proper shipping name	Class	ID No.	PG	Label	Special provisions	Guide	Placard
Refrigerating machines, containing non-flammable, non-toxic gases, or ammonia solutions (UN2672)	2.2	UN2857		2.2	A53	126	NONFLAMMABLE GAS
Regulated medical waste, n.o.s. or (BIO) Medical waste, n.o.s. or Clinical waste, unspecified, n.o.s. or Biomedical waste, n.o.s. or Medical waste, n.o.s.	6.2	UN3291	II	6.2	41, 337, A13	158	NONE
Release devices, explosive	1.4S	UN0173		1.4S		114	EXPLOSIVES 1.4
Resin Solution, *flammable*	3	UN1866	I	3	B52, T11, TP1, TP8, TP28	127	FLAMMABLE
			II	3	149, B52, IB2, T4, TP1, TP8	127	FLAMMABLE
			III	3	B1, B52, IB3, T2, TP1	127	FLAMMABLE
Resorcinol	6.1	UN2876	III	6.1	IB8, IP3, T1, TP33	153	POISON
Rifle grenade, see Grenades, hand or rifle, etc.							
Rifle powder, see Powder, smokeless (UN 0160)							
Rivets, explosive	1.4S	UN0174		1.4S		114	EXPLOSIVES 1.4
Road asphalt or tar liquid, see Tars, liquid, etc.							
Rocket motors	1.3C	UN0186		1.3C	109	112	EXPLOSIVES 1.3*
Rocket motors	1.1C	UN0280		1.1C	109	112	EXPLOSIVES 1.1*
Rocket motors	1.2C	UN0281		1.2C	109	112	EXPLOSIVES 1.2*
Rocket motors	1.4C	UN0510		1.4C	109	114	EXPLOSIVES 1.4
Rocket motors, liquid fueled	1.2J	UN0395		1.2J	109	112	EXPLOSIVES 1.2*
Rocket motors, liquid fueled	1.3J	UN0396		1.3J	109	112	EXPLOSIVES 1.3*
Rocket motors with hypergolic liquids *with or without an expelling charge*	1.3L	UN0250		1.3L	109	112	EXPLOSIVES 1.3*
Rocket motors with hypergolic liquids *with or without an expelling charge*	1.2L	UN0322		1.2L	109	112	EXPLOSIVES 1.2*
Rockets, line-throwing	1.2G	UN0238		1.2G		112	EXPLOSIVES 1.2*
Rockets, line-throwing	1.3G	UN0240		1.3G		112	EXPLOSIVES 1.3*
Rockets, line-throwing	1.4G	UN0453		1.4G		114	EXPLOSIVES 1.4
Rockets, liquid fueled *with bursting charge*	1.1J	UN0397		1.1J		112	EXPLOSIVES 1.1*
Rockets, liquid fueled *with bursting charge*	1.2J	UN0398		1.2J		112	EXPLOSIVES 1.2*
Rockets, *with bursting charge*	1.1F	UN0180		1.1F		112	EXPLOSIVES 1.1*

Symbols (1)	Hazardous materials descriptions and proper shipping names (2)	Hazard class or Division (3)	Identification Numbers (4)	PG (5)	Label Codes (6)	Special Provisions (§172.102) (7)	ERG Guide No.	Placard Advisory Consult §172.504 & §172.505 *Placard any quantity
	Rockets, with bursting charge	1.1E	UN0181		1.1E		112	EXPLOSIVES 1.1*
	Rockets, with bursting charge	1.2E	UN0182		1.2E		112	EXPLOSIVES 1.2*
	Rockets, with bursting charge	1.2F	UN0295		1.2F		112	EXPLOSIVES 1.2*
	Rockets, with expelling charge	1.2C	UN0436		1.2C		112	EXPLOSIVES 1.2*
	Rockets, with expelling charge	1.3C	UN0437		1.3C		112	EXPLOSIVES 1.3*
	Rockets, with expelling charge	1.4C	UN0438		1.4C		114	EXPLOSIVES 1.4
	Rockets, with inert head	1.3C	UN0183		1.3C		112	EXPLOSIVES 1.3*
	Rockets, with inert head	1.2C	UN0502		1.2C		112	EXPLOSIVES 1.2*
	Rosin oil	3	UN1286	II	3	IB2, T4, TP1	127	FLAMMABLE
				III	3	B1, IB3, T2, TP1	127	FLAMMABLE
	Rubber scrap or shoddy, *powdered or granulated, not exceeding 840 microns and rubber content exceeding 45%*	4.1	UN1345	II	4.1	IB8, IP2, IP4, T3, TP33	133	FLAMMABLE SOLID
	Rubber solution	3	UN1287	II	3	149, IB2, T4, TP1, TP8	127	FLAMMABLE
				III	3	B1, IB3, T2, TP1	127	FLAMMABLE
	Rubidium	4.3	UN1423	I	4.3	22, A7, A19, IB4, IP1, N34, N40, N45, W31	138	DANGEROUS WHEN WET*
	Rubidium hydroxide	8	UN2678	II	8	IB8, IP2, IP4, T3, TP33	154	CORROSIVE
	Rubidium hydroxide solution	8	UN2677	II	8	B2, IB2, T7, TP2	154	CORROSIVE
				III	8	IB3, T4, TP1	154	CORROSIVE
	Safety devices, *electrically initiated*	9	UN3268		9	160, A200	171	CLASS 9
	Safety devices, pyrotechnic	1.4G	UN0503		1.4G	A200	114	EXPLOSIVES 1.4
	Safety fuse, see **Fuse, safety**							
G	**Samples, explosive,** *other than initiating explosives*					113	—	—
	Sand acid, see **Fluorosilicic acid**		UN0190					

Symbols	Hazardous materials descriptions and proper shipping names	Hazard class or Division	Identification Numbers	PG	Label Codes	Special Provisions	Guide No.	Placard
	Seed cake, containing vegetable oil solvent extractions and expelled seeds, with not more than 10 percent of oil and when the amount of moisture is higher than 11 percent, with not more than 20 percent of oil and moisture combined.	4.2	UN1386	III	None	B136, IB8, IP3, IP7, N7	135	SPONTANEOUSLY COMBUSTIBLE
I	Seed cake with more than 1.5 percent oil and not more than 11 percent moisture	4.2	UN1386	III	None	B136, IB8, IP3, IP7, N7	135	SPONTANEOUSLY COMBUSTIBLE
I	Seed cake with more than 1.5 percent oil and not more than 11 percent moisture	4.2	UN2217	III	None	B136, IB8, IP3, P7, N7	135	SPONTANEOUSLY COMBUSTIBLE
G	Selenates or Selenites	6.1	UN2630	I	6.1	IB7, IP1, T6, TP33	151	POISON
	Selenic acid	8	UN1905	I	8	IB7, IP1, N34, T6, TP33	154	CORROSIVE
G	Selenium compound, liquid, n.o.s.	6.1	UN3440	I	6.1	T14, TP2, TP27	151	POISON
				II	6.1	IB2, T11, TP2, TP27	151	POISON
				III	6.1	IB3, T7, TP1, TP28	151	POISON
G	Selenium compound, solid, n.o.s.	6.1	UN3283	I	6.1	IB7, IP1, T6, TP33	151	POISON
				II	6.1	IB8, IP2, IP4, T3, TP33	151	POISON
				III	6.1	IB8, IP3, T1, TP33	151	POISON
	Selenium disulfide	6.1	UN2657	II	6.1	IB8, IP2, IP4, T3, TP33	153	POISON
	Selenium hexafluoride	2.3	UN2194		2.3, 8	1	125	INHALATION HAZARD CLASS 2*
	Selenium nitride	Forbidden						
	Selenium oxychloride	8	UN2879	I	8, 6.1	A7, N34, T10, TP2, TP13	157	CORROSIVE
+ A D	*Self-defense spray, aerosol, see Aerosols, etc.*	9	NA3334	III	9	A37	171	CLASS 9
G	Self-heating liquid, corrosive, inorganic, n.o.s.	4.2	UN3188	II	4.2, 8	IB2, W31	136	SPONTANEOUSLY COMBUSTIBLE
				III	4.2, 8	IB2, W31	136	SPONTANEOUSLY COMBUSTIBLE
G	Self-heating liquid, corrosive, organic, n.o.s.	4.2	UN3185	II	4.2, 8	IB2, W31	136	SPONTANEOUSLY COMBUSTIBLE
				III	4.2, 8	IB2, W31	136	SPONTANEOUSLY COMBUSTIBLE

Symbols (1)	Hazardous materials descriptions and proper shipping names (2)	Hazard class or Division (3)	Identification Numbers (4)	PG (5)	Label Codes (6)	Special Provisions (§172.102) (7)	ERG Guide No.	Placard Advisory Consult §172.504 & §172.505 *Placard any quantity
G	Self-heating liquid, inorganic, n.o.s.	4.2	UN3186	II	4.2	IB2, W31	135	SPONTANEOUSLY COMBUSTIBLE
				III	4.2	IB2, W31	135	SPONTANEOUSLY COMBUSTIBLE
G	Self-heating liquid, organic, n.o.s.	4.2	UN3183	II	4.2	IB2, W31	135	SPONTANEOUSLY COMBUSTIBLE
				III	4.2	IB2, W31	135	SPONTANEOUSLY COMBUSTIBLE
G	Self-heating liquid, toxic, inorganic, n.o.s.	4.2	UN3187	II	4.2, 6.1	IB2, W31	136	SPONTANEOUSLY COMBUSTIBLE
				III	4.2, 6.1	IB2, W31	136	SPONTANEOUSLY COMBUSTIBLE
G	Self-heating liquid, toxic, organic, n.o.s.	4.2	UN3184	II	4.2, 6.1	IB2, W31	136	SPONTANEOUSLY COMBUSTIBLE
				III	4.2, 6.1	IB2, W31	136	SPONTANEOUSLY COMBUSTIBLE
G	Self-heating solid, corrosive, inorganic, n.o.s.	4.2	UN3192	II	4.2, 8	IB5, IP2, T3, TP33	136	SPONTANEOUSLY COMBUSTIBLE
				III	4.2, 8	IB8, IP3, T1, TP33	136	SPONTANEOUSLY COMBUSTIBLE
G	Self-heating solid, corrosive, organic, n.o.s.	4.2	UN3126	II	4.2, 8	IB5, IP2, T3, TP33	136	SPONTANEOUSLY COMBUSTIBLE
				III	4.2, 8	IB8, IP3, T1, TP33	136	SPONTANEOUSLY COMBUSTIBLE
G	Self-heating solid, inorganic, n.c.s.	4.2	UN3190	II	4.2	IB6, IP2, T3, TP33, W31	135	SPONTANEOUSLY COMBUSTIBLE
				III	4.2	IB8, IP3, T1, TP33, W31	135	SPONTANEOUSLY COMBUSTIBLE
G	Self-heating solid, organic, n.o.s.	4.2	UN3088	II	4.2	IB6, IP2, T3, TP33, W31	135	SPONTANEOUSLY COMBUSTIBLE

Symbol	Hazardous materials descriptions and proper shipping names	Hazard class or Division	Identification Numbers	PG	Label Codes	Special Provisions	ERG Guide No.	
G	Self-heating solid, oxidizing, n.o.s.	4.2	UN3127	II	4.2, 5.1	B116, B130, IB8, IP3, T1, TP33, W31	135	SPONTANEOUSLY COMBUSTIBLE
G	Self-heating solid, toxic, inorganic, n.o.s.	4.2	UN3191	II	4.2, 6.1	IB5, IP2, T3, TP33	135	SPONTANEOUSLY COMBUSTIBLE
				III	4.2, 6.1	IB8, IP3, T1, TP33	136	SPONTANEOUSLY COMBUSTIBLE
G	Self-heating solid, toxic, organic, n.o.s.	4.2	UN3128	II	4.2, 6.1	IB5, IP2, T3, TP33	136	SPONTANEOUSLY COMBUSTIBLE
				III	4.2, 6.1	IB8, IP3, T1, TP33	136	SPONTANEOUSLY COMBUSTIBLE
	Self-propelled vehicle, see Engines or Batteries etc.							
G	Self-reactive liquid type B	4.1	UN3221		4.1	53	149	FLAMMABLE SOLID
G	Self-reactive liquid type B, temperature controlled	4.1	UN3231		4.1	53	150	FLAMMABLE SOLID
G	Self-reactive liquid type C	4.1	UN3223		4.1		149	FLAMMABLE SOLID
G	Self-reactive liquid type C, temperature controlled	4.1	UN3233		4.1		150	FLAMMABLE SOLID
G	Self-reactive liquid type D	4.1	UN3225		4.1		149	FLAMMABLE SOLID
G	Self-reactive liquid type D, temperature controlled	4.1	UN3235		4.1		150	FLAMMABLE SOLID
G	Self-reactive liquid type E	4.1	UN3227		4.1		149	FLAMMABLE SOLID
G	Self-reactive liquid type E, temperature controlled	4.1	UN3237		4.1		150	FLAMMABLE SOLID
G	Self-reactive liquid type F	4.1	UN3229		4.1		149	FLAMMABLE SOLID
G	Self-reactive liquid type F, temperature controlled	4.1	UN3239		4.1		150	FLAMMABLE SOLID
G	Self-reactive solid type B	4.1	UN3222		4.1	53	149	FLAMMABLE SOLID
G	Self-reactive solid type B, temperature controlled	4.1	UN3232		4.1	53	150	FLAMMABLE SOLID
G	Self-reactive solid type C	4.1	UN3224		4.1		149	FLAMMABLE SOLID
G	Self-reactive solid type C, temperature controlled	4.1	UN3234		4.1		150	FLAMMABLE SOLID
G	Self-reactive solid type D	4.1	UN3226		4.1		149	FLAMMABLE SOLID
G	Self-reactive solid type D, temperature controlled	4.1	UN3236		4.1		150	FLAMMABLE SOLID
G	Self-reactive solid type E	4.1	UN3228		4.1		149	FLAMMABLE SOLID
G	Self-reactive solid type E, temperature controlled	4.1	UN3238		4.1		150	FLAMMABLE SOLID

Symbols (1)	Hazardous materials descriptions and proper shipping names (2)	Hazard class or Division (3)	Identification Numbers (4)	PG (5)	Label Codes (6)	Special Provisions (§172.102) (7)	ERG Guide No.	Placard Advisory Consult §172.504 & §172.505 *Placard any quantity
G	**Self-reactive solid type F**	4.1	UN3230		4.1		149	FLAMMABLE SOLID
G	**Self-reactive solid type F, temperature controlled**	4.1	UN3240		4.1		150	FLAMMABLE SOLID
	Shale oil	3	UN1288	I	3	T11, TP1, TP8, TP27	128	FLAMMABLE
				II	3	IB2, T4, TP1, TP8	128	FLAMMABLE
				III	3	B1, IB3, T2, TP1	128	FLAMMABLE
	Shaped charges, see Charges, shaped, etc.							
	Signal devices, hand	1.4G	UN0191		1.4G	381	114	EXPLOSIVES 1.4
	Signal devices, hand	1.4S	UN0373		1.4S	381	114	EXPLOSIVES 1.4
	Signals, distress, ship	1.1G	UN0194		1.1G		112	EXPLOSIVES 1.1*
	Signals, distress, ship	1.3G	UN0195		1.3G		112	EXPLOSIVES 1.3*
	Signals, distress, ship	1.4G	UN0505		1.4G		114	EXPLOSIVES 1.4
	Signals, distress, ship	1.4S	UN0506		1.4S		114	EXPLOSIVES 1.4
	Signals, highway, see Signal devices, hand							
	Signals, railway track, explosive	1.1G	UN0192		1.1G		112	EXPLOSIVES 1.1*
	Signals, railway track, explosive	1.4S	UN0193		1.4S	381	114	EXPLOSIVES 1.4
	Signals, railway track, explosive	1.3G	UN0492		1.3G		112	EXPLOSIVES 1.3*
	Signals, railway track, explosive	1.4G	UN0493		1.4G		114	EXPLOSIVES 1.4
	Signals, ship distress, water-activated, see Contrivances, water-activated, etc.							
	Signals, smoke	1.1G	UN0196		1.1G		112	EXPLOSIVES 1.1*
	Signals, smoke	1.4G	UN0197		1.4G		114	EXPLOSIVES 1.4
	Signals, smoke	1.2G	UN0313		1.2G		112	EXPLOSIVES 1.2*
	Signals, smoke	1.4S	UN0507		1.4S		114	EXPLOSIVES 1.4
	Signals, smoke	1.3G	UN0487		1.3G		112	EXPLOSIVES 1.3*
	Silane	2.1	UN2203		2.1		116	FLAMMABLE GAS
	Silicofluoric acid, see Fluorosilicic acid							
	Silicon chloride, see Silicon tetrachloride							

	Hazardous material	Class	ID No.	PG	Labels	Special provisions	Pkg	
	Silicon powder, amorphous	4.1	UN1346	III	4.1	A1, IB8, IP3, T1, TP33	170	FLAMMABLE SOLID
	Silicon tetrachloride	8	UN1818	II	8	A3, B2, B6, T10, TP2, TP7, TP13	157	CORROSIVE
	Silicon tetrafluoride	2.3	UN1859		2.3, 8	2	125	INHALATION HAZARD CLASS 2*
	Silicon tetrafluoride, adsorbed	2.3	UN3521		2.3, 8	2	173	INHALATION HAZARD CLASS 2*
	Silver acetylide (dry)	Forbidden						
	Silver arsenite	6.1	UN1683	II	6.1	IB8, IP2, IP4, T3, TP33	151	POISON
	Silver azide (dry)	Forbidden						
	Silver chlorite (dry)	Forbidden						
	Silver cyanide	6.1	UN1684	II	6.1	IB8, IP2, IP4, T3, TP33	151	POISON
	Silver fulminate (dry)	Forbidden						
	Silver nitrate	5.1	UN1493	II	5.1	IB8, IP2, IP4, T3, TP33	140	OXIDIZER
	Silver oxalate (dry)	Forbidden						
	Silver picrate (dry)	Forbidden						
	Silver picrate, wetted with not less than 30 percent water, by mass	4.1	UN1347	I	4.1	23, W31	113	FLAMMABLE SOLID
	Sludge, acid	8	UN1906	II	8	A3, A7, B2, IB2, N34, T8, TP2, TP28	153	CORROSIVE
D	Smokeless powder for small arms (100 pounds or less)	4.1	NA3178	I	4.1	16	133	FLAMMABLE SOLID
	Soda lime with more than 4 percent sodium hydroxide	8	UN1907	III	8	IB8, IP3, T1, TP33	154	CORROSIVE
	Sodium	4.3	UN1428	I	4.3	A7, A8, A19, A20, B9, B48, B68, IB4, IP1, N34, T9, TP7, TP33, TP46, W31	138	DANGEROUS WHEN WET*
A	Sodium aluminate, solid	8	UN2812	III	8	IB8, IP3, T1, TP33	154	CORROSIVE
	Sodium aluminate, solution	8	UN1819	II	8	B2, IB2, T7, TP2	154	CORROSIVE
				III	8	IB3, T4, TP1	154	CORROSIVE
	Sodium aluminum hydride	4.3	UN2835	II	4.3	A8, A19, A20, IB4, T3, TP33, W31, W40	138	DANGEROUS WHEN WET*
	Sodium ammonium vanadate	6.1	UN2863	II	6.1	IB8, IP2, IP4, T3, TP33	154	POISON
	Sodium arsanilate	6.1	UN2473	III	6.1	IB8, IP3, T1, TP33	154	POISON

Symbols (1)	Hazardous materials descriptions and proper shipping names (2)	Hazard class or Division (3)	Identification Numbers (4)	PG (5)	Label Codes (6)	Special Provisions (§172.102) (7)	ERG Guide No.	Placard Advisory Consult §172.504 & §172.505 *Placard any quantity
	Sodium arsenate	6.1	UN1685	II	6.1	IB8, IP2, IP4, T3, TP33	151	POISON
	Sodium arsenite, aqueous solutions	6.1	UN1686	II	6.1	IB2, T7, TP2	154	POISON
				III	6.1	IB3, T4, TP2	154	POISON
	Sodium arsenite, solid	6.1	UN2027	II	6.1	IB8, IP2, IP4, T3, TP33	151	POISON
	Sodium azide	6.1	UN1667	II	6.1	IB8, IP2, IP4	153	POISON
	Sodium bifluoride, see Sodium hydrogendifluoride							
	Sodium bisulfite, solution, see Bisulfites, aqueous solutions, n.o.s.							
	Sodium borohydride	4.3	UN1426	I	4.3	N40, W31	138	DANGEROUS WHEN WET*
	Sodium borohydride and sodium hydroxide solution, with not more than 12 percent sodium borohydride and not more than 40 percent sodium hydroxide by mass	8	UN3320	II	8	B2, IB2, N34, T7, TP2	157	CORROSIVE
				III	8	B2, IB3, N34, T4, TP2	157	CORROSIVE
	Sodium bromate	5.1	UN1494	II	5.1	IB8, IP2, IP4, T3, TP33	140	OXIDIZER
	Sodium cacodylate	6.1	UN1688	II	6.1	IB8, IP2, IP4, T3, TP33	152	POISON
	Sodium carbonate peroxyhydrate	5.1	UN3378	II	5.1	B120, IB8, IP2, IP4, T3, TP33	140	OXIDIZER
				III	5.1	B120, IB8, IP3, T1, TP33	140	OXIDIZER
	Sodium chlorate	5.1	UN1495	II	5.1	A9, IB8, IP2, IP4, N34, T3, TP33	140	OXIDIZER
	Sodium chlorate, aqueous solution	5.1	UN2428	II	5.1	A2, IB2, T4, TP1	140	OXIDIZER
				III	5.1	A2, IB2, T4, TP1	140	OXIDIZER
	Sodium chlorate mixed with dinitrotoluene, see Explosive blasting, type C							
	Sodium chlorite	5.1	UN1496	II	5.1	A9, IB8, IP2, IP4, N34, T3, TP33	143	OXIDIZER
	Sodium chloroacetate	6.1	UN2659	III	6.1	IB8, IP3, T1, TP33	151	POISON

Hazardous materials descriptions and proper shipping names	Hazard class or division	Identification Numbers	PG	Label Codes	Special provisions	ERG Guide No.	Placard
Sodium cuprocyanide, solid	6.1	UN2316	I	6.1	IB7, IP1, T6, TP33	157	POISON
Sodium cuprocyanide, solution	6.1	UN2317	I	6.1	T14, TP2, TP13	157	POISON
Sodium cyanide, solid	6.1	UN1689	I	6.1	B69, B77, IB7, N74, N75, T6, TP33, W31	157	POISON
Sodium cyanide solution	6.1	UN3414	I	6.1	B69, B77, N74, N75, T14, TP2, TP13, W31	157	POISON
			II	6.1	B69, B77, IB2, N74, N75, T11, TP2, TP13, TP27, W31	157	POISON
			III	6.1	B69, B77, IB3, N74, N75, T7, TP2, TP13, TP28, W31	157	POISON
Sodium dichloroisocyanurate or Sodium dichloro-s-triazinetrione, see Dichloroisocyanuric acid etc.							
Sodium dinitro-o-cresolate, dry or wetted with less than 15 percent water, by mass	1.3C	UN0234		1.3C		112	EXPLOSIVES 1.3*
Sodium dinitro-o-cresolate, wetted, with not less than 10% water, by mass	4.1	UN3369	I	4.1	162, A8, A19, N41, N84, W31	113	FLAMMABLE SOLID
Sodium dinitro-o-cresolate, wetted with not less than 15 percent water, by mass	4.1	UN1348	I	4.1, 6.1	23, A8, A19, A20, N41, W31	113	FLAMMABLE SOLID
Sodium dithionite or Sodium hydrosulfite	4.2	UN1384	II	4.2	A19, A20, IB6, IP2, T3, TP33, W31	135	SPONTANEOUSLY COMBUSTIBLE
Sodium fluoride, solid	6.1	UN1690	III	6.1	IB8, IP3, T1, TF8	154	POISON
Sodium fluoride solution	6.1	UN3415	III	6.1	IB3, T4, TP1	154	POISON
Sodium fluoroacetate	6.1	UN2629	I	6.1	IB7, IP1, T6, TP33	151	POISON
Sodium fluorosilicate	6.1	UN2674	III	6.1	IB8, IP3, T1, TP33	154	POISON
Sodium hydrate, see Sodium hydroxide, solid							
Sodium hydride	4.3	UN1427	I	4.3	A19, N40, W31	138	DANGEROUS WHEN WET*
Sodium hydrogendifluoride	8	UN2439	II	8	IB8, IP2, IP4, N3, N34, T3, TP33	154	CORROSIVE
Sodium hydrosulfide, with less than 25 percent water of crystallization	4.2	UN2318	II	4.2	A7, A19, A20, IB6, IP2, T3, TP33, W31	135	SPONTANEOUSLY COMBUSTIBLE

Symbols (1)	Hazardous materials descriptions and proper shipping names (2)	Hazard class or Division (3)	Identification Numbers (4)	PG (5)	Label Codes (6)	Special Provisions (§172.102) (7)	ERG Guide No.	Placard Advisory Consult §172.504 & §172.505 *Placard any quantity
	Sodium hydrosulfide with not less than 25 percent water of crystallization	8	UN2949	II	8	A7, IB8, IP2, IP4, T7, TP2	154	CORROSIVE
	Sodium hydrosulfite, see Sodium dithionite							
	Sodium hydroxide, solid	8	UN1823	II	8	IB8, IP2, IP4, T3, TP33	154	CORROSIVE
	Sodium hydroxide solution	8	UN1824	II	8	B2, IB2, N34, T7, TP2	154	CORROSIVE
				III	8	IB3, N34, T4, TP1	154	CORROSIVE
	Sodium hypochlorite, solution, see Hypochlorite solutions etc.							
	Sodium metal, liquid alloy, see Alkali metal alloys, liquid, n.o.s.							
	Sodium methylate	4.2	UN1431	II	4.2, 8	A7, A19, IB5, IP2, T3, TP33, W31	138	SPONTANEOUSLY COMBUSTIBLE
	Sodium methylate solutions in alcohol	3	UN1289	II	3, 8	IB2, T7, TP1, TP8	132	FLAMMABLE
				III	3, 8	B1, IB3, T4, TP1	132	FLAMMABLE
	Sodium monoxide	8	UN1825	II	8	IB8, IP2, IP4, T3, TP33	157	CORROSIVE
	Sodium nitrate	5.1	UN1498	III	5.1	A1, A29, B120, IB8, IP3, T1, TP33, W1	140	OXIDIZER
	Sodium nitrate and potassium nitrate mixtures	5.1	UN1499	III	5.1	A1, A29, B120, IB8, IP3, T1, TP33, W1	140	OXIDIZER
	Sodium nitrite	5.1	UN1500	III	5.1, 6.1	A1, A29, IB8, IP3, T1, TP33	141	OXIDIZER
	Sodium pentachlorophenate	6.1	UN2567	II	6.1	IB8, IP2, IP4, T3, TP33	154	POISON
	Sodium perborate monohydrate	5.1	UN3377	III	5.1	B120, IB8, IP3, T1, TP33	140	OXIDIZER
	Sodium perchlorate	5.1	UN1502	II	5.1	IB6, IP2, T3, TP33	140	OXIDIZER
	Sodium permanganate	5.1	UN1503	II	5.1	IB6, IP2, T3, TP33	140	OXIDIZER
	Sodium peroxide	5.1	UN1504	I	5.1	A20, IB5, IP1, N34	144	OXIDIZER
	Sodium peroxoborate, anhydrous	5.1	UN3247	II	5.1	IB8, IP2, IP4, T3, TP33	140	OXIDIZER
	Sodium persulfate	5.1	UN1505	III	5.1	A1, IB8, IP3, T1, TP33	140	OXIDIZER
	Sodium phosphide	4.3	UN1432	I	4.3, 6.1	A19, N40, W31	139	DANGEROUS WHEN WET*

Symbol	Hazardous materials descriptions and proper shipping names	Hazard class or Division	ID No.	PG	Label Codes	Special Provisions	Guide	Description
	Sodium picramate, *dry or wetted with less than 20 percent water, by mass*	1.3C	UNC235		1.3C		112	EXPLOSIVES 1.3*
	Sodium picramate, *wetted with not less than 20 percent water, by mass*	4.1	UN1349	I	4.1	23, A8, A19, N41, W31	113	FLAMMABLE SOLID
	Sodium picryl peroxide	Forbidden						
	Sodium potassium alloys, see **Potassium sodium alloys**							
	Sodium selenate, see **Selenates or Selenites**							
	Sodium sulfide, anhydrous or Sodium sulfide *with less than 30 percent water of crystallization*	4.2	UN1385	II	4.2	A19, A20, IB6, IF2, N34, T3, TP33, W31, W40	135	SPONTANEOUSLY COMBUSTIBLE
	Sodium sulfide, hydrated *with not less than 30 percent water*	8	UN-849	II	8	IB8, IP2, IP4, T3, TP33	153	CORROSIVE
	Sodium superoxide	5.1	UN2547	I	5.1	A20, IB6, IP1, N34	143	OXIDIZER
	Sodium tetranitride	Forbidden						
G	Solids containing corrosive liquid, n.o.s.	8	UN3244	II	8	49, IB5, T3, TP33	154	CORROSIVE
G	Solids containing flammable liquid, n.o.s.	4.1	UN3175	II	4.1	47, IB6, IP2, T3, TP33	133	FLAMMABLE SOLID
G	Solids containing toxic liquid, n.o.s.	6.1	UN3243	II	6.1	48, IB2, T2, TP33	151	POISON
	Sounding devices, explosive	1.2F	UN0204		1.2F		112	EXPLOSIVES 1.2*
	Sounding devices, explosive	1.1F	UN0296		1.1F		112	EXPLOSIVES 1.1*
	Sounding devices, explosive	1.1D	UN0374		1.1D		112	EXPLOSIVES 1.1*
	Sounding devices, explosive	1.2D	UN0375		1.2D		112	EXPLOSIVES 1.2*
	Spirits of salt, see **Hydrochloric acid**							
	Squibs, see **Igniters** etc.							
	Stannic chloride, anhydrous	8	UN1827	II	8	B2, IB2, T7, TP2	137	CORROSIVE
	Stannic chloride pentahydrate	8	UN2440	III	8	IB8, IP3, T1, TP33	154	CORROSIVE
	Stannic phosphide	4.3	UN1433	I	4.3, 6.1	A19, N40, W31	139	DANGEROUS WHEN WET*
	Steel swarf, see **Ferrous metal borings**, etc.							
	Stibine	2.3	UN2676		2.3, 2.1	1	119	INHALATION HAZARD CLASS 2*
	Storage batteries, wet, see **Batteries, wet** etc.							
	Strontium arsenite	6.1	UN1691	II	6.1	IB8, IP2, IP4, T3, TP33	151	POISON

Symbols (1)	Hazardous materials descriptions and proper shipping names (2)	Hazard class or Division (3)	Identification Numbers (4)	PG (5)	Label Codes (6)	Special Provisions (§172.102) (7)	ERG Guide No.	Placard Advisory Consult §172.504 & §172.505 *Placard any quantity
	Strontium chlorate	5.1	UN1506	II	5.1	A1, A9, IB8, IP2, IP4, N34, T3, TP33	143	OXIDIZER
	Strontium nitrate	5.1	UN1507	III	5.1	A1, A29, IB8, IP3, T1, TP33	140	OXIDIZER
	Strontium perchlorate	5.1	UN1508	II	5.1	IB6, IP2, T3, TP33	140	OXIDIZER
	Strontium peroxide	5.1	UN1509	II	5.1	IB6, IP2, T3, TP33, W100	143	OXIDIZER
	Strontium phosphide	4.3	UN2013	I	4.3, 6.1	A19, N40, W31	139	DANGEROUS WHEN WET*
	Strychnine or Strychnine salts	6.1	UN1692	I	6.1	IB7, IP1, T6, TP33	151	POISON
	Styphnic acid, see Trinitroresorcinol, etc.							
	Styrene monomer, stabilized	3	UN2055	III	3	387, B1, IB3, T2, TP1	128P	FLAMMABLE
G	Substances, explosive, n.o.s.	1.1L	UN0357	II	1.1L	101	112	EXPLOSIVES 1.1*
G	Substances, explosive, n.o.s.	1.2L	UN0358	II	1.2L	101	112	EXPLOSIVES 1.2*
G	Substances, explosive, n.o.s.	1.3L	UN0359	II	1.3L	101	112	EXPLOSIVES 1.3*
G	Substances, explosive, n.o.s.	1.1A	UN0473	II	1.1A	101, 111	112	EXPLOSIVES 1.1*
G	Substances, explosive, n.o.s.	1.1C	UN0474	II	1.1C	101	112	EXPLOSIVES 1.1*
G	Substances, explosive, n.o.s.	1.1D	UN0475	II	1.1D	101	112	EXPLOSIVES 1.1*
G	Substances, explosive, n.o.s.	1.1G	UN0476	II	1.1G	101	112	EXPLOSIVES 1.1*
G	Substances, explosive, n.o.s.	1.3C	UN0477	II	1.3C	101	112	EXPLOSIVES 1.3*
G	Substances, explosive, n.o.s.	1.3G	UN0478	II	1.3G	101	112	EXPLOSIVES 1.3*
G	Substances, explosive, n.o.s.	1.4C	UN0479	II	1.4C	101	114	EXPLOSIVES 1.4
G	Substances, explosive, n.o.s.	1.4D	UN0480	II	1.4D	101	114	EXPLOSIVES 1.4
G	Substances, explosive, n.o.s.	1.4S	UN0481	II	1.4S	101, 347	114	EXPLOSIVES 1.4
G	Substances, explosive, n.o.s.	1.4G	UN0485	II	1.4G	101	114	EXPLOSIVES 1.4
G	Substances, explosive, very insensitive, n.o.s., or Substances, EVI, n.o.s	1.5D	UN0482	II	1.5D	101	112	EXPLOSIVES 1.5

Sym	Name	Hazard class	ID No.	PG	Label/Class Codes	Special Provisions	Guide	Label
	Substituted nitrophenol pesticides, liquid, flammable, toxic, flash point less than 23 degrees C	3	UN2780	I	3, 6.1	T14, TP2, TP13, TP27	131	FLAMMABLE
				II	3, 6.1	IB2, T11, TP2, TP13, TP27	131	FLAMMABLE
	Substituted nitrophenol pesticides, liquid, toxic	6.1	UN3014	I	6.1	T14, TP2, TP13, TP27	153	POISON
				II	6.1	IB2, T11, TP2, TP13, TP27	153	POISON
				III	6.1	IB3, T7, TP2, TP28	153	POISON
	Substituted nitrophenol pesticides, liquid, toxic, flammable flash point not less than 23 degrees C	6.1	UN3013	I	6.1, 3	T14, TP2, TP13, TP27	131	POISON
				II	6.1, 3	IB2, T11, TP2, TP13, TP27	131	POISON
				III	6.1, 3	B1, IB3, T7, TP2, TP28	153	POISON
	Substituted nitrophenol pesticides, solid, toxic	6.1	UN2779	I	6.1	IB7, IP1, T6, TP33	153	POISON
				II	6.1	IB8, IP2, IP4, T3, TP33	153	POISON
				III	6.1	IB8, IP3, T1, TP33	153	POISON
	Sucrose octanitrate (dry)	Forbidden						
	Sulfamic acid	8	UN2967	III	8	IB8, IP3, T1, TP33	154	CORROSIVE
D	Sulfur	9	NA1350	III	9	30, B120, IB8, IP2	133	CLASS 9
I	Sulfur	4.1	UN1350	III	4.1	30, B120, IB8, IP3, T1, TP33	133	FLAMMABLE SOLID
	Sulfur and chlorate, loose mixtures of	Forbidden						
	Sulfur chlorides	8	UN1828	I	8	5, A7, A10, B10, B77, N34, T20, TP2	137	CORROSIVE
	Sulfur dichloride, see Sulfur chlorides							
	Sulfur dioxide	2.3	UN1079		2.3, 8	3, B14, T50, TP19	125	INHALATION HAZARD CLASS 2*
	Sulfur dioxide solution, see Sulfurous acid							
	Sulfur hexafluoride	2.2	UN1080		2.2		126	NONFLAMMABLE GAS
D	Sulfur, molten	9	NA2448	III	9	30, B13, IB3, R1, T1, TP3	133	CLASS 9
I	Sulfur, molten	4.1	UN2448	III	4.1	30, B13, IB1, R1, T1, TP3	133	FLAMMABLE SOLID
	Sulfur tetrafluoride	2.3	UN2418		2.3, 8	1	125	INHALATION HAZARD CLASS 2*

Symbols (1)	Hazardous materials descriptions and proper shipping names (2)	Hazard class or Division (3)	Identification Numbers (4)	PG (5)	Label Codes (6)	Special Provisions (§172.102) (7)	ERG Guide No.	Placard Advisory Consult §172.504 & §172.505 *Placard any quantity
+	Sulfur trioxide, stabilized	8	UN1829	I	8, 6.1	2, 387, B9, B14, B32, B49, B77, N34, T20, TP4, TP13, TP25, TP26, TP38, TP45	137	CORROSIVE, INHALATION HAZARD CLASS 6*
	Sulfuretted hydrogen, see Hydrogen sulfide							
	Sulfuric acid, fuming with less than 30 percent free sulfur trioxide	8	UN1831	I	8	A7, N34, T20, TP2, TP13	137	CORROSIVE
	Sulfuric acid, fuming with 30 percent or more free sulfur trioxide	8	UN1831	I	8, 6.1	2, B9, B14, B32, B77, B84, N34, T20, TP2, TP12, TP13	137	CORROSIVE, INHALATION HAZARD CLASS 6*
	Sulfuric acid, spent	8	UN1832	II	8	A3, A7, B2, B83, B84, IB2, N34, T8, TP2	137	CORROSIVE
	Sulfuric acid with more than 51 percent acid	8	UN1830	II	8	A3, A7, B3, B83, B84, IB2, N34, T8, TP2	137	CORROSIVE
	Sulfuric acid with not more than 51% acid	8	UN2796	II	8	386, A3, A7, B2, B15, IB2, N6, N34, T8, TP2	157	CORROSIVE
	Sulfuric and hydrofluoric acid mixtures, see Hydrofluoric and sulfuric acid mixtures							
	Sulfuric anhydride, see Sulfur trioxide, stabilized							
	Sulfurous acid	8	UN1833	II	8	B3, IB2, T7, TP2	154	CORROSIVE
+	Sulfuryl chloride	6.1	UN1834	I	6.1, 8	1, B6, B9, B10, B14, B30, B77, N34, T22, TP2, TP13, TP38, TP44	137	INHALATION HAZARD CLASS 6*
	Sulfuryl fluoride	2.3	UN2191		2.3	4	123	INHALATION HAZARD CLASS 2*
	Tars, liquid including road oils and cutback bitumens	3	UN1999	II	3	149, B13, IB2, T3, TP3, TP29	130	FLAMMABLE
				III	3	B1, B13, IB3, T1, TP3	130	FLAMMABLE
	Tear gas candles	6.1	UN1700		6.1, 4.1		159	POISON
	Tear gas cartridges, see Ammunition, tear-producing, etc.							

Sym	Hazardous materials descriptions and proper shipping names	Class	ID No.	PG	Label	Special provisions	Guide	Placard
D	Tear gas devices with more than 2 percent tear gas substances, by mass	6.1	NA1693	I	6.1		159	POISON
				II	6.1		159	POISON
	Tear gas devices, with not more than 2 percent tear gas substances, by mass, see Aerosols, etc.							
	Tear gas grenades, see Tear gas candles							
G	Tear gas substances, liquid, n.o.s.	6.1	UN1693	I	6.1	W31	159	POISON
				II	6.1	IB2, W31	159	POISON
G	Tear gas substance, solid, n.o.s.	6.1	UN3448	I	6.1	T6, TP33, W31	159	POISON
				II	6.1	IB8, IP2, IP4, T3, TP33, W31	159	POISON
G	Tellurium compound, n.o.s.	6.1	UN3284	I	6.1	IB7, IP1, T6, TP33	151	POISON
				II	6.1	IB8, IP2, IP4, T3, TP33	151	POISON
				III	6.1	IB8, IP3, T1, TF33	151	POISON
	Tellurium hexafluoride	2.3	UN2195		2.3, 8	1	125	INHALATION HAZARD CLASS 2*
	Terpene hydrocarbons, n.o.s.	3	UN2319	III	3	B1, IB3, T4, TP1, TP29	128	FLAMMABLE
	Terpinolene	3	UN2541	III	3	B1, IB3, T2, TP1	128	FLAMMABLE
	Tetraazido benzene quinone	Forbidden						
	Tetrabromoethane	6.1	UN2504	III	6.1	IB3, T4, TP1	159	POISON
	1,1,2,2-Tetrachloroethane	6.1	UN1702	II	6.1	IB2, N36, T7, TP2	151	POISON
	Tetrachloroethylene	6.1	UN1897	III	6.1	IB3, N36, T4, TP1	160	POISON
	Tetraethyl dithiopyrophosphate	6.1	UN1704	II	6.1	IB2, T7, TP2	153	POISON
	Tetraethyl silicate	3	UN1292	III	3	B1, IB3, T2, TP1	129	FLAMMABLE
	Tetraethylammonium perchlorate (dry)	Forbidden						
	Tetraethylenepentamine	8	UN2320	III	8	IB3, T4, TP1	153	CORROSIVE
	1,1,1,2-Tetrafluoroethane *or Refrigerant gas R 134a*	2.2	UN3159		2.2	T50	126	NONFLAMMABLE GAS
	Tetrafluoroethylene, stabilized	2.1	UN1081		2.1	387	116P	FLAMMABLE GAS
	Tetrafluoromethane, *or Refrigerant gas R 14*	2.2	UN1982		2.2		126	NONFLAMMABLE GAS
	1,2,3,6-Tetrahydrobenzaldehyde	3	UN2498	III	3	B1, IB3, T2, TF1	129	FLAMMABLE
	Tetrahydrofuran	3	UN2056	II	3	IB2, T4, TP1	127	FLAMMABLE

HAZMAT TABLE

Symbols (1)	Hazardous materials descriptions and proper shipping names (2)	Hazard class or Division (3)	Identification Numbers (4)	PG (5)	Label Codes (6)	Special Provisions (§172.102) (7)	ERG Guide No.	Placard Advisory Consult §172.504 & §172.505 *Placard any quantity
	Tetrahydrofurfurylamine	3	UN2943	III	3	B1, IB3, T2, TP1	129	FLAMMABLE
	Tetrahydrophthalic anhydrides with more than 0.05 percent of maleic anhydride	8	UN2698	III	8	IB8, IP3, T1, TP33	156	CORROSIVE
	1,2,3,6-Tetrahydropyridine	3	UN2410	II	3	IB2, T4, TP1	129	FLAMMABLE
	Tetrahydrothiophene	3	UN2412	II	3	IB2, T4, TP1	130	FLAMMABLE
	Tetramethylammonium hydroxide, solid	8	UN3423	II	8	B2, IB8, IP2, IP4, T3, TP33	153	CORROSIVE
	Tetramethylammonium hydroxide solution	8	UN1835	II	8	B2, IB2, T7, TP2	153	CORROSIVE
				III	8	B2, IB3, T7, TP2	153	CORROSIVE
	Tetramethylene diperoxide dicarbamide	Forbidden						
	Tetramethylsilane	3	UN2749	I	3	A7, T14, TP2	130	FLAMMABLE
	Tetranitro diglycerin	Forbidden						
	Tetranitroaniline	1.1D	UN0207		1.1D		112	EXPLOSIVES 1.1*
+	**Tetranitromethane**	6.1	UN1510	I	6.1, 5.1	2, B32, T20, TP2, TP13, TP38, TP44	143	INHALATION HAZARD CLASS 6*
	2,3,4,6-Tetranitrophenol	Forbidden						
	2,3,4,6-Tetranitrophenyl methyl nitramine	Forbidden						
	2,3,4,6-Tetranitrophenylnitramine	Forbidden						
	Tetranitroresorcinol (dry)	Forbidden						
	2,3,5,6-Tetranitroso-1,4-dinitrobenzene	Forbidden						
	2,3,5,6-Tetranitroso nitrobenzene (dry)	Forbidden						
	Tetrapropylorthotitanate	3	UN2413	III	3	B1, IB3, T4, TP1	128	FLAMMABLE
	Tetrazene, *see Guanyl nitrosaminoguanyltetrazene*							
	Tetrazine (dry)	Forbidden						
	Tetrazol-1-acetic acid	1.4C	UN0407		1.4C		114	EXPLOSIVES 1.4
	1H-Tetrazole	1.1D	UN0504		1.1D		112	EXPLOSIVES 1.1*
	Tetrazolyl azide (dry)	Forbidden						
	Tetryl, *see Trinitrophenylmethylnitramine*							

Sym	Hazardous materials descriptions and proper shipping names	Hazard class or Division	Identification Numbers	PG	Label Codes	Special Provisions	ERG Guide	Hazard Label
A I W	Textile waste, wet	4.2	UN1857	III	4.2		133	SPONTANEOUSLY COMBUSTIBLE
	Thallium chlorate	5.1	UN2573	II	5.1, 6.1	IB6, IP2, T3, TP33	141	OXIDIZER
G	Thallium compounds, n.o.s.	6.1	UN1707	II	6.1	IB8, IP2, IP4, T3, TP33	151	POISON
	Thallium nitrate	6.1	UN2727	II	6.1, 5.1	IB6, IP2, T3, TP33	141	POISON
	4-Thiapentanal	6.1	UN2785	III	6.1	IB3, T4, TP1, W31	152	POISON
	Thioacetic acid	3	UN2436	II	3	IB2, T4, TP1	129	FLAMMABLE
	Thiocarbamate pesticide, liquid, flammable, toxic, *flash point less than 23 degrees C*	3	UN2772	I	3, 6.1	T14, TP2, TP13, TP27	131	FLAMMABLE
				II	3, 6.1	IB2, T11, TP13, TP27	131	FLAMMABLE
	Thiocarbamate pesticide, liquid, toxic, flammable, *flash point not less than 23 degrees C*	6.1	UN3005	I	6.1, 3	T14, TP2, TP13	131	POISON
				II	6.1, 3	IB2, T11, TP2, TP13, TP27	131	POISON
				III	6.1	IB3, T7, TP2, TP28	131	POISON
	Thiocarbamate pesticide, liquid, toxic	6.1	UN3006	I	6.1	T14, TP2, TP13	151	POISON
				II	6.1	IB2, T11, TP2, TP13, TP27	151	POISON
				III	6.1	IB3, T7, TP2, TP28	151	POISON
	Thiocarbamate pesticides, solid, toxic	6.1	UN2771	I	6.1	IB7, IP1, T6, TF33	151	POISON
				II	6.1	IB8, IP2, IP4, T3, TP33	151	POISON
				III	6.1	IB8, IP3, T1, TF33	151	POISON
	Thiocarbonylchloride, see Thiophosgene							
	Thioglycol	6.1	UN2966	II	6.1	IB2, T7, TP2	153	POISON
	Thioglycolic acid	8	UN1940	II	8	A7, B2, IB2, N34, T7, TP2	153	CORROSIVE
	Thiolactic acid	6.1	UN2936	II	6.1	IB2, T7, TP2	153	POISON
	Thionyl chloride	8	UN1836	I	8	B6, B10, N34, T10, TP2, TP13	137	CORROSIVE
	Thiophene	3	UN2414	II	3	IB2, T4, TP1	130	FLAMMABLE
+	Thiophosgene	6.1	UN2474	I	6.1	2, B9, B14, B32, N33, N34, T20, TP2, TP15, TP38, TP45	157	INHALATION HAZARD CLASS 6"

HAZMAT TABLE

Symbols (1)	Hazardous materials descriptions and proper shipping names (2)	Hazard class or Division (3)	Identification Numbers (4)	PG (5)	Label Codes (6)	Special Provisions (§172.102) (7)	ERG Guide No.	Placard Advisory Consult §172.504 & §172.505 *Placard any quantity
	Thiophosphoryl chloride	8	UN1837	II	8	A3, A7, B2, B8, B25, IB2, N34, T7, TP2	157	CORROSIVE
	Thiourea dioxide	4.2	UN3341	II	4.2	IB6, IP2, T3, TP33, W31	135	SPONTANEOUSLY COMBUSTIBLE
				III	4.2	IB8, IP3, T1, TP33, W31	135	SPONTANEOUSLY COMBUSTIBLE
	Tin chloride, fuming, see Stannic chloride, anhydrous							
	Tin perchloride or Tin tetrachloride, see Stannic chloride, anhydrous							
	Tinctures, medicinal	3	UN1293	II	3	IB2, T4, TP1, TP8	127	FLAMMABLE
				III	3	B1, IB3, T2, TP1	127	FLAMMABLE
	Tinning flux, see Zinc chloride							
	Tires and tire assemblies, see Air, compressed or Nitrogen, compressed							
	Titanium disulphide	4.2	UN3174	III	4.2	IB8, IP3, T1, TP33, W31	135	SPONTANEOUSLY COMBUSTIBLE
	Titanium hydride	4.1	UN1871	II	4.1	A19, A20, IB4, N34, T3, TP33, W31, W40	170	FLAMMABLE SOLID
	Titanium powder, dry	4.2	UN2546	I	4.2	W31	135	SPONTANEOUSLY COMBUSTIBLE
				II	4.2	A19, A20, IB6, IP2, N5, N34, T3, TP33, W31	135	SPONTANEOUSLY COMBUSTIBLE
				III	4.2	B135, IB8, IP21, T1, TP33, W31	135	SPONTANEOUSLY COMBUSTIBLE
	Titanium powder, wetted *with not less than 25 percent water (a visible excess of water must be present) (a) mechanically produced, particle size less than 53 microns; (b) chemically produced, particle size less than 840 microns*	4.1	UN1352	II	4.1	A19, A20, IB6, IP2, N34, T3, TP33, W31, W40	170	FLAMMABLE SOLID

Sym	Hazardous materials descriptions	Hazard class	ID number	PG	Label codes	Special provisions	Guide	Hazard
	Titanium sponge granules *or* Titanium sponge powders	4.1	UN2878	III	4.1	A1, B134, IB8, IP21, T1, TP33, W100	170	FLAMMABLE SOLID
+	Titanium tetrachloride	6.1	UN1838	I	6.1, 8	2, B7, B9, B14, B32, B77, T20, TP2, TP13, TP38, TP45	137	INHALATION HAZARD CLASS 6*
	Titanium trichloride mixtures	8	UN2869	II	8	A7, IB8, IP2, IP4, N34, T3, TP33	157	CORROSIVE
				III	8	A7, IB8, IP3, N34, T1, TP33	157	CORROSIVE
	Titanium trichloride, pyrophoric *or* Titanium trichloride mixtures, pyrophoric	4.2	UN2441	I	4.2, 8	N34, W31	135	SPONTANEOUSLY COMBUSTIBLE
	TNT mixed with aluminum, see Tritonal							
	TNT, see Trinitrotoluene, etc.							
	Toluene	3	UN1294	II	3	IB2, T4, TP1	130	FLAMMABLE
+	Toluene diisocyanate	6.1	UN2078	II	6.1	IB2, T7, TP2, TP13	156	POISON
	Toluene sulfonic acid, see Alkyl, or Aryl sulfonic acid etc.							
+	Toluidines, liquid	6.1	UN1708	II	6.1	IB2, T7, TP2	153	POISON
	Toluidines, solid	6.1	UN3451	II	6.1	IB8, IP2, IP4, T3, TP33	153	POISON
	2,4-Toluylenediamine, solid *or* 2,4-Toluenediamine, solid	6.1	UN1709	III	6.1	IB8, IP3, T1, TP33	151	POISON
	2,4-Toluylenediamine solution *or* 2,4-Toluenediamine solution	6.1	UN3418	III	6.1	IB3, T4, TP1	151	POISON
	Torpedoes, liquid fueled, with inert head	1.3J	UN0450		1.3J		112	EXPLOSIVES 1.3*
	Torpedoes, liquid fueled, with or without bursting charge	1.1J	UN0449		1.1J		112	EXPLOSIVES 1.1*
	Torpedoes with bursting charge	1.1E	UN0329		1.1E		112	EXPLOSIVES 1.1*
	Torpedoes with bursting charge	1.1F	UN0330		1.1F		112	EXPLOSIVES 1.1*
	Torpedoes with bursting charge	1.1D	UN0451		1.1D		112	EXPLOSIVES 1.1*
G	Toxic by inhalation liquid, flammable, corrosive, n.o.s. *with an LC50 lower than or equal to 200 ml/m³ and saturated vapor concentration greater than or equal to 500 LC50*	6.1	UN3488	I	6.1, 3, 8	1, B9, B14, B3C, T22, TP2, TP13, TP27, TP38, TP44	131	INHALATION HAZARD CLASS 6*
G	Toxic by inhalation liquid, flammable, corrosive, n.o.s. *with an LC50 lower than or equal to 1000 ml/m³ and saturated vapor concentration greater than or equal to 10 LC50*	6.1	UN3489	I	6.1, 3, 8	2, B9, B14, B32, T20, TP2, TP13, TP27, TP38, TP45	131	INHALATION HAZARD CLASS 6*

Symbols (1)	Hazardous materials descriptions and proper shipping names (2)	Hazard class or Division (3)	Identification Numbers (4)	PG (5)	Label Codes (6)	Special Provisions (§172.102) (7)	ERG Guide No.	Placard Advisory Consult §172.504 & §172.505 *Placard any quantity
G	Toxic by inhalation liquid, n.o.s. with an inhalation LC50 than or equal to 200 ml/m³ and saturated vapor concentration great than or equal to 500 LC50	6.1	UN3381	I	6.1	1, B9, B14, B30, T22, TP2, TP13, TP27, TP38, TP44	151	INHALATION HAZARD CLASS 6*
G	Toxic by inhalation liquid, n.o.s. with an LC50 lower than or equal to 1000 ml/m³ and saturated vapor concentration greater than or equal to 10 LC50	6.1	UN3382	I	6.1	2, B9, B14, B32, T20, TP2, TP13, TP27, TP38, TP45	151	INHALATION HAZARD CLASS 6*
G	Toxic by inhalation liquid, flammable, n.o.s. with an LC50 lower than or equal to 200 ml/m³ and saturated vapor concentration greater than or equal to 500 LC50	6.1	UN3383	I	6.1, 3	1, B9, B14, B30, T22, TP2, TP13, TP27, TP38, TP44	131	INHALATION HAZARD CLASS 6*
G	Toxic by inhalation liquid, flammable, n.o.s. with an LC50 lower than or equal to 1000 ml/m³ and saturated vapor concentration greater than or equal to 10 LC50	6.1	UN3384	I	6.1, 3	2, B9, B14, B32, T20, TP2, TP13, TP27, TP38, TP45	131	INHALATION HAZARD CLASS 6*
G	Toxic by inhalation liquid, water-reactive, n.o.s. with an LC50 lower than or equal to 200 ml/m³ and saturated vapor concentration greater than or equal to 500 LC50	6.1	UN3385	I	6.1, 4.3	1, B9, B14, B30, T22, TP2, TP13, TP38, TP44	139	INHALATION HAZARD CLASS 6*
G	Toxic by inhalation liquid, water-reactive, n.o.s. with an LC50 lower than or equal to 1000 ml/m³ and saturated vapor concentration greater than or equal to 10 LC50	6.1	UN3386	I	6.1, 4.3	2, B9, B14, B32, T20, TP2, TP13, TP38, TP44	139	INHALATION HAZARD CLASS 6*
G	Toxic by inhalation liquid, water-reactive, flammable, n.o.s. with an LC50 lower than or equal to 200 ml/m³ and saturated vapor concentration greater than or equal to 500 LC50	6.1	UN3490	I	6.1, 4.3, 3	1, B9, B14, B30, T22, TP2, TP13, TP27, TP38, TP44	155	INHALATION HAZARD CLASS 6*
G	Toxic by inhalation liquid, water-reactive, flammable, n.o.s. with an LC50 lower than or equal to 1000 ml/m³ and saturated vapor concentration greater than or equal to 10 LC50	6.1	UN3491	I	6.1, 4.3, 3	2, B9, B14, B32, T20, TP2, TP13, TP27, TP38, TP45	155	INHALATION HAZARD CLASS 6*
G	Toxic by inhalation liquid, oxidizing, n.o.s. with an LC50 lower than or equal to 200 ml/m³ and saturated vapor concentration greater than or equal to 500 LC50	6.1	UN3387	I	6.1, 5.1	1, B9, B14, B30, T22, TP2, TP13, TP38, TP44	142	INHALATION HAZARD CLASS 6*
G	Toxic by inhalation liquid, oxidizing, n.o.s. with an LC50 lower than or equal to 1000 ml/m³ and saturated vapor concentration greater than or equal to 10 LC50	6.1	UN3388	I	6.1, 5.1	2, B9, B14, B32, T20, TP2, TP13, TP38, TP44	142	INHALATION HAZARD CLASS 6*

Symbol	Hazardous materials description	Hazard class	ID number	PG	Label codes	Special provisions	Guide no.	Inhalation hazard Class 6*
G	Toxic by inhalation liquid, corrosive, n.o.s. with an LC50 lower than or equal to 200 ml/m³ and saturated vapor concentration greater than or equal to 500 LC50	6.1	UN3389	I	6.1, 8	1, B9, B14, B3C, T22, TP2, TP13, TP27, TP38, TP44	154	INHALATION HAZARD CLASS 6*
G	Toxic by inhalation liquid, corrosive, n.o.s. with an LC50 lower than or equal to 1000 ml/m³ and saturated vapor concentration greater than or equal to 10 LC50	6.1	UN3390	I	6.1, 8	2, B9, B14, B3C, T20, TP2, TP13, TP27, TP38, TP45	154	INHALATION HAZARD CLASS 6*
G	Toxic liquid, corrosive, inorganic, n.o.s.	6.1	UN3289	I	6.1, 8	T14, TP2, TP13, TP27	154	POISON
				II	6.1, 8	IB2, T11, TP2, TP27	154	POISON
G	Toxic liquid, inorganic, n.o.s.	6.1	UN3287	I	6.1	T14, TP2, TP13, TP27	151	POISON
				II	6.1	IB2, T11, TP2, TP27	151	POISON
				III	6.1	IB3, T7, TP1, TP28	151	POISON
G	Toxic liquids, corrosive, organic, n.o.s.	6.1	UN2927	I	6.1, 8	T14, TP2, TP13, TP27	154	POISON
				II	6.1, 8	IB2, T11, TP2, TP27	154	POISON
G	Toxic liquids, flammable, organic, n.o.s.	6.1	UN2929	I	6.1, 3	T14, TP2, TP13, TP27	131	POISON
				II	6.1, 3	IB2, T11, TP2, TP13, TP27	131	POISON
G	Toxic, liquids, organic, n.o.s.	6.1	UN2810	I	6.1	T14, TP2, TP13, TP27	153	POISON
				II	6.1	IB2, T11, TP2, TP13, TP27	153	POISON
				III	6.1	IB3, T7, TP1, TP28	153	POISON
G	Toxic liquids, oxidizing, n.o.s.	6.1	UN3122	I	6.1, 5.1	A4	142	POISON
				II	6.1, 5.1	IB2	142	POISON
G	Toxic liquids, water-reactive, n.o.s.	6.1	UN3123	I	6.1, 4.3	A4	139	POISON, DANGEROUS WHEN WET*
				II	6.1, 4.3	IB2	139	POISON, DANGEROUS WHEN WET*
G	Toxic solid, corrosive, inorganic, n.o.s.	6.1	UN3290	I	6.1, 8	IB7, T6, TP33	154	POISON
				II	6.1, 8	IB6, IP2, T3, TP33	154	POISON
G	Toxic solid, flammable, inorganic, n.o.s.	6.1	UN3535	I	6.1, 4.1	IB6, T6, TP33	134	POISON

Symbols (1)	Hazardous materials descriptions and proper shipping names (2)	Hazard class or Division (3)	Identification Numbers (4)	PG (5)	Label Codes (6)	Special Provisions (§172.102) (7)	ERG Guide No.	Placard Advisory Consult §172.504 & §172.505 *Placard any quantity
				II	6.1, 4.1	IB8, IP2, IP4, T3, TP33	134	POISON
G	Toxic solid, inorganic, n.o.s.	6.1	UN3288	I	6.1	IB7, T6, TP33	151	POISON
				II	6.1	IB8, IP2, IP4, T3, TP33	151	POISON
				III	6.1	IB8, IP3, T1, TP33	151	POISON
G	Toxic solids, corrosive, organic, n.o.s.	6.1	UN2928	I	6.1, 8	IB7, T6, TP33	154	POISON
				II	6.1, 8	IB6, IP2, T3, TP33	154	POISON
G	Toxic solids, flammable, organic, n.o.s.	6.1	UN2930	I	6.1, 4.1	IB6, T6, TP33	134	POISON
				II	6.1, 4.1	IB8, IP2, IP4, T3, TP33	134	POISON
G	Toxic solids, organic, n.o.s.	6.1	UN2811	I	6.1	IB7, T6, TP33	154	POISON
				II	6.1	IB8, IP2, IP4, T3, TP33	154	POISON
				III	6.1	IB8, IP3, T1, TP33	154	POISON
G	Toxic solids, oxidizing, n.o.s.	6.1	UN3086	I	6.1, 5.1	T6, TP33	141	POISON
				II	6.1, 5.1	IB6, IP2, T3, TP33	141	POISON
G	Toxic solids, self-heating, n.o.s.	6.1	UN3124	I	6.1, 4.2	A5, T6, TP33	136	POISON
				II	6.1, 4.2	IB6, IP2, T3, TP33	136	POISON
G	Toxic solids, water-reactive, n.o.s.	6.1	UN3125	I	6.1, 4.3	A5, T6, TP33, W100	139	POISON, DANGEROUS WHEN WET*
G	Toxins extracted from living sources, liquid, n.o.s.	6.1	UN3172	I	6.1	141	153	POISON
				II	6.1	141, IB2	153	POISON
				III	6.1	141, IB3	153	POISON

Sym	Hazardous materials description and proper shipping names	Class/Div	ID No.	PG	Label codes	Special provisions	ERG	Placard
G	Toxins extracted from living sources, solid, n.o.s.	6.1	UN3462	I	6.1	141, IB7, IP1, T5, TP33	153	POISON
				II	6.1	141, IB8, IP2, IP4, T3, TP33	153	POISON
				III	6.1	141, IB8, IP3, T1, TP33	153	POISON
D	Toy Caps	1.4S	NA0337		1.4S		114	EXPLOSIVES 1.4
	Tracers for ammunition	1.3G	UN0212		1.3G		112	EXPLOSIVES 1.3*
	Tracers for ammunition	1.4G	UN0306		1.4G		114	EXPLOSIVES 1.4
	Tractors, see Vehicle, etc.							
	Tri-(b-nitroxyethyl) ammonium nitrate	Forbidden						
	Triallyl borate	6.1	UN2609	III	6.1	IB3	156	POISON
	Triallylamine	3	UN2610	III	3, 8	B1, IB3, T4, TP1	132	FLAMMABLE
	Triazine pesticides, liquid, flammable, toxic, *flash point less than 23 degrees C*	3	UN2764	I	3, 6.1	T14, TP2, TP13, TP27	131	FLAMMABLE
				II	3, 6.1	IB2, T11, TP2, TP13, TP27	131	FLAMMABLE
	Triazine pesticides, liquid, toxic	6.1	UN2998	I	6.1	T14, TP2, TP13, TP27	151	POISON
				II	6.1	IB2, T11, TP2, TP13, TP27	151	POISON
				III	6.1	IB3, T7, TP2, TP28	151	POISON
	Triazine pesticides, liquid, toxic, flammable, *flash point not less than 23 degrees C*	6.1	UN2997	I	6.1, 3	T14, TP2, TP13, TP27	131	POISON
				II	6.1, 3	IB2, T11, TP2, TP13, TP27	131	POISON
				III	6.1, 3	IB3, T7, TP2, T28	131	POISON
	Triazine pesticides, solid, toxic	6.1	UN2763	I	6.1	IB7, IP1, T6, TP33	151	POISON
				II	6.1	IB8, IP2, IP4, T3, TP33	151	POISON
				III	6.1	IB8, IP3, T1, TP33	151	POISON
	Tributylamine	6.1	UN2542	II	6.1	IB2, T7, TP2	153	POISON
	Tributylphosphane	4.2	UN3254	I	4.2	T21, TP7, TP35	135	SPONTANEOUSLY COMBUSTIBLE
	Trichloro-s-triazinetrione dry, with more than 39 percent available chlorine, see Trichloroisocyanuric acid, dry							
	Trichloroacetic acid	8	UN1839	II	8	A7, IB8, IP2, IF4, N34, T3, TP33	153	CORROSIVE

Symbols (1)	Hazardous materials descriptions and proper shipping names (2)	Hazard class or Division (3)	Identification Numbers (4)	PG (5)	Label Codes (6)	Special Provisions (§172.102) (7)	ERG Guide No.	Placard Advisory Consult §172.504 & §172.505 *Placard any quantity
	Trichloroacetic acid, solution	8	UN2564	II	8	A3, A7, B2, IB2, N34, T7, TP2	153	CORROSIVE
				III	8	A3, A7, IB3, N34, T4, TP1	153	CORROSIVE
+	**Trichloroacetyl chloride**	8	UN2442	II	8, 6.1	2, B9, B14, B32, N34, T20, TP2, TP38, TP45	156	CORROSIVE, INHALATION HAZARD CLASS 6*
	Trichlorobenzenes, liquid	6.1	UN2321	III	6.1	IB3, T4, TP1	153	POISON
	Trichlorobutene	6.1	UN2322	II	6.1	IB2, T7, TP2	152	POISON
	1,1,1-Trichloroethane	6.1	UN2831	III	6.1	IB3, N36, T4, TP1	160	POISON
	Trichloroethylene	6.1	UN1710	III	6.1	IB3, N36, T4, TP1	160	POISON
	Trichloroisocyanuric acid, dry	5.1	UN2468	II	5.1	IB8, IP2, IP4, T3, TP33	140	OXIDIZER
	Trichloromethyl perchlorate	Forbidden						
	Trichlorosilane	4.3	UN1295	I	4.3, 3, 8	N34, T14, TP2, TP7, TP13, W31	139	DANGEROUS WHEN WET*
	Tricresyl phosphate with more than 3 percent ortho isomer	6.1	UN2574	II	6.1	A3, IB2, N33, N34, T7, TP2	151	POISON
	Triethyl phosphite	3	UN2323	III	3	B1, IB3, T2, TP1	130	FLAMMABLE
	Triethylamine	3	UN1296	II	3, 8	IB2, T7, TP1	132	FLAMMABLE
	Triethylenetetramine	8	UN2259	II	8	B2, IB2, T7, TP2	153	CORROSIVE
	Trifluoroacetic acid	8	UN2699	I	8	A7, B4, N3, N34, N36, T10, TP2	154	CORROSIVE
	Trifluoroacetyl chloride	2.3	UN3057		2.3, 8	2, B7, B9, B14, T50, TP21	125	INHALATION HAZARD CLASS 2*
	Trifluorochloroethylene, stabilized *or* **Refrigerant gas R 1113**	2.3	UN1082		2.3, 2.1	3, 387, B14, T50	119P	INHALATION HAZARD CLASS 2*
	1,1,1-Trifluoroethane *or* **Refrigerant gas R 143a**	2.1	UN2035		2.1	T50	115	FLAMMABLE GAS
	Trifluoromethane *or* **Refrigerant gas R 23**	2.2	UN1984		2.2		126	NONFLAMMABLE GAS
	Trifluoromethane, refrigerated liquid	2.2	UN3136		2.2	T75, TP5	120	NONFLAMMABLE GAS
	2-Trifluoromethylaniline	6.1	UN2942	III	6.1	IB3	153	POISON

	Hazardous materials descriptions	Hazard class	ID number	PG	Special provisions	ERG	Label/Placard
	3-Trifluoromethylaniline	6.1	UN2948	II	6.1	IB2, T7, TP2	153	POISON
	Triformoxime trinitrate	Forbidden						
	Triisobutylene	3	UN2324	III	3	B1, IB3, T4, TP1	128	FLAMMABLE
	Triisopropyl borate	3	UN2616	II	3	IB2, T4, TP1	129	FLAMMABLE
				III	3	B1, IB3, T2, TP1	129	FLAMMABLE
D	Trimethoxysilane	6.1	NA9269	I	6.1, 3	2, B9, B14, B32, T20, TP4, TP13, TP38, TP45	132	INHALATION HAZARD CLASS 6"
	Trimethyl borate	3	UN2416	II	3	IB2, T7, TP1	129	FLAMMABLE
	Trimethyl phosphite	3	UN2329	III	3	B1, IB3, T2, TP1	130	FLAMMABLE
	1,3,5-Trimethyl-2,4,6-trinitrobenzene	Forbidden						
	Trimethylacetyl chloride	6.1	UN2438	I	6.1, 8, 3	2, B3, B9, B14, B32, N34, T20, TP2, TP13, TP38, TP45	131	INHALATION HAZARD CLASS 6"
	Trimethylamine, anhydrous	2.1	UN1083		2.1	N87, T50	118	FLAMMABLE GAS
	Trimethylamine, aqueous solutions *with not more than 50 percent trimethylamine by mass*	3	UN1297	I	3, 8	T11, TP1	132	FLAMMABLE
				II	3, 8	B1, IB2, T7, TP1	132	FLAMMABLE
				III	3, 8	B1, IB3, T7, TP1	132	FLAMMABLE
	1,3,5-Trimethylbenzene	3	UN2325	III	3	B1, IB3, T2, TP2	129	FLAMMABLE
	Trimethylchlorosilane	3	UN1298	II	3, 8	A3, A7, B77, N34, T10, TP2, TP7, TP13	155	FLAMMABLE
	Trimethylcyclohexylamine	8	UN2326	III	8	IB3, T4, TP1	153	CORROSIVE
	Trimethylene glycol diperchlorate	Forbidden						
	Trimethylhexamethylene diisocyanate	6.1	UN2328	III	6.1	IB3, T4, TP2, TP13	156	POISON
	Trimethylhexamethylenediamines	8	UN2327	III	8	IB3, T4, TP1	153	CORROSIVE
	Trimethylol nitromethane trinitrate	Forbidden						
	Trinitro-m-cresol	1.1D	UN0216	II	1.1D		112	EXPLOSIVES 1.1*
	2,4,6-Trinitro-1,3-diazobenzene	Forbidden						
	2,4,6-Trinitro-1,3,5-triazido benzene (dry)	Forbidden						
	Trinitroacetic acid	Forbidden						
	Trinitroacetonitrile	Forbidden						

Symbols (1)	Hazardous materials descriptions and proper shipping names (2)	Hazard class or Division (3)	Identification Numbers (4)	PG (5)	Label Codes (6)	Special Provisions (§172.102) (7)	ERG Guide No.	Placard Advisory Consult §172.504 & §172.505 *Placard any quantity
	Trinitroamine cobalt	Forbidden						
	Trinitroaniline or **Picramide**	1.1D	UN0153		1.1D		112	EXPLOSIVES 1.1*
	Trinitroanisole	1.1D	UN0213		1.1D		112	EXPLOSIVES 1.1*
	Trinitrobenzene, dry or wetted with less than 30 percent water, by mass	1.1D	UN0214		1.1D		112	EXPLOSIVES 1.1*
	Trinitrobenzene, wetted, with not less than 10% water by mass	4.1	UN3367	I	4.1	162, A8, A19, N41, N84, W31	113	FLAMMABLE SOLID
	Trinitrobenzene, wetted with not less than 30 percent water, by mass	4.1	UN1354	I	4.1	23, A2, A8, A19, N41, W31	113	FLAMMABLE SOLID
	Trinitrobenzenesulfonic acid	1.1D	UN0386		1.1D		112	EXPLOSIVES 1.1*
	Trinitrobenzoic acid, dry or wetted with less than 30 percent water, by mass	1.1D	UN0215		1.1D		112	EXPLOSIVES 1.1*
	Trinitrobenzoic acid, wetted with not less than 10% water by mass	4.1	UN3368	I	4.1	162, A8, A19, N41, N84, W31	113	FLAMMABLE SOLID
	Trinitrobenzoic acid, wetted with not less than 30 percent water, by mass	4.1	UN1355	I	4.1	23, A2, A8, A19, N41, W31	113	FLAMMABLE SOLID
	Trinitrochlorobenzene or **Picryl chloride**	1.1D	UN0155		1.1D		112	EXPLOSIVES 1.1*
	Trinitrochlorobenzene (picryl chloride), wetted, with not less than 10% water by mass	4.1	UN3365	I	4.1	162, A8, A19, N41, N84, W31	113	FLAMMABLE SOLID
	Trinitroethanol	Forbidden						
	Trinitroethylnitrate	Forbidden						
	Trinitrofluorenone	1.1D	UN0387		1.1D		112	EXPLOSIVES 1.1*
	Trinitromethane	Forbidden						
	1,3,5-Trinitronaphthalene	Forbidden						
	Trinitronaphthalene	1.1D	UN0217		1.1D		112	EXPLOSIVES 1.1*
	Trinitrophenetole	1.1D	UN0218		1.1D		112	EXPLOSIVES 1.1*
	Trinitrophenol or **Picric acid**, dry or wetted with less than 30 percent water, by mass	1.1D	UN0154		1.1D		112	EXPLOSIVES 1.1*

Hazardous materials descriptions and proper shipping names	Hazard class or Division	Identification Number	PG	Label Codes	Special Provisions		
Trinitrophenol (picric acid), wetted, with not less than 10 percent water by mass	4.1	UN3364	I	4.1	23, A8, A19, N41, N84, W31	113	FLAMMABLE SOLID
Trinitrophenol, wetted with not less than 30 percent water, by mass	4.1	UN1344	I	4.1	162, A8, A19, N41, W31	113	FLAMMABLE SOLID
2,4,6-Trinitrophenyl guanidine (dry)	Forbidden						
2,4,6-Trinitrophenyl nitramine	Forbidden						
2,4,6-Trinitrophenyl trimethylol methyl nitramine trinitrate (dry)	Forbidden						
Trinitrophenylmethylnitramine or Tetryl	1.1D	UN0208		1.1D		112	EXPLOSIVES 1.1*
Trinitroresorcinol or Styphnic acid, dry or wetted with less than 20 percent water, or mixture of alcohol and water, by mass	1.1D	UN0219		1.1D		112	EXPLOSIVES 1.1*
Trinitroresorcinol, wetted or Styphnic acid, wetted with not less than 20 percent water, or mixture of alcohol and water by mass	1.1D	UN0394		1.1D	385	112	EXPLOSIVES 1.1*
2,4,6-Trinitroso-3-methyl nitraminoanisole	Forbidden						
Trinitrotetramine cobalt nitrate	Forbidden						
Trinitrotoluene and Trinitrobenzene mixtures or TNT and trinitrobenzene mixtures or TNT and hexanitrostilbene mixtures or Trinitrotoluene and hexanitrostilbene mixtures	1.1D	UN0388		1.1D		112	EXPLOSIVES 1.1*
Trinitrotoluene mixtures containing Trinitrobenzene and Hexanitrostilbene or TNT mixtures containing trinitrobenzene and hexanitrostilbene	1.1D	UN0389		1.1D		112	EXPLOSIVES 1.1*
Trinitrotoluene or TNT, dry or wetted with less than 30 percent water, by mass	1.1D	UN0209		1.1D		112	EXPLOSIVES 1.1*
Trinitrotoluene (TNT), wetted, with not less than 10 percent water by mass	4.1	UN3366	I	4.1	162, A8, A19, N41, N84, W31	113	FLAMMABLE SOLID
Trinitrotoluene, wetted or TNT, wetted, with not less than 30 percent water by mass	4.1	UN1356	I	4.1	23, A2, A8, A19, N41, W31	113	FLAMMABLE SOLID
Tripropylamine	3	UN2260	III	3, 8	B1, IB3, T4, TP*	132	FLAMMABLE
Tripropylene	3	UN2057	II	3	IB2, T4, TP2	128	FLAMMABLE
	3		III	3	B1, IB3, T2, TP2	128	FLAMMABLE
Tris-(1-aziridinyl)phosphine oxide, solution	6.1	UN2501	II	6.1	IB2, T7, TP2	152	POISON
	6.1		III	6.1	IB3, T4, TP1	152	POISON
Tris, bis-bifluoroamino diethoxy propane (TVOPA)	Forbidden						

Symbols (1)	Hazardous materials descriptions and proper shipping names (2)	Hazard class or Division (3)	Identification Numbers (4)	PG (5)	Label Codes (6)	Special Provisions (§172.102) (7)	ERG Guide No.	Placard Advisory Consult §172.504 & §172.505 *Placard any quantity
	Tritonal	1.1D	UN0390		1.1D		112	EXPLOSIVES 1.1*
	Tungsten hexafluoride	2.3	UN2196		2.3, 8	2, N86	125	INHALATION HAZARD CLASS 2*
	Turpentine	3	UN1299	III	3	B1, IB3, T2, TP2	128	FLAMMABLE
	Turpentine substitute	3	UN1300	I	3	T11, TP1, TP8, TP27	128	FLAMMABLE
				II	3	IB2, T4, TP1	128	FLAMMABLE
				III	3	B1, IB3, T2, TP1	128	FLAMMABLE
	Undecane	3	UN2330	III	3	B1, IB3, T2, TP1	128	FLAMMABLE
	Uranium hexafluoride, radioactive material, excepted package, less than 0.1 kg per package, non-fissile or fissile-excepted	6.1	UN3507	I	6.1, 7, 8	369	166	CORROSIVE
	Urea hydrogen peroxide	5.1	UN1511	III	5.1, 8	A1, A7, A29, IB8, IP3, T1, TP33	140	OXIDIZER
	Urea nitrate, dry or wetted with less than 20 percent water, by mass	1.1D	UN0220		1.1D	119	112	EXPLOSIVES 1.1*
	Urea nitrate, wetted, with not less than 10 percent water by mass	4.1	UN3370	I	4.1	162, A8, A19, N41, N84, W31	113	FLAMMABLE SOLID
	Urea nitrate, wetted with not less than 20 percent water, by mass	4.1	UN1357	I	4.1	23, 39, A8, A19, N41, W31	113	FLAMMABLE SOLID
	Urea peroxide, see Urea hydrogen peroxide							
	Valeraldehyde	3	UN2058	II	3	IB2, T4, TP1	129	FLAMMABLE
	Valeric acid, see Corrosive liquids, n.o.s.							
	Valeryl chloride	8	UN2502	II	8, 3	A3, A7, B2, IB2, N34, T7, TP2	132	CORROSIVE
G	Vanadium compound, n.o.s.	6.1	UN3285	I	6.1	IB7, IP1, T6, TP33	151	POISON
				II	6.1	IB8, IP2, IP4, T3, TP33	151	POISON
				III	6.1	IB8, IP3, T1, TP33	151	POISON
	Vanadium oxytrichloride	8	UN2443	II	8	A3, A7, B2, B16, IB2, N34, T7, TP2	137	CORROSIVE
	Vanadium pentoxide, non-fused form	6.1	UN2862	III	6.1	IB8, IP3, T1, TP33	151	POISON

Name	Class or Division	ID No.	PG	Label Codes	Special Provisions	Guide No.	Placard
Vanadium tetrachloride	8	UN2444	I	8	A7, B4, N34, T10, TP2	137	CORROSIVE
Vanadium trichloride	8	UN2475	III	8	IB8, IP3, T1, TP33	157	CORROSIVE
Vanadyl sulfate	6.1	UN2931	II	6.1	IB8, IP2, IP4, T3, TP33	151	POISON
Vehicle, flammable gas powered *or* Vehicle, fuel cell, flammable gas powered	9	UN3166		9	135, A200	115	CLASS 9
Vehicle, flammable liquid powered *or* Vehicle, fuel cell, flammable liquid powered	9	UN3166		9	135, A200	128	CLASS 9
Very signal cartridge, see Cartridges, signal							
Vinyl acetate, stabilized	3	UN1301	II	3	387, IB2, T4, TP1	129P	FLAMMABLE
Vinyl bromide, stabilized	2.1	UN1085		2.1	387, N86, T50	116P	FLAMMABLE GAS
Vinyl butyrate, stabilized	3	UN2838	II	3	387, IB2, T4, TP1	129P	FLAMMABLE
Vinyl chloride, stabilized	2.1	UN1086		2.1	21, 387, B44, N86, T50	116P	FLAMMABLE GAS
Vinyl chloroacetate	6.1	UN2589	II	6.1, 3	IB2, T7, TP2	155	POISON
Vinyl ethyl ether, stabilized	3	UN1302	I	3	387, T11, TP2	127P	FLAMMABLE
Vinyl fluoride, stabilized	2.1	UN1860		2.1	387, N86	116P	FLAMMABLE GAS
Vinyl isobutyl ether, stabilized	3	UN1304	II	3	387, IB2, T4, TP1	127P	FLAMMABLE
Vinyl methyl ether, stabilized	2.1	UN1087		2.1	387, B44, T50	116P	FLAMMABLE GAS
Vinyl nitrate polymer	Forbidden						
Vinylidene chloride, stabilized	3	UN1303	I	3	387, T12, TP2, TP7	130P	FLAMMABLE
Vinylpyridines, stabilized	6.1	UN3073	II	6.1, 3, 8	387, IB1, T7, TP2, TP13	131P	POISON
Vinyltoluenes, stabilized	3	UN2618	III	3	387, B1, IB3, T2, TP1	130P	FLAMMABLE
Vinyltrichlorosilane	3	UN1305	II	3, 8	A3, A7, B6, N34, T10, TP2, TP7, TP13	155P	FLAMMABLE
Warheads, rocket *with burster or expelling charge*	1.4D	UN0370		1.4D		114	EXPLOSIVES 1.4
Warheads, rocket *with burster or expelling charge*	1.4F	UN0371		1.4F		114	EXPLOSIVES 1.4
Warheads, rocket *with bursting charge*	1.1D	UN0286		1.1D		112	EXPLOSIVES 1.1*
Warheads, rocket *with bursting charge*	1.2D	UN0287		1.2D		112	EXPLOSIVES 1.2*
Warheads, rocket *with bursting charge*	1.1F	UN0369		1.1F		112	EXPLOSIVES 1.1*
Warheads, torpedo *with bursting charge*	1.1D	UN0221		1.1D		112	EXPLOSIVES 1.1*

Symbols (1)	Hazardous materials descriptions and proper shipping names (2)	Hazard class or Division (3)	Identification Numbers (4)	PG (5)	Label Codes (6)	Special Provisions (§172.102) (7)	ERG Guide No.	Placard Advisory Consult §172.504 & §172.505 *Placard any quantity
G	Water-reactive liquid, corrosive, n.o.s.	4.3	UN3129	I	4.3, 8	T14, TP2, TP7, TP13	138	DANGEROUS WHEN WET*
				II	4.3, 8	IB1, T11, TP2, TP7	138	DANGEROUS WHEN WET*
				III	4.3, 8	IB2, T7, TP2, TP7	138	DANGEROUS WHEN WET*
G	Water-reactive liquid, n.o.s.	4.3	UN3148	I	4.3	T13, TP2, TP7, TP41, W31	138	DANGEROUS WHEN WET*
				II	4.3	IB1, T7, TP2, TP7, W31	138	DANGEROUS WHEN WET*
				III	4.3	IB2, T7, TP2, TP7, W31	138	DANGEROUS WHEN WET*
G	Water-reactive liquid, toxic, n.o.s.	4.3	UN3130	I	4.3, 6.1	A4	139	DANGEROUS WHEN WET*
				II	4.3, 6.1	IB1	139	DANGEROUS WHEN WET*
				III	4.3, 6.1	IB2	139	DANGEROUS WHEN WET*
G	Water-reactive solid, corrosive, n.o.s.	4.3	UN3131	I	4.3, 8	IB4, IP1, N40, T9, TP7, TP33, W31	138	DANGEROUS WHEN WET*
				II	4.3, 8	IB6, IP2, T3, TP33, W31, W40	138	DANGEROUS WHEN WET*
				III	4.3, 8	IB8, IP4, T1, TP33, W31	138	DANGEROUS WHEN WET*
G	Water-reactive solid, flammable, n.o.s.	4.3	UN3132	I	4.3, 4.1	IB4, N40, W31	138	DANGEROUS WHEN WET*
				II	4.3, 4.1	IB4, T3, TP33, W31, W40	138	DANGEROUS WHEN WET*
				III	4.3, 4.1	IB6, T1, TP33, W31	138	DANGEROUS WHEN WET*

Symbol	Hazardous materials descriptions and proper shipping names	Hazard class	Identification Numbers	PG	Label codes	Special provisions	Guide	Response
G	Water-reactive solid, n.o.s.	4.3	UN2813	I	4.3	IB4, N40, T9, TP7, TP33, W31	138	DANGEROUS WHEN WET*
				II	4.3	B132, IB7, IP2, IP21, T3, TP33, W31, W40	138	DANGEROUS WHEN WET*
				III	4.3	B132, IB8, IP2, IP21, T1, TP33, W31	138	DANGEROUS WHEN WET*
G	Water-reactive solid, oxidizing, n.o.s.	4.3	UN3133	II	4.3, 5.1		138	DANGEROUS WHEN WET*
				III	4.3, 5.1		138	DANGEROUS WHEN WET*
G	Water-reactive solid, self-heating, n.o.s.	4.3	UN3135	I	4.3, 4.2	N40, W31	138	DANGEROUS WHEN WET*
				II	4.3, 4.2	IB5, IP2, T3, TP33, W31, W40	138	DANGEROUS WHEN WET*
				III	4.3, 4.2	IB8, IP4, T1, TP33, W31	138	DANGEROUS WHEN WET*
G	Water-reactive solid, toxic, n.o.s.	4.3	UN3134	I	4.3, 6.1	A8, IB4, IP1, N40, W31	139	DANGEROUS WHEN WET*
				II	4.3, 6.1	IB5, IP2, T3, TP33, W31, W40	139	DANGEROUS WHEN WET*
				III	4.3, 6.1	IB8, IP4, T1, TP33, W31	139	DANGEROUS WHEN WET*
	Wheel chair, electric, see Battery powered vehicle or Battery powered equipment							
	White acid, see Hydrofluoric acid							
	Wood preservatives, liquid	3	UN1306	II	3	149, IB2, T4, TP1, TP8	129	FLAMMABLE
				III	3	B1, IB3, T2, TP1	129	FLAMMABLE
A I W	Wool waste, wet	4.2	UN1387	III	4.2		133	SPONTANEOUSLY COMBUSTIBLE
	Xanthates	4.2	UN3342	II	4.2	IB6, IP2, T3, TP33, W31	135	SPONTANEOUSLY COMBUSTIBLE
				III	4.2	IB8, IP3, T1, TP33, W31	135	SPONTANEOUSLY COMBUSTIBLE

HAZMAT TABLE

Symbols (1)	Hazardous materials descriptions and proper shipping names (2)	Hazard class or Division (3)	Identification Numbers (4)	PG (5)	Label Codes (6)	Special Provisions (§172.102) (7)	ERG Guide No.	Placard Advisory Consult §172.504 & §172.505 *Placard any quantity
	Xenon, compressed	2.2	UN2036		2.2		120	NONFLAMMABLE GAS
	Xenon, refrigerated liquid *(cryogenic liquids)*	2.2	UN2591		2.2	T75, TP5	120	NONFLAMMABLE GAS
	Xylenes	3	UN1307	II	3	IB2, T4, TP1	130	FLAMMABLE
				III	3	B1, IB3, T2, TP1	130	FLAMMABLE
	Xylenols, solid	6.1	UN2261	II	6.1	IB8, IP2, IP4, T7, T3, TP33	153	POISON
	Xylenols, liquid	6.1	UN3430	II	6.1	IB2, T7, TP2	153	POISON
	Xylidines, liquid	6.1	UN1711	II	6.1	IB2, T7, TP2	153	POISON
	Xylidines, solid	6.1	UN3452	II	6.1	IB8, IP2, IP4, T7, T3, TP33	153	POISON
	Xylyl bromide, liquid	6.1	UN1701	II	6.1	A3, A7, IB2, N33, T7, TP2, TP13, W31	152	POISON
	Xylyl bromide, solid	6.1	UN3417	II	6.1	A3, A6, A7, IB8, IP2, IP4, N33, T3, TP33	152	POISON
	p-Xylyl diazide	Forbidden						
	Zinc ammonium nitrite	5.1	UN1512	II	5.1	IB8, IP4, T3, TP33	140	OXIDIZER
	Zinc arsenate *or* Zinc arsenite *or* Zinc arsenate and zinc arsenite mixtures.	6.1	UN1712	II	6.1	IB8, IP2, IP4, T3, TP33	151	POISON
	Zinc ashes	4.3	UN1435	III	4.3	A1, A19, B136, IB8, IP4, T1, TP33, W100	138	DANGEROUS WHEN WET*
	Zinc bisulfite solution, see Bisulfites, aqueous solutions, n.o.s.							
	Zinc bromate	5.1	UN2469	III	5.1	A1, A29, IB8, IP3, T1, TP33	140	OXIDIZER
	Zinc chlorate	5.1	UN1513	II	5.1	A9, IB8, IP2, IP4, N34, T3, TP33	140	OXIDIZER
	Zinc chloride, anhydrous	8	UN2331	III	8	IB8, IP3, T1, TP33	154	CORROSIVE
	Zinc chloride, solution	8	UN1840	III	8	IB3, T4, TP2	154	CORROSIVE
	Zinc cyanide	6.1	UN1713	I	6.1	IB7, IP1, T6, TP33	151	POISON
	Zinc dithionite *or* Zinc hydrosulfite	9	UN1931	III	None	IB8, IP3, T1, TP33	171	CLASS 9
	Zinc fluorosilicate	6.1	UN2855	III	6.1	IB8, IP3, T1, TP33	151	POISON

Name	Class	ID number	PG	Label codes	Special provisions	ERG	Description
Zinc hydrosulfite, see Zinc dithionite							
Zinc muriate solution, see Zinc chloride, solution							
Zinc nitrate	5.1	UN1514	II	5.1	IB8, IP2, IP4, T3, TP33	140	OXIDIZER
Zinc permanganate	5.1	UN1515	II	5.1	IB6, IP2, T3, TP33	140	OXIDIZER
Zinc peroxide	5.1	UN1516	II	5.1	IB6, IP2, T3, TP33, W100	143	OXIDIZER
Zinc phosphide	4.3	UN1714	I	4.3, 6.1	A19, N40, W31	139	DANGEROUS WHEN WET*
Zinc powder or Zinc dust	4.3	UN1436	I	4.3, 4.2	A19, IB4, IP1, N40, W31	138	DANGEROUS WHEN WET*
			II	4.3, 4.2	A19, IB7, IP2, T3, TP33, W31, W40	138	DANGEROUS WHEN WET*
			III	4.3, 4.2	IB8, IP4, T1, TP33, W31	138	DANGEROUS WHEN WET*
Zinc resinate	4.1	UN2714	III	4.1	A1, IB6, T1, TP33	133	FLAMMABLE SOLID
Zinc selenate, see Selenates or Selenites							
Zinc selenite, see Selenates or Selenites							
Zinc silicofluoride, see Zinc fluorosilicate							
Zirconium, dry, coiled wire, finished metal sheets, strip (thinner than 254 microns but not thinner than 18 microns)	4.1	UN2858	III	4.1	A1, W100	170	FLAMMABLE SOLID
Zirconium, dry, finished sheets, strip or coiled wire	4.2	UN2009	III	4.2	A1, A19, W31	135	SPONTANEOUSLY COMBUSTIBLE
Zirconium hydride	4.1	UN1437	II	4.1	A19, A20, IB4, N34, T3, TP33, W31, W40	138	FLAMMABLE SOLID
Zirconium nitrate	5.1	UN2728	III	5.1	A1, A29, IB8, IP3, T1, TP33	140	OXIDIZER
Zirconium picramate, dry or wetted with less than 20 percent water, by mass	1.3C	UN0236		1.3C		112	EXPLOSIVES 1.3*
Zirconium picramate, wetted with not less than 20 percent water, by mass	4.1	UN1517	I	4.1	23, N41, W31	113	FLAMMABLE SOLID
Zirconium powder, dry	4.2	UN2008	I	4.2	T21, TP7, TP33, W31	135	SPONTANEOUSLY COMBUSTIBLE
			II	4.2	A19, A20, IB6, IP2, N5, N34, T3, TP33, W31	135	SPONTANEOUSLY COMBUSTIBLE

Symbols (1)	Hazardous materials descriptions and proper shipping names (2)	Hazard class or Division (3)	Identification Numbers (4)	PG (5)	Label Codes (6)	Special Provisions (§172.102) (7)	ERG Guide No.	Placard Advisory Consult §172.504 & §172.505 *Placard any quantity
				III	4.2	B135, IB8, IP4, T1, TP33, W31	135	SPONTANEOUSLY COMBUSTIBLE
	Zirconium powder, wetted with not less than 25 percent water (a visible excess of water must be present) (a) mechanically produced, particle size less than 53 microns; (b) chemically produced, particle size less than 840 microns	4.1	UN1358	II	4.1	A19, A20, IB6, IP2, N34, T3, TP33, W31, W40	170	FLAMMABLE SOLID
	Zirconium scrap	4.2	UN1932	III	4.2	B135, IB8, IP21, N34, T1, TP33, W31	135	SPONTANEOUSLY COMBUSTIBLE
	Zirconium suspended in a liquid	3	UN1308	I	3		170	FLAMMABLE
				II	3	IB2	170	FLAMMABLE
				III	3	B1, IB2	170	FLAMMABLE
	Zirconium tetrachloride	8	UN2503	III	8	IB8, IP3, T1, TP33	137	CORROSIVE

Appendix A to §172.101—List of Hazardous Substances and Reportable Quantities

1. This Appendix lists materials and their corresponding reportable quantities (RQs) that are listed or designated as "hazardous substances" under section 101(14) of the Comprehensive Environmental Response, Compensation, and Liability Act, 42 U.S.C. 9601(14) (CERCLA; 42 U.S.C. 9601 *et seq*). This listing fulfills the requirement of CERCLA, 42 U.S.C. 9656 (a), that all "hazardous substances," as defined in 42 U.S.C. 9601 (14), be listed and regulated as hazardous materials under 49 U.S.C. 5101-5127. That definition includes substances listed under sections 311(b)(2)(A) and 307(a) of the Federal Water Pollution Control Act, 33 U.S.C. 1321(b)(2)(A) and 1317(a), section 3001 of the Solid Waste Disposal Act, 42 U.S.C. 6921, and Section 112 of the Clean Air Act, 42 U.S.C. 7412. In addition, this list contains materials that the Administrator of the Environmental Protection Agency has determined to be hazardous substances in accordance with section 102 of CERCLA, 42 U.S.C. 9602. It should be noted that 42 U.S.C. 9656(b) provides that common and contract carriers may be held liable under laws other than CERCLA for the release of a hazardous substance as defined in that Act, during transportation that commenced before the effective date of the listing and regulating of that substance as a hazardous material under 49 U.S.C. 5101-5127.

2. This Appendix is divided into two TABLES which are entitled "TABLE 1– HAZARDOUS SUBSTANCES OTHER THAN RADIONUCLIDES" and "TABLE 2–RADIONUCLIDES." A material listed in this Appendix is regulated as a hazardous material and a hazardous substance under this subchapter if it meets the definition of a hazardous substance in §171.8 of this subchapter.

3. The procedure for selecting a proper shipping name for a hazardous substance is set forth in §172.101(c).

4. Column 1 of TABLE 1, entitled *"Hazardous substance"*, contains the names of those elements and compounds that are hazardous substances. Following the listing of elements and compounds is a listing of waste streams. These waste streams appear on the list in numerical sequence and are referenced by the appropriate "D", "F", or "K" numbers. Column 2 of TABLE 1, entitled *"Reportable quantity (RQ)"*, contains the reportable quantity (RQ), in pounds and kilograms, for each hazardous substance listed in Column 1 of TABLE 1.

5. A series of notes is used throughout TABLE 1 and TABLE 2 to provide additional information concerning certain hazardous substances. These notes are explained at the end of each TABLE.

6. TABLE 2 lists radionuclides that are hazardous substances and their corresponding RQ's. The RQ's in TABLE 2 for radionuclides are expressed in units of curies and terabecquerels, whereas those in TABLE 1 are expressed in units of pounds and kilograms. If a material is listed in both TABLE 1 and TABLE 2, the lower RQ shall apply. Radionuclides are listed in alphabetical order. The RQs for radionuclides are given in the radiological unit of measure of curie, abbreviated "Ci," followed, in parentheses, by an equivalent unit measured in terabecquerels, abbreviated "TBq".

7. For mixtures of radionuclides, the following requirements shall be used in determining if a package contains an RQ of a hazardous substance: (i) if the identity and quantity (in curies or terabecquerels) of each radionuclide in a mixture or solution is known, the ratio between the quantity per package (in curies or terabecquerels) and the RQ for the radionuclide must be determined for each radionuclide. A package contains an RQ of a hazardous substance when the sum of the ratios for the radionuclides in the mixture or solution is equal to or greater than one; (ii) if the identity of each radionuclide in a mixture or solution is known but the quantity per package (in curies or terabecquerels) of one or more of the radionuclides is unknown, an RQ of a hazardous substance is present in a package when the total quantity (in curies or terabecquerels) of the mixture or solution is

equal to or greater than the lowest RQ of any individual radionuclide in the mixture or solution; and (iii) if the identity of one or more radionuclides in a mixture or solution is unknown (or if the identity of a radionuclide by itself is unknown), an RQ of a hazardous substance is present when the total quantity (in curies or terabecquerels) in a package is equal to or greater than either one curie or the lowest RQ of any known individual radionuclide in the mixture or solution, whichever is lower.

Table 1 — Hazardous substances

Hazardous substance	Reportable quantity (RQ) pounds (kilograms)
A2213	5000 (2270)
Acenaphthene	100 (45.4)
Acenaphthylene	5000 (2270)
Acetaldehyde	1000 (454)
Acetaldehyde, chloro-	1000 (454)
Acetaldehyde, trichloro-	5000 (2270)
Acetamide	100 (45.4)
Acetamide, N-(aminothloxomethyl)-	1000 (454)
Acetamide, N-(4-ethoxyphenyl)-	100 (45.4)
Acetamide, N-9H-fluoren-2-yl-	1 (0.454)
Acetamide 2-fluoro-	100 (45.4)
Acetic acid	5000 (2270)
Acetic acid, (2,4-dichlorophenoxy)-, salts & esters	100 (45.4)
Acetic acid, ethyl ester	5000 (2270)
Acetic acid, fluoro-, sodium salt	10 (4.54)
Acetic acid, lead(2+) salt	10 (4.54)
Acetic acid, thallium(1+) salt	100 (45.4)
Acetic acid, (2,4,5-trichlorophenoxy)-	1000 (454)
Acetic anhydride	5000 (2270)
Acetone	5000 (2270)
Acetone cyanohydrin	10 (4.54)
Acetonitrile	5000 (2270)
Acetophenone	5000 (2270)
2-Acetylaminofluorene	1 (0.454)
Acetyl bromide	5000 (2270)
Acetyl chloride	5000 (2270)
1-Acetyl-2-thiourea	1000 (454)
Acrolein	1 (0.454)
Acrylamide	5000 (2270)
Acrylic acid	5000 (2270)
Acrylonitrile	100 (45.4)
Adipic acid	5000 (2270)
Aldicarb	1 (0.454)
Aldicarb sulfone	100 (45.4)
Aldrin	1 (0.454)
Allyl alcohol	100 (45.4)
Allyl chloride	1000 (454)
Aluminum phosphide	100 (45.4)
Aluminum sulfate	5000 (2270)
4-Aminobiphenyl	1 (0.454)
5-(Aminomethyl)-3-isoxazolol	1000 (454)
4-Aminopyridine	1000 (454)
Amitrole	10 (4.54)
Ammonia	100 (45.4)
Ammonium acetate	5000 (2270)
Ammonium benzoate	5000 (2270)
Ammonium bicarbonate	5000 (2270)
Ammonium bichromate	10 (4.54)
Ammonium bifluoride	100 (45.4)

Hazardous substance	Reportable quantity (RQ) pounds (kilograms)
Ammonium bisulfite	5000 (2270)
Ammonium carbamate	5000 (2270)
Ammonium carbonate	5000 (2270)
Ammonium chloride	5000 (2270)
Ammonium chromate	10 (4.54)
Ammonium citrate, dibasic	5000 (2270)
Ammonium dichromate [@]	10 (4.54)
Ammonium fluoborate	5000 (2270)
Ammonium fluoride	100 (45.4)
Ammonium hydroxide	1000 (454)
Ammonium oxalate	5000 (2270)
Ammonium picrate	10 (4.54)
Ammonium silicofluoride	1000 (454)
Ammonium sulfamate	5000 (2270)
Ammonium sulfide	100 (45.4)
Ammonium sulfite	5000 (2270)
Ammonium tartrate	5000 (2270)
Ammonium thiocyanate	5000 (2270)
Ammonium vanadate	1000 (454)
Amyl acetate	5000 (2270)
iso-Amyl acetate	....
sec-Amyl acetate	....
tert-Amyl acetate	....
Aniline	5000 (2270)
o-Anisidine	100 (45.4)
Anthracene	5000 (2270)
Antimony [c]	5000 (2270)
Antimony pentachloride	1000 (454)
Antimony potassium tartrate	100 (45.4)
Antimony tribromide	1000 (454)
Antimony trichloride	1000 (454)
Antimony trifluoride	1000 (454)
Antimony trioxide	1000 (454)
Argentate(1-), bis(cyano-C)-, potassium	1 (0.454)
Aroclor 1016	1 (0.454)
Aroclor 1221	1 (0.454)
Aroclor 1232	1 (0.454)
Aroclor 1242	1 (0.454)
Aroclor 1248	1 (0.454)
Aroclor 1254	1 (0.454)
Aroclor 1260	1 (0.454)
Aroclors	1 (0.454)
Arsenic [c]	1 (0.454)
Arsenic acid H_3AsO_4	1 (0.454)
Arsenic disulfide	1 (0.454)
Arsenic oxide As_2O_3	1 (0.454)
Arsenic oxide As_2O_5	1 (0.454)
Arsenic pentoxide	1 (0.454)
Arsenic trichloride	1 (0.454)
Arsenic trioxide	1 (0.454)
Arsenic trisulfide	1 (0.454)

TABLE 1 — HAZARDOUS SUBSTANCES 313

Hazardous substance	Reportable quantity (RQ) pounds (kilograms)
Arsine, diethyl-	1 (0.454)
Arsinic acid, dimethyl-	1 (0.454)
Arsonous dichloride, phenyl-	1 (0.454)
Asbestos cc	1 (0.454)
Auramine	100 (45.4)
Azaserine	1 (0.454)
Aziridine	1 (0.454)
Aziridine, 2-methyl-	1 (0.454)
Azirino[2',3':3,4]pyrrolo[1,2-a]indole-4,7-dione, 6-amino-8-[[(aminocarbonyl)oxy]methyl]-1,1a,2,8,8a,8b-hexahydro-8a-methoxy-5-methyl-, [1aS-(1aalpha,8beta,8aalpha, 8balpha)]-	10 (4.54)
Barban	10 (4.54)
Barium cyanide	10 (4.54)
Bendiocarb	100 (45.4)
Bendiocarb phenol	1000 (454)
Benomyl	10 (4.54)
Benz[j]aceanthrylene, 1,2-dihydro-3-methyl-	10 (4.54)
Benz[c]acridine	100 (45.4)
Benzal chloride	5000 (2270)
Benzamide, 3,5-dichloro-N-(1,1-dimethyl-2-propynyl)-	5000 (2270)
Benz[a]anthracene	10 (4.54)
1,2-Benzanthracene	10 (4.54)
Benz[a]anthracene, 7,12-dimethyl-	1 (0.454)
Benzenamine	5000 (2270)
Benzenamine, 4,4'-carbonimidoylbis (N,N dimethyl-	100 (45.4)
Benzenamine, 4-chloro-	1000 (454)
Benzenamine, 4-chloro-2-methyl-, hydrochloride	100 (45.4)
Benzenamine, N,N-dimethyl-4-(phenylazo)-	10 (4.54)
Benzenamine, 2-methyl-	100 (45.4)
Benzenamine, 4-methyl-	100 (45.4)
Benzenamine, 4,4'-methylenebis[2-chloro-	10 (4.54)
Benzenamine, 2-methyl-, hydrochloride	100 (45.4)
Benzenamine, 2-methyl-5-nitro-	100 (45.4)
Benzenamine, 4-nitro-	5000 (2270)
Benzene	10 (4.54)
Benzeneacetic acid, 4-chloro-α-(4-chlorophenyl)-α-hydroxy-, ethyl ester	10 (4.54)
Benzene, 1-bromo-4-phenoxy-	100 (45.4)
Benzenebutanoic acid, 4-[bis(2-chloroethyl)amino]-	10 (4.54)
Benzene, chloro-	100 (45.4)
Benzene, (chloromethyl)-	100 (45.4)
Benzenediamine, ar-methyl-	10 (4.54)
1,2-Benzenedicarboxylic acid, bis(2-ethylhexyl) ester	100 (45.4)
1,2-Benzenedicarboxylic acid, dibutyl ester	10 (4.54)
1,2-Benzenedicarboxylic acid, diethyl ester	1000 (454)
1,2-Benzenedicarboxylic acid, dimethyl ester	5000 (2270)
1,2-Benzenedicarboxylic acid, dioctyl ester	5000 (2270)
Benzene, 1,2-dichloro-	100 (45.4)
Benzene, 1,3-dichloro-	100 (45.4)
Benzene, 1,4-dichloro-	100 (45.4)
Benzene, 1,1'-(2,2-dichloroethylidene) bis[4-chloro-	1 (0.454)
Benzene, (dichloromethyl)-	5000 (2270)

Hazardous substance	Reportable quantity (RQ) pounds (kilograms)
Benzene, 1,3-diisocyanatomethyl-	100 (45.4)
Benzene, dimethyl-	100 (45.4)
1,3-Benzenediol	5000 (2270)
1,2-Benzenediol,4-[1-hydroxy-2-(methylamino) ethyl]-	1000 (454)
Benzeneethanamine, alpha,alpha-dimethyl-	5000 (2270)
Benzene, hexachloro-	10 (4.54)
Benzene, hexahydro-	1000 (454)
Benzene, methyl-	1000 (454)
Benzene, 1-methyl-2,4-dinitro-	10 (4.54)
Benzene, 2-methyl-1,3-dinitro-	100 (45.4)
Benzene, (1-methylethyl)-	5000 (2270)
Benzene, nitro-	1000 (454)
Benzene, pentachloro-	10 (4.54)
Benzene, pentachloronitro-	100 (45.4)
Benzenesulfonic acid chloride	100 (45.4)
Benzenesulfonyl chloride	100 (45.4)
Benzene,1,2,4,5-tetrachloro-	5000 (2270)
Benzenethiol	100 (45.4)
Benzene,1,1'-(2,2,2-trichloroethylidene) bis[4-chloro-	1 (0.454)
Benzene,1,1'-(2,2,2-trichloroethylidene) bis[4-methoxy-	1 (0.454)
Benzene, (trichloromethyl)-	10 (4.54)
Benzene, 1,3,5-trinitro-	10 (4.54)
Benzidine	1 (0.454)
Benzo[a]anthracene	10 (4.54)
1,3-Benzodioxole, 5-(1-propenyl)-1	100 (45.4)
1,3-Benzodioxole, 5-(2-propenyl)-	100 (45.4)
1,3-Benzodioxole, 5-propyl-	10 (4.54)
1,3-Benzodioxol-4-ol, 2,2-dimethyl-	1000 (454)
1,3-Benzodioxol-4-ol, 2,2-dimethyl-, methyl carbamate	100 (45.4)
Benzo[b]fluoranthene	1 (0.454)
Benzo[k]fluoranthene	5000 (2270)
7-Benzofuranol, 2,3-dihydro-2,2-dimethyl-	10 (4.54)
7-Benzofuranol, 2,3-dihydro-2,2-dimethyl-, methylcarbamate	10 (4.54)
Benzoic acid	5000 (2270)
Benzoic acid, 2-hydroxy-, compd. With (3aS-cis)-1,2,3,3a,8,8a-hexahydro-1,3a,8-trimethylpyrrolo [2,3-b]indol-5-yl methylcarbamate ester (1:1)	100 (45.4)
Benzonitrile	5000 (2270)
Benzo[rst]pentaphene	10 (4.54)
Benzo[ghi]perylene	5000 (2270)
2H-1-Benzopyran-2-one, 4-hydroxy-3-(3-oxo-1-phenylbutyl)-, & salts	100 (45.4)
Benzo[a]pyrene	1 (0.454)
3,4-Benzopyrene	1 (0.454)
p-Benzoquinone	10 (4.54)
Benzotrichloride	10 (4.54)
Benzoyl chloride	1000 (454)
Benzyl chloride	100 (45.4)
Beryllium [c]	10 (4.54)
Beryllium chloride	1 (0.454)
Beryllium fluoride	1 (0.454)
Beryllium nitrate	1 (0.454)
Beryllium powder [c]	10 (4.54)

TABLE 1 — HAZARDOUS SUBSTANCES   315

Hazardous substance	Reportable quantity (RQ) pounds (kilograms)
alpha-BHC	10 (4.54)
beta-BHC	1 (0.454)
delta-BHC	1 (0.454)
gamma-BHC	1 (0.454)
2,2'-Bioxirane	10 (4.54)
Biphenyl	100 (45.4)
[1,1'-Biphenyl]-4,4'-diamine	1 (0.454)
[1,1'-Biphenyl]-4,4'-diamine,3,3'-dichloro-	1 (0.454)
[1,1'-Biphenyl]-4,4'-diamine,3,3'-dimethoxy-	100 (45.4)
[1,1'-Biphenyl]-4,4'-diamine,3,3'-dimethyl-	10 (4.54)
Bis(2-chloroethoxy) methane	1000 (454)
Bis(2-chloroethyl) ether	10 (4.54)
Bis(chloromethyl) ether	10 (4.54)
Bis(2-ethylhexyl) phthalate	100 (45.4)
Bromoacetone	1000 (454)
Bromoform	100 (45.4)
Bromomethane	1000 (454)
4-Bromophenyl phenyl ether	100 (45.4)
Brucine	100 (45.4)
1,3-Butadiene	10 (4.54)
1,3-Butadiene, 1,1,2,3,4,4-hexachloro-	1 (0.454)
1-Butanamine, N-butyl-N-nitroso-	10 (4.54)
1-Butanol	5000 (2270)
2-Butanone	5000 (2270)
2-Butanone, 3,3-dimethyl-1(methylthio)-, O [(methylamino) carbonyl] oxime	100 (45.4)
2-Butanone peroxide	10 (4.54)
2-Butenal	100 (45.4)
2-Butene, 1,4-dichloro-	1 (0.454)
2-Butenoic acid, 2-methyl-, 7-[[2,3-dihydroxy-2-(1-methoxyethyl)-3-methyl-1-oxobutoxy] methyl]-2,3,5,7a-tetrahydro-1H-pyrrolizin-1-yl ester, [1S-[1alpha(Z),7(2S*,3R*),7aalpha]]-	10 (4.54)
Butyl acetate	5000 (2270)
iso-Butyl acetate	....
sec-Butyl acetate	....
tert-Butyl acetate	....
n-Butyl alcohol	5000 (2270)
Butylamine	1000 (454)
iso-Butylamine	....
sec-Butylamine	....
tert-Butylamine	....
Butyl benzyl phthalate	100 (45.4)
n-Butyl phthalate	10 (4.54)
Butyric acid	5000 (2270)
iso-Butyric acid	....
Cacodylic acid	1 (0.454)
Cadmium [c]	10 (4.54)
Cadmium acetate	10 (4.54)
Cadmium bromide	10 (4.54)
Cadmium chloride	10 (4.54)
Calcium arsenate	1 (0.454)
Calcium arsenite	1 (0.454)

Hazardous substance	Reportable quantity (RQ) pounds (kilograms)
Calcium carbide	10 (4.54)
Calcium chromate	10 (4.54)
Calcium cyanamide	1000 (454)
Calcium cyanide Ca(CN)$_2$	10 (4.54)
Calcium dodecylbenzenesulfonate	1000 (454)
Calcium hypochlorite	10 (4.54)
Captan	10 (4.54)
Carbamic acid, 1H-benzimidazol-2-yl, methyl ester	10 (4.54)
Carbamic acid, [1-[(butylamino)carbonyl]-1H-benzimidazol-2-yl]-, methyl ester	10 (4.54)
Carbamic acid, (3-chlorophenyl)-, 4-chloro-2-butynyl ester	10 (4.54)
Carbamic acid, [(dibutylamino)-thio]methyl-, 2,3-dihydro-2,2-dimethyl-7-benzofuranyl ester	1000 (454)
Carbamic acid, dimethyl-,1-[(dimethyl-amino)carbonyl]-5-methyl-1H-pyrazol-3-yl ester	1 (0.454)
Carbamic acid, dimethyl-, 3-methyl-1-(1-methylethyl)-1H-pyrazol-5-yl ester	100 (45.4)
Carbamic acid, ethyl ester	100 (45.4)
Carbamic acid, methyl-, 3-methylphenyl ester	1000 (454)
Carbamic acid, methylnitroso-, ethyl ester	1 (0.454)
Carbamic acid, [1,2-phenylenebis(iminocarbonothioyl)] bis-, dimethyl ester	10 (4.54)
Carbamic acid, phenyl-, 1-methylethyl ester	1000 (454)
Carbamic chloride, dimethyl-	1 (0.454)
Carbamodithioic acid, 1,2-ethanediylbis-, salts & esters	5000 (2270)
Carbamothioic acid, bis(1-methylethyl)-, S-(2,3-dichloro-2-propenyl) ester	100 (45.4)
Carbamothioic acid, bis(1-methylethyl)-, S-(2,3,3-trichloro-2-propenyl) ester	100 (45.4)
Carbamothioic acid, dipropyl-, S-(phenylmethyl) ester	5000 (2270)
Carbaryl	100 (45.4)
Carbendazim	10 (4.54)
Carbofuran	10 (4.54)
Carbofuran phenol	10 (4.54)
Carbon disulfide	100 (45.4)
Carbonic acid, dithallium(1+) salt	100 (45.4)
Carbonic dichloride	10 (4.54)
Carbonic difluoride	1000 (454)
Carbonochloridic acid, methyl ester	1000 (454)
Carbon oxyfluoride	1000 (454)
Carbon tetrachloride	10 (4.54)
Carbonyl sulfide	100 (45.4)
Carbosulfan	1000 (454)
Catechol	100 (45.4)
Chloral	5000 (2270)
Chloramben	100 (45.4)
Chlorambucil	10 (4.54)
Chlordane	1 (0.454)
Chlordane, alpha & gamma isomers	1 (0.454)
CHLORDANE (TECHNICAL MIXTURE AND METABOLITES)	1 (0.454)
Chlorinated camphene	1 (0.454)
Chlorine	10 (4.54)
Chlornaphazine	100 (45.4)
Chloroacetaldehyde	1000 (454)
Chloroacetic acid	100 (45.4)
2-Chloroacetophenone	100 (45.4)

TABLE 1 — HAZARDOUS SUBSTANCES   317

Hazardous substance	Reportable quantity (RQ) pounds (kilograms)
p-Chloroaniline	1000 (454)
Chlorobenzene	100 (45.4)
Chlorobenzilate	10 (4.54)
p-Chloro-m-cresol	5000 (2270)
Chlorodlbromomethane	100 (45.4)
1-Chloro-2,3-epoxypropane	100 (45.4)
Chloroethane	100 (45.4)
2-Chloroethyl vinyl ether	1000 (454)
Chloroform	10 (4.54)
Chloromethane	100 (45.4)
Chloromethyl methyl ether	10 (4.54)
beta-Chloronaphthalene	5000 (2270)
2-Chloronaphthalene	5000 (2270)
2-Chlorophenol	100 (45.4)
o-Chlorophenol	100 (45.4)
4-Chlorophenyl phenyl ether	5000 (2270)
1-(o-Chlorophenyl)thiourea	100 (45.4)
Chloroprene	100 (45.4)
3-Chloropropionitrile	1000 (454)
Chlorosulfonic acid	1000 (454)
4-Chloro-o-toluidine, hydrochloride	100 (45.4)
Chlorpyrifos	1 (0.454)
Chromic acetate	1000 (454)
Chromic acid	10 (4.54)
Chromic acid H_2CrO_4, calcium salt	10 (4.54)
Chromic sulfate	1000 (454)
Chromium [c]	5000 (2270)
Chromous chloride	1000 (454)
Chrysene	100 (45.4)
Cobaltous bromide	1000 (454)
Cobaltous formate	1000 (454)
Cobaltous sulfamate	1000 (454)
Coke Oven Emissions	1 (0.454)
Copper [c]	5000 (2270)
Copper chloride [@]	10 (4.54)
Copper cyanide Cu(CN)	10 (4.54)
Coumaphos	10 (4.54)
Creosote	1 (0.454)
Cresol (cresylic acid)	100 (45.4)
m-Cresol	100 (45.4)
o-Cresol	100 (45.4)
p-Cresol	100 (45.4)
Cresols (isomers and mixture)	100 (45.4)
Cresylic acid (isomers and mixture)	100 (45.4)
Crotonaldehyde	100 (45.4)
Cumene	5000 (2270)
m-Cumenyl methylcarbamate	10 (4.54)
Cupric acetate	100 (45.4)
Cupric acetoarsenite	1 (0.454)
Cupric chloride	10 (4.54)
Cupric nitrate	100 (45.4)

Hazardous substance	Reportable quantity (RQ) pounds (kilograms)
Cupric oxalate	100 (45.4)
Cupric sulfate	10 (4.54)
Cupric sulfate, ammoniated	100 (45.4)
Cupric tartrate	100 (45.4)
Cyanides (soluble salts and complexes) not otherwise specified	10 (4.54)
Cyanogen	100 (45.4)
Cyanogen bromide (CN)Br	1000 (454)
Cyanogen chloride (CN)Cl	10 (4.54)
2,5-Cyclohexadiene-1,4-dione	10 (4.54)
Cyclohexane	1000 (454)
Cyclohexane, 1,2,3,4,5,6-hexachloro-, (1α, 2α, 3β-, 4α, 5α, 6β)	1 (0.454)
Cyclohexanone	5000 (2270)
2-Cyclohexyl-4,6-dinitrophenol	100 (45.4)
1,3-Cyclopentadiene, 1,2,3,4,5,5-hexachloro-	10 (4.54)
Cyclophosphamide	10 (4.54)
2,4-D Acid	100 (45.4)
2,4-D Ester	100 (45.4)
2,4-D, salts and esters	100 (45.4)
Daunomycin	10 (4.54)
DDD	1 (0.454)
4,4'-DDD	1 (0.454)
DDE (72-55-9) #	1 (0.454)
DDE (3547-04-4) #	5000 (2270)
4,4'-DDE	1 (0.454)
DDT	1 (0.454)
4,4'-DDT	1 (0.454)
DEHP	100 (45.4)
Diallate	100 (45.4)
Diazinon	1 (0.454)
Diazomethane	100 (45.4)
Dibenz[a,h]anthracene	1 (0.454)
1,2:5,6-Dibenzanthracene	1 (0.454)
Dibenzo[a,h]anthracene	1 (0.454)
Dibenzofuran	100 (45.4)
Dibenzo[a,i]pyrene	10 (4.54)
1,2-Dibromo-3-chloropropane	1 (0.454)
Dibromoethane	1 (0.454)
Dibutyl phthalate	10 (4.54)
Di-n-butyl phthalate	10 (4.54)
Dicamba	1000 (454)
Dichlobenil	100 (45.4)
Dichlone	1 (0.454)
Dichlorobenzene	100 (45.4)
1,2-Dichlorobenzene	100 (45.4)
1,3-Dichlorobenzene	100 (45.4)
1,4-Dichlorobenzene	100 (45.4)
m-Dichlorobenzene	100 (45.4)
o-Dichlorobenzene	100 (45.4)
p-Dichlorobenzene	100 (45.4)
3,3'-Dichlorobenzidine	1 (0.454)
Dichlorobromomethane	5000 (2270)

TABLE 1 — HAZARDOUS SUBSTANCES   319

Hazardous substance	Reportable quantity (RQ) pounds (kilograms)
1,4-Dichloro-2-butene	1 (0.454)
Dichlorodifluoromethane	5000 (2270)
1,1-Dichloroethane	1000 (454)
1,2-Dichloroethane	100 (45.4)
1,1-Dichloroethylene	100 (45.4)
1,2-Dichloroethylene	1000 (454)
Dichloroethyl ether	10 (4.54)
Dichloroisopropyl ether	1000 (454)
Dichloromethane	1000 (454)
Dichloromethoxyethane	1000 (454)
Dichloromethyl ether	10 (4.54)
2,4-Dichlorophenol	100 (45.4)
2,6-Dichlorophenol	100 (45.4)
Dichlorophenylarsine	1 (0.454)
Dichloropropane	1000 (454)
1,1-Dichloropropane	
1,3-Dichloropropane	
1,2-Dichloropropane	1000 (454)
Dichloropropane-Dichloropropene (mixture)	100 (45.4)
Dichloropropene	100 (45.4)
2,3-Dichloropropene	
1,3-Dichloropropene	100 (45.4)
2,2-Dichloropropionic acid	5000 (2270)
Dichlorvos	10 (4.54)
Dicofol	10 (4.54)
Dieldrin	1 (0.454)
1,2:3,4-Diepoxybutane	10 (4.54)
Diethanolamine	100 (45.4)
Diethylamine	100 (45.4)
N,N-Diethylaniline	1000 (454)
Diethylarsine	1 (0.454)
Diethylene glycol, dicarbamate	5000 (2270)
1,4-Diethyleneoxide	100 (45.4)
Diethylhexyl phthalate	100 (45.4)
N,N'-Diethylhydrazine	10 (4.54)
O,O-Diethyl S-methyl dithiophosphate	5000 (2270)
Diethyl-p-nitrophenyl phosphate	100 (45.4)
Diethyl phthalate	1000 (454)
O,O-Diethyl O-pyrazinyl phosphorothioate	100 (45.4)
Diethylstilbestrol	1 (0.454)
Diethyl sulfate	10 (4.54)
Dihydrosafrole	10 (4.54)
Diisopropylfluorophosphate (DFP)	100 (45.4)
1,4:5,8-Dimethanonaphthalene, 1,2,3,4,10,10-hexachloro-1,4,4a,5,8,8a-hexahydro-, (1alpha, 4alpha, 4abeta, 5alpha, 8alpha, 8abeta)-	1 (0.454)
1,4:5,8-Dimethanonaphthalene, 1,2,3,4,10,10-hexachloro-1,4,4a,5,8,8a-hexahydro-, (1alpha, 4alpha, 4abeta, 5beta, 8beta, 8abeta)-	1 (0.454)
2,7:3,6-Dimethanonaphth[2,3-b]oxirene,3,4,5,6,9,9-hexachloro-1a,2,2a,3,6,6a,7,7a-octahydro-, (1aalpha, 2beta, 2aalpha, 3beta, 6beta, 6aalpha, 7beta, 7aalpha)-	1 (0.454)

Hazardous substance	Reportable quantity (RQ) pounds (kilograms)
2,7:3,6-Dimethanonaphth[2, 3-b]oxirene,3,4,5,6,9,9-hexachloro-1a,2,2a,3,6,6a,7,7a-octahydro-, (1aalpha, 2beta, 2abeta, 3alpha, 6alpha, 6abeta, 7beta, 7aalpha)-, & metabolites	1 (0.454)
Dimethoate	10 (4.54)
3,3'-Dimethoxybenzidine	100 (45.4)
Dimethylamine	1000 (454)
Dimethyl aminoazobenzene	10 (4.54)
p-Dimethylaminoazobenzene	10 (4.54)
N,N-Dimethylaniline	100 (45.4)
7,12-Dimethylbenz[a]anthracene	1 (0.454)
3,3'-Dimethylbenzidine	10 (4.54)
alpha,alpha-Dimethylbenzylhydroperoxide	10 (4.54)
Dimethylcarbamoyl chloride	1 (0.454)
Dimethylformamide	100 (45.4)
1,1-Dimethylhydrazine	10 (4.54)
1,2-Dimethylhydrazine	1 (0.454)
Dimethylhydrazine, unsymmetrical [@]	10 (4.54)
alpha,alpha-Dimethylphenethylamine	5000 (2270)
2,4-Dimethylphenol	100 (45.4)
Dimethyl phthalate	5000 (2270)
Dimethyl sulfate	100 (45.4)
Dimetilan	1 (0.454)
Dinitrobenzene (mixed)	100 (45.4)
m-Dinitrobenzene	
o-Dinitrobenzene	
p-Dinitrobenzene	
4,6-Dinitro-o-cresol, and salts	10 (4.54)
Dinitrogen tetroxide [@]	10 (4.54)
Dinitrophenol	10 (4.54)
2,5-Dinitrophenol	
2,6-Dinitrophenol	
2,4-Dinitrophenol	10 (4.54)
Dinitrotoluene	10 (4.54)
3,4-Dinitrotoluene	
2,4-Dinitrotoluene	10 (4.54)
2,6-Dinitrotoluene	100 (45.4)
Dinoseb	1000 (454)
Di-n-octyl phthalate	5000 (2270)
1,4-Dioxane	100 (45.4)
1,2-Diphenylhydrazine	10 (4.54)
Diphosphoramide, octamethyl-	100 (45.4)
Diphosphoric acid, tetraethyl ester	10 (4.54)
Dipropylamine	5000 (2270)
Di-n-propylnitrosamine	10 (4.54)
Diquat	1000 (454)
Disulfoton	1 (0.454)
Dithiobiuret	100 (45.4)
1,3-Dithiolane-2-carboxaldehyde, 2,4-dimethyl-, O-[(methylamino)-carbonyl]oxime	100 (45.4)
Diuron	100 (45.4)
Dodecylbenzenesulfonic acid	1000 (454)
Endosulfan	1 (0.454)

TABLE 1 — HAZARDOUS SUBSTANCES 321

Hazardous substance	Reportable quantity (RQ) pounds (kilograms)
alpha-Endosulfan	1 (0.454)
beta-Endosulfan	1 (0.454)
Endosulfan sulfate	1 (0.454)
Endothall	1000 (454)
Endrin	1 (0.454)
Endrin aldehyde	1 (0.454)
Endrin, & metabolites	1 (0.454)
Epichlorohydrin	100 (45.4)
Epinephrine	1000 (454)
1,2-Epoxybutane	100 (45.4)
Ethanal	1000 (454)
Ethanamine, N,N-diethyl-	5000 (2270)
Ethanamine, N-ethyl-N-nitroso-	1 (0.454)
1,2-Ethanediamine, N,N-dimethyl-N'-2-pyridinyl-N'-(2-thienylmethyl)-	5000 (2270)
Ethane, 1,2-dibromo-	1 (0.454)
Ethane, 1,1-dichloro-	1000 (454)
Ethane, 1,2-dichloro-	100 (45.4)
Ethanedinitrile	100 (45.4)
Ethane, hexachloro-	100 (45.4)
Ethane, 1,1'-[methylenebis(oxy)]bis[2-chloro-	1000 (454)
Ethane, 1,1'-oxybis-	100 (45.4)
Ethane, 1,1'-oxybis[2-chloro-	10 (4.54)
Ethane, pentachloro-	10 (4.54)
Ethane, 1,1,1,2-tetrachloro-	100 (45.4)
Ethane, 1,1,2,2-tetrachloro-	100 (45.4)
Ethanethioamide	10 (4.54)
Ethane, 1,1,1-trichloro-	1000 (454)
Ethane, 1,1,2-trichloro-	100 (45.4)
Ethanimidothioic acid, 2-(dimethylamino)-N-hydroxy-2-oxo-, methyl ester	5000 (2270)
Ethanimidothioic acid, 2-(dimethylamino)-N-[[(methylamino) carbonyl]oxy]-2-oxo-, methyl ester	100 (45.4)
Ethanimidothioic acid, N-[[(methylamino) carbonyl]oxy]-, methyl ester	100 (45.4)
Ethanimidothioic acid, N,N'[thiobis[(methylimino)carbonyloxy]] bis-, dimethyl ester	100 (45.4)
Ethanol, 2-ethoxy-	1000 (454)
Ethanol, 2,2'-(nitrosoimino)bis-	1 (0.454)
Ethanol, 2,2'-oxybis-, dicarbamate	5000 (2270)
Ethanone, 1-phenyl-	5000 (2270)
Ethene, chloro-	1 (0.454)
Ethene, (2-chloroethoxy)-	1000 (454)
Ethene, 1,1-dichloro-	100 (45.4)
Ethene, 1,2-dichloro-(E)	1000 (454)
Ethene, tetrachloro-	100 (45.4)
Ethene, trichloro-	100 (45.4)
Ethion	10 (4.54)
Ethyl acetate	5000 (2270)
Ethyl acrylate	1000 (454)
Ethylbenzene	1000 (454)
Ethyl carbamate	100 (45.4)
Ethyl chloride	100 (45.4)
Ethyl cyanide	10 (4.54)
Ethylenebisdithiocarbamic acid, salts & esters	5000 (2270)

Hazardous substance	Reportable quantity (RQ) pounds (kilograms)
Ethylenediamine	5000 (2270)
Ethylenediamine-tetraacetic acid (EDTA)	5000 (2270)
Ethylene dibromide	1 (0.454)
Ethylene dichloride	100 (45.4)
Ethylene glycol	5000 (2270)
Ethylene glycol monoethyl ether	1000 (454)
Ethylene oxide	10 (4.54)
Ethylenethiourea	10 (4.54)
Ethylenimine	1 (0.454)
Ethyl ether	100 (45.4)
Ethylidene dichloride	1000 (454)
Ethyl methacrylate	1000 (454)
Ethyl methanesulfonate	1 (0.454)
Ethyl methyl ketone[@]	5000 (2270)
Famphur	1000 (454)
Ferric ammonium citrate	1000 (454)
Ferric ammonium oxalate	1000 (454)
Ferric chloride	1000 (454)
Ferric fluoride	100 (45.4)
Ferric nitrate	1000 (454)
Ferric sulfate	1000 (454)
Ferrous ammonium sulfate	1000 (454)
Ferrous chloride	100 (45.4)
Ferrous sulfate	1000 (454)
Fluoranthene	100 (45.4)
Fluorene	5000 (2270)
Fluorine	10 (4.54)
Fluoroacetamide	100 (45.4)
Fluoroacetic acid, sodium salt	10 (4.54)
Formaldehyde	100 (45.4)
Formetanate hydrochloride	100 (45.4)
Formic acid	5000 (2270)
Formparanate	100 (45.4)
Fulminic acid, mercury(2+)salt	10 (4.54)
Fumaric acid	5000 (2270)
Furan	100 (45.4)
2-Furancarboxyaldehyde	5000 (2270)
2,5-Furandione	5000 (2270)
Furan, tetrahydro-	1000 (454)
Furfural	5000 (2270)
Furfuran	100 (45.4)
Glucopyranose, 2-deoxy-2-(3-methyl-3-nitrosoureido)-, D-	1 (0.454)
D-Glucose, 2-deoxy-2-[[(methylnitrosoamino)-carbonyl]amino]-	1 (0.454)
Glycidylaldehyde	10 (4.54)
Guanidine, N-methyl-N'-nitro-N-nitroso-	10 (4.54)
Guthion	1 (0.454)
Heptachlor	1 (0.454)
Heptachlor epoxide	1 (0.454)
Hexachlorobenzene	10 (4.54)
Hexachlorobutadiene	1 (0.454)
Hexachlorocyclopentadiene	10 (4.54)

TABLE 1 — HAZARDOUS SUBSTANCES 323

Hazardous substance	Reportable quantity (RQ) pounds (kilograms)
Hexachloroethane	100 (45.4)
Hexachlorophene	100 (45.4)
Hexachloropropene	1000 (454)
Hexaethyl tetraphosphate	100 (45.4)
Hexamethylene-1,6-diisocyanate	100 (45.4)
Hexamethylphosphoramide	1 (0.454)
Hexane	5000 (2270)
Hexone	5000 (2270)
Hydrazine	1 (0.454)
Hydrazinecarbothioamide	100 (45.4)
Hydrazine, 1,2-diethyl-	10 (4.54)
Hydrazine, 1,1-dimethyl-	10 (4.54)
Hydrazine, 1,2-dimethyl-	1 (0.454)
Hydrazine, 1,2-diphenyl-	10 (4.54)
Hydrazine, methyl-	10 (4.54)
Hydrochloric acid	5000 (2270)
Hydrocyanic acid	10 (4.54)
Hydrofluoric acid	100 (45.4)
Hydrogen chloride	5000 (2270)
Hydrogen cyanide	10 (4.54)
Hydrogen fluoride	100 (45.4)
Hydrogen phosphide	100 (45.4)
Hydrogen sulfide H2S	100 (45.4)
Hydroperoxide, 1-methyl-1-phenylethyl-	10 (4.54)
Hydroquinone	100 (45.4)
2-Imidazolidinethione	10 (4.54)
Indeno(1,2,3-cd)pyrene	100 (45.4)
Iodomethane	100 (45.4)
1,3-Isobenzofurandione	5000 (2270)
Isobutyl alcohol	5000 (2270)
Isodrin	1 (0.454)
Isolan	100 (45.4)
Isophorone	5000 (2270)
Isoprene	100 (45.4)
Isopropanolamine dodecylbenzenesulfonate	1000 (454)
3-Isopropylphenyl N-methylcarbamate	10 (4.54)
Isosafrole	100 (45.4)
3(2H)-Isoxazolone, 5-(aminomethyl)-	1000 (454)
Kepone	1 (0.454)
Lasiocarpine	10 (4.54)
Lead [c]	10 (4.54)
Lead acetate	10 (4.54)
Lead arsenate	1 (0.454)
Lead, bis(acetato-O)tetrahydroxytri-	10 (4.54)
Lead chloride	10 (4.54)
Lead fluoborate	10 (4.54)
Lead fluoride	10 (4.54)
Lead iodide	10 (4.54)
Lead nitrate	10 (4.54)
Lead phosphate	10 (4.54)
Lead stearate	10 (4.54)

Hazardous substance	Reportable quantity (RQ) pounds (kilograms)
Lead subacetate	10 (4.54)
Lead sulfate	10 (4.54)
Lead sulfide	10 (4.54)
Lead thiocyanate	10 (4.54)
Lindane	1 (0.454)
Lindane (all isomers)	1 (0.454)
Lithium chromate	10 (4.54)
Malathion	100 (45.4)
Maleic acid	5000 (2270)
Maleic anhydride	5000 (2270)
Maleic hydrazide	5000 (2270)
Malononitrile	1000 (454)
Manganese, bis(dimethylcarbamodithioato-S,S')-	10 (4.54)
Manganese dimethyldithiocarbamate	10 (4.54)
MDI	5000 (2270)
MEK	5000 (2270)
Melphalan	1 (0.454)
Mercaptodimethur	10 (4.54)
Mercuric cyanide	1 (0.454)
Mercuric nitrate	10 (4.54)
Mercuric sulfate	10 (4.54)
Mercuric thiocyanate	10 (4.54)
Mercurous nitrate	10 (4.54)
Mercury	1 (0.454)
Mercury, (acetato-O)phenyl-	100 (45.4)
Mercury fulminate	10 (4.54)
Methacrylonitrile	1000 (454)
Methanamine, N-methyl-	1000 (454)
Methanamine, N-methyl-N-nitroso-	10 (4.54)
Methane, bromo-	1000 (454)
Methane, chloro-	100 (45.4)
Methane, chloromethoxy-	10 (4.54)
Methane, dibromo-	1000 (454)
Methane, dichloro-	1000 (454)
Methane, dichlorodifluoro-	5000 (2270)
Methane, iodo-	100 (45.4)
Methane, isocyanato-	10 (4.54)
Methane, oxybis(chloro-	10 (4.54)
Methanesulfenyl chloride, trichloro-	100 (45.4)
Methanesulfonic acid, ethyl ester	1 (0.454)
Methane, tetrachloro-	10 (4.54)
Methane, tetranitro-	10 (4.54)
Methanethiol	100 (45.4)
Methane, tribromo-	100 (45.4)
Methane, trichloro-	10 (4.54)
Methane, trichlorofluoro-	5000 (2270)
Methanimidamide, N,N-dimethyl-N'-[3-[[(methylamino) carbonyl] oxy] phenyl]-, monohydrochloride	100 (45.4)
Methanimidamide, N,N-dimethyl-N'-[2-methyl-4-[[(methylamino)carbonyl] oxy]phenyl]-	100 (45.4)
6,9-Methano-2,4,3-benzodioxathiepin,6,7,8,9,10,10-hexachloro-1,5,5a,6,9,9a-hexahydro-, 3-oxide	1 (0.454)

TABLE 1 — HAZARDOUS SUBSTANCES   325

Hazardous substance	Reportable quantity (RQ) pounds (kilograms)
4,7-Methano-1H-indene, 1,4,5,6,7,8,8-heptachloro-3a,4,7,7a-tetrahydro-	1 (0.454)
4,7-Methano-1H-indene, 1,2,4,5,6,7,8,8-octachloro-2,3,3a,4,7,7a-hexahydro-	1 (0.454)
Methanol	5000 (2270)
Methapyrilene	5000 (2270)
1,3,4-Metheno-2H-cyclobuta[cd]pentalen-2-one, 1,1a,3,3a,4,5,5,5a,5b,6-decachlorooctahydro-	1 (0.454)
Methiocarb	10 (4.54)
Methomyl	100 (45.4)
Methoxychlor	1 (0.454)
Methyl alcohol	5000 (2270)
Methylamine [@]	100 (45.4)
2-Methyl aziridine	1 (0.454)
Methyl bromide	1000 (454)
1-Methylbutadiene	100 (45.4)
Methyl chloride	100 (45.4)
Methyl chlorocarbonate	1000 (454)
Methyl chloroform	1000 (454)
Methyl chloroformate [@]	1000 (454)
Methyl chloromethyl ether [@]	10 (4.54)
3-Methylcholanthrene	10 (4.54)
4,4'-Methylenebis(2-chloroaniline)	10 (4.54)
Methylene bromide	1000 (454)
Methylene chloride	1000 (454)
4,4'-Methylenedianiline	10 (4.54)
Methylene diphenyl diisocyanate	5000 (2270)
Methyl ethyl ketone	5000 (2270)
Methyl ethyl ketone peroxide	10 (4.54)
Methyl hydrazine	10 (4.54)
Methyl iodide	100 (45.4)
Methyl isobutyl ketone	5000 (2270)
Methyl isocyanate	10 (4.54)
2-Methyllactonitrile	10 (4.54)
Methyl mercaptan	100 (45.4)
Methyl methacrylate	1000 (454)
Methyl parathion	100 (45.4)
4-Methyl-2-pentanone	5000 (2270)
Methyl tert-butyl ether	1000 (454)
Methylthiouracil	10 (4.54)
Metolcarb	1000 (454)
Mevinphos	10 (4.54)
Mexacarbate	1000 (454)
Mitomycin C	10 (4.54)
MNNG	10 (4.54)
Monoethylamine	100 (45.4)
Monomethylamine	100 (45.4)
Naled	10 (4.54)
5,12-Naphthacenedione, 8-acetyl-10-[(3-amino-2,3,6-trideoxy-alpha-L-lyxo-hexopyranosyl)oxy]-7,8,9,10-tetrahydro-6,8,11-trihydroxy-1-methoxy-, (8S-cis)-	10 (4.54)
1-Naphthalenamine	100 (45.4)
2-Naphthalenamine	10 (4.54)
Naphthalenamine, N,N'-bis(2-chloroethyl)-	100 (45.4)

Hazardous substance	Reportable quantity (RQ) pounds (kilograms)
Naphthalene	100 (45.4)
Naphthalene, 2-chloro-	5000 (2270)
1,4-Naphthalenedione	5000 (2270)
2,7-Naphthalenedisulfonic acid, 3,3'-[(3,3'-dimethyl-(1,1'-biphenyl)-4,4'-diyl)-bis(azo)]bis(5-amino-4-hydroxy)-tetrasodium salt	10 (4.54)
1-Naphthalenol, methylcarbamate	100 (45.4)
Naphthenic acid	100 (45.4)
1,4-Naphthoquinone	5000 (2270)
alpha-Naphthylamine	100 (45.4)
beta-Naphthylamine	10 (4.54)
alpha-Naphthylthiourea	100 (45.4)
Nickel [c]	100 (45.4)
Nickel ammonium sulfate	100 (45.4)
Nickel carbonyl Ni(CO)4, (T-4)-	10 (4.54)
Nickel chloride	100 (45.4)
Nickel cyanide Ni(CN)$_2$	10 (4.54)
Nickel hydroxide	10 (4.54)
Nickel nitrate	100 (45.4)
Nickel sulfate	100 (45.4)
Nicotine, & salts	100 (45.4)
Nitric acid	1000 (454)
Nitric acid, thallium (1+) salt	100 (45.4)
Nitric oxide	10 (4.54)
p-Nitroaniline	5000 (2270)
Nitrobenzene	1000 (454)
4-Nitrobiphenyl	10 (4.54)
Nitrogen dioxide	10 (4.54)
Nitrogen oxide NO	10 (4.54)
Nitrogen oxide NO$_2$	10 (4.54)
Nitroglycerine	10 (4.54)
Nitrophenol (mixed)	100 (45.4)
m-Nitrophenol	....
o-Nitrophenol	100 (45.4)
p-Nitrophenol	100 (45.4)
2-Nitrophenol	100 (45.4)
4-Nitrophenol	100 (45.4)
2-Nitropropane	10 (4.54)
N-Nitrosodi-n-butylamine	10 (4.54)
N-Nitrosodiethanolamine	1 (0.454)
N-Nitrosodiethylamine	1 (0.454)
N-Nitrosodimethylamine	10 (4.54)
N-Nitrosodiphenylamine	100 (45.4)
N-Nitroso-N-ethylurea	1 (0.454)
N-Nitroso-N-methylurea	1 (0.454)
N-Nitroso-N-methylurethane	1 (0.454)
N-Nitrosomethylvinylamine	10 (4.54)
N-Nitrosomorpholine	1 (0.454)
N-Nitrosopiperidine	10 (4.54)
N-Nitrosopyrrolidine	1 (0.454)
Nitrotoluene	1000 (454)
m-Nitrotoluene	....

TABLE 1 — HAZARDOUS SUBSTANCES   327

Hazardous substance	Reportable quantity (RQ) pounds (kilograms)
o-Nitrotoluene	....
p-Nitrotoluene	....
5-Nitro-o-toluidine	100 (45.4)
Octamethylpyrophosphoramide	100 (45.4)
Osmium oxide OsO₄, (T-4)-	1000 (454)
Osmium tetroxide	1000 (454)
7-Oxabicyclo[2.2.1]heptane-2,3-dicarboxylic acid	1000 (454)
Oxamyl	100 (45.4)
1,2-Oxathiolane, 2,2-dioxide	10 (4.54)
2H-1,3,2-Oxazaphosphorin-2-amine, N,N-bis(2-chloroethyl) tetrahydro-, 2-oxide	10 (4.54)
Oxirane	10 (4.54)
Oxiranecarboxyaldehyde	10 (4.54)
Oxirane, (chloromethyl)-	100 (45.4)
Paraformaldehyde	1000 (454)
Paraldehyde	1000 (454)
Parathion	10 (4.54)
PCBs	1 (0.454)
PCNB	100 (45.4)
Pentachlorobenzene	10 (4.54)
Pentachloroethane	10 (4.54)
Pentachloronitrobenzene	100 (45.4)
Pentachlorophenol	10 (4.54)
1,3-Pentadiene	100 (45.4)
Perchloroethylene	100 (45.4)
Perchloromethyl mercaptan[@]	100 (45.4)
Phenacetin	100 (45.4)
Phenanthrene	5000 (2270)
Phenol	1000 (454)
Phenol, 2-chloro-	100 (45.4)
Phenol, 4-chloro-3-methyl-	5000 (2270)
Phenol, 2-cyclohexyl-4,6-dinitro-	100 (45.4)
Phenol, 2,4-dichloro-	100 (45.4)
Phenol, 2,6-dichloro-	100 (45.4)
Phenol, 4,4'-(1,2-diethyl-1,2-ethenediyl)bis-, (E)	1 (0.454)
Phenol, 2,4-dimethyl-	100 (45.4)
Phenol, 4-(dimethylamino)-3,5-dimethyl-, methylcarbamate (ester)	1000 (454)
Phenol, (3,5-dimethyl-4-(methylthio)-, methylcarbamate	10 (4.54)
Phenol, 2,4-dinitro-	10 (4.54)
Phenol, methyl-	100 (45.4)
Phenol, 2-methyl-4,6-dinitro-, & salts	10 (4.54)
Phenol, 2,2'-methylenebis[3,4,6-trichloro-	100 (45.4)
Phenol, 2-(1-methylethoxy)-, methylcarbamate	100 (45.4)
Phenol, 3-(1-methylethyl)-, methyl carbamate	10 (4.54)
Phenol, 3-methyl-5-(1-methylethyl)-, methyl carbamate	1000 (454)
Phenol, 2-(1-methylpropyl)-4,6-dinitro-	1000 (454)
Phenol, 4-nitro-	100 (45.4)
Phenol, pentachloro-	10 (4.54)
Phenol, 2,3,4,6-tetrachloro-	10 (4.54)
Phenol, 2,4,5-trichloro-	10 (4.54)
Phenol, 2,4,6-trichloro-	10 (4.54)
Phenol, 2,4,6-trinitro-, ammonium salt	10 (4.54)

Hazardous substance	Reportable quantity (RQ) pounds (kilograms)
L-Phenylalanine, 4-[bis(2-chloroethyl)amino]-	1 (0.454)
p-Phenylenediamine	5000 (2270)
Phenyl mercaptan[@]	100 (45.4)
Phenylmercury acetate	100 (45.4)
Phenylthiourea	100 (45.4)
Phorate	10 (4.54)
Phosgene	10 (4.54)
Phosphine	100 (45.4)
Phosphoric acid	5000 (2270)
Phosphoric acid, diethyl 4-nitrophenyl ester	100 (45.4)
Phosphoric acid, lead(2+) salt (2:3)	10 (4.54)
Phosphorodithioic acid, O,O-diethyl S-[2-(ethylthio)ethyl] ester	1 (0.454)
Phosphorodithioic acid, O,O-diethyl S-[(ethylthio)methyl] ester	10 (4.54)
Phosphorodithioic acid, O,O-diethyl S-methyl ester	5000 (2270)
Phosphorodithioic acid, O,O-dimethyl S-[2-(methylamino)-2-oxoethyl] ester	10 (4.54)
Phosphorofluoridic acid, bis(1-methylethyl) ester	100 (45.4)
Phosphorothioic acid, O,O-diethyl O-(4-nitrophenyl) ester	10 (4.54)
Phosphorothioic acid, O,O-diethyl O-pyrazinyl ester	100 (45.4)
Phosphorothioic acid, O-[4-[(dimethylamino) sulfonyl]phenyl] O,O-dimethyl ester	1000 (454)
Phosphorothioic acid, O,O-dimethyl O-(4-nitrophenyl) ester	100 (45.4)
Phosphorus	1 (0.454)
Phosphorus oxychloride	1000 (454)
Phosphorus pentasulfide	100 (45.4)
Phosphorus sulfide	100 (45.4)
Phosphorus trichloride	1000 (454)
Phthalic anhydride	5000 (2270)
Physostigmine	100 (45.4)
Physostigmine salicylate	100 (45.4)
2-Picoline	5000 (2270)
Piperidine, 1-nitroso-	10 (4.54)
Plumbane, tetraethyl-	10 (4.54)
POLYCHLORINATED BIPHENYLS	1 (0.454)
Potassium arsenate	1 (0.454)
Potassium arsenite	1 (0.454)
Potassium bichromate	10 (4.54)
Potassium chromate	10 (4.54)
Potassium cyanide K(CN)	10 (4.54)
Potassium hydroxide	1000 (454)
Potassium permanganate	100 (45.4)
Potassium silver cyanide	1 (0.454)
Promecarb	1000 (454)
Pronamide	5000 (2270)
Propanal, 2-methyl-2-(methyl-sulfonyl)-, O-[(methylamino)carbonyl] oxime	100 (45.4)
Propanal, 2-methyl-2-(methylthio)-, O-[(methylamino)carbonyl] oxime	1 (0.454)
1-Propanamine	5000 (2270)
1-Propanamine, N-propyl-	5000 (2270)
1-Propanamine, N-nitroso-N-propyl-	10 (4.54)
Propane, 1,2-dibromo-3-chloro-	1 (0.454)
Propane, 1,2-dichloro-	1000 (454)
Propanedinitrile	1000 (454)
Propanenitrile	10 (4.54)

TABLE 1 — HAZARDOUS SUBSTANCES 329

Hazardous substance	Reportable quantity (RQ) pounds (kilograms)
Propanenitrile, 3-chloro-	1000 (454)
Propanenitrile, 2-hydroxy-2-methyl-	10 (4.54)
Propane, 2-nitro-	10 (4.54)
Propane, 2,2'-oxybis[2-chloro-	1000 (454)
1,3-Propane sultone	10 (4.54)
1,2,3-Propanetriol, trinitrate	10 (4.54)
Propanoic acid, 2-(2,4,5-trichlorophenoxy)-	100 (45.4)
1-Propanol, 2,3-dibromo-, phosphate (3:1)	10 (4.54)
1-Propanol, 2-methyl-	5000 (2270)
2-Propanone	5000 (2270)
2-Propanone, 1-bromo-	1000 (454)
Propargite	10 (4.54)
Propargyl alcohol	1000 (454)
2-Propenal	1 (0.454)
2-Propenamide	5000 (2270)
1-Propene, 1,3-dichloro-	100 (45.4)
1-Propene, 1,1,2,3,3,3-hexachloro-	1000 (454)
2-Propenenitrile	100 (45.4)
2-Propenenitrile, 2-methyl-	1000 (454)
2-Propenoic acid	5000 (2270)
2-Propenoic acid, ethyl ester	1000 (454)
2-Propenoic acid, 2-methyl-, ethyl ester	1000 (454)
2-Propenoic acid, 2-methyl-, methyl ester	1000 (454)
2-Propen-1-ol	100 (45.4)
Propham	1000 (454)
beta-Propiolactone	10 (4.54)
Propionaldehyde	1000 (454)
Propionic acid	5000 (2270)
Propionic anhydride	5000 (2270)
Propoxur (Baygon)	100 (45.4)
n-Propylamine	5000 (2270)
Propylene dichloride	1000 (454)
Propylene oxide	100 (45.4)
1,2-Propylenimine	1 (0.454)
2-Propyn-1-ol	1000 (454)
Prosulfocarb	5000 (2270)
Pyrene	5000 (2270)
Pyrethrins	1 (0.454)
3,6-Pyridazinedione, 1,2-dihydro-	5000 (2270)
4-Pyridinamine	1000 (454)
Pyridine	1000 (454)
Pyridine, 2-methyl-	5000 (2270)
Pyridine, 3-(1-methyl-2-pyrrolidinyl)-, (S)-, & salts	100 (45.4)
2,4-(1H,3H)-Pyrimidinedione, 5-[bis(2-chloroethyl)amino]-	10 (4.54)
4(1H)-Pyrimidinone, 2,3-dihydro-6-methyl-2-thioxo-	10 (4.54)
Pyrrolidine, 1-nitroso-	1 (0.454)
Pyrrolo[2,3-b] indol-5-ol,1,2,3,3a,8,8a-hexahydro-1,3a,8-trimethyl-, methylcarbamate (ester), (3aS-cis)-	100 (45.4)
Quinoline	5000 (2270)
Quinone	10 (4.54)
Quintobenzene	100 (45.4)

HAZ. SUBSTANCES

Hazardous substance	Reportable quantity (RQ) pounds (kilograms)
RADIONUCLIDES	See Table 2
Reserpine	5000 (2270)
Resorcinol	5000 (2270)
Safrole	100 (45.4)
Selenious acid	10 (4.54)
Selenious acid, dithallium (1+) salt	1000 (454)
Selenium [c]	100 (45.4)
Selenium dioxide	10 (4.54)
Selenium oxide	10 (4.54)
Selenium sulfide SeS2	10 (4.54)
Selenourea	1000 (454)
L-Serine, diazoacetate (ester)	1 (0.454)
Silver [c]	1000 (454)
Silver cyanide Ag(CN)	1 (0.454)
Silver nitrate	1 (0.454)
Silvex (2,4,5-TP)	100 (45.4)
Sodium	10 (4.54)
Sodium arsenate	1 (0.454)
Sodium arsenite	1 (0.454)
Sodium azide	1000 (454)
Sodium bichromate	10 (4.54)
Sodium bifluoride	100 (45.4)
Sodium bisulfite	5000 (2270)
Sodium chromate	10 (4.54)
Sodium cyanide Na(CN)	10 (4.54)
Sodium dodecylbenzenesulfonate	1000 (454)
Sodium fluoride	1000 (454)
Sodium hydrosulfide	5000 (2270)
Sodium hydroxide	1000 (454)
Sodium hypochlorite	100 (45.4)
Sodium methylate	1000 (454)
Sodium nitrite	100 (45.4)
Sodium phosphate, dibasic	5000 (2270)
Sodium phosphate, tribasic	5000 (2270)
Sodium selenite	100 (45.4)
Streptozotocin	1 (0.454)
Strontium chromate	10 (4.54)
Strychnidin-10-one, & salts	10 (4.54)
Strychnidin-10-one, 2,3-dimethoxy-	100 (45.4)
Strychnine, & salts	10 (4.54)
Styrene	1000 (454)
Styrene oxide	100 (45.4)
Sulfur chlorides [e]	1000 (454)
Sulfuric acid	1000 (454)
Sulfuric acid, dimethyl ester	100 (45.4)
Sulfuric acid, dithallium (1+) salt	100 (45.4)
Sulfur monochloride	1000 (454)
Sulfur phosphide	100 (45.4)
2,4,5-T	1000 (454)
2,4,5-T acid	1000 (454)
2,4,5-T amines	5000 (2270)

TABLE 1 — HAZARDOUS SUBSTANCES   331

Hazardous substance	Reportable quantity (RQ) pounds (kilograms)
2,4,5-T esters	1000 (454)
2,4,5-T salts	1000 (454)
TCDD	1 (0.454)
TDE	1 (0.454)
1,2,4,5-Tetrachlorobenzene	5000 (2270)
2,3,7,8-Tetrachlorodibenzo-p-dioxin	1 (0.454)
1,1,1,2-Tetrachloroethane	100 (45.4)
1,1,2,2-Tetrachloroethane	100 (45.4)
Tetrachloroethylene	100 (45.4)
2,3,4,6-Tetrachlorophenol	10 (4.54)
Tetraethyl pyrophosphate	10 (4.54)
Tetraethyl lead	10 (4.54)
Tetraethyldithiopyrophosphate	100 (45.4)
Tetrahydrofuran	1000 (454)
Tetranitromethane	10 (4.54)
Tetraphosphoric acid, hexaethyl ester	100 (45.4)
Thallic oxide	100 (45.4)
Thallium	1000 (454)
Thallium (I) acetate	100 (45.4)
Thallium (I) carbonate	100 (45.4)
Thallium chloride TlCl	100 (45.4)
Thallium (I) nitrate	100 (45.4)
Thallium oxide Tl_2O_3	100 (45.4)
Thallium (I) selenite	1000 (454)
Thallium (I) sulfate	100 (45.4)
Thioacetamide	10 (4.54)
Thiodicarb	100 (45.4)
Thiodiphosphoric acid, tetraethyl ester	100 (45.4)
Thiofanox	100 (45.4)
Thioimidodicarbonic diamide [$(H_2N)C(S)]_2NH$	100 (45.4)
Thiomethanol	100 (45.4)
Thioperoxydicarbonic diamide [$(H_2N)C(S)]_2S_2$, tetramethyl-	10 (4.54)
Thiophanate-methyl	10 (4.54)
Thiophenol	100 (45.4)
Thiosemicarbazide	100 (45.4)
Thiourea	10 (4.54)
Thiourea, (2-chlorophenyl)-	100 (45.4)
Thiourea, 1-naphthalenyl-	100 (45.4)
Thiourea, phenyl-	100 (45.4)
Thiram	10 (4.54)
Tirpate	100 (45.4)
Titanium tetrachloride	1000 (454)
Toluene	1000 (454)
Toluenediamine	10 (4.54)
2,4-Toluene diamine	10 (4.54)
Toluene diisocyanate	100 (45.4)
2,4-Toluene diisocyanate	100 (45.4)
o-Toluidine	100 (45.4)
p-Toluidine	100 (45.4)
o-Toluidine hydrochloride	100 (45.4)
Toxaphene	1 (0.454)

Hazardous substance	Reportable quantity (RQ) pounds (kilograms)
2,4,5-TP acid	100 (45.4)
2,4,5-TP esters	100 (45.4)
Triallate	100 (45.4)
1H-1,2,4-Triazol-3-amine	10 (4.54)
Trichlorfon	100 (45.4)
1,2,4-Trichlorobenzene	100 (45.4)
1,1,1-Trichloroethane	1000 (454)
1,1,2-Trichloroethane	100 (45.4)
Trichloroethylene	100 (45.4)
Trichloromethanesulfenyl chloride	100 (45.4)
Trichloromonofluoromethane	5000 (2270)
Trichlorophenol	10 (4.54)
2,3,4-Trichlorophenol	....
2,3,5-Trichlorophenol	....
2,3,6-Trichlorophenol	....
3,4,5-Trichlorophenol	....
2,4,5-Trichlorophenol	10 (4.54)
2,4,6-Trichlorophenol	10 (4.54)
Triethanolamine dodecylbenzenesulfonate	1000 (454)
Triethylamine	5000 (2270)
Trifluralin	10 (4.54)
Trimethylamine	100 (45.4)
2,2,4-Trimethylpentane	1000 (454)
1,3,5-Trinitrobenzene	10 (4.54)
1,3,5-Trioxane, 2,4,6-trimethyl-	1000 (454)
Tris(2,3-dibromopropyl) phosphate	10 (4.54)
Trypan blue	10 (4.54)
D002 Unlisted Hazardous Wastes Characteristic of Corrosivity	100 (45.4)
D001 Unlisted Hazardous Wastes Characteristic of Ignitability	100 (45.4)
D003 Unlisted Hazardous Wastes Characteristic of Reactivity	100 (45.4)
D004–D043 Unlisted Hazardous Wastes Characteristic of Toxicity:	
Arsenic (D004)	1 (0.454)
Barium (D005)	1000 (454)
Benzene (D018)	10 (4.54)
Cadmium (D006)	10 (4.54)
Carbon tetrachloride (D019)	10 (4.54)
Chlordane (D020)	1 (0.454)
Chlorobenzene (D021)	100 (45.4)
Chloroform (D022)	10 (4.54)
Chromium (D007)	10 (4.54)
o-Cresol (D023)	100 (45.4)
m-Cresol (D024)	100 (45.4)
p-Cresol (D025)	100 (45.4)
Cresol (D026)	100 (45.4)
2,4-D (D016)	100 (45.4)
1,4-Dichlorobenzene (D027)	100 (45.4)
1,2-Dichloroethane (D028)	100 (45.4)
1,1-Dichloroethylene (D029)	100 (45.4)
2,4-Dinitrotoluene (D030)	10 (4.54)
Endrin (D012)	1 (0.454)
Heptachlor (and epoxide) (D031)	1 (0.454)

TABLE 1 — HAZARDOUS SUBSTANCES   333

Hazardous substance	Reportable quantity (RQ) pounds (kilograms)
Hexachlorobenzene (D032)	10 (4.54)
Hexachlorobutadiene (D033)	1 (0.454)
Hexachloroethane (D034)	100 (45.4)
Lead (D008)	10 (4.54)
Lindane (D013)	1 (0.454)
Mercury (D009)	1 (0.454)
Methoxychlor (D014)	1 (0.454)
Methyl ethyl ketone (D035)	5000 (2270)
Nitrobenzene (D036)	1000 (454)
Pentachlorophenol (D037)	10 (4.54)
Pyridine (D038)	1000 (454)
Selenium (D010)	10 (4.54)
Silver (D011)	1 (0.454)
Tetrachloroethylene (D039)	100 (45.4)
Toxaphene (D015)	1 (0.454)
Trichloroethylene (D040)	100 (45.4)
2,4,5-Trichlorophenol (D041)	10 (4.54)
2,4,6-Trichlorophenol (D042)	10 (4.54)
2,4,5-TP (D017)	100 (45.4)
Vinyl chloride (D043)	1 (0.454)
Uracil mustard	10 (4.54)
Uranyl acetate	100 (45.4)
Uranyl nitrate	100 (45.4)
Urea, N-ethyl-N-nitroso-	1 (0.454)
Urea, N-methyl-N-nitroso-	1 (0.454)
Urethane	100 (45.4)
Vanadic acid, ammonium salt	1000 (454)
Vanadium oxide V_2O_5	1000 (454)
Vanadium pentoxide	1000 (454)
Vanadyl sulfate	1000 (454)
Vinyl acetate	5000 (2270)
Vinyl acetate monomer	5000 (2270)
Vinylamine, N-methyl-N-nitroso-	10 (4.54)
Vinyl bromide	100 (45.4)
Vinyl chloride	1 (0.454)
Vinylidene chloride	100 (45.4)
Warfarin, & salts	100 (45.4)
Xylene	100 (45.4)
m-Xylene	1000 (454)
o-Xylene	1000 (454)
p-Xylene	100 (45.4)
Xylene (mixed)	100 (45.4)
Xylenes (isomers and mixture)	100 (45.4)
Xylenol	1000 (454)
Yohimban-16-carboxylic acid,11,17-dimethoxy-18-[(3,4,5-trimethoxybenzoyl)oxy]-, methyl ester (3beta,16beta,17alpha,18beta, 20alpha)	5000 (2270)
Zinc [c]	1000 (454)
Zinc acetate	1000 (454)
Zinc ammonium chloride	1000 (454)
Zinc, bis(dimethylcarbamodithioato-S,S')-	10 (4.54)
Zinc borate	1000 (454)

Hazardous substance	Reportable quantity (RQ) pounds (kilograms)
Zinc bromide	1000 (454)
Zinc carbonate	1000 (454)
Zinc chloride	1000 (454)
Zinc cyanide $Zn(CN)_2$	10 (4.54)
Zinc fluoride	1000 (454)
Zinc formate	1000 (454)
Zinc hydrosulfite	1000 (454)
Zinc nitrate	1000 (454)
Zinc phenolsulfonate	5000 (2270)
Zinc phosphide Zn_3P_2	100 (45.4)
Zinc silicofluoride	5000 (2270)
Zinc sulfate	1000 (454)
Ziram	10 (4.54)
Zirconium nitrate	5000 (2270)
Zirconium potassium fluoride	1000 (454)
Zirconium sulfate	5000 (2270)
Zirconium tetrachloride	5000 (2270)
F001	10 (4.54)
(a) Tetrachloroethylene	100 (45.4)
(b) Trichloroethylene	100 (45.4)
(c) Methylene chloride	1000 (454)
(d) 1,1,1-Trichloroethane	1000 (454)
(e) Carbon tetrachloride	10 (4.54)
(f) Chlorinated fluorocarbons	5000 (2270)
F002	10 (4.54)
(a) Tetrachloroethylene	100 (45.4)
(b) Methylene chloride	1000 (454)
(c) Trichloroethylene	100 (45.4)
(d) 1,1,1-Trichloroethane	1000 (454)
(e) Chlorobenzene	100 (45.4)
(f) 1,1,2-Trichloro-1,2,2-trifluoroethane	5000 (2270)
(g) o-Dichlorobenzene	100 (45.4)
(h) Trichlorofluoromethane	5000 (2270)
(i) 1,1,2-Trichloroethane	100 (45.4)
F003	100 (45.4)
(a) Xylene	1000 (454)
(b) Acetone	5000 (2270)
(c) Ethyl acetate	5000 (2270)
(d) Ethylbenzene	1000 (454)
(e) Ethyl ether	100 (45.4)
(f) Methyl isobutyl ketone	5000 (2270)
(g) n-Butyl alcohol	5000 (2270)
(h) Cyclohexanone	5000 (2270)
(i) Methanol	5000 (2270)
F004	100 (45.4)
(a) Cresols/Cresylic acid	100 (45.4)
(b) Nitrobenzene	1000 (454)
F005	100 (45.4)
(a) Toluene	1000 (454)
(b) Methyl ethyl ketone	5000 (2270)
(c) Carbon disulfide	100 (45.4)

TABLE 1 — HAZARDOUS SUBSTANCES 335

Hazardous substance	Reportable quantity (RQ) pounds (kilograms)
(d) Isobutanol	5000 (2270)
(e) Pyridine	1000 (454)
F006	10 (4.54)
F007	10 (4.54)
F008	10 (4.54)
F009	10 (4.54)
F010	10 (4.54)
F011	10 (4.54)
F012	10 (4.54)
F019	10 (4.54)
F020	1 (0.454)
F021	1 (0.454)
F022	1 (0.454)
F023	1 (0.454)
F024	1 (0.454)
F025	1 (0.454)
F026	1 (0.454)
F027	1 (0.454)
F028	1 (0.454)
F032	1 (0.454)
F034	1 (0.454)
F035	1 (0.454)
F037	1 (0.454)
F038	1 (0.454)
F039	1 (0.454)
K001	1 (0.454)
K002	10 (4.54)
K003	10 (4.54)
K004	10 (4.54)
K005	10 (4.54)
K006	10 (4.54)
K007	10 (4.54)
K008	10 (4.54)
K009	10 (4.54)
K010	10 (4.54)
K011	10 (4.54)
K013	10 (4.54)
K014	5000 (2270)
K015	10 (4.54)
K016	1 (0.454)
K017	10 (4.54)
K018	1 (0.454)
K019	1 (0.454)
K020	1 (0.454)
K021	10 (4.54)
K022	1 (0.454)
K023	5000 (2270)
K024	5000 (2270)
K025	10 (4.54)
K026	1000 (454)
K027	10 (4.54)

Hazardous substance	Reportable quantity (RQ) pounds (kilograms)
K028.	1 (0.454)
K029.	1 (0.454)
K030.	1 (0.454)
K031.	1 (0.454)
K032.	10 (4.54)
K033.	10 (4.54)
K034.	10 (4.54)
K035.	1 (0.454)
K036.	1 (0.454)
K037.	1 (0.454)
K038.	10 (4.54)
K039.	10 (4.54)
K040.	10 (4.54)
K041.	1 (0.454)
K042.	10 (4.54)
K043.	10 (4.54)
K044.	10 (4.54)
K045.	10 (4.54)
K046.	10 (4.54)
K047.	10 (4.54)
K048.	10 (4.54)
K049.	10 (4.54)
K050.	10 (4.54)
K051.	10 (4.54)
K052.	10 (4.54)
K060.	1 (0.454)
K061.	10 (4.54)
K062.	10 (4.54)
K064.	10 (4.54)
K065.	10 (4.54)
K066.	10 (4.54)
K069.	10 (4.54)
K071.	1 (0.454)
K073.	10 (4.54)
K083.	100 (45.4)
K084.	1 (0.454)
K085.	10 (4.54)
K086.	10 (4.54)
K087.	100 (45.4)
K088.	10 (4.54)
K090.	10 (4.54)
K091.	10 (4.54)
K093.	5000 (2270)
K094.	5000 (2270)
K095.	100 (45.4)
K096.	100 (45.4)
K097.	1 (0.454)
K098.	1 (0.454)
K099.	10 (4.54)
K100.	10 (4.54)
K101.	1 (0.454)

TABLE 1 — HAZARDOUS SUBSTANCES 337

Hazardous substance	Reportable quantity (RQ) pounds (kilograms)
K102	1 (0.454)
K103	100 (45.4)
K104	10 (4.54)
K105	10 (4.54)
K106	1 (0.454)
K107	10 (4.54)
K108	10 (4.54)
K109	10 (4.54)
K110	10 (4.54)
K111	10 (4.54)
K112	10 (4.54)
K113	10 (4.54)
K114	10 (4.54)
K115	10 (4.54)
K116	10 (4.54)
K117	1 (0.454)
K118	1 (0.454)
K123	10 (4.54)
K124	10 (4.54)
K125	10 (4.54)
K126	10 (4.54)
K131	100 (45.4)
K132	1000 (454)
K136	1 (0.454)
K141	1 (0.454)
K142	1 (0.454)
K143	1 (0.454)
K144	1 (0.454)
K145	1 (0.454)
K147	1 (0.454)
K148	1 (0.454)
K149	10 (4.54)
K150	10 (4.54)
K151	10 (4.54)
K156	10 (4.54)
K157	10 (4.54)
K158	10 (4.54)
K159	10 (4.54)
K161	1 (0.454)
K169	10 (4.54)
K170	1 (0.454)
K171	1 (0.454)
K172	1 (0.454)
K174	1 (0.454)
K175	1 (0.454)
K176	1 (0.454)
K177	5000 (2270)
K178	1000 (454)
K181	1 (0.454)

¢ The RQ for these hazardous substances is limited to those pieces of the metal having a diameter smaller than 100 micrometers (0.004 inches).

¢¢ The RQ for asbestos is limited to friable forms only.

@ Indicates that the name was added by PHMSA because (1) the name is a synonym for a specific hazardous substance and (2) the name appears in the Hazardous Materials Table as a proper shipping name.

To provide consistency with EPA regulations, two entries with different CAS numbers are provided. Refer to the EPA Table 302.4—List of Hazardous Substances and Reportable Quantities for an explanation of the two entries.

Table 2—Radionuclides

(1)-Radionuclide	(2)-Atomic Number	(3)-Reportable Quantity (RQ) Ci(TBq)
Actinium-224	89	100 (3.7)
Actinium-225	89	1 (.037)
Actinium-226	89	10 (.37)
Actinium-227	89	0.001 (.000037)
Actinium-228	89	10 (.37)
Aluminum-26	13	10 (.37)
Americium-237	95	1000 (37)
Americium-238	95	100 (3.7)
Americium-239	95	100 (3.7)
Americium-240	95	10 (.37)
Americium-241	95	0.01 (.00037)
Americium-242	95	100 (3.7)
Americium-242m	95	0.01 (.00037)
Americium-243	95	0. 01 (.00037)
Americium-244	95	10 (.37)
Americium-244m	95	1000 (37)
Americium-245	95	1000 (37)
Americium-246	95	1000 (37)
Americium-246m	95	1000 (37)
Antimony-115	51	1000 (37)
Antimony-116	51	1000 (37)
Antimony-116m	51	100 (3.7)
Antimony-117	51	1000 (37)
Antimony-118m	51	10 (.37)
Antimony-119	51	1000 (37)
Antimony-120 (16 min)	51	1000 (37)
Antimony-120 (5.76 day)	51	10 (.37)
Antimony-122	51	10 (.37)
Antimony-124	51	10 (.37)
Antimony-124m	51	1000 (37)
Antimony-125	51	10 (.37)
Antimony-126	51	10 (.37)
Antimony-126m	51	1000 (37)
Antimony-127	51	10 (.37)
Antimony-128 (10.4 min)	51	1000 (37)
Antimony-128 (9.01 hr)	51	10 (.37)
Antimony-129	51	100 (3.7)
Antimony-130	51	100 (3.7)
Antimony-131	51	1000 (37)
Argon-39	18	1000 (37)
Argon-41	18	10 (.37)
Arsenic-69	33	1000 (37)
Arsenic-70	33	100 (3.7)
Arsenic-71	33	100 (3.7)
Arsenic-72	33	10 (.37)
Arsenic-73	33	100 (3.7)
Arsenic-74	33	10 (.37)
Arsenic-76	33	100 (3.7)
Arsenic-77	33	1000 (37)

(1)-Radionuclide	(2)-Atomic Number	(3)-Reportable Quantity (RQ) Ci(TBq)
Arsenic-78.	33	100 (3.7)
Astatine-207	85	100 (3.7)
Astatine-211	85	100 (3.7)
Barium-126	56	1000 (37)
Barium-128	56	10 (.37)
Barium-131	56	10 (.37)
Barium-131m	56	1000 (37)
Barium-133	56	10 (.37)
Barium-133m	56	100 (3.7)
Barium-135m	56	1000 (37)
Barium-139	56	1000 (37)
Barium-140	56	10 (.37)
Barium-141	56	1000 (37)
Barium-142	56	1000 (37)
Berkelium-245	97	100 (3.7)
Berkelium-246	97	10 (.37)
Berkelium-247	97	0. 01 (.00037)
Berkelium-249	97	1 (.037)
Berkelium-250	97	100 (3.7)
Beryllium-7	4	100 (3.7)
Beryllium-10	4	1 (.037)
Bismuth-200	83	100 (3.7)
Bismuth-201	83	100 (3.7)
Bismuth-202	83	1000 (37)
Bismuth-203	83	10 (.37)
Bismuth-205	83	10 (.37)
Bismuth-206	83	10 (.37)
Bismuth-207	83	10 (.37)
Bismuth-210	83	10 (.37)
Bismuth-210m	83	0.1 (.0037)
Bismuth-212	83	100 (3.7)
Bismuth-213	83	100 (3.7)
Bismuth-214	83	100 (3.7)
Bromine-74	35	100 (3.7)
Bromine-74m	35	100 (3.7)
Bromine-75	35	100 (3.7)
Bromine-76	35	10 (.37)
Bromine-77	35	100 (3.7)
Bromine-80m	35	1000 (37)
Bromine-80	35	1000 (37)
Bromine-82	35	10 (.37)
Bromine-83	35	1000 (37)
Bromine-84	35	100 (3.7)
Cadmium-104	48	1000 (37)
Cadmium-107	48	1000 (37)
Cadmium-109	48	1 (.037)
Cadmium-113	48	0.1 (.0037)
Cadmium-113m	48	0.1 (.0037)
Cadmium-115	48	100 (3.7)
Cadmium-115m	48	10 (.37)
Cadmium-117	48	100 (3.7)

TABLE 2 — RADIONUCLIDES 341

(1)-Radionuclide	(2)-Atomic Number	(3)-Reportable Quantity (RQ) Ci(TBq)
Cadmium-117m	48	10 (.37)
Calcium-41	20	10 (.37)
Calcium-45	20	10 (.37)
Calcium-47	20	10 (.37)
Californium-244	98	1000 (37)
Californium-246	98	10 (.37)
Californium-248	98	0.1 (.0037)
Californium-249	98	0.01 (.00037)
Californium-250	98	0.01 (.00037)
Californium-251	98	0.01 (.00037)
Californium-252	98	0.1 (.0037)
Californium-253	98	10 (.37)
Californium-254	98	0.1 (.0037)
Carbon-11	6	1000 (37)
Carbon-14	6	10 (.37)
Cerium-134	58	10 (.37)
Cerium-135	58	10 (.37)
Cerium-137	58	1000 (37)
Cerium-137m	58	100 (3.7)
Cerium-139	58	100 (3.7)
Cerium-141	58	10 (.37)
Cerium-143	58	100 (3.7)
Cerium-144	58	1 (.037)
Cesium-125	55	1000 (37)
Cesium-127	55	100 (3.7)
Cesium-129	55	100 (3.7)
Cesium-130	55	1000 (37)
Cesium-131	55	1000 (37)
Cesium-132	55	10 (.37)
Cesium-134	55	1 (.037)
Cesium-134m	55	1000 (37)
Cesium-135	55	10 (.37)
Cesium-135m	55	100 (3.7)
Cesium-136	55	10 (.37)
Cesium-137	55	1 (.037)
Cesium-138	55	100 (3.7)
Chlorine-36	17	10 (.37)
Chlorine-38	17	100 (3.7)
Chlorine-39	17	100 (3.7)
Chromium-48	24	100 (3.7)
Chromium-49	24	1000 (37)
Chromium-49	24	1000 (37)
Chromium-51	24	1000 (37)
Cobalt-55	27	10 (.37)
Cobalt-56	27	10 (.37)
Cobalt-57	27	100 (3.7)
Cobalt-58	27	10 (.37)
Cobalt-58m	27	1000 (37)
Cobalt-60	7	10 (.37)
Cobalt-60m	27	1000 (37)
Cobalt-61	27	1000 (37)

(1)-Radionuclide	(2)-Atomic Number	(3)-Reportable Quantity (RQ) Ci(TBq)
Cobalt-62m	27	1000 (37)
Copper-60	29	100 (3.7)
Copper-61	29	100 (3.7)
Copper-64	29	1000 (37)
Copper-67	29	100 (3.7)
Curium-238	96	1000 (37)
Curium-240	96	1 (.037)
Curium-241	96	10 (.37)
Curium-242	96	1 (.037)
Curium-243	96	0.01 (.00037)
Curium-244	96	0.01 (.00037)
Curium-245	96	0.01 (.00037)
Curium-246	96	0.01 (.00037)
Curium-247	96	0.01 (.00037)
Curium-248	96	0.001 (.000037)
Curium-249	96	1000 (37)
Dysprosium-155	66	100 (3.7)
Dysprosium-157	66	100 (3.7)
Dysprosium-159	66	100 (3.7)
Dysprosium-165	66	1000 (37)
Dysprosium-166	66	10 (.37)
Einsteinium-250	99	10 (.37)
Einsteinium-251	99	1000 (37)
Einsteinium-253	99	10 (.37)
Einsteinium-254	99	0.1 (.0037)
Einsteinium-254m	99	1 (.037)
Erbium-161	68	100 (3.7)
Erbium-165	68	1000 (37)
Erbium-169	68	100 (3.7)
Erbium-171	68	100 (3.7)
Erbium-172	68	10 (.37)
Europium-145	63	10 (.37)
Europium-146	63	10 (.37)
Europium-147	63	10 (.37)
Europium-148	63	10 (.37)
Europium-149	63	100 (3.7)
Europium-150 (12.6 hr)	63	1000 (37)
Europium-150 (34.2 yr)	63	10 (.37)
Europium-152	63	10 (.37)
Europium-152m	63	100 (3.7)
Europium-154	63	10 (.37)
Europium-155	63	10 (.37)
Europium-156	63	10 (.37)
Europium-157	63	10 (.37)
Europium-158	63	1000 (37)
Fermium-252	100	10 (.37)
Fermium-253	100	10 (.37)
Fermium-254	100	100 (3.7)
Fermium-255	100	100 (3.7)
Fermium-257	100	1 (.037)
Fluorine-18	9	1000 (37)

TABLE 2 — RADIONUCLIDES   343

(1)-Radionuclide	(2)-Atomic Number	(3)-Reportable Quantity (RQ) Ci(TBq)
Francium-222	87	100 (3.7)
Francium-223	87	100 (3.7)
Gadolinium-145	64	100 (3.7)
Gadolinium-146	64	10 (.37)
Gadolinium-147	64	10 (.37)
Gadolinium-148	64	0.001 (.000037)
Gadolinium-149	64	100 (3.7)
Gadolinium-151	64	100 (3.7)
Gadolinium-152	64	0.001 (.000037)
Gadolinium-153	64	10 (.37)
Gadolinium-159	64	1000 (37)
Gallium-65	31	1000 (37)
Gallium-66	31	10 (.37)
Gallium-67	31	100 (3.7)
Gallium-68	31	1000 (37)
Gallium-70	31	1000 (37)
Gallium-72	31	10 (.37)
Gallium-73	31	100 (3.7)
Germanium-66	32	100 (3.7)
Germanium-67	32	1000 (37)
Germanium-68	32	10 (.37)
Germanium-69	32	10 (.37)
Germanium-71	32	1000 (37)
Germanium-75	32	1000 (37)
Germanium-77	32	10 (.37)
Germanium-78	32	1000 (37)
Gold-193	79	100 (3.7)
Gold-194	79	10 (.37)
Gold-195	79	100 (3.7)
Gold-198	79	100 (3.7)
Gold-198m	79	10 (.37)
Gold-199	79	100 (3.7)
Gold-200	79	1000 (37)
Gold-200m	79	10 (.37)
Gold-201	79	1000 (37)
Hafnium-170	72	100 (3.7)
Hafnium-172	72	1 (.037)
Hafnium-173	72	100 (3.7)
Hafnium-175	72	100 (3.7)
Hafnium-177m	72	1000 (37)
Hafnium-178m	72	0.1 (.0037)
Hafnium-179m	72	100 (3.7)
Hafnium-180m	72	100 (3.7)
Hafnium-181	72	10 (.37)
Hafnium-182	72	0.1 (.0037)
Hafnium-182m	72	100 (3.7)
Hafnium-183	72	100 (3.7)
Hafnium-184	72	100 (3.7)
Holmium-155	67	1000 (37)
Holmium-157	67	1000 (37)
Holmium-159	67	1000 (37)

RADIONUCLIDES

TABLE 2 — RADIONUCLIDES

(1)-Radionuclide	(2)-Atomic Number	(3)-Reportable Quantity (RQ) Ci(TBq)
Holmium-161	67	1000 (37)
Holmium-162	67	1000 (37)
Holmium-162m	67	1000 (37)
Holmium-164	67	1000 (37)
Holmium-164m	67	1000 (37)
Holmium-166	67	100 (3.7)
Holmium-166m	67	1 (.037)
Holmium-167	67	100 (3.7)
Hydrogen-3	1	100 (3.7)
Indium-109	49	100 (3.7)
Indium-110 (69.1 min)	49	100 (3.7)
Indium-110 (4.9 hr)	49	10 (.37)
Indium-111	49	100 (3.7)
Indium-112	49	1000 (37)
Indium-113m	49	1000 (37)
Indium-114m	49	10 (.37)
Indium-115	49	0.1 (.0037)
Indium-115m	49	100 (3.7)
Indium-116m	49	100 (3.7)
Indium-117	49	1000 (37)
Indium-117m	49	100 (3.7)
Indium-119m	49	1000 (37)
Iodine-120	53	10 (.37)
Iodine-120m	53	100 (3.7)
Iodine-121	53	100 (3.7)
Iodine-123	53	10 (.37)
Iodine-124	53	0.1 (.0037)
Iodine-125	53	0.01 (.00037)
Iodine-126	53	0.01 (.00037)
Iodine-128	53	1000 (37)
Iodine-129	53	0.001 (.000037)
Iodine-130	53	1 (.037)
Iodine-131	53	0.01 (.00037)
Iodine-132	53	10 (.37)
Iodine-132m	53	10 (.37)
Iodine-133	53	0.1 (.0037)
Iodine-134	53	100 (3.7)
Iodine-135	3	10 (.37)
Iridium-182	7	1000 (37)
Iridium-184	77	100 (3.7)
Iridium-185	77	100 (3.7)
Iridium-186	77	10 (.37)
Iridium-187	77	100 (3.7)
Iridium-188	77	10 (.37)
Iridium-189	77	100 (3.7)
Iridium-190	77	10 (.37)
Iridium-190m	77	1000 (37)
Iridium-192	77	10 (.37)
Iridium-192m	77	100 (3.7)
Iridium-194	77	100 (3.7)
Iridium-194m	77	10 (.37)

TABLE 2 — RADIONUCLIDES   345

(1)-Radionuclide	(2)-Atomic Number	(3)-Reportable Quantity (RQ) Ci(TBq)
Iridium-195	77	1000 (37)
Iridium-195m	77	100 (3.7)
Iron-52	26	100 (3.7)
Iron-55	26	100 (3.7)
Iron-59	26	10 (.37)
Iron-60	26	0.1 (.0037)
Krypton-74	36	10 (.37)
Krypton-76	36	10 (.37)
Krypton-77	36	10 (.37)
Krypton-79	36	100 (3.7)
Krypton-81	36	1000 (37)
Krypton-83m	36	1000 (37)
Krypton-85	36	1000 (37)
Krypton-85m	36	100 (3.7)
Krypton-87	36	10 (.37)
Krypton-88	36	10 (.37)
Lanthanum-131	57	1000 (37)
Lanthanum-132	57	100 (3.7)
Lanthanum-135	57	1000 (37)
Lanthanum-137	57	10 (.37)
Lanthanum-138	57	1 (.037)
Lanthanum-140	57	10 (.37)
Lanthanum-141	57	1000 (37)
Lanthanum-142	57	100 (3.7)
Lanthanum-143	57	1000 (37)
Lead-195m	82	1000 (37)
Lead-198	82	100 (3.7)
Lead-199	82	100 (3.7)
Lead-200	82	100 (3.7)
Lead-201	82	100 (3.7)
Lead-202	82	1 (.037)
Lead-202m	82	10 (.37)
Lead-203	82	100 (3.7)
Lead-205	82	100 (3.7)
Lead-209	82	1000 (37)
Lead-210	82	0.01 (.00037)
Lead-211	82	100 (3.7)
Lead-212	82	10 (.37)
Lead-214	82	100 (3.7)
Lutetium-169	71	10 (.37)
Lutetium-170	71	10 (.37)
Lutetium-171	71	10 (.37)
Lutetium-172	71	10 (.37)
Lutetium-173	71	100 (3.7)
Lutetium-174	71	10 (.37)
Lutetium-174m	71	10 (.37)
Lutetium-176	71	1 (.037)
Lutetium-176m	71	1000 (37)
Lutetium-177	71	100 (3.7)
Lutetium-177m	71	10 (.37)
Lutetium-178	71	1000 (37)

TABLE 2 — RADIONUCLIDES

(1)-Radionuclide	(2)-Atomic Number	(3)-Reportable Quantity (RQ) Ci(TBq)
Lutetium-178m	71	1000 (37)
Lutetium-179	71	1000 (37)
Magnesium-28	12	10 (.37)
Manganese-51	25	1000 (37)
Manganese-52	25	10 (.37)
Manganese-52m	25	1000 (37)
Manganese-53	25	1000 (37)
Manganese-54	25	10 (.37)
Manganese-56	25	100 (3.7)
Mendelevium-257	101	100 (3.7)
Mendelevium-258	101	1 (.037)
Mercury-193	80	100 (3.7)
Mercury-193m	80	10 (.37)
Mercury-194	80	0.1 (.0037)
Mercury-195	80	100 (3.7)
Mercury-195m	80	100 (3.7)
Mercury-197	80	1000 (37)
Mercury-197m	80	1000 (37)
Mercury-199m	80	1000 (37)
Mercury-203	80	10 (.37)
Molybdenum-90	42	100 (3.7)
Molybdenum-93	42	100 (3.7)
Molybdenum-93m	42	10 (.37)
Molybdenum-99	42	100 (3.7)
Molybdenum-101	42	1000 (37)
Neodymium-136	60	1000 (37)
Neodymium-138	60	1000 (37)
Neodymium-139	60	1000 (37)
Neodymium-139m	60	100 (3.7)
Neodymium-141	60	1000 (37)
Neodymium-147	60	10 (.37)
Neodymium-149	60	100 (3.7)
Neodymium-151	60	1000 (37)
Neptunium-232	93	1000 (37)
Neptunium-233	93	1000 (37)
Neptunium-234	93	10 (.37)
Neptunium-235	93	1000 (37)
Neptunium-236 (1.2 E 5 yr)	93	0.1 (.0037)
Neptunium-236 (22.5 hr)	93	100 (3.7)
Neptunium-237	93	0.01 (.00037)
Neptunium-238	93	10 (.37)
Neptunium-239	93	100 (3.7)
Neptunium-240	93	100 (3.7)
Nickel-56	28	10 (.37)
Nickel-57	28	10 (.37)
Nickel-59	28	100 (3.7)
Nickel-63	28	100 (3.7)
Nickel-65	28	100 (3.7)
Nickel-66	28	10 (.37)
Niobium-88	41	100 (3.7)
Niobium-89 (66 min)	41	100 (3.7)

TABLE 2 — RADIONUCLIDES 347

(1)-Radionuclide	(2)-Atomic Number	(3)-Reportable Quantity (RQ) Ci(TBq)
Niobium-89 (122 min)...................	41	100 (3.7)
Niobium-90.............................	41	10 (.37)
Niobium-93m...........................	41	100 (3.7)
Niobium-94.............................	41	10 (.37)
Niobium-95.............................	41	10 (.37)
Niobium-95m...........................	41	100 (3.7)
Niobium-96.............................	41	10 (.37)
Niobium-97.............................	41	100 (3.7)
Niobium-98.............................	41	1000 (37)
Osmium-180............................	76	1000 (37)
Osmium-181............................	76	100 (3.7)
Osmium-182............................	76	100 (3.7)
Osmium-185............................	76	10 (.37)
Osmium-189m..........................	76	1000 (37)
Osmium-191............................	76	100 (3.7)
Osmium-191m..........................	76	1000 (37)
Osmium-193............................	76	100 (3.7)
Osmium-194............................	76	1 (.037)
Palladium-100	46	100 (3.7)
Palladium-101	46	100 (3.7)
Palladium-103	46	100 (3.7)
Palladium-107	46	100 (3.7)
Palladium-109	46	1000 (37)
Phosphorus-32	15	0.1 (.0037)
Phosphorus-33	15	1 (.037)
Platinum-186	78	100 (3.7)
Platinum-188	78	100 (3.7)
Platinum-189	78	100 (3.7)
Platinum-191	78	100 (3.7)
Platinum-193	78	1000 (37)
Platinum-193m.........................	78	100 (3.7)
Platinum-195m.........................	78	100 (3.7)
Platinum-197	78	1000 (37)
Platinum-197m.........................	78	1000 (37)
Platinum-199	78	1000 (37)
Platinum-200	78	100 (3.7)
Plutonium-234	94	1000 (37)
Plutonium-235	94	1000 (37)
Plutonium-236	94	0.1 (.0037)
Plutonium-237	94	1000 (37)
Plutonium-238	94	0.01 (.00037)
Plutonium-239	94	0.01 (.00037)
Plutonium-240	94	0.01 (.00037)
Plutonium-241	94	1 (.037)
Plutonium-242	94	0.01 (.00037)
Plutonium-243	94	1000 (37)
Plutonium-244	94	0.01 (.00037)
Plutonium-245	94	100 (3.7)
Polonium-203..........................	84	100 (3.7)
Polonium-205..........................	84	100 (3.7)
Polonium-207..........................	84	10 (.37)

TABLE 2 — RADIONUCLIDES

(1)-Radionuclide	(2)-Atomic Number	(3)-Reportable Quantity (RQ) Ci(TBq)
Polonium-210	84	0.01 (.00037)
Potassium-40	19	1 (.037)
Potassium-42	19	100 (3.7)
Potassium-43	19	10 (.37)
Potassium-44	19	100 (3.7)
Potassium-45	19	1000 (37)
Praseodymium-136	59	1000 (37)
Praseodymium-137	59	1000 (37)
Praseodymium-138m	59	100 (3.7)
Praseodymium-139	59	1000 (37)
Praseodymium-142	59	100 (3.7)
Praseodymium-142m	59	1000 (37)
Praseodymium-143	59	10 (.37)
Praseodymium-144	59	1000 (37)
Praseodymium-145	59	1000 (37)
Praseodymium-147	59	1000 (37)
Promethium-141	61	1000 (37)
Promethium-143	61	100 (3.7)
Promethium-144	61	10 (.37)
Promethium-145	61	100 (3.7)
Promethium-146	61	10 (.37)
Promethium-147	61	10 (.37)
Promethium-148	61	10 (.37)
Promethium-148m	61	10 (.37)
Promethium-149	61	100 (3.7)
Promethium-150	61	100 (3.7)
Promethium-151	61	100 (3.7)
Protactinium-227	91	100 (3.7)
Protactinium-228	91	10 (.37)
Protactinium-230	91	10 (.37)
Protactinium-231	91	0.01 (.00037)
Protactinium-232	91	10 (.37)
Protactinium-233	91	100 (3.7)
Protactinium-234	91	10 (.37)
RADIONUCLIDES§†		1 (.037)
Radium-223	88	1 (.037)
Radium-224	88	10 (.37)
Radium-225	88	1 (.037)
Radium-226**	88	0.1 (.0037)
Radium-227	88	1000 (37)
Radium-228	88	0.1 (.0037)
Radon-220	86	0.1 (.0037)
Radon-222	86	0.1 (.0037)
Rhenium-177	75	1000 (37)
Rhenium-178	75	1000 (37)
Rhenium-181	75	100 (3.7)
Rhenium-182 (12.7 hr)	75	10 (.37)
Rhenium-182 (64.0 hr)	75	10 (.37)
Rhenium-184	75	10 (.37)
Rhenium-184m	75	10 (.37)
Rhenium-186	75	100 (3.7)

TABLE 2 — RADIONUCLIDES   349

(1)-Radionuclide	(2)-Atomic Number	(3)-Reportable Quantity (RQ) Ci(TBq)
Rhenium-186m	75	10 (.37)
Rhenium-187	75	1000 (37)
Rhenium-188	75	1000 (37)
Rhenium-188m	75	1000 (37)
Rhenium-189	75	1000 (37)
Rhodium-99	45	10 (.37)
Rhodium-99m	45	100 (3.7)
Rhodium-100	45	10 (.37)
Rhodium-101	45	10 (.37)
Rhodium-101m	45	100 (3.7)
Rhodium-102	45	10 (.37)
Rhodium-102m	45	10 (.37)
Rhodium-103m	45	1000 (37)
Rhodium-105	45	100 (3.7)
Rhodium-106m	45	10 (.37)
Rhodium-107	45	1000 (37)
Rubidium-79	37	1000 (37)
Rubidium-81	37	100 (3.7)
Rubidium-81m	37	1000 (37)
Rubidium-82m	37	10 (.37)
Rubidium-83	37	10 (.37)
Rubidium-84	37	10 (.37)
Rubidium-86	37	10 (.37)
Rubidium-88	37	1000 (37)
Rubidium-89	37	1000 (37)
Rubidium-87	37	10 (.37)
Ruthenium-94	44	1000 (37)
Ruthenium-97	44	100 (3.7)
Ruthenium-103	44	10 (.37)
Ruthenium-105	44	100 (3.7)
Ruthenium-106	44	1 (.037)
Samarium-141	62	1000 (37)
Samarium-141m	62	1000 (37)
Samarium-142	62	1000 (37)
Samarium-145	62	100 (3.7)
Samarium-146	62	0.01 (.00037)
Samarium-147	62	0.01 (.00037)
Samarium-151	62	10 (.37)
Samarium-153	62	100 (3.7)
Samarium-155	62	1000 (37)
Samarium-156	62	100 (3.7)
Scandium-43	21	1000 (37)
Scandium-44	21	100 (3.7)
Scandium-44m	21	10 (.37)
Scandium-46	21	10 (.37)
Scandium-47	21	100 (3.7)
Scandium-48	21	10 (.37)
Scandium-49	21	1000 (37)
Selenium-70	34	1000 (37)
Selenium-73	34	10 (.37)
Selenium-73m	34	100 (3.7)

(1)-Radionuclide	(2)-Atomic Number	(3)-Reportable Quantity (RQ) Ci(TBq)
Selenium-75	34	10 (.37)
Selenium-79	34	10 (.37)
Selenium-81	34	1000 (37)
Selenium-81m	34	1000 (37)
Selenium-83	34	1000 (37)
Silicon-31	14	1000 (37)
Silicon-32	14	1 (.037)
Silver-102	47	100 (3.7)
Silver-103	47	1000 (37)
Silver-104	47	1000 (37)
Silver-104m	47	1000 (37)
Silver-105	47	10 (.37)
Silver-106	47	1000 (37)
Silver-106m	47	10 (.37)
Silver-108m	47	10 (.37)
Silver-110m	47	10 (.37)
Silver-111	47	10 (.37)
Silver-112	47	100 (3.7)
Silver-115	47	1000 (37)
Sodium-22	11	10 (.37)
Sodium-24	11	10 (.37)
Strontium-80	38	100 (3.7)
Strontium-81	38	1000 (37)
Strontium-83	38	100 (3.7)
Strontium-85	38	10 (.37)
Strontium-85m	38	1000 (37)
Strontium-87m	38	100 (3.7)
Strontium-89	38	10 (.37)
Strontium-90	38	0.1 (.0037)
Strontium-91	38	10 (.37)
Strontium-92	38	100 (3.7)
Sulfur-35	16	1 (.037)
Tantalum-172	73	100 (3.7)
Tantalum-173	73	100 (3.7)
Tantalum-174	73	100 (3.7)
Tantalum-175	73	100 (3.7)
Tantalum-176	73	10 (.37)
Tantalum-177	73	1000 (37)
Tantalum-178	73	1000 (37)
Tantalum-179	73	1000 (37)
Tantalum-180	73	100 (3.7)
Tantalum-180m	73	1000 (37)
Tantalum-182	73	10 (.37)
Tantalum-182m	73	1000 (37)
Tantalum-183	73	100 (3.7)
Tantalum-184	73	10 (.37)
Tantalum-185	73	1000 (37)
Tantalum-186	73	1000 (37)
Technetium-93	43	100 (3.7)
Technetium-93m	43	1000 (37)
Technetium-94	43	10 (.37)

TABLE 2 — RADIONUCLIDES   351

(1)-Radionuclide	(2)-Atomic Number	(3)-Reportable Quantity (RQ) Ci(TBq)
Technetium-94m	43	100 (3.7)
Technetium-96	43	10 (.37)
Technetium-96m	43	1000 (37)
Technetium-97	43	100 (3.7)
Technetium-97m	43	100 (3.7)
Technetium-98	43	10 (.37)
Technetium-99	43	10 (.37)
Technetium-99m	43	100 (3.7)
Technetium-101	43	1000 (37)
Technetium-104	43	1000 (37)
Tellurium-116	52	1000 (37)
Tellurium-121	52	10 (.37)
Tellurium-121m	52	10 (.37)
Tellurium-123	52	10 (.37)
Tellurium-123m	52	10 (.37)
Tellurium-125m	52	10 (.37)
Tellurium-127	52	1000 (37)
Tellurium-127m	52	10 (.37)
Tellurium-129	52	1000 (37)
Tellurium-129m	52	10 (.37)
Tellurium-131	52	1000 (37)
Tellurium-131m	52	10 (.37)
Tellurium-132	52	10 (.37)
Tellurium-133	52	1000 (37)
Tellurium-133m	52	1000 (37)
Tellurium-134	52	1000 (37)
Terbium-147	65	100 (3.7)
Terbium-149	65	100 (3.7)
Terbium-150	65	100 (3.7)
Terbium-151	65	10 (.37)
Terbium-153	65	100 (3.7)
Terbium-154	65	10 (.37)
Terbium-155	65	100 (3.7)
Terbium-156m (5.0 hr)	65	1000 (37)
Terbium-156m (24.4 hr)	65	1000 (37)
Terbium-156	65	10 (.37)
Terbium-157	65	100 (3.7)
Terbium-158	65	10 (.37)
Terbium-160	65	10 (.37)
Terbium-161	65	100 (3.7)
Thallium-194	81	1000 (37)
Thallium-194m	81	100 (3.7)
Thallium-195	81	100 (3.7)
Thallium-197	81	100 (3.7)
Thallium-198	81	10 (.37)
Thallium-198m	81	100 (3.7)
Thallium-199	81	100 (3.7)
Thallium-200	81	10 (.37)
Thallium-201	81	1000 (37)
Thallium-202	81	10 (.37)
Thallium-204	81	10 (.37)

TABLE 2 — RADIONUCLIDES

(1)-Radionuclide	(2)-Atomic Number	(3)-Reportable Quantity (RQ) Ci(TBq)
Thorium (Irradiated)	90	***
Thorium (Natural)	90	**
Thorium-226	90	100 (3.7)
Thorium-227	90	1 (.037)
Thorium-228	90	0.01 (.00037)
Thorium-229	90	0.001 (.000037)
Thorium-230	90	0.01 (.00037)
Thorium-231	90	100 (3.7)
Thorium-232**	90	0.001 (.000037)
Thorium-234	90	100 (3.7)
Thulium-162	69	1000 (37)
Thulium-166	69	10 (.37)
Thulium-167	69	100 (3.7)
Thulium-170	69	10 (.37)
Thulium-171	69	100 (3.7)
Thulium-172	69	100 (3.7)
Thulium-173	69	100 (3.7)
Thulium-175	69	1000 (37)
Tin-110	50	100 (3.7)
Tin-111	50	1000 (37)
Tin-113	50	10 (.37)
Tin-117m	50	100 (3.7)
Tin-119m	50	10 (.37)
Tin-121	50	1000 (37)
Tin-121m	50	10 (.37)
Tin-123	50	10 (.37)
Tin-123m	50	1000 (37)
Tin-125	50	10 (.37)
Tin-126	50	1 (.037)
Tin-127	50	100 (3.7)
Tin-128	50	1000 (37)
Titanium-44	22	1 (.037)
Titanium-45	22	1000 (37)
Tungsten-176	74	1000 (37)
Tungsten-177	74	100 (3.7)
Tungsten-178	74	100 (3.7)
Tungsten-179	74	1000 (37)
Tungsten-181	74	100 (3.7)
Tungsten-185	74	10 (.37)
Tungsten-187	74	100 (3.7)
Tungsten-188	74	10 (.37)
Uranium (Depleted)	92	***
Uranium (Irradiated)	92	***
Uranium (Natural)	92	**
Uranium Enriched 20% or greater	92	***
Uranium Enriched less than 20%	92	***
Uranium-230	92	1 (.037)
Uranium-231	92	1000 (37)
Uranium-232	92	0.01 (.00037)
Uranium-233	92	0.1 (.0037)
Uranium-234**	92	0.1 (.0037)

TABLE 2 — RADIONUCLIDES 353

(1)-Radionuclide	(2)-Atomic Number	(3)-Reportable Quantity (RQ). Ci(TBq)
Uranium-235**	92	0.1 (.0037)
Uranium-236	92	0.1 (.0037)
Uranium-237	92	100 (3.7)
Uranium-238**	92	0.1 (.0037)
Uranium-239	92	1000 (37)
Uranium-240	92	1000 (37)
Vanadium-47	23	1000 (37)
Vanadium-48	23	10 (.37)
Vanadium-49	23	1000 (37)
Xenon-120	54	100 (3.7)
Xenon-121	54	10 (.37)
Xenon-122	54	100 (3.7)
Xenon-123	54	10 (.37)
Xenon-125	54	100 (3.7)
Xenon-127	54	100 (3.7)
Xenon-129m	54	1000 (37)
Xenon-131m	54	1000 (37)
Xenon-133	54	1000 (37)
Xenon-133m	54	1000 (37)
Xenon-135	54	100 (3.7)
Xenon-135m	54	10 (.37)
Xenon-138	54	10 (.37)
Ytterbium-162	70	1000 (37)
Ytterbium-166	70	10 (.37)
Ytterbium-167	70	1000 (37)
Ytterbium-169	70	10 (.37)
Ytterbium-175	70	100 (3.7)
Ytterbium-177	70	1000 (37)
Ytterbium-178	70	1000 (37)
Yttrium-86	39	10 (.37)
Yttrium-86m	39	1000 (37)
Yttrium-87	39	10 (.37)
Yttrium-88	39	10 (.37)
Yttrium-90	39	10 (.37)
Yttrium-90m	39	100 (3.7)
Yttrium-91	39	10 (.37)
Yttrium-91m	39	1000 (37)
Yttrium-92	39	100 (3.7)
Yttrium-93	39	100 (3.7)
Yttrium-94	39	1000 (37)
Yttrium-95	39	1000 (37)
Zinc-62	30	100 (3.7)
Zinc-63	30	1000 (37)
Zinc-65	30	10 (.37)
Zinc-69	30	1000 (37)
Zinc-69m	30	100 (3.7)
Zinc-71m	30	100 (3.7)
Zinc-72	30	100 (3.7)
Zirconium-86	40	100 (3.7)
Zirconium-88	40	10 (.37)
Zirconium-89	40	100 (3.7)

TABLE 2 — RADIONUCLIDES

(1)-Radionuclide	(2)-Atomic Number	(3)-Reportable Quantity (RQ) Ci(TBq)
Zirconium-93	40	1 (.037)
Zirconium-95	40	10 (.37)
Zirconium-97	40	10 (.37)

§ The RQs for all radionuclides apply to chemical compounds containing the radionuclides and elemental forms regardless of the diameter of pieces of solid material.

† The RQ of one curie applies to all radionuclides not otherwise listed. Whenever the RQs in Table 1—HAZARDOUS SUBSTANCES OTHER THAN RADIONUCLIDES and this table conflict, the lowest RQ shall apply. For example, uranyl acetate and uranyl nitrate have RQs shown in TABLE 1 of 100 pounds, equivalent to about one-tenth the RQ level for uranium-238 in this table.

** The method to determine RQs for mixtures or solutions of radionuclides can be found in paragraph 7 of the note preceding TABLE 1 of this appendix. RQs for the following four common radionuclide mixtures are provided: radium-226 in secular equilibrium with its daughters (0.053 curie); natural uranium (0.1 curie); natural uranium in secular equilibrium with its daughters (0.052 curie); and natural thorium in secular equilibrium with its daughters (0.011 curie).

*** Indicates that the name was added by PHMSA because it appears in the list of radionuclides in 49 CFR 173.435. The reportable quantity (RQ), if not specifically listed elsewhere in this appendix, shall be determined in accordance with the procedures in paragraph 7 of this appendix.

Appendix B to §172.101—List of Marine Pollutants

1. See §171.4 of this subchapter for applicability to marine pollutants. This appendix lists potential marine pollutants as defined in §171.8 of this subchapter.

2. Marine pollutants listed in this appendix are not necessarily listed by name in the §172.101 Table. If a marine pollutant not listed by name or by synonym in the §172.101 Table meets the definition of any hazard Class 1 through 8, then you must determine the class and division of the material in accordance with §173.2a of this subchapter. You must also select the most appropriate hazardous material description and proper shipping name. If a marine pollutant not listed by name or by synonym in the §172.101 Table does not meet the definition of any Class 1 through 8, then you must offer it for transportation under the most appropriate of the following two Class 9 entries: "Environmentally hazardous substances, liquid, n.o.s." UN 3082, or "Environmentally hazardous substances, solid, n.o.s." UN3077.

3. This appendix contains two columns. The first column, entitled "S.M.P." (for severe marine pollutants), identifies whether a material is a severe marine pollutant. If the letters "PP" appear in this column for a material, the material is a severe marine pollutant, otherwise it is not. The second column, entitled "Marine Pollutant", lists the marine pollutants.

4. If a material is not listed in this appendix and meets the criteria for a marine pollutant as provided in Chapter 2.9 of the IMDG Code, (incorporated by reference; see §171.7 of this subchapter), the material may be transported as a marine pollutant in accordance with the applicable requirements of this subchapter.

5. If a material or a solution meeting the definition of a marine pollutant in §171.8 of this subchapter does not meet the criteria for a marine pollutant as provided in section 2.9.3.3 and 2.9.3.4 of the IMDG Code, (incorporated by reference; see §171.7 of this subchapter), it may be excepted from the requirements of this subchapter as a marine pollutant if that exception is approved by the Associate Administrator.

LIST OF MARINE POLLUTANTS

S.M.P. (1)	Marine Pollutant (2)
....	Acetone cyanohydrin, stabilized
....	Acetylene tetrabromide
....	Acetylene tetrachloride
....	Acraldehyde, inhibited
....	Acroleic acid, stabilized
....	Acrolein, inhibited
....	Acrolein stabilized
....	Acrylic Acid, Stabilized
....	Acrylic aldehyde, inhibited
....	Alcohol C-12 - C-16 poly(1-6) ethoxylate
....	Alcohol C-6 C-17 (secondary)poly(3-6) ethoxylate
....	Aldicarb
PP	Aldrin
....	Alkybenzenesulphonates, branched and straight chain (excluding C11-C13 straight chain or branched chain homologues)
....	Alkyl (C12-C14) dimethylamine
....	Alkyl (C7-C9) nitrates
....	Allyl alcohol
....	Allyl bromide
....	ortho-Aminoanisole
....	Aminobenzene
....	Aminocarb

S.M.P. (1)	Marine Pollutant (2)
....	Ammonia, anhydrous (I)
....	Ammonia solution, *relative density less than 0.880 at 15 degrees C in water, with more than 50 percent ammonia*
....	Ammonia Solution *relative density less than 0.880 at 15 degrees C in water, with more than 35% but not more than 50% ammonia*
....	Ammonia solution, *relative density between 0.880 and 0.957 at 15 degrees C in water, with more than 10 percent but not more than 35 percent ammonia, by mass*
....	Ammonium dinitro-o-cresolate
....	n-Amylbenzene
....	Aniline
....	Aniline oil
PP	Azinphos-ethyl
PP	Azinphos-methyl
....	Barium cyanide
....	Bendiocarb
....	Benomyl
....	Benquinox
....	Benzyl chlorocarbonate
....	Benzyl chloroformate
PP	Binapacryl
....	*N,N-Bis* (2-hydroxyethyl) oleamide (LOA)
....	Bleaching powder
PP	Brodifacoum
....	Bromine cyanide
....	Bromoacetone
....	Bromoallylene
....	Bromobenzene
....	ortho-Bromobenzyl cyanide
....	Bromocyane
....	Bromoform
PP	Bromophos-ethyl
....	3-Bromopropene
....	Bromoxynil
....	Butanedione
....	2-Butenal, stabilized
....	Butylbenzenes
....	Butyl benzyl phthalate
....	N-*tert*-butyl-N-cyclopropyl-6-methylthio-1,3,5-triazine- 2,4-diamine
....	para-tertiary-butyltoluene
PP	Cadmium compounds
....	Cadmium sulphide
....	Calcium arsenate
....	Calcium arsenate and calcium arsenite, mixtures, solid
....	Calcium cyanide
....	Calcium hypochlorite , dry *with more than 39% available chlorine (8.8% available oxygen)*
....	Calcium hypochlorite mixture, dry *with more than 10% but not more than 39% available chlorine*
....	Calcium hypochlorite mixture, dry *with more than 39% available chlorine (8.8% available oxygen)*
....	Calcium hypochlorite mixture, dry, corrosive *with more than 10% but not more than 39% available chlorine*
....	Calcium hypochlorite mixture, dry, corrosive *with more than 39% available chlorine (8.8% available oxygen)*

S.M.P. (1)	Marine Pollutant (2)
....	Calcium hypochlorite, hydrated *with not less than 5.5% but not more than 16% water*
....	Calcium hypochlorite, hydrated, corrosive *with not less than 5.5% but not more than 16% water*
....	Calcium hypochlorite, hydrated mixture *with not less than 5.5% but not more than 16% water*
....	Calcium hypochlorite, hydrated mixture, corrosive *with not less than 5.5% but not more than 16% water*
PP	Camphechlor
....	Carbaryl
....	Carbendazim
....	Carbofuran
....	Carbon tetrabromide
....	Carbon tetrachloride
PP	Carbophenothion
....	Cartap hydrochloride
PP	Chlordane
....	Chlorfenvinphos
PP	Chlorinated paraffins (C-10 - C-13)
PP	Chlorinated paraffins (C14 - C17), with more than 1% shorter chain length
....	Chlorine
....	Chlorine cyanide, inhibited
....	Chlomephos
....	Chloroacetone, stabilized
....	1-Chloro-2,3-Epoxypropane
....	2-Chloro-6-nitrotoluene
....	4-Chloro-2-nitrotoluene
....	Chloro-ortho-nitrotoluene
....	2-Chloro-5-trifluoromethylnitrobenzene
....	para-Chlorobenzyl chloride, liquid or solid
....	Chlorodinitrobenzenes, liquid or solid
....	1-Chloroheptane
....	1-Chlorohexane
....	Chloronitroanilines
....	Chloronitrotoluenes, *liquid*
....	Chloronitrotoluenes, *solid*
....	1-Chlorooctane
PP	Chlorophenolates, liquid
PP	Chlorophenolates, solid
....	Chlorophenyltrichlorosilane
....	Chloropicrin
....	ortho-Chlorotoluene
PP	Chlorpyriphos
PP	Chlorthiophos
....	Cocculus
....	Coconitrile
....	Copper acetoarsenite
....	Copper arsenite
PP	Copper chloride
PP	Copper chloride (solution)
PP	Copper cyanide
PP	Copper metal powder
PP	Copper sulphate, anhydrous, hydrates
....	Coumachlor

S.M.P. (1)	Marine Pollutant (2)
PP	Coumaphos
	Creosote salts
PP	Cresyl diphenyl phosphate
	Crotonaldehyde, stabilized
	Crotonic aldehyde, stabilized
	Crotoxyphos
	Cupric arsenite
PP	Cupric chloride
PP	Cupric cyanide
PP	Cupric sulfate
	Cupriethylenediamine solution
PP	Cuprous chloride
	Cyanide mixtures
	Cyanide solutions
	Cyanides, inorganic, n.o.s.
	Cyanogen bromide
	Cyanogen chloride, inhibited
	Cyanogen chloride, stabilized
	Cyanophos
PP	1,5,9-Cyclododecatriene
	Cycloheptane
PP	Cyhexatin
PP	Cymenes (o-;m-;p-)
PP	Cypermethrin
PP	DDT
	Decycloxytetrahydrothiophene dioxide
	Decyl acrylate
	DEF
	Desmedipham
	Di-allate
	Di-n-Butyl phthalate
	1,4-Di-tert-butylbenzene
PP	Dialifos
	4,4´-Diaminodiphenylmethane
PP	Diazinon
	1,3-Dibromobenzene
PP	Dichlofenthion
	Dichloroanilines
	1,3-Dichlorobenzene
	1,4-Dichlorobenzene
	Dichlorobenzene (meta-; para-)
	2,2-Dichlorodiethyl ether
	Dichlorodimethyl ether, symmetrical
	Di-(2-chloroethyl) ether
	1,1-Dichloroethylene, inhibited
	1,6-Dichlorohexane
	2,4-Dichlorophenol
	Dichlorophenyltrichlorosilane
	1,3-Dichloropropene
PP	Dichlorvos
PP	Diclofop-methyl
	Dicrotophos
PP	Dieldrin
	Diisopropylbenzenes

S.M.P. (1)	Marine Pollutant (2)
	Diisopropylnaphthalenes, mixed isomers
PP	Dimethoate
	Dimethyl Disulphide
PP	N,N-Dimethyldodecylamine
	Dimethylhydrazine, symmetrical
	Dimethylhydrazine, unsymmetrical
	Dinitro-o-cresol, *solid*
	Dinitro-o-cresol, *solution*
	Dinitrochlorobenzenes, liquid or solid
	Dinitrophenol, *dry or wetted with less than 15 percent water, by mass*
	Dinitrophenol solutions
	Dinitrophenol, *wetted with not less than 15 percent water, by mass*
	Dinitrophenolates *alkali metals, dry or wetted with less than 15 per cent water, by mass*
	Dinitrophenolates, *wetted with not less than 15 percent water, by mass*
	Dinitrotoluenes, Liquid
	Dinitrotoluenes, Molton
	Dintrotoluenes, Solid
	Dinobuton
	Dinoseb
	Dinoseb acetate
	Dioxacarb
	Dioxathion
	Dipentene
	Diphacinone
	Diphenyl
PP	Diphenylamine chloroarsine
PP	Diphenylchloroarsine, solid *or* liquid
	2,4-Di-tert-butylphenol
PP	2,6-Di-tert-Butylphenol
	Disulfoton
	DNOC
	DNOC (pesticide)
	Dodecene (except 1-dodecene).
	Dodecyl diphenyl oxide disulphonate
PP	Dodecyl hydroxypropyl sulfide
	1-Dodecylamine
PP	Dodecylphenol
	Drazoxolon
	Edifenphos
PP	Endosulfan
PP	Endrin
	Epibromohydrin
	Epichlorohydrin
PP	EPN
PP	Esfenvalerate
PP	Ethion
	Ethoprophos
	Ethyl fluid
	Ethyl mercaptan
	2-Ethyl-3-propylacrolein
	Ethyl tetraphosphate
	Ethyldichloroarsine

S.M.P. (1)	Marine Pollutant (2)
....	2-Ethylhexaldehyde
....	Ethylene dibromide and methyl bromide mixtures, liquid
....	2-Ethylhexyl nitrate
....	Fenamiphos
PP..........................	Fenbutatin oxide
PP..........................	Fenchlorazole-ethyl
PP..........................	Fenitrothion
PP..........................	Fenoxapro-ethyl
PP..........................	Fenoxaprop-P-ethyl
PP..........................	Fenpropathrin
....	Fensulfothion
PP..........................	Fenthion
PP..........................	Fentin acetate
PP..........................	Fentin hydroxide
....	Ferric arsenate
....	Ferric arsenite
....	Ferrous arsenate
PP..........................	Fonofos
....	Formetanate
PP..........................	Furathiocarb (ISO)
PP..........................	gamma-BHC
....	Gasoline, leaded
PP..........................	Heptachlor
....	n-Heptaldehyde
....	Heptanes
....	Heptenophos
....	normal-Heptyl chloride
....	n-Heptylbenzene
PP..........................	Hexachlorobutadiene
PP..........................	1,3-Hexachlorobutadiene
....	Hexaethyl tetraphosphate, *liquid*
....	Hexaethyl tetraphosphate, *solid*
....	Hexane
....	normal-Hexyl chloride
....	n-Hexylbenzene
....	Hydrocyanic acid, anhydrous, stabilized containing less than 3% water
....	Hydrocyanic acid, anhydrous, stabilized, containing less than 3% water and absorbed in a porous inert material
....	Hydrocyanic acid, aqueous solutions *not more than 20% hydrocyanic acid*
....	Hydrogen cyanide solution in alcohol, *with not more than 45% hydrogen cyanide*
....	Hydrogen cyanide, stabilized *with less than 3% water*
....	Hydrogen cyanide, stabilized *with less than 3% water and absorbed in a porous inert material*
....	Hydroxydimethylbenzenes, liquid or solid
....	Hypochlorite solutions
....	Ioxynil
....	Isobenzan
....	Isobutyl butyrate
....	Isobutylbenzene
....	Isodecyl acrylate
....	Isodecyl diphenyl phosphate
....	Isofenphos

S.M.P. (1)	Marine Pollutant (2)
....	Isooctane
....	Isooctyl nitrate
....	Isoprene, stabilized
....	Isoprocarb
....	Isotetramethylbenzene
PP........................	Isoxathion
....	Lead acetate
....	Lead arsenates
....	Lead arsenites
....	Lead compounds, soluble, n.o.s.
....	Lead cyanide
....	Lead nitrate
....	Lead perchlorate, solid or solution
....	Lead tetraethyl
....	Lead tetramethyl
PP........................	Lindane
....	Linuron
....	London Purple
....	Magnesium arsenate
....	Malathion
....	Mancozeb (ISO)
....	Maneb
....	Maneb preparation, stabilized against self-heating
....	Maneb preparations *with not less than 60% maneb*
....	Maneb stabilized or Maneb preparations, stabilized *against self-heating*
....	Manganese ethylene-1,2-bisdithiocarbamate
....	Manganeseethylene-1,2-bisdithiocarbamate, stabilized against self-heating
....	Mecarbam
....	Mephosfolan
....	Mercaptodimethur
PP........................	Mercuric acetate
PP........................	Mercuric ammonium chloride
PP........................	Mercuric arsenate
PP........................	Mercuric benzoate
PP........................	Mercuric bisulphate
PP........................	Mercuric bromide
PP........................	Mercuric chloride
PP........................	Mercuric cyanide
PP........................	Mercuric gluconate
....	Mercuric iodide
PP........................	Mercuric nitrate
PP........................	Mercuric oleate
PP........................	Mercuric oxide
PP........................	Mercuric oxycyanide, desensitized
PP........................	Mercuric potassium cyanide
PP........................	Mercuric Sulphate
PP........................	Mercuric thiocyanate
PP........................	Mercurol
PP........................	Mercurous acetate
PP........................	Mercurous bisulphate
PP........................	Mercurous bromide
PP........................	Mercurous chloride

MARINE POLLUTANTS

S.M.P. (1)	Marine Pollutant (2)
PP	Mercurous nitrate
PP	Mercurous salicylate
PP	Mercurous sulphate
PP	Mercury acetates
PP	Mercury ammonium chloride
PP	Mercury based pesticide, liquid, flammable, toxic
PP	Mercury based pesticide, liquid, toxic, flammable
PP	Mercury based pesticide, liquid, toxic
PP	Mercury based pesticide, solid, toxic
PP	Mercury benzoate
PP	Mercury bichloride
PP	Mercury bisulphates
PP	Mercury bromides
PP	Mercury compounds, liquid, n.o.s.
PP	Mercury compounds, solid, n.o.s.
PP	Mercury cyanide
PP	Mercury gluconate
PP	NMercury (I) (mercurous) compounds (pesticides)
PP	NMercury (II) (mercuric) compounds (pesticides)
	Mercury iodide
PP	Mercury nucleate
PP	Mercury oleate
PP	Mercury oxide
PP	Mercury oxycyanide, desensitized
PP	Mercury potassium cyanide
PP	Mercury potassium iodide
PP	Mercury salicylate
PP	Mercury sulfates
PP	Mercury thiocyanate
	Mesitylene
	Metam-sodium
	Methamidophos
	Methanethiol
	Methidathion
	Methomyl
	ortho-Methoxyaniline
	Methyl bromide and ethylene dibromide mixtures, liquid
	Methyl disulphide
	1-Methyl-2-ethylbenzene
	Methyl mercaptan
	2-Methyl-2-phenylpropane
	3-Methylacrolein, stabilized
	N-Methylaniline
	Methylchlorobenzenes
	Methylcyclohexane
	Methyldinitrobenzenes, liquid
	Methyldinitrobenzenes, molten
	Methyldinitrobenzenes, solid
	Methyldithiomethane
	2-Methylheptane
	Methylnitrophenols
	2-Methylpentane
	alpha-Methylstyrene
	Methyltrithion

S.M.P. (1)	Marine Pollutant (2)
	Methylvinylbenzenes, inhibited
PP	Mevinphos
	Mexacarbate
	Mirex
	Monocratophos
	Motor fuel anti-knock mixtures
	Motor fuel anti-knock mixtures or compunds
	Nabam
	Naled
	Naphthalene, crude or Naphthalene, refined
	Napthalene, molten
PP	Nickel carbonyl
PP	Nickel cyanide
PP	Nickel tetracarbonyl
	3-Nitro-4-chlorobenzotrifluoride
	Nitrobenzene
	Nitrobenzotrifluorides, liquid or solid
	Nitroxylenes, liquid or solid
	Nonanes
	Nonylphenol
	normal-Octaldehyde
	Octanes
	Oleylamine
PP	Organotin compounds, liquid, n.o.s.
PP	Organotin compounds, (pesticides)
PP	Organotin compounds, solid, n.o.s.
PP	Organotin pesticides, liquid, flammable, toxic, n.o.s. *flash point less than 23 deg.C*
PP	Organotin pesticides, liquid, toxic, flam-mable, n.o.s.
PP	Organotin pesticides, liquid, toxic, n.o.s.
PP	Organotin pesticides, solid, toxic, n.o.s.
	Orthoarsenic acid
PP	Osmium tetroxide
	Oxamyl
	Oxydisulfoton
	Paraoxon
PP	Parathion
PP	Parathion-methyl
PP	PCBs
	Pentachloroethane
PP	Pentachlorophenol
	Pentalin
	n-Pentylbenzene
	Perchloroethylene
	Perchloromethylmercaptan
	Petrol, leaded
PP	Phenarsazine chloride
	d-Phenothrin
PP	Phenthoate
	1-Phenylbutane
	2-Phenylbutane
	Phenylcyclohexane
	Phenylamine
PP	Phenylmercuric acetate

S.M.P. (1)	Marine Pollutant (2)
PP	Phenylmercuric compounds, n.o.s.
PP	Phenylmercuric hydroxide
PP	Phenylmercuric nitrate
PP	Phorate
PP	Phosaione
	Phosmet
PP	Phosphamidon
PP	Phosphorus, white, molten
PP	Phosphorus, white or yellow dry or under water or in solution
PP	Phosphorus white, or yellow, molten
PP	Phosphorus, yellow, molten
	Pindone (and salts of)
	Pine Oil
	alpha-Pinene
	Pirimicarb
PP	Pirimiphos-ethyl
PP	Polychlorinated biphenyls
PP	Polyhalogenated biphenyls, liquid or Ter-phenyls liquid
PP	Polyhalogenated biphenyls, solid or Ter-phenyls solid
PP	Potassium cuprocyanide
	Potassium cyanide, solid
	Potassium cyanide, solution
PP	Potassium cyanocuprate (I)
PP	Potassium cyanomercurate
PP	Potassium mercuric iodide
	Promecarb
	Propachlor
	Propaphos
	Propenal, inhibited
	Propenoic acid, stabilized
	Propenyl alcohol
	Propoxur
	Propylene Tetramer
	Prothoate
	Prussic acid, anhydrous, stabilized
	Prussic acid, anhydrous, stabilized, absorbed in a porous inert material
PP	Pyrazophos
	Quinalphos
PP	Quizalofop
PP	Quizalofop-p-ethyl
	Rotenone
	Salithion
PP	Silafluofen
	Silver arsenite
	Silver cyanide
	Silver orthoarsenite
PP	Sodium copper cyanide, solid
PP	Sodium copper cyanide solution
PP	Sodium cuprocyanide, solid
PP	Sodium cuprocyanide, solution
	Sodium cyanide, solid
	Sodium cyanide, solution

S.M.P. (1)	Marine Pollutant (2)
....	Sodium dinitro-o-cresolate, *dry or wetted* with less than 15 percent water, by mass
....	Sodium dinitro-ortho-cresolate, wetted *with not less than 15 percent water, by mass*
....	Sodium hypochlorite solution
PP..........................	Sodium pentachlorophenate
....	Strychnine *or* Strychnine salts
....	Sulfotep
PP..........................	Sulprophos
....	Tallow nitrile
....	Temephos
....	TEPP
PP..........................	Terbufos
....	Tetrabromoethane
....	Tetrabromomethane
....	1,1,2,2-Tetrachloroethane
....	Tetrachloroethylene
....	Tetrachloromethane
....	Tetraethyl dithiopyrophosphate
PP..........................	Tetraethyl lead, liquid
....	Tetramethrin
....	Tetramethyllead
....	Tetrapropylene
....	Thallium chlorate
....	Thallium compounds, n.o.s.
....	Thallium compounds (pesticides)
....	Thallium nitrate
....	Thallium sulfate
....	Thallous chlorate
....	Thiocarbonyl tetrachloride
....	Toluidines, liquid
....	Toluidines, Solid
....	Triaryl phosphates, isopropylated
PP..........................	Triaryl phosphates, n.o.s.
....	Triazophos
....	Tribromomethane
PP..........................	Tributyltin compounds
....	Trichlorfon
PP..........................	1,2,3-Trichlorobenzene
....	Trichlorobenzenes, liquid
....	Trichlorobutene
....	Trichlorobutylene
....	Trichloromethane sulphuryl chloride
....	Trichloromethyl sulphochloride
....	Trichloronat
....	Tricresyl phosphate (less than 1% ortho-isomer)
PP..........................	Tricresyl phosphate, not less than 1% ortho-isomer but not more than 3% orthoisomer
PP..........................	Tricresyl phosphate *with more than 3 per cent ortho isomer*
....	Triethylbenzene
....	Triisopropylated phenyl phosphates
....	1,3,5-Trimethylbenzene
....	Trimethylene dichloride
....	2,2,4-Trimethylpentane

S.M.P. (1)	Marine Pollutant (2)
....	Triphenyl phosphate/tert-butylated triphenyl phosphates mixtures containing 5% to 10% triphenyl phosphates
PP	Triphenyl phosphate/tert-butylated triphenyl phosphates mixtures containing 10% to 48% triphenyl phosphates
PP	Triphenylphosphate
PP	Triphenyltin compounds
....	Tripropylene
....	Tritolyl phosphate (less than 1% ortho-isomer)
PP	Tritolyl phosphate (not less than 1% ortho-isomer)
....	Trixylenyl phosphate
....	Turpentine
....	Vinylidene chloride, inhibited
....	Vinylidene chloride, stabilized
....	Warfarin (and salts of)
PP	White phosphorus, dry
PP	White phosphorus, wet
....	White spirit, low (15-20%) aromatic
PP	Yellow phosphorus, dry
PP	Yellow phosphorus, wet
....	Zinc bromide
....	Zinc Chloride, Anhydrous
....	Zinc Chloride Solution
....	Zinc cyanide

Special Provisions

§172.102 Special provisions.

(a) **General.** When Column 7 of the §172.101 Table refers to a special provision for a hazardous material, the meaning and requirements of that provision are as set forth in this section. When a special provision specifies packaging or packaging requirements—

(1) The special provision is in addition to the standard requirements for all packagings prescribed in §173.24 of this subchapter and any other applicable packaging requirements in subparts A and B of part 173 of this subchapter; and

(2) To the extent a special provision imposes limitations or additional requirements on the packaging provisions set forth in Column 8 of the §172.101 Table, packagings must conform to the requirements of the special provision.

(b) **Description of codes for special provisions.** Special provisions contain packaging provisions, prohibitions, exceptions from requirements for particular quantities or forms of materials and requirements or prohibitions applicable to specific modes of transportation, as follows:

(1) A code consisting only of numbers (for example, "11") is multi-modal in application and may apply to bulk and non-bulk packagings.

(2) A code containing the letter "A" refers to a special provision which applies only to transportation by aircraft.

(3) A code containing the letter "B" refers to a special provision that applies only to bulk packaging requirements. Unless otherwise provided in this subchapter, these special provisions do not apply to UN, IM Specification portable tanks or IBCs.

(4) A code containing the letters "IB" or "IP" refers to a special provision that applies only to transportation in IBCs.

(5) A code containing the letter "N" refers to a special provision which applies only to non-bulk packaging requirements.

(6) A code containing the letter "R" refers to a special provision which applies only to transportation by rail.

(7) A code containing the letter "T" refers to a special provision which applies only to transportation in UN or IM Specification portable tanks.

(8) A code containing the letters "TP" refers to a portable tank special provision for UN or IM Specification portable tanks that is in addition to those provided by the portable tank instructions or the requirements in part 178 of this subchapter.

(9) A code containing the letter "W" refers to a special provision that applies only to transportation by water.

(c) **Tables of special provisions.** The following tables list, and set forth the requirements of, the special provisions referred to in Column 7 of the §172.101 Table.

(1) *Numeric provisions.* These provisions are multi-modal and apply to bulk and non-bulk packagings:

Code/Special provisions

1   This material is poisonous by inhalation (see §171.8 of this subchapter) in Hazard Zone A (see §173.116(a) or §173.133(a) of this subchapter), and must be described as an inhalation hazard under the provisions of this subchapter.

2   This material is poisonous by inhalation (see §171.8 of this subchapter) in Hazard Zone B (see §173.116(a) or §173.133(a) of this subchapter), and must be described as an inhalation hazard under the provisions of this subchapter.

3   This material is poisonous by inhalation (see §171.8 of this subchapter) in Hazard Zone C (see §173.116(a) of this subchapter), and must be described as an inhalation hazard under the provisions of this subchapter.

4   This material is poisonous by inhalation (see §171.8 of this subchapter) in Hazard Zone D (see §173.116(a) of this subchapter), and must be described as an inhalation hazard under the provisions of this subchapter.

5   If this material meets the definition for a material poisonous by inhalation (see §171.8 of this subchapter), a shipping name must be selected which identifies the inhalation hazard, in Division 2.3 or Division 6.1, as appropriate.

6   This material is poisonous-by-inhalation and must be described as an inhalation hazard under the provisions of this subchapter.

8   A hazardous substance that is not a hazardous waste may be shipped under the shipping description "Other regulated substances, liquid or solid, n.o.s.", as appropriate. In addition, for solid materials, special provision B54 applies.

9   Packaging for certain PCBs for disposal and storage is prescribed by EPA in 40 CFR 761.60 and 761.65.

11   The hazardous material must be packaged as either a liquid or a solid, as appropriate, depending on its physical form at 55°C (131°F) at atmospheric pressure.

12   In concentrations greater than 40 percent, this material has strong oxidizing properties and is capable of starting fires in contact with combustible materials. If appropriate, a package containing this material must conform to the additional labeling requirements of §172.402 of this subchapter.

13   The words "Inhalation Hazard" shall be entered on each shipping paper in association with the shipping description, shall be marked on each non-bulk package in association with the proper shipping name and identification number, and shall be marked on two opposing sides of each bulk package. Size of marking on bulk package must conform to §172.302(b) of this subchapter. The requirements of §§172.203(m) and 172.505 of this subchapter do not apply.

14   Motor fuel antiknock mixtures are:

          a.   Mixtures of one or more organic lead mixtures (such as tetraethyl lead, triethylmethyl lead, diethyldimethyl lead, ethyltrimethyl lead, and tetramethyl lead) with one or more halogen compounds (such as ethylene dibromide and ethylene dichloride), hydrocarbon solvents or other equally efficient stabilizers; or

b.   tetraethyl lead.

15   This entry applies to "Chemical kits" and "First aid kits" containing one or more compatible items of hazardous materials in boxes, cases, etc. that, for example, are used for medical, analytical, diagnostic, testing, or repair purposes. Kits that are carried on board transport vehicles for first aid or operating purposes are not subject to the requirements of this subchapter.

16   This description applies to smokeless powder and other solid propellants that are used as powder for small arms and have been classed as Division 1.3C, 1.4C and Division 4.1 in accordance with §173.56 of this subchapter.

19   For domestic transportation only, the identification number "UN1075" may be used in place of the identification number specified in Column (4) of the §172.101 Table. The identification number used must be consistent on package markings, shipping papers and emergency response information.

21   This material must be stabilized by appropriate means (e.g., addition of chemical inhibitor, purging to remove oxygen) to prevent dangerous polymerization (see §173.21(f) of this subchapter).

22   If the hazardous material is in dispersion in organic liquid, the organic liquid must have a flash point above 50°C (122°F).

23   This material may be transported under the provisions of Division 4.1 only if it is so packed that the percentage of diluent will not fall below that stated in the shipping description at any time during transport. Quantities of not more than 500 g per package with not less than 10 percent water by mass may also be classed in Division 4.1, provided a negative test result is obtained when tested in accordance with test series 6(c) of the UN Manual of Tests and Criteria (IBR, see §171.7 of this subchapter).

24   Alcoholic beverages containing more than 70 percent alcohol by volume must be transported as materials in Packing Group II. Alcoholic beverages containing more than 24 percent but not more than 70 percent alcohol by volume must be transported as materials in Packing Group III.

26   This entry does not include ammonium permanganate, the transport of which is prohibited except when approved by the Associate Administrator.

28   The dihydrated sodium salt of dichloroisocyanuric acid does not meet the criteria for inclusion in Division 5.1 (Oxidizer) and is not subject to the requirements of this subchapter unless meeting the criteria for inclusion in another class or division.

30   Sulfur is not subject to the requirements of this subchapter if transported in a non-bulk packaging or if formed to a specific shape (for example, prills, granules, pellets, pastilles, or flakes). A bulk packaging containing sulfur is not subject to the placarding requirements of subpart F of this part, if it is marked with the appropriate identification number as required bysubpart D of this part. Molten sulfur must be marked as required by §172.325 of this subchapter.

31   Materials which have undergone sufficient heat treatment to render them non-hazardous are not subject to the requirements of this subchapter.

32   Polymeric beads and molding compounds may be made from polystyrene, poly(methyl methacrylate) or other polymeric material.

33   Ammonium nitrates and mixtures of an inorganic nitrite with an ammonium salt are prohibited.

34   The commercial grade of calcium nitrate fertilizer, when consisting mainly of a double salt (calcium nitrate and ammonium nitrate) containing not more than 10 percent ammonium nitrate and at least 12 percent water of crystallization, is not subject to the requirements of this subchapter.

35   Antimony sulphides and oxides which do not contain more than 0.5 percent of arsenic calculated on the total mass do not meet the definition of Division 6.1.

37   Unless it can be demonstrated by testing that the sensitivity of the substance in its frozen state is no greater than in its liquid state, the substance must remain liquid during normal transport conditions. It must not freeze at temperatures above -15°C (5°F).

38   If this material shows a violent effect in laboratory tests involving heating under confinement, the labeling requirements of Special Provision 53 apply, and the material must be packaged in accordance with packing method OP6 in §173.225 of this subchapter. If the SADT of the technically pure substance is higher than 75°C, the technically pure substance and formulations derived from it are not self-reactive materials and, if not meeting any other hazard class, are not subject to the requirements of this subchapter.

39   This substance may be carried under provisions other than those of Class 1 only if it is so packed that the percentage of water will not fall below that stated at any time during transport. When phlegmatized with water and inorganic inert material, the content of urea nitrate must not exceed 75 percent by mass and the mixture should not be capable of being detonated by test 1(a)(i) or test 1(a) (ii) in the UN Manual of Tests and Criteria (IBR, see §171.7 of this subchapter).

40   Polyester resin kits consist of two components: A base material (either Class 3 or Division 4.1, Packing Group II or III) and an activator (organic peroxide), each separately packed in an inner packaging. The organic peroxide must be type D, E, or F, not requiring temperature control. The components may be placed in the same outer packaging provided they will not interact dangerously in the event of leakage. The Packing Group assigned will be II or III, according to the classification criteria for either Class 3 or Division 4.1, as appropriate, applied to the base material. Additionally, unless otherwise excepted in this subchapter, polyester

resin kits must be packaged in specification combination packagings based on the performance level of the base material contained within the kit.

41   This material at the Packing Group II hazard criteria level may be transported in Large Packagings.

43   The membrane filters, including paper separators and coating or backing materials, that are present in transport, must not be able to propagate a detonation as tested by one of the tests de scribed in the UN Manual of Tests and Criteria, Part I, Test series 1(a) (IBR, see §171.7 of this subchapter). On the basis of the results of suitable burning rate tests, and taking into account the standard tests in the UN Manual of Tests and Criteria, Part III, subsection 33.2.1 (IBR, see §171.7 of this subchapter), nitrocellulose membrane filters in the form in which they are to be transported that do not meet the criteria for a Division 4.1 material are not subject to the requirements of this subchapter. Packagings must be so constructed that explosion is not possible by reason of increased internal pressure. Nitrocellulose membrane filters covered by this entry, each with a mass not exceeding 0.5 g, are not subject to the requirements of this subchapter when contained individually in an article or a sealed packet.

44   The formulation must be prepared so that it remains homogeneous and does not separate during transport. Formulations with low nitrocellulose contents and neither showing dangerous properties when tested for their ability to detonate, deflagrate or explode when heated under defined confinement by the appropriate test methods and criteria in the UN Manual of Tests and Criteria (IBR, see §171.7 of this subchapter), nor classed as a Division 4.1 (flammable solid) when tested in accordance with the procedures specified in §173.124 of this subchapter (chips, if necessary, crushed and sieved to a particle size of less than 1.25 mm), are not subject to the requirements of this subchapter.

45   Temperature should be maintained between 18°C (64.4°F) and 40°C (104°F). Tanks containing solidified methacrylic acid must not be reheated during transport.

46   This material must be packed in accordance with packing method OP6 (see §173.225 of this subchapter). During transport, it must be protected from direct sunshine and stored (or kept) in a cool and well-ventilated place, away from all sources of heat.

47   Mixtures of solids that are not subject to this subchapter and flammable liquids may be transported under this entry without first applying the classification criteria of Division 4.1, provided there is no free liquid visible at the time the material is loaded or at the time the packaging or transport unit is closed. Except when the liquids are fully absorbed in solid material contained in sealed bags, for single packagings, each packaging must correspond to a design type that has passed a leakproofness test at the Packing Group II level. Small inner packagings consisting of sealed packets and articles containing less than 10 mL of a Class 3 liquid in Packing Group II or III absorbed onto a solid material are not subject to this subchapter provided there is no free liquid in the packet or article.

48   Mixtures of solids that are not subject to this subchapter and toxic liquids may be transported under this entry without first applying the classification criteria of Division 6.1, provided there is no free liquid visible at the time the material is loaded or at the time the packaging or transport unit is closed. For single packagings, each packaging must correspond to a design type that has passed a leakproofness test at the Packing Group II level. This entry may not be used for solids containing a Packing Group I liquid.

49   Mixtures of solids that are not subject to this subchapter and corrosive liquids may be transported under this entry without first applying the classification criteria of Class 8, provided there is no free liquid visible at the time the material is loaded or at the time the packaging or transport unit is closed. For single packagings, each packaging must correspond to a design type that has passed a leakproofness test at the Packing Group II level.

50   Cases, cartridge, empty with primer which are made of metallic or plastic casings and meeting the classification criteria of Division 1.4 are not regulated for domestic transportation.

51   This description applies to items previously described as "Toy propellant devices, Class C" and includes reloadable kits. Model rocket motors containing 30 grams or less propellant are classed as Division 1.4S and items containing more than 30 grams of propellant but not more than 62.5 grams of propellant are classed as Division 1.4C.

52   This entry may only be used for substances that are too insensitive for acceptance into Class 1 (explosive) when tested in accordance with Test Series 2 in the UN Manual of Tests and Criteria, Part I (incorporated by reference; see §171.7 of this subchapter).

53   Packages of these materials must bear the subsidiary risk label, "EXPLOSIVE", and the subsidiary hazard class/division must be entered in parentheses immediately following the primary hazard class in the shipping description, unless otherwise provided in this subchapter or through an approval issued by the Associate Administrator, or the competent authority of the country of origin. A copy of the approval shall accompany the shipping papers.

54   Maneb or maneb preparations not meeting the definition of Division 4.3 or any other hazard class are not subject to the requirements of this subchapter when transported by motor vehicle, rail car, or aircraft.

55   This device must be approved in accordance with §173.56 of this subchapter by the Associate Administrator.

56   A means to interrupt and prevent detonation of the detonator from initiating the detonating cord must be installed between each electric detonator and the detonating cord ends of the jet perforating guns before the charged jet perforating guns are offered for transportation.

57   Maneb or Maneb preparations stabilized against self-heating need not be classified in Division 4.2 when it can be demonstrated by testing that a volume of 1 m^3 of substance does not self-ignite and that the temperature at the center of the sample does not exceed 200°C, when the sample is maintained at a temperature of not less than 75°C ± 2°C for a period of 24 hours, in accordance with procedures set forth for testing self-heating materials in the UN Manual of Tests and Criteria (IBR, see §171.7 of this subchapter).

58 Aqueous solutions of Division 5.1 inorganic solid nitrate substances are considered as not meeting the criteria of Division 5.1 if the concentration of the substances in solution at the minimum temperature encountered in transport is not greater than 80% of the saturation limit.

59 Ferrocerium, stabilized against corrosion, with a minimum iron content of 10 percent is not subject to the requirements of this subchapter.

61 A chemical oxygen generator is spent if its means of ignition and all or a part of its chemical contents have been expended.

62 Oxygen generators (see §171.8 of this subchapter) are not authorized for transportation under this entry.

64 The group of alkali metals includes lithium, sodium, potassium, rubidium, and caesium.

65 The group of alkaline earth metals includes magnesium, calcium, strontium, and barium.

66 Formulations of these substances containing not less than 30 percent non-volatile, non-flammable phlegmatizer are not subject to this subchapter.

70 Black powder that has been classed in accordance with the requirements of §173.56 of this subchapter may be reclassed and offered for domestic transportation as a Division 4.1 material if it is offered for transportation and transported in accordance with the limitations and packaging requirements of §173.170 of this subchapter.

74 During transport, this material must be protected from direct sunshine and stored or kept in a cool and well-ventilated place, away from all sources of heat.

78 This entry may not be used to describe compressed air which contains more than 23.5 percent oxygen. Compressed air containing greater than 23.5 percent oxygen must be shipped using the description "Compressed gas, oxidizing, n.o.s., UN3156."

79 This entry may not be used for mixtures that meet the definition for oxidizing gas.

81 Polychlorinated biphenyl items, as defined in 40 CFR 761.3, for which specification packagings are impractical, may be packaged in non-specification packagings meeting the general packaging requirements of subparts A and B of part 173 of this subchapter. Alternatively, the item itself may be used as a packaging if it meets the general packaging requirements of subparts A and B of part 173 of this subchapter.

101 The name of the particular substance or article must be specified.

102   The ends of the detonating cord must be tied fast so that the explosive cannot escape. The articles may be transported as in Division 1.4 Compatibility Group D (1.4D) if all of the conditions specified in §173.63(a) of this subchapter are met.

103   Detonators which will not mass detonate and undergo only limited propagation in the shipping package may be assigned to 1.4B classification code. Mass detonate means that more than 90 percent of the devices tested in a package explode practically simultaneously. Limited propagation means that if one detonator near the center of a shipping package is exploded, the aggregate weight of explosives, excluding ignition and delay charges, in this and all additional detonators in the outside packaging that explode may not exceed 25 grams.

105   The word "Agents" may be used instead of "Explosives" when approved by the Associate Administrator.

106   The recognized name of the particular explosive may be specified in addition to the type.

107   The classification of the substance is expected to vary especially with the particle size and packaging but the border lines have not been experimentally determined; appropriate classifications should be verified following the test procedures in §§173.57 and 173.58 of this subchapter.

108   Fireworks must be so constructed and packaged that loose pyrotechnic composition will not be present in packages during transportation.

109   Rocket motors must be nonpropulsive in transportation unless approved in accordance with §173.56 of this subchapter. A rocket motor to be considered "nonpropulsive" must be capable of unrestrained burning and must not appreciably move in any direction when ignited by any means.

110   Fire extinguishers transported under UN1044 and oxygen cylinders transported for emergency use under UN1072 may include installed actuating cartridges (cartridges, power device of Division 1.4C or 1.4S), without changing the classification of Division 2.2, provided the aggregate quantity of deflagrating (propellant) explosives does not exceed 3.2 grams per cylinder. Oxygen cylinders with installed actuating cartridges as prepared for transportation must have an effective means of preventing inadvertent activation.

111   Explosive substances of Division 1.1 Compatibility Group A (1.1A) are forbidden for transportation if dry or not desensitized, unless incorporated in a device.

113   The sample must be given a tentative approval by an agency or laboratory in accordance with §173.56 of this subchapter.

114   Jet perforating guns, charged, oil well, without detonator may be reclassed to Division 1.4 Compatibility Group D (1.4D) if the following conditions are met:

       a.   The total weight of the explosive contents of the shaped charges assembled in the guns does not exceed 90.5 kg (200 pounds) per vehicle; and

b.   The guns are packaged in accordance with Packing Method US1 as specified in §173.62 of this subchapter.

115   Boosters with detonator, detonator assemblies and boosters with detonators in which the total explosive charge per unit does not exceed 25 g, and which will not mass detonate and undergo only limited propagation in the shipping package may be assigned to 1.4B classification code. Mass detonate means more than 90 percent of the devices tested in a package explode practically simultaneously. Limited propagation means that if one booster near the center of the package is exploded, the aggregate weight of explosives, excluding ignition and delay charges, in this and all additional boosters in the outside packaging that explode may not exceed 25 g.

116   Fuzes, detonating may be classed in Division 1.4 if the fuzes do not contain more than 25 g of explosive per fuze and are made and packaged so that they will not cause functioning of other fuzes, explosives or other explosive devices if one of the fuzes detonates in a shipping packaging or in adjacent packages.

117   If shipment of the explosive substance is to take place at a time that freezing weather is anticipated, the water contained in the explosive substance must be mixed with denatured alcohol so that freezing will not occur.

118   This substance may not be transported under the provisions of Division 4.1 unless specifically authorized by the Associate Administrator (see UN0143 or UN0150 as appropriate).

119   This substance, when in quantities of not more than 11.5 kg (25.3 pounds), with not less than 10 percent water, by mass, also may be classed as Division 4.1, provided a negative test result is obtained when tested in accordance with test series 6(c) of the UN Manual of Tests and Criteria (IBR, see §171.7 of this subchapter).

120   The phlegmatized substance must be significantly less sensitive than dry PETN.

121   This substance, when containing less alcohol, water or phlegmatizer than specified, may not be transported unless approved by the Associate Administrator.

123   Any explosives, blasting, type C containing chlorates must be segregated from explosives containing ammonium nitrate or other ammonium salts.

125   Lactose or glucose or similar materials may be used as a phlegmatizer provided that the substance contains not less than 90%, by mass, of phlegmatizer. These mixtures may be classified in Division 4.1 when tested in accordance with test series 6(c) of the UN Manual of Tests and Criteria (IBR, see §171.7 of this subchapter) and approved by the Associate Administrator. Testing must be conducted on at least three packages as prepared for transport. Mixtures containing at least 98%, by mass, of phlegmatizer are not subject to the requirements of this subchapter. Packages containing mixtures with not less than 90% by mass, of phlegmatizer need not bear a POISON subsidiary risk label.

127 Mixtures containing oxidizing and organic materials transported under this entry may not meet the definition and criteria of a Class 1 material. (See §173.50 of this subchapter.)

128 Regardless of the provisions of §172.101(c)(12), aluminum smelting by-products and aluminum remelting by-products described under this entry, meeting the definition of Class 8, Packing Group II and III may be classed as a Division 4.3 material and transported under this entry. The presence of a Class 8 hazard must be communicated as required by this Part for subsidiary hazards.

129 These materials may not be classified and transported unless authorized by the Associate Administrator on the basis of results from Series 2 Test and a Series 6(c) Test from the UN Manual of Tests and Criteria (IBR, see §171.7 of this subchapter) on packages as prepared for transport. The packing group assignment and packaging must be approved by the Associate Administrator on the basis of the criteria in §173.21 of this subchapter and the package type used for the Series 6(c) test.

130 "Batteries, dry, sealed, n.o.s.," commonly referred to as dry batteries, are hermetically sealed and generally utilize metals (other than lead) and/or carbon as electrodes. These batteries are typically used for portable power applications. The rechargeable (and some non-rechargeable) types have gelled alkaline electrolytes (rather than acidic) making it difficult for them to generate hydrogen or oxygen when overcharged and therefore, differentiating them from non-spillable batteries. Dry batteries specifically covered by another entry in the §172.101 Table must be transported in accordance with the requirements applicable to that entry. For example, nickel-metal hydride batteries transported by vessel in certain quantities are covered by another entry (see Batteries, nickel-metal hydride, UN3496). Dry batteries not specifically covered by another entry in the §172.101 Table are covered by this entry (i.e., Batteries, dry, sealed, n.o.s.) and are not subject to requirements of this subchapter except for the following:

(a) *Incident reporting.* For transportation by aircraft, a telephone report in accordance with §171.15(a) is required if a fire, violent rupture, explosion or dangerous evolution of heat (i.e., an amount of heat sufficient to be dangerous to packaging or personal safety to include charring of packaging, melting of packaging, scorching of packaging, or other evidence) occurs as a direct result of a dry battery. For all modes of transportation, a written report submitted, retained, and updated in accordance with §171.16 is required if a fire, violent rupture, explosion or dangerous evolution of heat occurs as a direct result of a dry battery or batterypowered device.

(b) *Preparation for transport.* Batteries and battery-powered device(s) containing batteries must be prepared and packaged for transport in a manner to prevent:

(1) A dangerous evolution of heat;

(2) Short circuits, including but not limited to the following methods:

(i)   Packaging each battery or each battery-powered device when practicable, in fully enclosed inner packagings made of non-conductive material;

(ii)   Separating or packaging batteries in a manner to prevent contact with other batteries, devices or conductive materials (*e.g.*, metal) in the packagings; or

(iii)   Ensuring exposed terminals or connectors are protected with non-conductive caps, non-conductive tape, or by other appropriate means; and

(3)   Damage to terminals. If not impact resistant, the outer packaging should not be used as the sole means of protecting the battery terminals from damage or short circuiting. Batteries must be securely cushioned and packed to prevent shifting which could loosen terminal caps or reorient the terminals to produce short circuits. Batteries contained in devices must be securely installed. Terminal protection methods include but are not limited to the following:

(i)   Securely attaching covers of sufficient strength to protect the terminals;

(ii)   Packaging the battery in a rigid plastic packaging; or

(iii)   Constructing the battery with terminals that are recessed or otherwise protected so that the terminals will not be subjected to damage if the package is dropped.

(c)   *Additional air transport requirements*. For a battery whose voltage (electrical potential) exceeds 9 volts—

(1)   When contained in a device, the device must be packaged in a manner that prevents unintentional activation or must have an independent means of preventing unintentional activation (*e.g.*, packaging restricts access to activation switch, switch caps or locks, recessed switches, trigger locks, temperature sensitive circuit breakers, *etc.*); and

(2)   An indication of compliance with this special provision must be provided by marking each package with the words "not restricted" or by including the words "not restricted" on a transport document such as an air waybill accompanying the shipment.

(d)   *Used or spent battery exception*. Used or spent dry batteries of both nonrechargeable and rechargeable designs, with a marked rating up to 9-volt that are combined in the same package and transported by highway or rail for recycling, reconditioning, or disposal are not subject to this special provision or any other requirement of the HMR. Note that batteries utilizing different chemistries (*i.e.*, those battery chemistries specifically covered by another entry in the §172.101 Table) as well as dry batteries with a marked rating greater than 9-volt may not be combined with used or spent batteries in the same package. Note also that this exception does not apply to batteries that have been reconditioned for reuse.

131   This material may not be offered for transportation unless approved by
       the Associate Administrator.

132   This description may only be used for ammonium nitrate-based com-
       pound fertilizers. They must be classified in accordance with the
       procedure as set out in the Manual of Tests and Criteria, part III, section
       39 (IBR, *see* §171.7 of this subchapter). Fertilizers meeting the criteria
       for this identification number are only subject to the requirements of this
       subchapter when offered for transportation and transported by air or
       vessel.

134   This entry only applies to vehicles powered by wet batteries, sodium
       batteries, lithium metal batteries or lithium ion batteries and equipment
       powered by wet batteries or sodium batteries that are transported with
       these batteries installed.

       a.   For the purpose of this special provision, vehicles are self-
             propelled apparatus designed to carry one or more persons or
             goods. Examples of such vehicles are electrically-powered cars,
             motorcycles, scooters, three- and four-wheeled vehicles or motor-
             cycles, trucks, locomotives, bicycles (pedal cycles with an electric
             motor) and other vehicles of this type (*e.g.* self-balancing vehicles
             or vehicles not equipped with at least one seating position), lawn
             tractors, self-propelled farming and construction equipment, boats,
             aircraft, wheelchairs and other mobility aids. This includes vehicles
             transported in a packaging. In this case some parts of the vehicle
             may be detached from its frame to fit into the packaging.

       b.   Examples of equipment are lawnmowers, cleaning machines or
             model boats and model aircraft. Equipment powered by lithium
             metal batteries or lithium ion batteries must be consigned under the
             entries "Lithium metal batteries contained in equipment" or "Lithium
             metal batteries packed with equipment" or "Lithium ion batteries
             contained in equipment" or "Lithium ion batteries packed with
             equipment" as appropriate.

       c.   Self-propelled vehicles or equipment that also contain an internal
             combustion engine must be consigned under the entries "Engine,
             internal combustion, flammable gas powered" or "Engine, internal
             combustion, flammable liquid powered" or "Vehicle, flammable gas
             powered" or "Vehicle, flammable liquid powered," as appropriate.
             These entries include hybrid electric vehicles powered by both an
             internal combustion engine and batteries. Additionally, self-
             propelled vehicles or equipment that contain a fuel cell engine must
             be consigned under the entries "Engine, fuel cell, flammable gas
             powered" or "Engine, fuel cell, flammable liquid powered" or
             "Vehicle, fuel cell, flammable gas powered" or "Vehicle, fuel cell,
             flammable liquid powered," as appropriate. These entries include
             hybrid electric vehicles powered by a fuel cell engine, an internal
             combustion engine, and batteries.

135   Internal combustion engines installed in a vehicle must be consigned
       under the entries "Vehicle, flammable gas powered" or "Vehicle, flam-
       mable liquid powered," as appropriate. If a vehicle is powered by a
       flammable liquid and a flammable gas internal combustion engine, it

must be consigned under the entry "Vehicle, flammable gas powered." These entries include hybrid electric vehicles powered by both an internal combustion engine and wet, sodium or lithium batteries installed. If a fuel cell engine is installed in a vehicle, the vehicle must be consigned using the entries "Vehicle, fuel cell, flammable gas powered" or "Vehicle, fuel cell, flammable liquid powered," as appropriate. These entries include hybrid electric vehicles powered by a fuel cell, an internal combustion engine, and wet, sodium or lithium batteries installed. For the purpose of this special provision, vehicles are self-propelled apparatus designed to carry one or more persons or goods. Examples of such vehicles are cars, motorcycles, trucks, locomotives, scooters, three- and four-wheeled vehicles or motorcycles, lawn tractors, self-propelled farming and construction equipment, boats and aircraft.

136   This entry only applies to machinery and apparatus containing hazardous materials as an integral element of the machinery or apparatus. It may not be used to describe machinery or apparatus for which a proper shipping name exists in the §172.101 Table. Except when approved by the Associate Administrator, machinery or apparatus may only contain hazardous materials for which exceptions are referenced in Column (8) of the §172.101 Table and are provided in part 173, subparts D and G, of this subchapter. Hazardous materials shipped under this entry are excepted from the labeling requirements of this subchapter unless offered for transportation or transported by aircraft and are not subject to the placarding requirements of subpart F of this part. Orientation markings as described in §172.312(a)(2) are required when liquid hazardous materials may escape due to incorrect orientation. The machinery or apparatus, if unpackaged, or the packaging in which it is contained shall be marked "Dangerous goods in machinery" or "Dangerous goods in apparatus," as appropriate, with the identification number UN3363. For transportation by aircraft, machinery or apparatus may not contain any material forbidden for transportation by passenger or cargo aircraft. The Associate Administrator may except from the requirements of this subchapter equipment, machinery and apparatus provided:

a.   It is shown that it does not pose a significant risk in transportation;

b.   The quantities of hazardous materials do not exceed those specified in §173.4a of this subchapter; and

c.   The equipment, machinery or apparatus conforms with §173.222 of this subchapter.

137   Cotton, dry; flax, dry; sisal, dry; and tampico fiber, dry are not subject to the requirements of this subchapter when they are baled in accordance with ISO 8115, "Cotton Bales—Dimensions and Density" (IBR, see §171.7 of this subchapter) to a density of not less than 360 kg/m^3 (22.1 lb/ft^3) for cotton, 400 kg/m^3 (24.97 lb/ft^3) for flax, 620 kg/m^3 (38.71 lb/ft^3) for sisal and 360 kg/m^3 (22.1 lb/ft^3) for tampico fiber and transported in a freight container or closed transport vehicle.

138   This entry applies to lead compounds which, when mixed in a ratio of 1:1,000 with 0.07 M (Molar concentration) hydrochloric acid and stirred for one hour at a temperature of 23°C ± 2°C, exhibit a solubility of more than 5%. Lead compounds which, when mixed in a ratio of 1:1,000 with

0.07 M (Molar concentration) hydrochloric acid and stirred for one hour at a temperature of 23°C ± 2°C, exhibit a solubility of 5% or less are not subject to the requirements of this subchapter unless they meet criteria as another hazard class or division. Lead compounds that have a solubility of 5% or less in accordance with this special provision are not subject to the requirements of this subchapter that pertain to Marine Pollutants.

139   Use of the "special arrangement" proper shipping names for international shipments must be made under an IAEA Certificate of Competent Authority issued by the Associate Administrator in accordance with the requirements in §173.471, §173.472, or §173.473 of this subchapter. Use of these proper shipping names for domestic shipments may be made only under a DOT special permit, as defined in, and in accordance with the requirements of subpart B of part 107 of this subchapter.

140   This material is regulated only when it meets the defining criteria for a hazardous substance or a marine pollutant. In addition, the column 5 reference is modified to read "III" on those occasions when this material is offered for transportation or transported by highway or rail.

141   A toxin obtained from a plant, animal, or bacterial source containing an infectious substance, or a toxin contained in an infectious substance, must be classed as Division 6.2, described as an infectious substance, and assigned to UN 2814 or UN 2900, as appropriate.

142   These hazardous materials may not be classified and transported unless authorized by the Associate Administrator. The Associate Administrator will base the authorization on results from Series 2 tests and a Series 6(c) test from the UN Manual of Tests and Criteria (IBR, see §171.7 of this subchapter) on packages as prepared for transport in accordance with the requirements of this subchapter.

144   If transported as a residue in an underground storage tank (UST), as defined in 40 CFR 280.12, that has been cleaned and purged or rendered inert according to the American Petroleum Institute (API) Standard 1604 (IBR, see §171.7 of this subchapter), then the tank and this material are not subject to any other requirements of this subchapter. However, sediments remaining in the tank that meet the definition for a hazardous material are subject to the applicable regulations of this subchapter.

145   This entry applies to formulations that neither detonate in the cavitated state nor deflagrate in laboratory testing, show no effect when heated under confinement, exhibit no explosive power, and are thermally stable (self-accelerating decomposition temperature (SADT) at 60°C (140°F) or higher for a 50 kg (110.2 lbs.) package). Formulations not meeting these criteria must be transported under the provisions applicable to the appropriate entry in the Organic Peroxide Table in §173.225 of this subchapter.

146   This description may be used for a material that poses a hazard to the environment but does not meet the definition for a hazardous waste or a hazardous substance, as defined in §171.8 of this subchapter, or any hazard class, as defined in part 173 of this subchapter, if it is designated

as environmentally hazardous by another Competent Authority. This provision may be used for both domestic and international shipments.

147   This entry applies to non-sensitized emulsions, suspensions, and gels consisting primarily of a mixture of ammonium nitrate and fuel, intended to produce a Type E blasting explosive only after further processing prior to use. The mixture for emulsions typically has the following composition: 60-85% ammonium nitrate; 5-30% water; 2-8% fuel; 0.5-4% emulsifier or thickening agent; 0-10% soluble flame suppressants; and trace additives. Other inorganic nitrate salts may replace part of the ammonium nitrate. The mixture for suspensions and gels typically has the following composition: 60-85% ammonium nitrate; 0-5% sodium or potassium perchlorate; 0-17% hexamine nitrate or monomethylamine nitrate; 5-30% water; 2-15% fuel; 0.5-4% thickening agent; 0-10% soluble flame suppressants; and trace additives. Other inorganic nitrate salts may replace part of the ammonium nitrate. These substances must satisfactorily pass Tests 8(a), (b) and (c) of Test Series 8 of the UN Manual of Tests and Criteria, Part I, Section 18 (IBR, see §171.7 of this subchapter), and may not be classified and transported unless approved by the Associate Administrator.

148   For domestic transportation, this entry directs to §173.66 for:

   a.   The standards for transporting a single bulk hazardous material for blasting by cargo tank motor vehicles (CTMV); and

   b.   The standards for CTMVs capable of transporting multiple hazardous materials for blasting in bulk and non-bulk packagings (i.e., a multipurpose bulk truck (MBT)).

149   Except for transportation by aircraft, when transported as a limited quantity or a consumer commodity, the maximum net capacity specified in §173.150(b)(2) of this subchapter for inner packagings may be increased to 5 L (1.3 gallons).

150   This description may only be used for ammonium nitrate-based fertilizers. They must be classified in accordance with the procedure as set out in the Manual of Tests and Criteria, part III, section 39 (IBR, see §171.7 of this subchapter).

151   If this material meets the definition of a flammable liquid in §173.120 of this subchapter, a FLAMMABLE LIQUID label is also required and the basic description on the shipping paper must indicate the Class 3 subsidiary hazard.

155   Fish meal, fish scrap and krill meal may not be transported if the temperature at the time of loading either exceeds 35°C (95°F), or exceeds 5°C (41°F) above the ambient temperature, whichever is higher.

156   Asbestos that is immersed or fixed in a natural or artificial binder material, such as cement, plastic, asphalt, resins or mineral ore, or contained in manufactured products is not subject to the requirements of this subchapter.

157   When transported as a limited quantity or a consumer commodity, the maximum net capacity specified in §173.151(b)(1)(i) of this subchapter for inner packagings may be increased to 5 kg (11 pounds).

159   This material must be protected from direct sunshine and kept in a cool, well-ventilated place away from sources of heat.

160   This entry applies to safety devices for vehicles, vessels or aircraft, *e.g.* air bag inflators, air bag modules, seat-belt pretensioners, and pyromechanical devices containing Class 1 (explosive) materials or materials of other hazard classes. These articles must be tested in accordance with Test series 6(c) of Part I of the UN Manual of Tests and Criteria (incorporated by reference; see §171.7 of this subchapter), with no explosion of the device, no fragmentation of device casing or pressure vessel, and no projection hazard or thermal effect that would significantly hinder fire-fighting or other emergency response efforts in the immediate vicinity. If the air bag inflator unit satisfactorily passes the series 6(c) test, it is not necessary to repeat the test on the air bag module. This entry does not apply to life saving appliances described in §173.219 (UN2990 and UN3072).

162   This material may be transported under the provisions of Division 4.1 only if it is packed so that at no time during transport will the percentage of diluent fall below the percentage that is stated in the shipping description.

163   Substances must satisfactorily pass Test Series 8 of the UN Manual of Tests and Criteria, Part I, Section 18 (IBR, see §171.7 of this subchapter).

164   Substances must not be transported under this entry unless approved by the Associate Administrator on the basis of the results of appropriate tests according to Part I of the UN Manual of Tests and Criteria (IBR, see §171.7 of this subchapter). The material must be packaged so that the percentage of diluent does not fall below that stated in the approval at any time during transportation.

165   These substances are susceptible to exothermic decomposition at elevated temperatures. Decomposition can be initiated by heat, moisture or by impurities (e.g., powdered metals (iron, manganese, cobalt, magnesium)). During the course of transportation, these substances must be shaded from direct sunlight and all sources of heat and be placed in adequately ventilated areas.

166   When transported in non-friable tablet form, calcium hypochlorite, dry, may be transported as a Packing Group III material.

167   These storage systems must always be considered as containing hydrogen. A metal hydride storage system installed in or intended to be installed in a vehicle or equipment or in vehicle or equipment components must be approved for transport by the Associate Administrator. A copy of the approval must accompany each shipment.

168   For lighters containing a Division 2.1 gas (see §171.8 of this subchapter), representative samples of each new lighter design must be examined and successfully tested as specified in §173.308(b)(3). For criteria in determining what is a new lighter design, see §173.308(b)(1). For transportation of new lighter design samples for examination and testing, see §173.308(b)(2). The examination and testing of each lighter design must be performed by a person authorized by the Associate Administrator under the provisions of subpart E of part 107 of this chapter, as specified in §173.308(a)(4). For continued use of approvals dated prior to January 1, 2012, see §173.308(b)(5).

For non-pressurized lighters containing a Class 3 (flammable liquid) material, its design, description, and packaging must be approved by the Associate Administrator prior to being offered for transportation or transported in commerce. In addition, a lighter design intended to contain a non-pressurized Class 3 material is excepted from the examination and testing criteria specified in §173.308(b)(3). An unused lighter or a lighter that is cleaned of residue and purged of vapors is not subject to the requirements of this subchapter.

169 This entry applies to lighter refills (see §171.8 of this subchapter) that contain a Division 2.1 (flammable) gas but do not contain an ignition device. Lighter refills offered for transportation under this entry may not exceed 4 fluid ounces capacity (7.22 cubic inches) or contain more than 65 grams of fuel. A lighter refill exceeding 4 fluid ounces capacity (7.22 cubic inches) or containing more than 65 grams of fuel must be classed as a Division 2.1 material, described with the proper shipping name appropriate for the material, and packaged in the packaging specified in part 173 of this subchapter for the flammable gas contained therein. In addition, a container exceeding 4 fluid ounces volumetric capacity (7.22 cubic inches) or containing more than 65 grams of fuel may not be connected or manifolded to a lighter or similar device and must also be described and packaged according to the fuel contained therein. For transportation by passenger-carrying aircraft, the net mass of lighter refills may not exceed 1 kg per package, and, for cargo-only aircraft, the net mass of lighter refills may not exceed 15 kg per package. See §173.306(h) of this subchapter.

170 Air must be eliminated from the vapor space by nitrogen or other means.

171 This entry may only be used when the material is transported in non-friable tablet form or for granular or powered mixtures that have been shown to meet the PG III criteria in §173.127.

172 This entry includes alcohol mixtures containing up to 5% petroleum products.

173 For adhesives, printing inks, printing ink-related materials, paints, paint-related materials, and resin solutions which are assigned to UN3082, and do not meet the definition of another hazard class, metal or plastic packaging for substances of packing groups II and III in quantities of 5 L (1.3 gallons) or less per packaging are not required to meet the UN performance package testing when transported:

a. Except for transportation by aircraft, in palletized loads, a pallet box or unit load device (*e.g.* individual packaging placed or stacked and secured by strapping, shrink or stretch-wrapping or other suitable means to a pallet). For vessel transport, the palletized loads, pallet boxes or unit load devices must be firmly packed and secured in closed cargo transport units; or

b.   Except for transportation by aircraft, as an inner packaging of a combination packaging with a maximum net mass of 40 kg (88 pounds). For transportation by aircraft, as an inner packaging of a combination packaging with a maximum gross mass of 30 kg when packaged as a limited quantity in accordance with §173.27(f).

175   This substance must be stabilized when in concentrations of not more than 99%.

176   This entry must be used for formaldehyde solutions containing methanol as a stabilizer. Formaldehyde solutions not containing methanol and not meeting the Class 3 flammable liquid criteria must be described using a different proper shipping name.

177   Gasoline, or, ethanol and gasoline mixtures, for use in internal combustion engines (*e.g.*, in automobiles, stationary engines and other engines) must be assigned to Packing Group II regardless of variations in volatility.

181   When a package contains a combination of lithium batteries contained in equipment and lithium batteries packed with equipment, the following requirements apply:

a.   The shipper must ensure that all applicable requirements of §173.185 of this subchapter are met. The total mass of lithium batteries contained in any package must not exceed the quantity limits in columns (9A) and (9B) for passenger aircraft or cargo aircraft, as applicable;

b.   Except as provided in §173.185(c)(3) of this subchapter, the package must be marked "UN3091 Lithium metal batteries packed with equipment", or "UN3481 Lithium ion batteries packed with equipment," as appropriate. If a package contains both lithium metal batteries and lithium ion batteries packed with and contained in equipment, the package must be marked as required for both battery types. However, button cell batteries installed in equipment (including circuit boards) need not be considered; and

c.   The shipping paper must indicate "UN3091 Lithium metal batteries packed with equipment" or "UN3481 Lithium ion batteries packed with equipment," as appropriate. If a package contains both lithium metal batteries and lithium ion batteries packed with and contained in equipment, then the shipping paper must indicate both "UN3091 Lithium metal batteries packed with equipment" and "UN3481 Lithium ion batteries packed with equipment."

182   Equipment containing only lithium batteries must be classified as either UN3091 or UN3481.

198   Nitrocellulose solutions containing not more than 20% nitrocellulose may be transported as paint, perfumery products, or printing ink, as applicable, provided the nitrocellulose contains no more 12.6% nitrogen (by dry mass). *See* UN1210, UN1263, UN1266, UN3066, UN3469, and UN3470.

200 Division 1.4G consumer fireworks may be certified for transportation by a DOT-approved Fireworks Certification Agency in accordance with the provisions of §173.65 of this subchapter.

222 Shipments offered for transportation by aircraft may not be reclassed as ORM-D.

237 "Batteries, dry, containing potassium hydroxide solid, *electric storage*" must be prepared and packaged in accordance with the requirements of §173.159(a) and (c). For transportation by aircraft, the provisions of §173.159(b)(2) apply. This entry may only be used for the transport of non-activated batteries that contain dry potassium hydroxide and that are intended to be activated prior to use by the addition of an appropriate amount of water to the individual cells.

238 Neutron radiation detectors: Neutron radiation detectors containing non-pressurized boron trifluoride gas in excess of 1 gram (0.035 ounces) and radiation detection systems containing such neutron radiation detectors as components may be transported by highway, rail, vessel, or cargo aircraft in accordance with the following:

    a. Each radiation detector must meet the following conditions:

    (1) The pressure in each neutron radiation detector must not exceed 105 kPa absolute at 20°C (68°F);

    (2) The amount of gas must not exceed 13 grams (0.45 ounces) per detector; and

    (3) Each neutron radiation detector must be of welded metal construction with brazed metal to ceramic feed through assemblies. These detectors must have a minimum burst pressure of 1800 kPa as demonstrated by design type qualification testing; and

    (4) Each detector must be tested to a 1×10^{-10} cm^3/s leaktightness standard before filling.

    b. Radiation detectors transported as individual components must be transported as follows:

    (1) They must be packed in a sealed intermediate plastic liner with sufficient absorbent or adsorbent material to absorb or adsorb the entire gas contents.

    (2) They must be packed in strong outer packagings and the completed package must be capable of withstanding a 1.8 meter (5.9 feet) drop without leakage of gas contents from detectors.

    (3) The total amount of gas from all detectors per outer packaging must not exceed 52 grams (1.83 ounces).

    c. Completed neutron radiation detection systems containing detectors meeting the conditions of paragraph a of this special provision must be transported as follows:

(1) The detectors must be contained in a strong sealed outer casing;

(2) The casing must contain include sufficient absorbent or adsorbent material to absorb or adsorb the entire gas contents;

(3) The completed system must be packed in strong outer packagings capable of withstanding a 1.8 meter (5.9 feet) drop test without leakage unless a system's outer casing affords equivalent protection.

d. Except for transportation by aircraft, neutron radiation detectors and radiation detection systems containing such detectors transported in accordance with paragraph a of this special provision are not subject to the labeling and placarding requirements of part 172 of this subchapter.

e. When transported by highway, rail, vessel, or as cargo on an aircraft, neutron radiation detectors containing not more than 1 gram of boron trifluoride, including those with solder glass joints are not subject to any other requirements of this subchapter provided they meet the requirements in paragraph a of this special provision and are packed in accordance with paragraph b of this special provision. Radiation detection systems containing such detectors are not subject to any other requirements of this subchapter provided they are packed in accordance with paragraph c of this special provision.

325   In the case of non-fissile or fissile-excepted uranium hexafluoride, the material must be classified under UN 2978.

328   When lithium metal or lithium ion batteries are contained in the fuel cell system, the item must be described under this entry and the appropriate entries for "Lithium metal batteries contained in equipment" or "Lithium ion batteries contained in equipment".

332   Magnesium nitrate hexahydrate is not subject to the requirements of this subchapter.

335   Mixtures of solids that are not subject to this subchapter and environmentally hazardous liquids or solids may be classified as "Environmentally hazardous substances, solid, n.o.s," UN3077 and may be transported under this entry, provided there is no free liquid visible at the time the material is loaded or at the time the packaging or transport unit is closed. Each transport unit must be leakproof when used as bulk packaging.

336   The use of UN1H1 drums, UN3H1 jerricans, and UN6HA1 composite packagings which meet the requirements of Part 178 of the HMR at the Packing Group I or II performance level. These packagings are not required to: (1.) meet the venting requirements in §173.24(g) or (2.) be marked with the hydrostatic pressure test marking specified in §173.24a(b)(4). Shipment of packages under this special provision must be made by private or contract motor carrier. Transportation of these packages also requires the door of each van trailer to be marked with "Warning trailer may contain chemical vapor. Do not enter until vapors

have dissipated." The driver of the transport vehicle and the consignee(s) must be trained not to enter the transport vehicle until the ammonia vapors have dissipated, and the emergency response information on the shipping paper must indicate that the vehicle contains ammonia vapors. This training must be documented in training records required by §172.704(d). Transport vehicles must be vented to prevent accumulation of vapors at a poisonous or flammable concentration.

337 Authorizes the use of regulated waste containers manufactured prior to October 1, 2006 to be marked with the alternative shipping name of Regulated medical waste, UN3291 and arrows that deviate as prescribed in §172.312(a)(2) in that they may be black or white.

338 Life Saving appliances, self-inflating transported by motor vehicle only between an U.S. Coast Guard approved inflatable life raft servicing facility and a vessel are only subject to the following requirements:

a. Prior to repacking into the life-saving appliance, an installed inflation cylinder must successfully meet and pass all inspection and test criteria and standards of the raft manufacturer and the vessel Flag State requirements for cylinders installed as part of life-saving appliances, self-inflating (UN2990) used on marine vessels. Additionally, each cylinder must be visually inspected in accordance with CGA pamphlet, CGA C-6 (incorporated by reference, see §171.7). A current copy of CGA pamphlet, CGA C-6 must be available at the facility servicing the life-saving appliance.

b. An installed inflation cylinder that requires recharging must be filled in accordance with §173.301(l).

c. Every installed inflation cylinder, as associated equipment of the life-saving appliance, must be packed within the protective packaging of the life raft and the life raft itself must otherwise be in compliance with §173.219.

d. The serial number for each cylinder must be recorded as part of the life-saving appliance service record by the U.S. Coast Guard-approved servicing facility.

340 This entry applies only to the vessel transportation of nickel-metal hydride batteries as cargo. Nickel-metal hydride button cells or nickel-metal hydride cells or batteries packed with or contained in battery-powered devices transported by vessel are not subject to the requirements of this special provision. See "Batteries, dry, sealed, n.o.s." in the §172.101 Hazardous Materials Table (HMT) of this part for transportation requirements for nickelmetal hydride batteries transported by other modes and for nickel-metal hydride button cells or nickel-metal hydride cells or batteries packed with or contained in battery-powered devices transported by vessel. Nickel-metal hydride batteries subject to this special provision are subject only to the following requirements: (1) The batteries must be prepared and packaged for transport in a manner to prevent a dangerous evolution of heat, short circuits, and damage to terminals; and are subject to the incident reporting in accordance with §171.16 of this subchapter if a fire, violent rupture, explosion or dangerous evolution of heat (*i.e.*, an amount of heat sufficient to be dangerous to packaging or personal safety to include charring of packaging, melting of packaging, scorching of packaging, or other evidence) occurs as a direct result of a nickel metal hydride battery; and (2) when loaded in a cargo transport unit in a total quantity of 100 kg gross mass or more, the shipping paper requirements of Subpart C of this part, the manifest requirements of §176.30 of this subchapter, and the vessel stowage requirements assigned to this entry in Column (10) of the §172.101 Hazardous Materials Table.

342   Glass inner packagings (such as ampoules or capsules) intended only for use in sterilization devices, when containing less than 30 mL of ethylene oxide per inner packaging with not more than 300 mL per outer packaging, may be transported in accordance with §173.4a of this subchapter, irrespective of the restriction of §173.4a(b) and the indication of "forbidden" in columns (9A) and (9B) of the §172.101 table provided that:

a.   After filling, each glass inner packaging must be determined to be leak-tight by placing the glass inner packaging in a hot water bath at a temperature and for a period of time sufficient to ensure that an internal pressure equal to the vapor pressure of ethylene oxide at 55°C is achieved. Any glass inner packaging showing evidence of leakage, distortion or other defect under this test must not be transported under the terms of this special provision;

b.   In addition to the packaging required in §173.4a, each glass inner packaging must be placed in a sealed plastic bag compatible with ethylene oxide and capable of containing the contents in the event of breakage or leakage of the glass inner packaging; and

c.   Each glass inner packaging is protected by a means of preventing puncture of the plastic bag (*e.g.*, sleeves or cushioning) in the event of damage to the packaging (*e.g.*, by crushing).

343   A bulk packaging that emits hydrogen sulfide in sufficient concentration that vapors evolved from the crude oil can present an inhalation hazard must be marked as specified in §172.327 of this part.

345   "Nitrogen, refrigerated liquid (*cryogenic liquid*), UN1977" transported in open cryogenic receptacles with a maximum capacity of 1 L are not subject to the requirements of this subchapter. The receptacles must be constructed with glass double walls having the space between the walls vacuum insulated and each receptacle must be transported in an outer packaging with sufficient cushioning and absorbent materials to protect the receptacle from damage.

346   "Nitrogen, refrigerated liquid (*cryogenic liquid*), UN1977" transported in accordance with the requirements for open cryogenic receptacles in §173.320 and this special provision are not subject to any other requirements of this subchapter. The receptacle must contain no hazardous materials other than the liquid nitrogen which must be fully absorbed in a porous material in the receptacle.

347   Effective July 1, 2011, for transportation by aircraft, this entry may only be used if the results of Test series 6(d) of Part I of the UN Manual of Tests and Criteria (IBR, *see* §171.7 of this subchapter) have demonstrated that any hazardous effects from accidental functioning are confined to within the package. Effective January 1, 2012, for transportation by vessel, this entry may only be used if the results of Test Series 6(d) of Part I of the UN Manual of Tests and Criteria (IBR, *see* §171.7 of this subchapter) have demonstrated that any hazardous effects from accidental functioning are confined to within the package. Effective January 1, 2014, for transportation domestically by highway or rail, this entry may only be used if the results of Test Series 6(d) of Part I of the UN Manual of Tests and Criteria (IBR, *see* §171.7 of this subchapter) have demonstrated that any hazardous effects from accidental functioning are confined to within the package. Testing must be performed or witnessed by a person who is approved by the Associate Administrator (see §173.56(b) of this subchapter). All successfully conducted tests or reassignment to another compatibility group require the issuance of a new or revised approval by the Associate Administrator prior to transportation on or after the dates specified for each authorized mode of transport in this special provision.

349   Mixtures of hypochlorite with an ammonium salt are forbidden for transport. A hypochlorite solution, UN1791, is a Class 8 corrosive material.

350   Ammonium bromate, ammonium bromate aqueous solutions, and mixtures of a bromate with an ammonium salt are forbidden for transport.

351   Ammonium chlorate, ammonium chlorate aqueous solutions, and mixtures of a chlorate with an ammonium salt are forbidden for transport.

352   Ammonium chlorite, ammonium chlorite aqueous solutions, and mixtures of a chlorite with an ammonium salt are forbidden for transport.

353   Ammonium permanganate, ammonium permanganate aqueous solutions, and mixtures of a permanganate with an ammonium salt are forbidden for transport.

357   A bulk packaging that emits hydrogen sulfide in sufficient concentration that vapors evolved from the crude oil can present an inhalation hazard must be marked as specified in §172.327 of this part.

360   Vehicles only powered by lithium batteries must be assigned the identification number UN3171.

361   Capacitors with an energy storage capacity of 0.3 Wh or less are not subject to the requirements of this subchapter. Energy storage capacity means the energy held by a capacitor, as calculated using the nominal voltage and capacitance. This entry does not apply to capacitors that by design maintain a terminal voltage (e.g., asymmetrical capacitors.)

362   This entry applies to liquids, pastes or powders, pressurized with a propellant that meets the definition of a gas in §173.115. A chemical under pressure packaged in an aerosol dispenser must be transported under UN1950. The chemical under pressure must be classed based on the hazard characteristics of the components in the propellant; the liquid; or the solid. The following provisions also apply:

(a) If one of the components, which can be a pure substance or a mixture, is classed as flammable, the chemical under pressure must be classed as flammable in Division 2.1. Flammable components are flammable liquids and liquid mixtures, flammable solids and solid mixtures or flammable gases and gas mixtures meeting the following criteria:

(1) A flammable liquid is a liquid having a flashpoint of not more than 93°C (200°F);

(2) A flammable solid is a solid that meets the criteria in §173.124 of this subchapter; or

(3) A flammable gas is a gas that meets the criteria in §173.115 of this subchapter.

(b) Gases of Division 2.3 and gases with a subsidiary risk of 5.1 must not be used as a propellant in a chemical under pressure.

(c) Where the liquid or solid components are classed as Division 6.1, Packing Group II or III, or Class 8, Packing Group II or III, the chemical under pressure must be assigned a subsidiary risk of Division 6.1 or Class 8 and the appropriate identification number must be assigned. Components classed as Division 6.1, Packing Group I, or Class 8, Packing Group I, must not be offered for transportation and transported under this description.

(d) A chemical under pressure with components meeting the properties of: Class 1 (explosives); Class 3 (liquid desensitized explosives); Division 4.1 (self-reactive substances and solid desensitized explosives); Division 4.2 (substances liable to spontaneous combustion); Division 4.3 (substances which, in contact with water, emit flammable gases or toxic gases); Division 5.1 (oxidizing substances); Division 5.2 (organic peroxides); Division 6.2 (Infectious substances); or, Class 7 (Radioactive material), must not be offered for transportation under this description.

(e) A description to which special provision 170 or TP7 is assigned in Column 7 of the §172.101 Hazardous Materials Table, and therefore requires air to be eliminated from the package vapor space by nitrogen or other means, must not be offered for transportation under this description.

(f) Chemicals under pressure containing components forbidden for transport on both passenger and cargo aircraft in Columns (9A) and (9B) of the §172.101 Hazardous Materials Table must not be transported by air.

365 For manufactured instruments and articles containing mercury, see UN3506.

367 For the purposes of documentation and package marking:

a. The proper shipping name "Paint related material" may be used for consignments of packages containing "Paint" and "Paint related material" in the same package;

b. The proper shipping name "Paint related material, corrosive, flammable" may be used for consignments of packages containing "Paint, corrosive, flammable" and "Paint related material, corrosive, flammable" in the same package;

c. The proper shipping name "Paint related material, flammable, corrosive" may be used for consignments of packages containing "Paint, flammable, corrosive" and "Paint related material, flammable, corrosive" In the same package; and

d. The proper shipping name "Printing ink related material" may be used for consignments of packages containing "Printing ink" and "Printing ink related material" in the same package.

368 In the case of non-fissile or fissile-excepted uranium hexafluoride, the material must be classified under UN3507 or UN2978.

369 In accordance with §173.2a of this subchapter, this radioactive material in an excepted package possessing toxic and corrosive properties is classified in Division 6.1 with radioactivity and corrosive subsidiary risks. Uranium hexafluoride may be classified under this entry only if the conditions of §§173.420(a)(4) and (6) and (d) and 173.421(b) and (d) of this subchapter, and, for fissile-excepted material, the conditions of §173.453 of this subchapter are met. In addition to the provisions applicable to the transport of Division 6.1 substances, the provisions of §§173.421(c) and 173.443(a) of this subchapter apply. In addition, packages shall be legibly and durably marked with an identification of the consignor, the consignee, or both. No Class 7 label is required to be displayed. The consignor shall be in possession of a copy of each applicable certificate when packages include fissile material excepted by competent authority approval. When a consignment is undeliverable, the consignment shall be placed in a safe location and the appropriate competent authority shall be informed as soon as possible and a request made for instructions on further action. If it is evident that a package of radioactive material, or conveyance carrying unpackaged radioactive material, is leaking, or if it is suspected that the package, or conveyance carrying unpackaged material, may have leaked, the requirements of §173.443(e) of this subchapter apply.

370 This entry also applies to Ammonium nitrate with not more than 0.2% combustible substances, including any organic substance calculated as carbon, to the exclusion of any added substance, that gives a positive result when tested in accordance with Test Series 2 of the UN Manual of Tests and Criteria, Part I (incorporated by reference; see §171.7 of this subchapter). See also UN No. 1942.

371 a. This entry also applies to articles not conforming to the requirements of §§173.302, 173.304, or 173.306 of this subchapter, containing a small pressure receptacle with a release device. Such articles must comply with the following requirements:

(1) The water capacity of the pressure receptacle must not exceed 0.5 L and the working pressure must not exceed 25 bar at 15°C (59°F);

    (2)   The minimum burst pressure of the pressure receptacle must be at least four times the pressure of the gas at 15°C (59°F);

    (3)   Each article must be manufactured in such a way that unintentional firing or release is avoided under normal conditions of handling, packing, transport and use. This may be fulfilled by an additional locking device linked to the activator;

    (4)   Each article must be manufactured in such a way as to prevent hazardous projections of the pressure receptacle or parts of the pressure receptacle;

    (5)   Each pressure receptacle must be manufactured from material which will not fragment upon rupture;

    (6)   The design type of the article must be subjected to a fire test. For this test, the provisions of paragraphs 16.6.1.2 except letter g, 16.6.1.3.1 to 16.6.1.3.6, 16.6.1.3.7(b) and 16.6.1.3.8 of the UN Manual of Tests and Criteria must be applied. It must be demonstrated that the article relieves its pressure by means of a fire degradable seal or other pressure relief device, in such a way that the pressure receptacle will not fragment and that the article or fragments of the article do not rocket more than 10 meters; and

    (7)   The design type of the article must be subjected to the following test. A stimulating mechanism must be used to initiate one article in the middle of the packaging. There must be no hazardous effects outside the package such as disruption of the package, metal fragments or a receptacle which passes through the packaging.

  b.   The manufacturer must produce technical documentation of the design type, manufacture as well as the tests and their results. The manufacturer must apply procedures to ensure that articles produced in series are made of good quality, conform to the design type and are able to meet the requirements in (a). The manufacturer must provide such information to a representative of the Department upon request.

372   This entry applies to asymmetric capacitors with an energy storage capacity greater than 0.3 Wh. Capacitors with an energy storage capacity of 0.3 Wh or less are not subject to the requirements of this subchapter.

Energy storage capacity means the energy stored in a capacitor, as calculated according to the following equation,

$$Wh = 1/2C_N(U_R{}^2 - U_L{}^2) \times (1/3600)$$

Using the nominal capacitance (C_N), rated voltage (U_R) and the rated lower limit voltage (U_L).

Nickel-carbon asymmetric capacitors containing Class 8 alkaline electrolytes must be transported as UN2795, Batteries, wet, filled with alkali, electric storage.

379 When offered for transport by highway, rail, or cargo vessel, anhydrous ammonia adsorbed or absorbed on a solid contained in ammonia dispensing systems or receptacles intended to form part of such systems is not subject to the requirements of this subchapter if the following conditions in this provision are met. In addition to meeting the conditions in this provision, transport on cargo aircraft only may be authorized with prior approval of the Associate Administrator.

a. The adsorption or absorption presents the following properties:

(1) The pressure at a temperature of 20°C (68°F) in the receptacle is less than 0.6 bar (60 kPa);

(2) The pressure at a temperature of 35°C (95°F) in the receptacle is less than 1 bar (100 kPa);

(3) The pressure at a temperature of 85°C (185°F) in the receptacle is less than 12 bar (1200 kPa).

b. The adsorbent or absorbent material shall not meet the definition or criteria for inclusion in Classes 1 to 8;

c. The maximum contents of a receptacle shall be 10 kg of ammonia; and

d. Receptacles containing adsorbed or absorbed ammonia shall meet the following conditions:

(1) Receptacles shall be made of a material compatible with ammonia as specified in ISO 11114-1:2012 (IBR, see §171.7 of this subchapter);

(2) Receptacles and their means of closure shall be hermetically sealed and able to contain the generated ammonia;

(3) Each receptacle shall be able to withstand the pressure generated at 85°C (185°F) with a volumetric expansion no greater than 0.1%;

(4) Each receptacle shall be fitted with a device that allows for gas evacuation once pressure exceeds 15 bar (1500 kPa) without violent rupture, explosion or projection; and

(5) Each receptacle shall be able to withstand a pressure of 20 bar (2000 kPa) without leakage when the pressure relief device is deactivated.

e. When offered for transport in an ammonia dispenser, the receptacles shall be connected to the dispenser in such a way that the assembly is guaranteed to have the same strength as a single receptacle.

f. The properties of mechanical strength mentioned in this special provision shall be tested using a prototype of a receptacle and/or dispenser filled to nominal capacity, by increasing the temperature until the specified pressures are reached.

g. The test results shall be documented, shall be traceable, and shall be made available to a representative of the Department upon request.

380   For transportation by private carrier in a motor carrier only, this material is not subject to the segregation requirements of §177.848(d) of this subchapter under the following conditions:

           a.   The material is packaged in a DOT Specification 4BW240 cylinder, or in a DOT-51 portable tank.

           b.   The material may only be loaded with Class 3, Class 8, and Division 4.1 materials in Packing Group II or III.

           c.   The motor carrier must maintain a satisfactory safety rating as prescribed in 49 CFR part 385.

381   For railroad flagging kits, see §173.184 (c) of this subchapter.

382   Packages containing toy plastic or paper caps for toy pistols described as "UN0349, Articles, explosive, n.o.s. (Toy caps), 1.4S" or "NA0337, Toy caps, 1.4S" are not subject to the subpart E (labeling) requirements of this part when offered for transportation by motor vehicle, rail freight, cargo vessel, and cargo aircraft and, notwithstanding the packing method assigned in §173.62 of this subchapter, in conformance with the following conditions:

           a.   The toy plastic or paper caps must be in the form of sheets, strips, rolls, or individual caps;

           b.   The caps must not contain more than an average of twenty-five hundredths of a grain of explosive composition per cap;

           c.   The caps must be packed inside packagings constructed of cardboard not less than 0.013-inch in thickness, metal not less than 0.008-inch in thickness, non-combustible plastic not less than 0.015-inch in thickness, or a composite blister package consisting of cardboard not less than 0.013-inch in thickness and non-combustible plastic not less than 0.005-inch in thickness that completely encloses the caps;

           d.   The minimum dimensions of each side and each end of the cardboard packaging must be ⅛th inch in height or more;

           e.   The number of caps inside each packaging must be limited so that not more than 10 grains of explosives composition may be packed into one cubic inch of space, and not more than 17.5 grains of the explosive composition of toy caps may be packed in any inner packaging;

           f.   Inner packagings must be packed in outer packagings meeting PG II performance criteria;

           g.   Toy caps may be packed with non-explosive or non-flammable articles provided the outer packagings are marked as prescribed in this paragraph;

           h.   Toy paper caps of any kind must not be packed in the same packaging with fireworks;

SPECIAL PROVISIONS

i.   The outside of each package must be plainly marked "ARTICLES, EXPLOSIVES, N.O.S. (TOY CAPS)—HANDLE CAREFULLY" OR "TOY CAPS—HANDLE CAREFULLY"; and

j.   Explosives shipped in conformance with this paragraph must have been examined in accordance with §173.56 of this subchapter and approved by the Associate Administrator.

383   For transportation by motor vehicle, substances meeting the conditions for high viscosity flammable liquids as prescribed in §173.121(b)(1)(i), (b)(1)(ii), and (b)(1)(iv) of this subchapter, may be reassigned to Packing Group III under the following conditions:

a.   Packaging must be UN standard metal drums attached with heavy duty steel strapping to a pallet; and

b.   The capacity of each drum must not exceed 220 L (58 gallons).

384   For green graphite electrodes and shapes that are large single component solid objects not subject to shifting, transport in open rail flat cars, open bed motor vehicles, and intermodal containers is also authorized. The objects must be secured to the flat car, motor vehicle, intermodal container, or unitized by steel banding to wooden runners or pallets and the units secured to the flat car, motor vehicle, or freight container to prevent shifting and movement, including relative motion between the objects, under conditions normally incident to transportation. Stacking is permitted two or more levels high to achieve maximum allowable utilization of the designated vehicle, rail car weight, or intermodal freight container weight or vessel hold volume.

385   Notwithstanding the provisions of §177.834(l) of this subchapter, cargo heaters may be used when weather conditions are such that the freezing of a wetted explosive material is likely. Shipments must be made by private, leased or contract carrier vehicles under exclusive use of the offeror. Cargo heaters must be reverse refrigeration (heat pump) units. Shipments made in accordance with this Special provision are excepted from the requirements of §173.60(b)(4) of this subchapter.

386   When transported by private motor carrier only, the following corrosive liquids may be packaged in polyethylene bottles with a capacity no greater than 3.785 L (one gallon), further packed inside an open-top, heavy wall, high density polyethylene box (*i.e.*, crate) in a manner that the polyethylene bottles are not subjected to any superimposed weight, and the boxes must be reasonably secured against movement within the transport vehicle and loaded so as to minimize the possibility of coming in contact with other lading:

Compounds, cleaning liquid, NA1760, PG II or III;

Corrosive liquid, acidic, inorganic, n.o.s., UN3264, PG II;

Corrosive liquid, acidic, organic, n.o.s., UN3265, PG III;

Corrosive liquid, basic, inorganic, n.o.s., UN3266, PG II;

Hypochlorite solutions, UN1791, PG III;

Hydrochloric acid solution, UN1789, PG II; and

Sulfuric acid, UN2796, PG II.

a.   No more than four bottles, securely closed with threaded caps, may be packed in each box.

b.   Each empty bottle must have a minimum weight of not less than 140 grams and a minimum wall thickness of not less than 0.020 inch (0.508 mm).

c.   The completed package must meet the Packing Group II performance level, as applicable for combination packagings with a plastic box outer packaging, in accordance with subpart M of part 178 of this subchapter.

(i)   Tests must be performed on each type and size of bottle, for each manufacturing location. Samples taken at random must withstand the prescribed tests without breakage or leakage.

(ii)   One bottle for every two hours of production, or for every 2500 bottles produced, must be tested by dropping a bottle filled to 98% capacity with water from a height of 1.2 meters (3.9 feet) onto solid concrete directly on the closure.

(iii)   A copy of the test results must be kept on file at each facility where packagings are offered for transportation, and must be made available to a representative of the Department upon request.

(iv)   The name or symbol of the bottle producer, and the month and year of manufacture, must be marked by embossing, ink-jet printing of permanent ink, or other permanent means on the face or bottom of each bottle, in letters and numbers at least 6 mm (0.2 inch) high. Symbols, if used, must be registered with the Associate Administrator.

(v)   The box must be constructed from high-density polyethylene in the density range 0.950-0.962, and be capable of holding liquid when in the upright position.

387   When materials are stabilized by temperature control, the provisions of §173.21(f) of this subchapter apply. When chemical stabilization is employed, the person offering the material for transport shall ensure that the level of stabilization is sufficient to prevent the material as packaged from dangerous polymerization at 50°C (122°F). If chemical stabilization becomes ineffective at lower temperatures within the anticipated duration of transport, temperature control is required and is forbidden by aircraft. In making this determination factors to be taken into consideration include, but are not limited to, the capacity and geometry of the packaging and the effect of any insulation present, the temperature of the material when offered for transport, the duration of the journey, and the ambient temperature conditions typically encountered in the journey (considering also the season of year), the effectiveness and other properties of the stabilizer employed, applicable operational controls imposed by regulation (e.g., requirements to protect from sources of heat, including other cargo carried at a temperature above ambient) and

any other relevant factors. The provisions of this special provision will be effective until January 2, 2023, unless we terminate them earlier or extend them beyond that date by notice of a final rule in the *Federal Register.*

388

a. Lithium batteries containing both primary lithium metal cells and rechargeable lithium ion cells that are not designed to be externally charged, must meet the following conditions:

i. The rechargeable lithium ion cells can only be charged from the primary lithium metal cells;

ii. Overcharge of the rechargeable lithium ion cells is precluded by design;

iii. The battery has been tested as a primary lithium battery; and

iv. Component cells of the battery must be of a type proved to meet the respective testing requirements of the Manual of Tests and Criteria, part III, subsection 38.3 (IBR, see §171.7 of this subchapter).

b. Lithium batteries conforming to paragraph a. of this special provision must be assigned to UN Nos. 3090 or 3091, as appropriate. When such batteries are transported in accordance with §173.185(c), the total lithium content of all lithium metal cells contained in the battery must not exceed 1.5 g and the total capacity of all lithium ion cells contained in the battery must not exceed 10 Wh.

389 This entry only applies to lithium ion batteries or lithium metal batteries installed in a cargo transport unit and designed only to provide power external to the cargo transport unit. The lithium batteries must meet the requirements of §173.185(a) and contain the necessary systems to prevent overcharge and over discharge between the batteries. The batteries must be securely attached to the interior structure of the cargo transport unit (*e.g.,* by means of placement in racks, cabinets, etc.) in such a manner as to prevent short circuits, accidental operation, and significant movement relative to the cargo transport unit under the shocks, loadings, and vibrations normally incident to transport. Hazardous materials necessary for the safe and proper operation of the cargo transport unit (*e.g.,* fire extinguishing systems and air conditioning systems), must be properly secured to or installed in the cargo transport unit and are not otherwise subject to this subchapter. Hazardous materials not necessary for the safe and proper operation of the cargo transport unit must not be transported within the cargo transport unit. The batteries inside the cargo transport unit are not subject to marking or labelling requirements of part 172 subparts D and E of this subchapter. The cargo transport unit shall display the UN number in a manner in accordance with §172.332 of this subchapter and be placarded on two opposing sides. For transportation by aircraft, cargo transport units may only be offered for transportation and transported under conditions approved by the Associate Administrator.

391 Except for articles being transported by motor vehicle as a material of trade in accordance with §173.6 of this subchapter, articles containing hazardous materials of Division 2.3, or Division 4.2, or Division 4.3, or Division 5.1, or Division 5.2, or Division 6.1 (substances with an inhalation toxicity of Packing Group I) and articles containing more than one of the following hazards: (1) Gases of Class 2; (2) Liquid desensitized explosives of Class 3; or (3) Self-reactive substances and solid desensitized explosives of Division 4.1, may only be offered for transportation and transported under conditions approved by the Associate Administrator.

420 This entry does not apply to manufactured articles (such as table tennis balls).

421 This entry will no longer be effective on January 2, 2023, unless we terminate it earlier or extend it beyond that date by notice of a final rule in the *Federal Register*.

422 When labelling is required, the label to be used must be the label shown in §172.447. When a placard is displayed, the placard must be the placard shown in §172.560.

440 When this material is transported by tank car, the offeror must ensure each tank car is remotely monitored for pressure and location. Additionally, the offeror must notify the carrier if the tank pressure rise exceeds 3 psig over any 24-hour period.

  (2) *"A" codes.* These provisions apply only to transportation by aircraft:

Code/Special provisions

A1 Single packagings are not permitted on passenger aircraft.

A2 Single packagings are not permitted on aircraft.

A3 For combination packagings, if glass inner packagings (including ampoules) are used, they must be packed with absorbent material in tightly closed rigid and leakproof receptacles before packing in outer packagings.

A4 Liquids having an inhalation toxicity of Packing Group I are not permitted on aircraft.

A5 Solids having an inhalation toxicity of Packing Group I are not permitted on passenger aircraft and may not exceed a maximum net quantity per package of 15 kg (33 pounds) on cargo aircraft.

A6 For combination packagings, if plastic inner packagings are used, they must be packed in tightly closed metal receptacles before packing in outer packagings.

A7 Steel packagings must be corrosion-resistant or have protection against corrosion.

A8 For combination packagings, if glass inner packagings (including ampoules) are used, they must be packed with cushioning material in tightly closed metal receptacles before packing in outer packagings.

A9 For combination packagings, if plastic bags are used, they must be packed in tightly closed metal receptacles before packing in outer packagings.

A10 When aluminum or aluminum alloy construction materials are used, they must be resistant to corrosion.

A11 For combination packagings, when metal inner packagings are permitted, only specification cylinders constructed of metals which are compatible with the hazardous material may be used.

A13 Bulk packagings are not authorized for transportation by aircraft.

A14 This material is not authorized to be transported as a limited quantity or consumer commodity in accordance with §173.306 of this subchapter when transported aboard an aircraft.

A19 Combination packagings consisting of outer fiber drums or plywood drums, with inner plastic packagings, are not authorized for transportation by aircraft.

A20 Plastic bags as inner receptacles of combination packagings are not authorized for transportation by aircraft.

A29 Combination packagings consisting of outer expanded plastic boxes with inner plastic bags are not authorized for transportation by aircraft.

A30 Ammonium permanganate is not authorized for transportation on aircraft.

A34 Aerosols containing a corrosive liquid in Packing Group II charged with a gas are not permitted for transportation by aircraft.

A35 This includes any material which is not covered by any of the other classes but which has an anesthetic, narcotic, noxious or other similar properties such that, in the event of spillage or leakage on an aircraft, extreme annoyance or discomfort could be caused to crew members so as to prevent the correct performance of assigned duties.

A37 This entry applies only to a material meeting the definition in §171.8 of this subchapter for self-defense spray.

A51 For aircraft batteries, irrespective of the quantity limitations specified in Column (9A) of the §172.101 Table or §175.75(c), wet cell batteries, UN2794 or UN2795, up to a limit of 100 kg net mass per package may be transported aboard passenger aircraft. Transport in accordance with this special provision must be noted on the shipping paper.

A53 Refrigerating machines and refrigerating machine components are not subject to the requirements of this subchapter when containing less than 12 kg (26.4 pounds) of a non-flammable gas or when containing 12 L (3 gallons) or less of ammonia solution (UN2672) (see §173.307 of this subchapter).

A54   Irrespective of the quantity limits in Column 9B of the §172.101 table, a lithium battery, including a lithium battery packed with, or contained in, equipment that otherwise meets the applicable requirements of §173.185, may have a mass exceeding 35 kg if approved by the Associate Administrator prior to shipment.

A56   Radioactive material with a subsidiary hazard of Division 4.2, Packing Group I, must be transported in Type B packages when offered for transportation by aircraft. Where the subsidiary hazard material is "Forbidden" in column (9A) or (9B) of the §172.101 Table, the radioactive material may only be offered for transportation and transported by aircraft under conditions approved by the Associate Administrator.

A60   Sterilization devices, when containing less than 30 mL per inner packaging with not more than 150 mL per outer packaging, may be transported in accordance with the provisions in §173.4a, irrespective of §173.4a(b), provided such packagings were first subjected to comparative fire testing. Comparative fire testing between a package as prepared for transport (including the substance to be transported) and an identical package filled with water must show that the maximum temperature measured inside the packages during testing does not differ by more than 200°C (392°F). Packagings may include a vent to permit the slow escape of gas (*i.e.* not more than 0.1 mL/hour per 30 mL inner packaging at 20°C (68°F) produced from gradual decomposition. The requirements of §§173.24(g)(1) and 173.27(c) do not apply.

A61   a. When used for purposes such as sterilization, inner packagings of peroxyacetic acid, stabilized, classified as UN 3107 Organic peroxide type E, liquid or UN 3109 Organic peroxide type F, liquid may be fitted with a vent consisting of hydrophobic membrane, provided:

    (1)   Each inner packaging contains not more than 70 mL;

    (2)   The inner packaging is designed so that the vent is not immersed in liquid in any orientation;

    (3)   Each inner packaging is enclosed in an intermediate rigid plastic packaging with a small opening to permit release of gas and contains a buffer that neutralizes the contents of the inner packaging in the event of leakage;

    (4)   Intermediate packagings are packed in a fiberboard box (4G) outer packaging;

    (5)   Each outer packaging contains not more than 1.4 L of liquid; and

    (6)   The rate of oxygen release from the outer packaging does not exceed 15 mL per hour.

    b.   Such packages must be transported on cargo aircraft only. The requirements of §§173.24(g)(1) and 173.27(c) do not apply.

A82   The quantity limits in columns (9A) and (9B) do not apply to human or animal body parts, whole organs or whole bodies known to contain or suspected of containing an infectious substance.

A100 Lithium ion cells and batteries must be offered for transport at a state of charge not exceeding 30 percent of their rated capacity. Lithium ion cells and batteries at a state of charge greater than 30 percent of their rated capacity may only be transported under conditions approved by the Associate Administrator in accordance with the requirements in 49 CFR part 107, subpart H. Guidance and methodology for determining the rated capacity can be found in sub-section 38.3.2.3 of the UN Manual of Tests and Criteria (IBR, *see* §171.7 of this subchapter).

A101 In addition to the applicable requirements of §173.185, the quantity of lithium metal in the batteries contained in any piece of equipment must not exceed 12 g per cell and 500 g per battery.

A105

a. This entry applies to machinery or apparatus containing hazardous materials as a residue or as an integral element of the machinery or apparatus. It must not be used for machinery or apparatus for which a proper shipping name already exists in the §172.101 Table.

b. Where the quantity of hazardous materials contained as an integral element in machinery or apparatus exceeds the limits permitted by §173.222(c)(2), and the hazardous materials meet the provisions of §173.222(c), the machinery or apparatus may be transported by aircraft only with the prior approval of the Associate Administrator.

A112 Notwithstanding the quantity limits shown in Column (9A) and (9B) for this entry, the following IBCs are authorized for transportation aboard passenger and cargo-only aircraft. Each IBC may not exceed a maximum net quantity of 1,000 kg:

a. Metal: 11A, 11B, 11N, 21A, 21B and 21N

b. Rigid plastics: 11H1, 11H2, 21H1 and 21H2

c. Composite with plastic inner receptacle: 11HZ1, 11HZ2, 21HZ1 and 21HZ2

d. Fiberboard: 11G

e. Wooden: 11C, 11D and 11F (with inner liners)

f. Flexible: 13H2, 13H3, 13H4, 13H5, 13L2, 13L3, 13L4, 13M1 and 13M2 (flexible IBCs must be sift-proof and water resistant or must be fitted with a sift-proof and water resistant liner).

A189 Except where the defining criteria of another class or division are met, concentrations of formaldehyde solution:

a. With less than 25 percent but not less than 10 percent formaldehyde, must be described as UN3334, Aviation regulated liquid, n.o.s.; and

b. With less than 10 percent formaldehyde, are not subject to this subchapter.

A191 Notwithstanding the Division 6.1 subsidiary risk for this description, the toxic subsidiary risk label and the requirement to indicate the subsidiary risk on the shipping paper are not required for manufactured articles containing less than 5 kg (11 pounds) of mercury.

A200 These articles must be transported as cargo and may not be carried aboard an aircraft by passengers or crewmembers in carry-on baggage, checked baggage, or on their person unless specifically authorized in §175.10.

A210 This substance is forbidden for transport by air. It may be transported on cargo aircraft only with the prior approval of the Associate Administrator.

A212 "UN 2031, Nitric acid, *other than red fuming, with more than 20% and less than 65% nitric acid*" intended for use in sterilization devices only, may be transported on passenger aircraft irrespective of the indication of "forbidden" in columns (9A) of the §172.101 table provided that:

     a.   Each inner packaging contains not more than 30 mL;

     b.   Each inner packaging is contained in a sealed leak-proof intermediate packaging with sufficient absorbent material capable of containing the contents of the inner packaging;

     c.   Intermediate packagings are securely packed in an outer packaging of a type permitted by §173.158(g) of this subchapter which meet the requirements of part 178 of this subchapter at the Packing Group I performance level;

     d.   The maximum quantity of nitric acid in the package does not exceed 300 mL; and

     e.   Transport in accordance with this special provision must be noted on the shipping paper.

     (3) *"B" codes.* These provisions apply only to bulk packagings. Except as otherwise provided in this subchapter, these special provisions do not apply to UN portable tanks or IBCs:

Code/Special provisions

B1 If the material has a flash point at or above 38°C (100°F) and below 93°C (200°F), then the bulk packaging requirements of §173.241 of this subchapter are applicable. If the material has a flash point of less than 38°C (100°F), then the bulk packaging requirements of §173.242 of this subchapter are applicable.

B2 MC 300, MC 301, MC 302, MC 303, MC 305, and MC 306, and DOT 406 cargo tanks are not authorized.

B3 MC 300, MC 301, MC 302, MC 303, MC 305, and MC 306, and DOT 406 cargo tanks and DOT 57 portable tanks are not authorized.

B4 MC 300, MC 301, MC 302, MC 303, MC 305, and MC 306, and DOT 406 cargo tanks are not authorized.

B5 Only ammonium nitrate solutions with 35 percent or less water that will remain completely in solution under all conditions of transport at a maximum lading temperature of 116°C (240°F) are authorized for transport in the following bulk packagings: MC 307, MC 312, DOT 407 and DOT 412 cargo tanks with at least 172 kPa (25 psig) design pressure. The packaging shall be designed for a working temperature of at least 121°C (250°F). Only Specifications MC 304, MC 307 or DOT 407 cargo tank motor vehicles are authorized for transportation by vessel.

B6 Packagings shall be made of steel.

B7 Safety relief devices are not authorized on multi-unit tank car tanks. Openings for safety relief devices on multi-unit tank car tanks shall be plugged or blank flanged.

B8 Packagings shall be made of nickel, stainless steel, or steel with nickel, stainless steel, lead or other suitable corrosion resistant metallic lining.

B9 Bottom outlets are not authorized.

B10 MC 300, MC 301, MC 302, MC 303, MC 305 and MC 306 and DOT 406 cargo tanks, and DOT 57 portable tanks are not authorized.

B11 Tank car tanks must have a test pressure of at least 2,068.5 kPa (300 psig). Cargo and portable tanks must have a design pressure of at least 1,207 kPa (175 psig).

B13 A nonspecification cargo tank motor vehicle authorized in §173.247 of this subchapter must be at least equivalent in design and in construction to a DOT 406 cargo tank or MC 306 cargo tank (if constructed before August 31, 1995), except as follows:

   a. Packagings equivalent to MC 306 cargo tanks are excepted from the certification, venting, and emergency flow requirements of the MC 306 specification.

   b. Packagings equivalent to DOT 406 cargo tanks are excepted from §§178.345-7(d)(5), circumferential reinforcements; 178.345-10, pressure relief; 178.345-11, outlets; 178.345-14, marking, and 178.345-15, certification.

   c. Packagings are excepted from the design stress limits at elevated temperatures, as described in Section VIII of the ASME Code (IBR, see §171.7 of this subchapter). However, the design stress limits may not exceed 25 percent of the stress for 0 temper at the maximum design temperature of the cargo tank, as specified in the Aluminum Association's "Aluminum Standards and Data" (IBR, see §171.7 of this subchapter).

B14 Each bulk packaging, except a tank car or a multi-unit-tank car tank, must be insulated with an insulating material so that the overall thermal conductance at 15.5°C (60°F) is no more than 1.5333 kilojoules per hour per square meter per degree Celsius (0.075 Btu per hour per square foot per degree Fahrenheit) temperature differential. Insulating materials must not promote corrosion to steel when wet.

B15   Packagings must be protected with non-metallic linings impervious to the lading or have a suitable corrosion allowance.

B16   The lading must be completely covered with nitrogen, inert gas or other inert materials.

B18   Open steel hoppers or bins are authorized.

B23   Tanks must be made of steel that is rubber lined or unlined. Unlined tanks must be passivated before being placed in service. If unlined tanks are washed out with water, they must be repassivated prior to return to service. Lading in unlined tanks must be inhibited so that the corrosive effect on steel is not greater than that of hydrofluoric acid of 65 percent concentration.

B25   Packagings must be made from monel or nickel or monel-lined or nickel-lined steel.

B26   Tanks must be insulated. Insulation must be at least 100 mm (3.9 inches) except that the insulation thickness may be reduced to 51 mm (2 inches) over the exterior heater coils. Interior heating coils are not authorized. The packaging may not be loaded with a material outside of the packaging's design temperature range. In addition, the material also must be covered with an inert gas or the container must be filled with water to the tank's capacity. After unloading, the residual material also must be covered with an inert gas or the container must be filled with water to the tank's capacity.

B27   Tanks must have a service pressure of 1,034 kPa (150 psig). Tank car tanks must have a test pressure rating of 1,379 kPa (200 psig). Lading must be blanketed at all times with a dry inert gas at a pressure not to exceed 103 kPa (15 psig).

B28   Packagings must be made of stainless steel.

B30   MC 312, MC 330, MC 331 and DOT 412 cargo tanks and DOT 51 portable tanks must be made of stainless steel, except that steel other than stainless steel may be used in accordance with the provisions of §173.24b(b) of this subchapter. Thickness of stainless steel for tank shell and heads for cargo tanks and portable tanks must be the greater of 7.62 mm (0.300 inch) or the thickness required for a tank with a design pressure at least equal to 1.5 times the vapor pressure of the lading at 46°C (115°F). In addition, MC 312 and DOT 412 cargo tank motor vehicles must:

a.   Be ASME Code (U) stamped for 100% radiography of all pressure-retaining welds;

b.   Have accident damage protection which conforms with §178.345-8 of this subchapter;

c.   Have a MAWP or design pressure of at least 87 psig: and

d.   Have a bolted manway cover.

B32 MC 312, MC 330, MC 331, DOT 412 cargo tanks and DOT 51 portable tanks must be made of stainless steel, except that steel other than stainless steel may be used in accordance with the provisions of §173.24b(b) of this subchapter. Thickness of stainless steel for tank shell and heads for cargo tanks and portable tanks must be the greater of 6.35 mm (0.250 inch) or the thickness required for a tank with a design pressure at least equal to 1.3 times the vapor pressure of the lading at 46°C (115°F). In addition, MC 312 and DOT 412 cargo tank motor vehicles must:

    a. Be ASME Code (U) stamped for 100% radiography of all pressure-retaining welds;

    b. Have accident damage protection which conforms with §178.345-8 of this subchapter;

    c. Have a MAWP or design pressure of at least 87 psig; and

    d. Have a bolted manway cover.

B33 MC 300, MC 301, MC 302, MC 303, MC 305, MC 306, and DOT 406 cargo tanks equipped with a 1 psig normal vent used to transport gasoline must conform to Table I of this Special Provision. Based on the volatility class determined by using ASTM D439 and the Reid vapor pressure (RVP) of the particular gasoline, the maximum lading pressure and maximum ambient temperature permitted during the loading of gasoline may not exceed that listed in Table I.

TABLE I—MAXIMUM AMBIENT TEMPERATURE—GASOLINE

ASTM D439 volatility class	Maximum lading and ambient temperature (see note 1)
A (RVP<=9.0 psia)	131°F
B (RVP<=10.0 psia)	124°F
C (RVP<=11.5 psia)	116°F
D (RVP<=13.5 psia)	107°F
E (RVP<=15.0 psia)	100°F

Note 1: Based on maximum lading pressure of 1 psig at top of cargo tank.

B35 Tank cars containing hydrogen cyanide may be alternatively marked "Hydrocyanic acid, liquefied" if otherwise conforming to marking requirements in subpart D of this part. Tank cars marked "HYDROCYANIC ACID" prior to October 1, 1991 do not need to be remarked.

B42 Tank cars constructed before March 16, 2009, must have a test pressure of 34.47 Bar (500 psig) or greater and conform to Class 105J. Each tank car must have a reclosing pressure relief device having a start-to-discharge pressure of 10.34 Bar (150 psig). The tank car specification may be marked to indicate a test pressure of 13.79 Bar (200 psig).

B44   All parts of valves and safety relief devices in contact with lading must be of a material which will not cause formation of acetylides.

B45   Each tank must have a reclosing combination pressure relief device equipped with stainless steel or platinum rupture discs approved by the AAR Tank Car Committee.

B46   The detachable protective housing for the loading and unloading valves of multi-unit tank car tanks must withstand tank test pressure and must be approved by the Associate Administrator.

B47   Each tank may have a reclosing pressure relief device having a start-to-discharge pressure setting of 310 kPa (45 psig).

B48   Portable tanks in sodium metal service may be visually inspected at least once every 5 years instead of being retested hydrostatically. Date of the visual inspection must be stenciled on the tank near the other required markings.

B49   Tanks equipped with interior heater coils are not authorized. Single unit tank car tanks must have a reclosing pressure relief device having a start-to-discharge pressure set at no more than 1551 kPa (225 psig).

B52   Notwithstanding the provisions of §173.24b of this subchapter, non-reclosing pressure relief devices are authorized on DOT 57 portable tanks.

B53   Packagings must be made of either aluminum or steel.

B54   Open-top, sift-proof rail cars are also authorized.

B55   Water-tight, sift-proof, closed-top, metal-covered hopper cars, equipped with a venting arrangement (including flame arrestors) approved by the Associate Administrator are also authorized.

B56   Water-tight, sift-proof, closed-top, metal-covered hopper cars also authorized if the particle size of the hazardous material is not less than 149 microns.

B57   Class 115A tank car tanks used to transport chloroprene must be equipped with a non-reclosing pressure relief device of a diameter not less than 305 mm (12 inches) with a maximum rupture disc burst pressure of 310 kPa (45 psig).

B59   Water-tight, sift-proof, closed-top, metal-covered hopper cars are also authorized provided that the lading is covered with a nitrogen blanket.

B61   Written procedures covering details of tank car appurtenances, dome fittings, safety devices, and marking, loading, handling, inspection, and testing practices must be approved by the Associate Administrator before any single unit tank car tank is offered for transportation.

B65   Tank cars constructed before March 16, 2009, must have a test pressure of 34.47 Bar (500 psig) or greater and conform to Class 105A. Each tank car must have a reclosing pressure relief device having a start-to-discharge pressure of 15.51 Bar (225 psig). The tank car specification may be marked to indicate a test pressure of 20.68 Bar (300 psig).

B66 Each tank must be equipped with gas tight valve protection caps. Outage must be sufficient to prevent tanks from becoming liquid full at 55°C (130°F). Specification 110A500W tanks must be stainless steel.

B67 All valves and fittings must be protected by a securely attached cover made of metal not subject to deterioration by the lading, and all valve openings, except safety valve, must be fitted with screw plugs or caps to prevent leakage in the event of valve failure.

B68 Sodium must be in a molten condition when loaded and allowed to solidify before shipment. Outage must be at least 5 percent at 98°C (208°F). Bulk packagings must have exterior heating coils fusion welded to the tank shell which have been properly stress relieved. The only tank car tanks authorized are Class DOT 105 tank cars having a test pressure of 2,069 kPa (300 psig) or greater.

B69 Dry sodium cyanide or potassium cyanide may be shipped in the following sift-proof and weather-resistant packagings: metal covered hopper cars, covered motor vehicles, portable tanks, or non-specification bins.

B70 If DOT 103ANW tank car tank is used: All cast metal in contact with the lading must have 96.7 percent nickel content; and the lading must be anhydrous and free from any impurities.

B76 Tank cars constructed before March 16, 2009, must have a test pressure of 20.68 Bar (300 psig) or greater and conform to Class 105S, 112J, 114J or 120S. Each tank car must have a reclosing pressure relief device having a start-to-discharge pressure of 10.34 Bar (150 psig). The tank car specification may be marked to indicate a test pressure of 13.79 Bar (200 psig).

B77 Other packaging are authorized when approved by the Associate Administrator.

B78 Tank cars must have a test pressure of 4.14 Bar (60 psig) or greater and conform to Class 103, 104, 105, 109, 111, 112, 114 or 120. Heater pipes must be of welded construction designed for a test pressure of 500 pounds per square inch. A 25 mm (1 inch) woven lining of asbestos or other approved material must be placed between the bolster slabbing and the bottom of the tank. If a tank car tank is equipped with a non-reclosing pressure relief device, the rupture disc must be perforated with a 3.2 mm (0.13 inch) diameter hole. If a tank car tank is equipped with a reclosing pressure relief valve, the tank must also be equipped with a vacuum relief valve.

B80 Each cargo tank must have a minimum design pressure of 276 kPa (40 psig).

B81 Venting and pressure relief devices for tank car tanks and cargo tanks must be approved by the Associate Administrator.

B82 Cargo tanks and portable tanks are not authorized.

B83 Bottom outlets are prohibited on tank car tanks transporting sulfuric acid in concentrations over 65.25 percent.

B84   Packagings must be protected with non-metallic linings impervious to the lading or have a suitable corrosion allowance for sulfuric acid or spent sulfuric acid in concentration up to 65.25 percent.

B85   Cargo tanks must be marked with the name of the lading accordance with the requirements of §172.302(b).

B90   Steel tanks conforming or equivalent to ASME specifications which contain solid or semisolid residual motor fuel antiknock mixture (including rust, scale, or other contaminants) may be shipped by rail freight or highway. The tank must have been designed and constructed to be capable of withstanding full vacuum. All openings must be closed with gasketed blank flanges or vapor tight threaded closures.

B115 Rail cars, highway trailers, roll-on/roll-off bins, or other non-specification bulk packagings are authorized. Packagings must be sift-proof, prevent liquid water from reaching the hazardous material, and be provided with sufficient venting to preclude dangerous accumulation of flammable, corrosive, or toxic gaseous emissions such as methane, hydrogen, and ammonia. The material must be loaded dry.

B116 The use of non specification, sift-proof dump or hopper type vehicles, and sift-proof roll-on/roll-off bulk bins, which must be covered by a tarpaulin, metal cover, or equivalent means is authorized for the transportation of spent bleaching earth by motor vehicle. The material is also be subject to operational controls which include not exceeding a temperature of 55°C (130°F) at the time it is offered or during transportation, not exceeding a transportation time of 24 hours, and drivers transporting spent bleaching earth must be trained in the properties and hazards of the spent bleaching earth. This training must be documented in training records required by §172.704(d).

B120 The use of flexible bulk containers conforming to the requirements in subpart R and subpart S of part 178 of this subchapter is permitted.

B130 When transported by motor vehicle, used diatomaceous earth filter material is not subject to any other requirements of this subchapter except for the shipping paper requirements of subpart C of part 172 of this subchapter; emergency response information as required by §172.602(a)(2) through (a)(7) of this subchapter; and the marking requirements of §172.302 of this subchapter, if the following requirements are met:

  a.   Packagings are non-DOT specification sift-proof motor vehicles or sift-proof roll-on/roll-off bulk bins, which are covered by a tarpaulin or other equivalent means.

  b.   The temperature of the material at the time it is offered for transport and during transportation may not exceed 55°C (130°F).

  c.   The time between offering the material for transportation at the point of origin, and unloading the material at the destination does not exceed 48 hours.

d. In addition to the training requirements prescribed in §§172.700 through 172.704, each driver must be trained regarding the properties and hazards of diatomaceous earth filter material, precautions to ensure safe transport of the material, and actions to be taken in the event of an emergency during transportation, or a substantial delay in transit.

B131 When transported by highway, rail, or cargo vessel, waste Paint and Paint related material (UN1263; PG II and PG III), when in plastic or metal inner packagings of not more than 26.5 L (7 gallons), are excepted from the marking requirements in §172.301(a) and (c) and the labeling requirements in §172.400(a), when further packed in the following specification and non-specification bulk outer packagings and under the following conditions:

a. Primary receptacles must conform to the general packaging requirements of subpart B of part 173 of this subchapter and may not leak. If they do leak, they must be overpacked in packagings conforming to the specification requirements of part 178 of this subchapter or in salvage packagings conforming to the requirements in §173.12 of this subchapter.

b. Primary receptacles must be further packed in non-specification bulk outer packagings such as cubic yard boxes, plastic rigid-wall bulk containers, dump trailers, and roll-off containers. Bulk outer packagings must be liquid tight through design or by the use of lining materials.

c. Primary receptacles may also be further packed in specification bulk outer packagings. Authorized specification bulk outer packagings are UN11G fiberboard intermediate bulk containers (IBC) and UN13H4 woven plastic, coated and with liner flexible intermediate bulk containers (FIBCs) meeting the Packing Group II performance level and lined with a plastic liner of at least 6 mil thickness.

d. All inner packagings placed inside bulk outer packagings must be blocked and braced to prevent movement during transportation that could cause the container to open or fall over. Specification IBCs and FIBCs are to be secured to a pallet.

B132 Except for transportation by aircraft, UN2813, Water reactive solid, n.o.s. (contains magnesium, magnesium nitrides) in PG II or III may be packaged in sift-proof bulk packagings that prevent liquid from reaching the hazardous material with sufficient venting to preclude dangerous accumulation of flammable, corrosive or toxic gaseous emissions such as methane, hydrogen and ammonia.

B133 Hydrochloric acid concentration not exceeding 38%, in Packing Group II, is authorized to be packaged in UN31H1 or UN31HH1 intermediate bulk containers when loaded in accordance with the requirements of §173.35(h) of this subchapter.

B134 For Large Packagings offered for transport by vessel, flexible or fibre inner packagings shall be sift-proof and water-resistant or shall be fitted with a sift-proof and water-resistant liner.

B135 For Large Packagings offered for transport by vessel, flexible or fibre inner packagings shall be hermetically sealed.

B136 Non-specification closed bulk bins are authorized.

(4) *IB Codes and IP Codes.* These provisions apply only to transportation in IBCs and Large Packagings. Table 1 authorizes IBCs for specific proper shipping names through the use of IB Codes assigned in the §172.101 table of this subchapter. Table 2 defines IP Codes on the use of IBCs that are assigned to specific commodities in the §172.101 Table of this subchapter. Table 3 authorizes Large Packagings for specific proper shipping names through the use of IB Codes assigned in the §172.101 table of this subchapter. Large Packagings are authorized for the Packing Group III entries of specific proper shipping names when either special provision IB3 or IB8 is assigned to that entry in the §172.101 Table. When no IB code is assigned in the §172.101 Table for a specific proper shipping name, or in §173.185 or §173.225(e) Organic Peroxide Table for Type F organic peroxides, use of an IBC or Large Packaging for the material may be authorized when approved by the Associate Administrator. The letter "Z" shown in the marking code for composite IBCs must be replaced with a capital code letter designation found in §178.702(a)(2) of this subchapter to specify the material used for the other packaging. Tables 1, 2, and 3 follow:

TABLE 1—IB CODES (IBC CODES)

IBC code	Authorized IBCs
IB1	*Authorized IBCs:* Metal (31A, 31B and 31N). *Additional Requirement:* Only liquids with a vapor pressure less than or equal to 110 kPa at 50°C (1.1 bar at 122°F), or 130 kPa at 55°C (1.3 bar at 131°F) are authorized.
IB2	*Authorized IBCs:* Metal (31A, 31B and 31N); Rigid plastics (31H1 and 31H2); Composite (31HZ1). *Additional Requirement:* Only liquids with a vapor pressure less than or equal to 110 kPa at 50°C (1.1 bar at 122°F), or 130 kPa at 55°C (1.3 bar at 131°F) are authorized.
IB3	*Authorized IBCs:* Metal (31A, 31B and 31N); Rigid plastics (31H1 and 31H2); Composite (31HZ1 and 31HA2, 31HB2, 31HN2, 31HD2 and 31HH2). *Additional Requirement:* Only liquids with a vapor pressure less than or equal to 110 kPa at 50°C (1.1 bar at 122°F), or 130 kPa at 55°C (1.3 bar at 131°F) are authorized, except for UN2672 (also see special provision IP8 in Table 2 for UN2672).
IB4	*Authorized IBCs:* Metal (11A, 11B, 11N, 21A, 21B, 21N, 31A, 31B and 31N).
IB5	*Authorized IBCs:* Metal (11A, 11B, 11N, 21A, 21B, 21N, 31A, 31B and 31N); Rigid plastics (11H1, 11H2, 21H1, 21H2, 31H1 and 31H2); Composite (11HZ1, 21HZ1 and 31HZ1).

TABLE 1—IB CODES (IBC CODES) , Continued

IBC code	Authorized IBCs
IB6	*Authorized IBCs:* Metal (11A, 11B, 11N, 21A, 21B, 21N, 31A, 31B and 31N); Rigid plastics (11H1, 11H2, 21H1, 21H2, 31H1 and 31H2); Composite (11HZ1, 11HZ2, 21HZ1, 21HZ2 and 31HZ1). *Additional Requirement:* Composite IBCs 11HZ2 and 21HZ2 may not be used when the hazardous materials being transported may become liquid during transport.
IB7	*Authorized IBCs:* Metal (11A, 11B, 11N, 21A, 21B, 21N, 31A, 31B and 31N); Rigid plastics (11H1, 11H2, 21H1, 21H2, 31H1 and 31H2); Composite (11HZ1, 11HZ2, 21HZ1, 21HZ2 and 31HZ1); Wooden (11C, 11D and 11F). *Additional Requirement:* Liners of wooden IBCs must be sift-proof.
IB8	*Authorized IBCs:* Metal (11A, 11B, 11N, 21A, 21B, 21N, 31A, 31B and 31N); Rigid plastics (11H1, 11H2, 21H1, 21H2, 31H1 and 31H2); Composite (11HZ1, 11HZ2, 21HZ1, 21HZ2 and 31HZ1); Fiberboard (11G); Wooden (11C, 11D and 11F); Flexible (13H1, 13H2, 13H3, 13H4, 13H5, 13L1, 13L2, 13L3, 13L4, 13M1 or 13M2).
IB9	IBCs are only authorized if approved by the Associate Administrator.

TABLE 2—IP CODES

IP code	
IP1	IBCs must be packed in closed freight containers or a closed transport vehicle.
IP2	When IBCs other than metal or rigid plastics IBCs are used, they must be offered for transportation in a closed freight container or a closed transport vehicle.
IP3	Flexible IBCs must be sift-proof and water-resistant or must be fitted with a sift-proof and water-resistant liner.
IP4	Flexible, fiberboard or wooden IBCs must be sift-proof and water-resistant or be fitted with a sift-proof and water-resistant liner.
IP5	IBCs must have a device to allow venting. The inlet to the venting device must be located in the vapor space of the IBC under maximum filling conditions.
IP6	Non-specification bulk bins are authorized.
IP7	For UN identification numbers 1327, 1363, 1364, 1365, 1386, 1841, 2211, 2217, 2793 and 3314, IBCs are not required to meet the IBC performance tests specified in part 178, subpart N, of this subchapter.
IP8	Ammonia solutions may be transported in rigid or composite plastic IBCs (31H1, 31H2 and 31HZ1) that have successfully passed, without leakage or permanent deformation, the hydrostatic test specified in §178.814 of this subchapter at a test pressure that is not less than 1.5 times the vapor pressure of the contents at 55°C (131°F).
IP13	Transportation by vessel in IBCs is prohibited.
IP14	Air must be eliminated from the vapor space by nitrogen or other means.
IP15	For UN2031 with more than 55% nitric acid, rigid plastic IBCs and composite IBCs with a rigid plastic inner receptacle are authorized for two years from the date of IBC manufacture.
IP16	IBCs of type 31A and 31N are only authorized if approved by the Associate Administrator.

TABLE 2—IP CODES, Continued

IP code	
IP19	For UN identification numbers 3531, 3532, 3533, and 3534, IBCs must be designed and constructed to permit the release of gas or vapor to prevent a build-up of pressure that could rupture the IBCs in the event of loss of stabilization.
IP20	Dry sodium cyanide or potassium cyanide is also permitted in siftproof, water-resistant, fiberboard IBCs when transported in closed freight containers or transport vehicles.
IP21	When transported by vessel, flexible, fiberboard or wooden IBCs must be sift-proof and water-resistant or be fitted with a sift-proof and water-resistant liner.

TABLE 3—IB CODES
[Large packaging authorizations]

IB3	Authorized Large Packagings (LIQUIDS) (PG III materials only)[2]
Inner packagings: Glass 10 liter Plastics 30 liter Metal 40 liter	Large outer packagings: steel (50A). aluminum (50B). metal other than steel or aluminum (50N). rigid plastics (50H). natural wood (50C). plywood (50D). reconstituted wood (50F). rigid fiverboard (50G).
IB8	Authorized Large Packagings (SOLIDS) (PG III materials only)[2]
Inner packagings: Glass 10 kg Plastics 50 kg Metal 50 kg Paper 50 kg Fiber 50 kg	Large outer packagings: steel (50A). aluminum (50B). metal other than steel or aluminum (50N). flexible plastics (51H)[1]. rigid plastics (50H). natural wood (50C). plywood (50D). reconstituted wood (50F). rigid fiberboard (50G).

[1]Flexible plastic (51H) Large Packagings are only authorized for use with flexible inner packagings.
[2]Except when authorized under Special Provision 41.

(5) *"N" codes.* These provisions apply only to non-bulk packagings:

Code/Special provisions

N3   Glass inner packagings are permitted in combination or composite packagings only if the hazardous material is free from hydrofluoric acid.

N4   For combination or composite packagings, glass inner packagings, other than ampoules, are not permitted.

N5   Glass materials of construction are not authorized for any part of a packaging which is normally in contact with the hazardous material.

N6 Battery fluid packaged with electric storage batteries, wet or dry, must conform to the packaging provisions of §173.159(g) or (h) of this subchapter.

N7 The hazard class or division number of the material must be marked on the package in accordance with §172.302 of this subchapter. However, the hazard label corresponding to the hazard class or division may be substituted for the marking.

N8 Nitroglycerin solution in alcohol may be transported under this entry only when the solution is packed in metal cans of not more than 1 L capacity each, overpacked in a wooden box containing not more than 5 L. Metal cans must be completely surrounded with absorbent cushioning material. Wooden boxes must be completely lined with a suitable material impervious to water and nitroglycerin.

N11 This material is excepted for the specification packaging requirements of this subchapter if the material is packaged in strong, tight non-bulk packaging meeting the requirements of subparts A and B of part 173 of this subchapter.

N12 Plastic packagings are not authorized.

N20 A 5M1 multi-wall paper bag is authorized if transported in a closed transport vehicle.

N25 Steel single packagings are not authorized.

N32 Aluminum materials of construction are not authorized for single packagings.

N33 Aluminum drums are not authorized.

N34 Aluminum construction materials are not authorized for any part of a packaging which is normally in contact with the hazardous material.

N36 Aluminum or aluminum alloy construction materials are permitted only for halogenated hydrocarbons that will not react with aluminum.

N37 This material may be shipped in an integrally-lined fiber drum (1G) which meets the general packaging requirements of subpart B of part 173 of this subchapter, the requirements of part 178 of this subchapter at the packing group assigned for the material and to any other special provisions of column 7 of the §172.101 table.

N40 This material is not authorized in the following packagings:

    a. A combination packaging consisting of a 4G fiberboard box with inner receptacles of glass or earthenware;

    b. A single packaging of a 4C2 sift-proof, natural wood box; or

    c. A composite packaging 6PG2 (glass, porcelain or stoneware receptacles within a fiberboard box).

N41 Metal construction materials are not authorized for any part of a packaging which is normally in contact with the hazardous material.

N42   1A1 drums made of carbon steel with thickness of body and heads of not less than 1.3 mm (0.050 inch) and with a corrosion-resistant phenolic lining are authorized for stabilized benzyl chloride if tested and certified to the Packing Group I performance level at a specific gravity of not less than 1.8.

N43   Metal drums are permitted as single packagings only if constructed of nickel or monel.

N45   Copper cartridges are authorized as inner packagings if the hazardous material is not in dispersion.

N65   Outage must be sufficient to prevent cylinders or spheres from becoming liquid full at 55°C (130°F). The vacant space (outage) may be charged with a nonflammable nonliquefied compressed gas if the pressure in the cylinder or sphere at 55°C (130°F) does not exceed 125 percent of the marked service pressure.

N73   Packagings consisting of outer wooden or fiberboard boxes with inner glass, metal or other strong containers; metal or fiber drums; kegs or barrels; or strong metal cans are authorized and need not conform to the requirements of part 178 of this subchapter.

N74   Packages consisting of tightly closed inner containers of glass, earthenware, metal or polyethylene, capacity not over 0.5 kg (1.1 pounds) securely cushioned and packed in outer wooden barrels or wooden or fiberboard boxes, not over 15 kg (33 pounds) net weight, are authorized and need not conform to the requirements of part 178 of this subchapter.

N75   Packages consisting of tightly closed inner packagings of glass, earthenware or metal, securely cushioned and packed in outer wooden barrels or wooden or fiberboard boxes, capacity not over 2.5 kg (5.5 pounds) net weight, are authorized and need not conform to the requirements of part 178 of this subchapter.

N76   For materials of not more than 25 percent active ingredient by weight, packages consisting of inner metal packagings not greater than 250 mL (8 ounces) capacity each, packed in strong outer packagings together with sufficient absorbent material to completely absorb the liquid contents are authorized and need not conform to the requirements of part 178 of this subchapter.

N77   For materials of not more than two percent active ingredients by weight, packagings need not conform to the requirements of part 178 of this subchapter, if liquid contents are absorbed in an inert material.

N78   Packages consisting of inner glass, earthenware, or polyethylene or other nonfragile plastic bottles or jars not over 0.5 kg (1.1 pounds) capacity each, or metal cans not over five pounds capacity each, packed in outer wooden boxes, barrels or kegs, or fiberboard boxes are authorized and need not conform to the requirements of part 178 of this subchapter. Net weight of contents in fiberboard boxes may not exceed 29 kg (64 pounds). Net weight of contents in wooden boxes, barrels or kegs may not exceed 45 kg (99 pounds).

N79 Packages consisting of tightly closed metal inner packagings not over 0.5 kg (1.1 pounds) capacity each, packed in outer wooden or fiberboard boxes, or wooden barrels, are authorized and need not conform to the requirements of part 178 of this subchapter. Net weight of contents may not exceed 15 kg (33 pounds).

N80 Packages consisting of one inner metal can, not over 2.5 kg (5.5 pounds) capacity, packed in an outer wooden or fiberboard box, or a wooden barrel, are authorized and need not conform to the requirements of part 178 of this subchapter.

N82 See §173.115 of this subchapter for classification criteria for flammable aerosols.

N83 This material may not be transported in quantities of more than 11.5 kg (25.4 lbs) per package.

N84 The maximum quantity per package is 500 g (1.1 lbs.).

N85 Packagings certified at the Packing Group I performance level may not be used.

N86 UN pressure receptacles made of aluminum alloy are not authorized.

N87 The use of copper valves on UN pressure receptacles is prohibited.

N88 Any metal part of a UN pressure receptacle in contact with the contents may not contain more than 65% copper, with a tolerance of 1%.

N89 When steel UN pressure receptacles are used, only those bearing the "H" mark are authorized.

N90 Metal packagings are not authorized. Packagings of other material with a small amount of metal, for example metal closures or other metal fittings such as those mentioned in part 178 of this subchapter, are not considered metal packagings. Packagings of other material constructed with a small amount of metal must be designed such that the hazardous material does not contact the metal.

N91 The use of a non specification sift-proof, non-bulk, metal can with or without lid, or a non specification sift-proof, non-bulk fiber drum, with or without lid is authorized when transporting coal tar pitch compounds by motor vehicle or rail freight. The fiber drum must to be fabricated with a three ply wall, as a minimum. The coal tar pitch compound must be in a solid mass during transportation.

N92 Notwithstanding the provisions of §173.24(g) of this subchapter, packagings shall be designed and constructed to permit the release of gas or vapor to prevent a build-up of pressure that could rupture the packagings in the event of loss of stabilization.

N95 UN1075, Liquefied petroleum gas and UN1978, Propane authorized for transport in DOT 4BA240 cylinders is not subject to the UN identification number and proper shipping name marking or the label requirements of this part subject to the following conditions:

    a.   The cylinder must be transported in a closed motor vehicle displaying FLAMMABLE GAS placards in accordance with subpart F of part 172 of this subchapter.

    b.   Shipping papers at all times must reflect a correct current accounting of all cylinders both full and expended.

    c.   The cylinders are collected and transported by a private or a contract carrier for reconditioning, reuse or disposal.

(6) *"R" codes.* These provisions apply only to transportation by rail.

R1   A person who offers for transportation tank cars containing sulfur, molten or residue of sulfur, molten may reference the Sulfur Institute's, "Molten Sulphur Rail Tank Car Guidance document" (see §171.7 of this subchapter) to identify tank cars that may pose a risk in transportation due to the accumulation of formed, solid sulfur on the outside of the tank.

(7) *"T" codes.* (i) These provisions apply to the transportation of hazardous materials in UN portable tanks. Portable tank instructions specify the requirements applicable to a portable tank when used for the transportation of a specific hazardous material. These requirements must be met in addition to the design and construction specifications in part 178 of this subchapter. Portable tank instructions T1 through T22 specify the applicable minimum test pressure, the mini mum shell thickness (in reference steel), bottom opening requirements and pressure relief requirements. Liquefied compressed gases are assigned to portable tank instruction T50. Refrigerated liquefied gases that are authorized to be transported in portable tanks are specified in tank instruction T75.

(ii) The following table specifies the portable tank requirements applicable to "T" Codes T1 through T22. Column 1 specifies the "T" Code. Column 2 specifies the minimum test pressure, in bar (1 bar = 14.5 psig), at which the periodic hydrostatic testing required by §180.605 of this subchapter must be conducted. Column 3 specifies the section reference for minimum shell thickness or, alternatively, the minimum shell thickness value. Column 4 specifies the applicability of §178.275(g)(3) of this subchapter for the pressure relief devices. When the word "Normal" is indicated, §178.275(g)(3)) of this subchapter does not apply. Column 5 references applicable requirements for bottom openings in part 178 of this subchapter. "Prohibited" means bottom openings are prohibited, and "Prohibited for liquids" means bottom openings are authorized for solid material only. The table follows:

TABLE OF PORTABLE TANK T CODES T1—T22

[Portable tank codes T1—T22 apply to liquid and solid hazardous materials of Classes 3 through 9 which are transported in portable tanks.]

Portable tank instruction (1)	Minimum test pressure (bar) (2)	Minimum shell thickness (in mm-reference steel) (*See* §178.274(d)) (3)	Pressure-relief requirements (*See* §178.275(g)) (4)	Bottom opening requirements (*See* §178.275(d)) (5)
T1	1.5	§178.274(d)(2)	Normal	§178.275(d)(2).
T2	1.5	§178.274(d)(2)	Normal	§178.275(d)(3).
T3	2.65	§178.274(d)(2)	Normal	§178.275(d)(2).
T4	2.65	§178.274(d)(2)	Normal	§178.275(d)(3).

TABLE OF PORTABLE TANK T CODES T1—T22, Continued

Portable tank instruction (1)	Minimum test pressure (bar) (2)	Minimum shell thickness (in mm-reference steel) (See §178.274(d)) (3)	Pressure-relief requirements (See §178.275(g)) (4)	Bottom opening requirements (See §178.275(d)) (5)
T5	2.65	§178.274(d)(2)	§178.275(g)(3)	Prohibited.
T6	4	§178.274(d)(2)	Normal	§178.275(d)(2).
T7	4	§178.274(d)(2)	Normal	§178.275(d)(3).
T8	4	§178.274(d)(2)	Normal	Prohibited.
T9	4	6 mm	Normal	Prohibited for liquids.
T10	4	6 mm	§178.275(g)(3)	Prohibited.
T11	6	§178.274(d)(2)	Normal	§178.275(d)(3).
T12	6	§178.274(d)(2)	§178.275(g)(3)	§178.275(d)(3).
T13	6	6 mm	Normal	Prohibited.
T14	6	6 mm	§178.275(g)(3)	Prohibited.
T15	10	§178.274(d)(2)	Normal	§178.275(d)(3).
T16	10	§178.274(d)(2)	§178.275(g)(3)	§178.275(d)(3).
T17	10	6 mm	Normal	§178.275(d)(3).
T18	10	6 mm	§178.275(g)(3)	§178.275(d)(3).
T19	10	6 mm	§178.275(g)(3)	Prohibited.
T20	10	8 mm	§178.275(g)(3)	Prohibited.
T21	10	10 mm	Normal	Prohibited for liquids. §178.275(d)(2).
T22	10	10 mm	§178.275(g)(3)	Prohibited.

(iii) T50 When portable tank instruction T50 is indicated in Column (7) of the §172.101 Hazardous Materials Table, the applicable liquefied compressed gas and chemical under pressure descriptions are authorized to be transported in portable tanks in accordance with the requirements of §173.313 of this subchapter.

(iv) T75. When portable tank instruction T75 is referenced in Column (7) of the §172.101 Table, the applicable refrigerated liquefied gases are authorized to be transported in portable tanks in accordance with the requirements of §178.277 of this subchapter.

(v) *UN and IM portable tank codes/special provisions.* When a specific portable tank instruction is specified by a "T" Code in Column (7) of the §172.101 Table for a specific hazardous material, a specification portable tank conforming to an alternative tank instruction may be used if:

(A) The alternative portable tank has a higher or equivalent test pressure (for example, 4 bar when 2.65 bar is specified);

(B) The alternative portable tank has greater or equivalent wall thickness (for example, 10 mm when 6 mm is specified);

(C) The alternative portable tank has a pressure relief device as specified in the "T" Code. If a frangible disc is required in series with the reclosing pressure relief device for the specified portable tank, the alternative portable tank must be fitted with a frangible disc in series with the reclosing pressure relief device; and

(D) With regard to bottom openings—

(1) When two effective means are specified, the alternative portable tank is fitted with bottom openings having two or three effective means of closure or no bottom openings; or

(2) When three effective means are specified, the portable tank has no bottom openings or three effective means of closure; or

(3) When no bottom openings are authorized, the alternative portable tank must not have bottom openings.

(vi) Except when an organic peroxide is authorized under §173.225(g), if a hazardous material is not assigned a portable tank "T" Code, the hazardous material may not be transported in a portable tank unless approved by the Associate Administrator.

(8) *"TP" codes.* (i) These provisions apply to the transportation of hazardous materials in IM and UN Specification portable tanks. Portable tank special provisions are assigned to certain hazardous materials to specify requirements that are in addition to those provided by the portable tank instructions or the requirements in part 178 of this subchapter. Portable tank special provisions are designated with the abbreviation TP (tank provision) and are assigned to specific hazardous materials in Column (7) of the §172.101 Table.

(ii) The following is a list of the portable tank special provisions:

Code/Special provisions

TP1   The maximum degree of filling must not exceed the degree of filling determined by the following:

$$\left(\text{Degree of filling} = \frac{97}{1 + \alpha(t_r - t_f)} \right).$$

Where:

t_r is the maximum mean bulk temperature during transport, and tf is the temperature in degrees celsius of the liquid during filling.

TP2   a. The maximum degree of filling must not exceed the degree of filling determined by the following:

$$\left(\text{Degree of filling} = \frac{95}{1 + \alpha(t_r - t_f)} \right).$$

Where:

t_r is the maximum mean bulk temperature during transport,

t_f is the temperature in degrees celsius of the liquid during filling, and

α is the mean coefficient of cubical expansion of the liquid between the mean temperature of the liquid during filling (t_f) and the maximum mean bulk temperature during transportation (t_r) both in degrees celsius.

b. For liquids transported under ambient conditions α may be calculated using the formula:

$$\alpha = \frac{d_{15} - d_{50}}{35\,d_{50}}$$

Where:

d_{15} and d_{50} are the densities (in units of mass per unit volume) of the liquid at 15°C (59°F) and 50°C (122°F), respectively.

TP3 The maximum degree of filling (in %) for solids transported above their melting points and for elevated temperature liquids shall be determined by the following:

$$\left(\text{Degree of filling} = 95\,\frac{d_r}{d_f} \right).$$

Where: d_f and d_r are the mean densities of the liquid at the mean temperature of the liquid during filling and the maximum mean bulk temperature during transport respectively.

TP4 The maximum degree of filling for portable tanks must not exceed 90%.

TP5 For a portable tank used for the transport of flammable refrigerated liquefied gases or refrigerated liquefied oxygen, the maximum rate at which the portable tank may be filled must not exceed the liquid flow capacity of the primary pressure relief system rated at a pressure not exceeding 120 percent of the portable tank's design pressure. For portable tanks used for the transport of refrigerated liquefied helium and refrigerated liquefied atmospheric gas (except oxygen), the maximum rate at which the tank is filled must not exceed the liquid flow capacity of the pressure relief device rated at 130 percent of the portable tank's design pressure. Except for a portable tank containing refrigerated liquefied helium, a portable tank shall have an outage of at least two percent below the inlet of the pressure relief device or pressure control valve, under conditions of incipient opening, with the portable tank in a level attitude. No outage is required for helium.

TP6 The tank must be equipped with a pressure release device which prevent a tank from bursting under fire engulfment conditions (the conditions prescribed in CGA pamphlet S-1.2 (see §171.7 of this subchapter) or alternative conditions approved by the Associate Administrator may be used to consider the fire engulfment condition), taking into account the properties of the hazardous material to be transported.

TP7 The vapor space must be purged of air by nitrogen or other means.

TP8 A portable tank having a minimum test pressure of 1.5 bar (150 kPa) may be used when the flash point of the hazardous material transported is greater than 0°C (32°F).

TP9   A hazardous material assigned to special provision TP9 in Column (7) of the §172.101 Table may only be transported in a portable tank if approved by the Associate Administrator.

TP10   A lead lining, not less than 5 mm thick, which shall be tested annually, or another suitable lining material approved by the competent authority, is required. A portable tank may be offered for transport after the date of expiry of the last lining inspection for a period not to exceed three months for purposes of performing the next required test or inspection, after emptying but before cleaning.

TP13   Self-contained breathing apparatus must be provided when this hazardous material is transported by sea.

TP16   The portable tank must be protected against over and under pressurization which may be experienced during transportation. The means of protection must be approved by the approval agency designated to approve the portable tank in accordance with the procedures in part 107, subpart E, of this subchapter. The pressure relief device must be preceded by a frangible disk in accordance with the requirements in §178.275(g)(3) of this subchapter to prevent crystallization of the product in the pressure relief device.

TP17   Only inorganic non-combustible materials may be used for thermal insulation of the tank.

TP18   The temperature of this material must be maintained between 18°C (64.4°F) and 40°C (104°F) while in transportation. Portable tanks containing solidified methacrylic acid must not be re heated during transportation.

TP19   The calculated wall thickness must be increased by 3 mm at the time of construction. Wall thickness must be verified ultrasonically at intervals midway between periodic hydraulic tests (every 2.5 years). The portable tank must not be used if the wall thickness is less than that prescribed by the applicable T code in Column (7) of the Table for this material.

TP20   This hazardous material must only be transported in insulated tanks under a nitrogen blanket.

TP21   The wall thickness must not be less than 8 mm. Portable tanks must be hydraulically tested and internally inspected at intervals not exceeding 2.5 years.

TP22   Lubricants for portable tank fittings (for example, gaskets, shut-off valves, flanges) must be oxygen compatible.

TP24   The portable tank may be fitted with a device to prevent the build up of excess pressure due to the slow decomposition of the hazardous material being transported. The device must be in the vapor space when the tank is filled under maximum filling conditions. This device must also prevent an unacceptable amount of leakage of liquid in the case of overturning.

TP25 Sulphur trioxide 99.95% pure and above may be transported in tanks without an inhibitor provided that it is maintained at a temperature equal to or above 32.5°C (90.5°F).

TP26 The heating device must be exterior to the shell. For UN3176, this requirement only applies when the hazardous material reacts dangerously with water.

TP27 A portable tank having a minimum test pressure of 4 bar (400 kPa) may be used provided the calculated test pressure is 4 bar or less based on the MAWP of the hazardous material, as defined in §178.275 of this subchapter, where the test pressure is 1.5 times the MAWP.

TP28 A portable tank having a minimum test pressure of 2.65 bar (265 kPa) may be used provided the calculated test pressure is 2.65 bar or less based on the MAWP of the hazardous material, as defined in §178.275 of this subchapter, where the test pressure is 1.5 times the MAWP.

TP29 A portable tank having a minimum test pressure of 1.5 bar (150.0 kPa) may be used provided the calculated test pressure is 1.5 bar or less based on the MAWP of the hazardous materials, as defined in §178.275 of this subchapter, where the test pressure is 1.5 times the MAWP.

TP30 This hazardous material may only be transported in insulated tanks.

TP31 This hazardous material may only be transported in tanks in the solid state.

TP32 Portable tanks may be used subject to the following conditions:

    a. Each portable tank constructed of metal must be fitted with a pressure-relief device consisting of a reclosing spring loaded type, a frangible disc or a fusible element. The set to discharge for the spring loaded pressure relief device and the burst pressure for the frangible disc, as applicable, must not be greater than 2.65 bar for portable tanks with minimum test pressures greater than 4 bar;

    b. The suitability for transport in tanks must be demonstrated using test 8(d) in Test Series 8 (see UN Manual of Tests and Criteria, Part 1, Subsection 18.7) (IBR, see §171.7 of this subchapter) or an alternative means approved by the Associate Administrator.

TP33 The portable tank instruction assigned for this substance applies for granular and powdered solids and for solids which are filled and discharged at temperatures above their melting point which are cooled and transported as a solid mass. Solid substances transported or offered for transport above their melting point are authorized for transportation in portable tanks conforming to the provisions of portable tank instruction T4 for solid substances of packing group III or T7 for solid substances of packing group II, unless a tank with more stringent requirements for minimum shell thickness, maximum allowable working pressure, pressure-relief devices or bottom outlets are assigned in which case the more stringent tank instruction and special provisions shall apply. Filling limits must be in accordance with portable tank special provision TP3.

Solids meeting the definition of an elevated temperature material must be transported in accordance with the applicable requirements of this subchapter.

TP36 For material assigned this portable tank special provision, portable tanks used to transport such material may be equipped with fusible elements in the vapor space of the portable tank.

TP37 IM portable tanks are only authorized for the shipment of hydrogen peroxide solutions in water containing 72% or less hydrogen peroxide by weight. Pressure relief devices shall be designed to prevent the entry of foreign matter, the leak age of liquid and the development of any dangerous excess pressure. In addition, the portable tank must be designed so that internal surfaces may be effectively cleaned and passivated. Each tank must be equipped with pressure relief de vices conforming to the following requirements:

Concentration of hydrogen per peroxide solution	Total[1]
52% or less	11
Over 52%, but not greater than 60%	22
Over 60%, but not greater than 72%	32

[1]Total venting capacity in standard cubic feet hour (S.C.F.H.) per pound of hydrogen peroxide solution.

TP38 Each portable tank must be Insulated with an insulating material so that the overall thermal conductance at 15.5°C (60°F) is no more than 1.5333 kilojoules per hour per square meter per degree Celsius (0.075 Btu per hour per square foot per degree Fahrenheit) temperature differential. Insulating materials may not promote corrosion to steel when wet.

TP39 The portable tank instruction T4 prescribed may continue to be applied until December 31, 2018.

TP40 The portable tank must not be transported when connected with spray application equipment.

TP41 The portable tank instruction T9 may continue to be applied until December 31, 2018.

TP44 Each portable tank must be made of stainless steel, except that steel other than stainless steel may be used in accordance with the provisions of §173.24b(b) of this subchapter. Thickness of stainless steel for tank shell and heads must be the greater of 7.62 mm (0.300 inch) or the thickness required for a portable tank with a design pressure at least equal to 1.5 times the vapor pressure of the hazardous material at 46°C (115°F).

TP45 Each portable tank must be made of stainless steel, except that steel other than stainless steel may be used in accordance with the provisions of 173.24b(b) of this subchapter. Thickness of stainless steel for portable tank shells and heads must be the greater of 6.35 mm (0.250 inch) or the thickness required for a portable tank with a design pressure at least equal to 1.3 times the vapor pressure of the hazardous material at 46°C (115°F).

SPECIAL PROVISIONS

TP46 Portable tanks in sodium metal service are not required to be hydrostatically retested.

TP47 The 2.5 year internal examination may be waived or substituted by other test methods or inspection procedures specified by the competent authority or its authorized body, provided that the portable tank is dedicated to the transport of the organometallic substances to which this tank special provision is assigned. However this examination is required when the conditions of §180.605(f) are met.

(9) *"W"codes.* These provisions apply only to transportation by water:

Code/Special provisions

W1 This substance in a non friable prill or granule form is not subject to the requirements of this subchapter when tested in accordance with the UN Manual of Test and Criteria (IBR, *see* §171.7 of this subchapter) and is found to not meet the definition or criteria for inclusion in Division 5.1.

W7 Vessel stowage category for uranyl nitrate hexahydrate solution is "D" as defined in §172.101(k)(4).

W8 Vessel stowage category for pyrophoric thorium metal or pyrophoric uranium metal is "D" as defined in §172.101(k)(4).

W9 When offered for transportation by water, the following Specification packagings are not authorized unless approved by the Associate Administrator: woven plastic bags, plastic film bags, textile bags, paper bags, IBCs and bulk packagings.

W10 When offered for transportation by vessel, the use of Large Packagings (see §171.8 of this subchapter) is prohibited.

W31 Non-bulk packagings must be hermetically sealed.

W40 Non-bulk bags are not allowed.

W41 When offered for transportation by water, this material must be packaged in bales and be securely and tightly bound with rope, wire or similar means.

W100 Non-bulk flexible, fibreboard or wooden packagings must be sift-proof and water-resistant or must be fitted with a sift-proof and water-resistant liner.

Reserved

Part 397 — Transportation of Hazardous Materials: Driving and Parking Rules

Subpart A—General

Sections

Subpart B—Reserved

Subpart C—Routing of Non-Radioactive Hazardous Materials

Subpart D—Routing of Class 7 (Radioactive) Materials

AUTHORITY: 49 U.S.C. 322; 49 CFR 1.48. Subpart A also issued under 49 U.S.C. 31136, 31502. Subparts C, D, and E also issued under 49 U.S.C. 5112, 5125.

Subpart A—General

§397.1 Application of the rules in this part.

(a) The rules in this part apply to each motor carrier engaged in the transportation of hazardous materials by a motor vehicle which must be marked or placarded in accordance with §177.823 of this title and to—

(1) Each officer or employee of the motor carrier who performs supervisory duties related to the transportation of hazardous materials; and

(2) Each person who operates or who is in charge of a motor vehicle containing hazardous materials.

(b) Each person designated in paragraph (a) of this section must know and obey the rules in this part.

§397.2 Compliance with Federal motor carrier safety regulations.

A motor carrier or other person to whom this part is applicable must comply with the rules in Part 390 through 397, inclusive, of this subchapter when he/she is transporting hazardous materials by a motor vehicle which must be marked or placarded in accordance with §177.823 of this title.

§397.3 State and local laws, ordinances and regulations.

Every motor vehicle containing hazardous materials must be driven and parked in compliance with the laws, ordinances, and regulations of the jurisdiction in which it is being operated, unless they are at variance with specific regulations of the Department of Transportation which are applicable to the operation of that vehicle and which impose a more stringent obligation or restraint.

§397.5 Attendance and surveillance of motor vehicles.

(a) Except as provided in paragraph (b) of this section, a motor vehicle which contains a Division 1.1, 1.2, or 1.3 (explosive) material must be attended at all times by its driver or a qualified representative of the motor carrier that operates it.

(b) The rules in paragraph (a) of this section do not apply to a motor vehicle which contains Division 1.1, 1.2, or 1.3 material if all the following conditions exist—

(1) The vehicle is located on the property of a motor carrier, on the property of a shipper or consignee of the explosives, in a safe haven, or, in the case of a vehicle containing 50 pounds or less of a Division 1.1, 1.2, or 1.3 material, on a construction or survey site; and

(2) The lawful bailee of the explosives is aware of the nature of the explosives the vehicle contains and has been instructed in the procedures which must be followed in emergencies; and

(3) The vehicle is within the bailee's unobstructed field of view or is located in a safe haven.

(c) A motor vehicle which contains hazardous materials other than Division 1.1, 1.2, or 1.3, materials, and which is located on a public street or highway, or the shoulder of a public highway, must be attended by its driver. However, the vehicle need not be attended while its driver is performing duties which are incident and necessary to the driver's duties as the operator of the vehicle.

(d) For purposes of this section—

(1) A motor vehicle is attended when the person in charge of the vehicle is on the vehicle, awake, and not in a sleeper berth, or is within 100 feet of the vehicle and has it within his/her unobstructed field of view.

(2) A qualified representative of a motor carrier is a person who—

(i) Has been designated by the carrier to attend the vehicle;

(ii) Is aware of the nature of the hazardous materials contained in the vehicle he/she attends;

(iii) Has been instructed in the procedures he/she must follow in emergencies; and

(iv) Is authorized to move the vehicle and has the means and ability to do so.

(3) A safe haven is an area specifically approved in writing by local, State, or Federal governmental authorities for the parking of unattended vehicles containing Division 1.1, 1.2, or 1.3 materials.

(e) The rules in this section do not relieve the driver from any obligation imposed by law relating to the placing of warning devices when a motor vehicle is stopped on a public street or highway.

§397.7 Parking.

(a) A motor vehicle which contains Division 1.1, 1.2, or 1.3 materials must not be parked under any of the following circumstances—

(1) On or within 5 feet of the traveled portion of a public street or highway;

(2) On private property (including premises of a fueling or eating facility) without the knowledge and consent of the person who is in charge of the property and who is aware of the nature of the hazardous materials the vehicle contains; or

(3) Within 300 feet of a bridge, tunnel, dwelling, or place where people work, congregate, or assemble, except for brief periods when the necessities of operation require the vehicle to be parked and make it impracticable to park the vehicle in any other place.

(b) A motor vehicle which contains hazardous materials other than Division 1.1, 1.2, or 1.3 materials must not be parked on or within five feet of the traveled portion of public street or highway except for brief periods when the necessities of operation require the vehicle to be parked and make it impracticable to park the vehicle in any other place.

§397.9 [Removed and Reserved]

§397.11 Fires.

(a) A motor vehicle containing hazardous materials must not be operated near an open fire unless its driver has first taken precautions to ascertain that the vehicle can safely pass the fire without stopping.

(b) A motor vehicle containing hazardous materials must not be parked within 300 feet of an open fire.

§397.13 Smoking.

No person may smoke or carry a lighted cigarette, cigar, or pipe on or within 25 feet of—

(a) A motor vehicle which contains Class 1 materials, Class 5 materials, or flammable materials classified as Division 2.1, Class 3, Divisions 4.1 and 4.2; or

(b) An empty tank motor vehicle which has been used to transport Class 3, flammable materials or Division 2.1 flammable gases, which, when so used, was required to be marked or placarded in accordance with the rules in §177.823 of this title.

§397.15 Fueling.

When a motor vehicle which contains hazardous materials is being fueled—

(a) Its engine must not be operating; and

(b) A person must be in control of the fueling process at the point where the fuel tank is filled.

§397.17 Tires.

(a) A driver must examine each tire on a motor vehicle at the beginning of each trip and each time the vehicle is parked.

(b) If, as the result of an examination pursuant to paragraph (a) of this section, or otherwise, a tire is found to be flat, leaking, or improperly inflated, the driver must cause the tire to be repaired, replaced, or properly inflated before the vehicle is driven. However, the vehicle may be driven to the nearest safe place to perform the required repair, replacement, or inflation.

(c) If, as the result of an examination pursuant to paragraph (a) of this section, or otherwise, a tire is found to be overheated, the driver shall immediately cause the overheated tire to be removed and placed at a safe distance from the vehicle. The driver shall not operate the vehicle until the cause of the overheating is corrected.

(d) Compliance with the rules in this section does not relieve a driver from the duty to comply with the rules in §§397.5 and 397.7.

§397.19 Instructions and documents.

(a) A motor carrier that transports Division 1.1, 1.2, or 1.3 (explosive) materials must furnish the driver of each motor vehicle in which the explosives are transported with the following documents:

(1) A copy of the rules in this part;

(2) [Reserved]

(3) A document containing instructions on procedures to be followed in the event of accident or delay. The documents must include the names and telephone numbers of persons (including representatives of carriers or shippers) to be contacted, the nature of the explosives being transported, and the precautions to be taken in emergencies such as fires, accidents, or leakages.

(b) A driver who receives documents in accordance with paragraph (a) of this section must sign a receipt for them. The motor carrier shall maintain the receipt for a period of one year from the date of signature.

(c) A driver of a motor vehicle which contains Division 1.1, 1.2, or 1.3 materials must be in possession of, be familiar with, and be In compliance with

(1) The documents specified in paragraph (a) of this section;

(2) The documents specified in §177.817 of this title; and

(3) The written route plan specified in §397.67.

Subpart B—[Reserved]

Subpart C—Routing of non-radioactive hazardous materials

§397.61 Purpose and scope.

This subpart contains routing requirements and procedures that States and Indian tribes are required to follow if they establish, maintain, or enforce routing designations over which a non-radioactive hazardous material (NRHM) in a quantity which requires placarding may or may not be transported by a motor vehicle. It also provides regulations for motor carriers transporting placarded or marked NRHM and procedures for dispute resolutions regarding NRHM routing designations.

§397.63 Applicability.

The provisions of this subpart apply to any State or Indian tribe that establishes, maintains, or enforces any routing designations over which NRHM may or may not be transported by motor vehicle. They also apply to any motor carrier that transports or causes to be transported placarded or marked NRHM in commerce.

§397.65 Definitions.

For purposes of this subpart, the following definitions apply:

Administrator. The Federal Motor Carrier Safety Administrator, who is the chief executive of the Federal Motor Carrier Safety Administration, an agency within the United States Department of Transportation, or his/her designate.

Commerce. Any trade, traffic, or transportation in the United States which:

(1) is between a place under the jurisdiction of a State or Indian tribe and any place outside of such jurisdiction; or

(2) is solely within a place under the jurisdiction of a State or Indian tribe but which affects trade, traffic, or transportation described in subparagraph (a).

FMCSA. The Federal Motor Carrier Safety Administration, an agency within the Department of Transportation.

Hazardous material. A substance or material, including a hazardous substance, which has been determined by the Secretary of Transportation to be capable of posing an unreasonable risk to health, safety, or property when transported in commerce, and which has been so designated.

Indian tribe. Has the same meaning as contained in section 4 of the Indian Self-Determination and Education Act, 25 U.S.C. 450b.

Motor carrier. A for-hire motor carrier or a private motor carrier of property. The term includes a motor carrier's agents, officers and representatives as well as employees responsible for hiring, supervising, training, assigning, or dispatching of drivers.

Motor vehicle. Any vehicle, machine, tractor, trailer, or semitrailer propelled or drawn by mechanical power and used upon the highways in the transportation of passengers or property, or any combination thereof.

NRHM. A non-radioactive hazardous material transported by motor vehicle in types and quantities which require placarding, pursuant to Table 1 or 2 of 49 CFR 172.504.

Political subdivision. A municipality, public agency or other instrumentality of one or more States, or a public corporation, board, or commission established under the laws of one or more States.

Radioactive material. As defined in 49 CFR 173.403, radioactive material means any material containing radionuclides where both the activity concentration and the total activity in the consignment exceed the values of the table in 49 CFR 173.436 or values derived according to the instructions in 49 CFR 173.433.

Routing agency. The State highway agency or other State agency designated by the Governor of that State, or an agency designated by an Indian tribe, to supervise, coordinate, and approve the NRHM routing designations for that State or Indian tribe.

Routing designations. Any regulation, limitation, restriction, curfew, time of travel restriction, lane restriction, routing ban, port-of-entry designation, or route weight restriction, applicable to the highway transportation of NRHM over a specific highway route or portion of a route.

Secretary. The Secretary of Transportation.

State. A State of the United States, the District of Columbia, the Commonwealth of Puerto Rico, the Commonwealth of the Northern Mariana Islands, the Virgin Islands, American Samoa or Guam.

§397.67 Motor carrier responsibility for routing.

(a) A motor carrier transporting NRHM shall comply with NRHM routing designations of a State or Indian tribe pursuant to this subpart.

(b) A motor carrier carrying hazardous materials required to be placarded or marked in accordance with 49 CFR 177.823 and not subject to NRHM routing designations pursuant to this subpart, shall operate the vehicle over routes which do not go through or near heavily populated areas, places where crowds are assembled, tunnels, narrow streets, or alleys, except where the motor carrier determines that:

(1) There is no practicable alternative;

(2) A reasonable deviation is necessary to reach terminals, points of loading and unloading, facilities for food, fuel, repairs, rest, or a safe haven; or

(3) A reasonable deviation is required by emergency conditions, such as a detour that has been established by a highway authority, or a situation exists where a law enforcement official requires the driver to take an alternative route.

(c) Operating convenience is not a basis for determining whether it is practicable to operate a motor vehicle in accordance with paragraph (b) of this section.

(d) Before a motor carrier requires or permits a motor vehicle containing explosives in Class 1, Divisions 1.1, 1.2, or 1.3, as defined in 49 CFR 173.50 and 173.53 respectively, to be operated, the carrier or its agent shall prepare a written route plan that complies with this section and shall furnish a copy to the driver. However, the driver may prepare the written plan as agent for the motor carrier when the trip begins at a location other than the carrier's terminal.

§397.69 Highway routing designations; preemption.

(a) Any State or Indian tribe that establishes or modifies a highway routing designation over which NRHM may or may not be transported on or after November 14, 1994, and maintains or enforces such designation, shall comply with the highway routing standards set forth in §397.71 of this subpart. For purposes of this subpart, any highway routing designation affecting the highway transportation of NRHM, made by a political subdivision of a State is considered as one made by that State, and all requirements of this subpart apply.

(b) Except as provided in §§397.75 and 397.219, an NRHM route designation made in violation of paragraph (a) of this section is preempted pursuant to 49 U.S.C. 5125(c).

(c) A highway routing designation established by a State, political subdivision, or Indian tribe before November 14, 1994 is subject to preemption in accordance with the preemption standards in paragraphs (a)(1) and (a)(2) of §397.203.

(d) A State, political subdivision, or Indian tribe may petition for a waiver of preemption in accordance with §397.213 of this part.

§397.71 Federal standards.

(a) A State or Indian tribe shall comply with the Federal standards under paragraph (b) of this section when establishing, maintaining or enforcing specific NRHM routing designations over which NRHM may or may not be transported.

(b) The Federal standards are as follows:

(1) **Enhancement of public safety**. The State or Indian tribe shall make a finding, supported by the record to be developed in accordance with paragraphs (b)(2)(ii) and (b)(3)(iv) of this section, that any NRHM routing

designation enhances public safety in the areas subject to its jurisdiction and in other areas which are directly affected by such highway routing designation. In making such a finding, the State or Indian tribe shall consider:

(i) The factors listed in paragraph (b)(9) of this section; and

(ii) The DOT "Guidelines for Applying Criteria to Designate Routes for Transporting Hazardous Materials," DOT/RSPA/OHMT-89-02, July 1989 [1] or its most current version; or an equivalent routing analysis which adequately considers overall risk to the public.

(2) **Public participation**. Prior to the establishment of any NRHM routing designation, the State or Indian tribe shall undertake the following actions to ensure participation by the public in the routing process:

(i) The State or Indian tribe shall provide the public with notice of any proposed NRHM routing designation and a 30-day period in which to comment. At any time during this period or following review of the comments received, the State or Indian tribe shall decide whether to hold a public hearing on the proposed NRHM route designation. The public shall be given 30 days prior notice of the public hearing which shall be conducted as described in paragraph (b)(2)(ii) of this section. Notice for both the comment period and the public hearing, if one is held, shall be given by publication in at least two newspapers of general circulation in the affected area or areas and shall contain a complete description of the proposed routing designation, together with the date, time, and location of any public hearings. Notice for both the comment period and any public hearing may also be published in the official register of the State.

(ii) If it is determined that a public hearing is necessary, the State or Indian tribe shall hold at least one public hearing on the record during which the public will be afforded the opportunity to present its views and any information or data related to the proposed NRHM routing designation. The State shall make available to the public, upon payment of prescribed costs, copies of the transcript of the hearing, which shall include all exhibits and documents presented during the hearing or submitted for the record.

(3) **Consultation with others**. Prior to the establishment of any NRHM routing designation, the State or Indian tribe shall provide notice to, and consult with, officials of affected political subdivisions, States and Indian tribes, and any other affected parties. Such actions shall include the following:

(i) At least 60 days prior to establishing a routing designation, the State or Indian tribe shall provide notice, in writing, of the proposed routing designation to officials responsible for highway routing in all other affected States or Indian tribes. A copy of this notice may also be sent to all affected political subdivisions. This notice shall request approval, in writing, by those States or Indian tribes, of the proposed routing designations. If no response is received within 60 days from the day of receipt of the notification of the proposed routing designation, the routing designation shall be considered approved by the affected State or Indian tribe.

(ii) The manner in which consultation under this paragraph is conducted is left to the discretion of the State or Indian tribe.

(iii) The State or Indian tribe shall attempt to resolve any concern or disagreement expressed by any consulted official related to the proposed routing designation.

---

[1] This document may be obtained from Federal Motor Carrier Safety Administration, Office of Enforcement and Compliance (MC-EC), 1200 New Jersey Ave., SE., Washington, DC 20590-0001.

(iv) The State or Indian tribe shall keep a record of the names and addresses of the officials notified pursuant to this section and of any consultation or meeting conducted with these officials or their representatives. Such record shall describe any concern or disagreement expressed by the officials and any action undertaken to resolve such disagreement or address any concern.

(4) **Through routing**. In establishing any NRHM routing designation, the State or Indian tribe shall ensure through highway routing for the transportation of NRHM between adjacent areas. The term "through highway routing" as used in this paragraph means that the routing designation must ensure continuity of movement so as to not impede or unnecessarily delay the transportation of NRHM. The State or Indian tribe shall utilize the procedures established in paragraphs (b)(2) and (b)(3) of this section in meeting these requirements. In addition, the State or Indian tribe shall make a finding, supported by a risk analysis conducted in accordance with paragraph (b)(1) of this section, that the routing designation enhances public safety. If the risk analysis shows—

(i) That the current routing presents at least 50 percent more risk to the public than the deviation under the proposed routing designation, then the proposed routing designation may go into effect.

(ii) That the current routing presents a greater risk but less than 50 percent more risk to the public than the deviation under the proposed routing restriction, then the proposed routing restriction made by a State or Indian tribe shall only go into effect if it does not force a deviation of more than 25 miles or result in an increase of more than 25 percent of that part of a trip affected by the deviation, whichever is shorter, from the most direct route through a jurisdiction as compared to the intended deviation.

(iii) That the current route has the same or less risk to the public than the deviation resulting from the proposed routing designation, then the routing designation shall not be allowed.

(5) **Agreement of other States; burden on commerce**. Any NRHM routing designation which affects another State or Indian tribe shall be established, maintained, or enforced only if:

(i) It does not unreasonably burden commerce, and

(ii) It is agreed to by the affected State or Indian tribe within 60 days of receipt of the notice sent pursuant to paragraph (b)(3)(i) of this section, or it is approved by the Administrator pursuant to §397.75.

(6) **Timeliness**. The establishment of an NRHM routing designation by any State or Indian tribe shall be completed within 18 months of the notice given in either paragraph (b)(2) or (b)(3) of this section, whichever occurs first.

(7) **Reasonable routes to terminals and other facilities**. In establishing or providing for reasonable access to and from designated routes, the State or Indian tribe shall use the shortest practicable route considering the factors listed in paragraph (b)(9) of this section. In establishing any NRHM routing designation, the State or Indian tribe shall provide reasonable access for motor vehicles transporting NRHM to reach:

(i) Terminals,

(ii) Points of loading, unloading, pickup and delivery, and

(iii) Facilities for food, fuel, repairs, rest, and safe havens.

(8) **Responsibility for local compliance**. The States shall be responsible for ensuring that all of their political subdivisions comply with the provisions of this subpart. The States shall be responsible for resolving all disputes between such political subdivisions within their jurisdictions. If a State or any political

subdivision thereof, or an Indian tribe chooses to establish, maintain, or enforce any NRHM routing designation, the Governor, or Indian tribe, shall designate a routing agency for the State or Indian tribe, respectively. The routing agency shall ensure that all NRHM routing designations within its jurisdiction comply with the Federal standards in this section. The State or Indian tribe shall comply with the public information and reporting requirements contained in §397.73.

(9) **Factors to consider**. In establishing any NRHM routing designation, the State or Indian tribe shall consider the following factors:

(i) **Population density**. The population potentially exposed to an NRHM release shall be estimated from the density of the residents, employees, motorists, and other persons in the area, using United States census tract maps or other reasonable means for determining the population within a potential impact zone along a designated highway route. The impact zone is the potential range of effects in the event of a release. Special populations such as schools, hospitals, prisons, and senior citizen homes shall, among other things, be considered when determining the potential risk to the populations along a highway routing. Consideration shall be given to the amount of time during which an area will experience a heavy population density.

(ii) **Type of highway**. The characteristics of each alternative NRHM highway routing designation shall be compared. Vehicle weight and size limits, underpass and bridge clearances, roadway geometrics, number of lanes, degree of access control, and median and shoulder structures are examples of characteristics which a State or Indian tribe shall consider.

(iii) **Types and quantities of NRHM**. An examination shall be made of the type and quantity of NRHM normally transported along highway routes which are included in a proposed NRHM routing designation, and consideration shall be given to the relative impact zone and risks of each type and quantity.

(iv) **Emergency response capabilities**. In consultation with the proper fire, law enforcement, and highway safety agencies, consideration shall be given to the emergency response capabilities which may be needed as a result of an NRHM routing designation. The analysis of the emergency response capabilities shall be based upon the proximity of the emergency response facilities and their capabilities to contain and suppress NRHM releases within the impact zones.

(v) **Results of consultation with affected persons**. Consideration shall be given to the comments and concerns of all affected persons and entities provided during public hearings and consultations conducted in accordance with this section.

(vi) **Exposure and other risk factors**. States and Indian tribes shall define the exposure and risk factors associated with any NRHM routing designations. The distance to sensitive areas shall be considered. Sensitive areas include, but are not limited to, homes and commercial buildings; special populations in hospitals, schools, handicapped facilities, prisons and stadiums; water sources such as streams and lakes; and natural areas such as parks, wetlands, and wildlife reserves.

(vii) **Terrain considerations**. Topography along and adjacent to the proposed NRHM routing designation that may affect the potential severity of an accident, the dispersion of the NRHM upon release and the control and clean up of NRHM if released shall be considered.

(viii) **Continuity of routes**. Adjacent jurisdictions shall be consulted to ensure routing continuity for NRHM across common borders. Deviations from the most direct route shall be minimized.

(ix) **Alternative routes**. Consideration shall be given to the alternative routes to, or resulting from, any NRHM route designation. Alternative routes shall be examined, reviewed, or evaluated to the extent necessary to demonstrate that the most probable alternative routing resulting from a routing designation is safer than the current routing.

(x) **Effects on commerce**. Any NRHM routing designation made in accordance with this subpart shall not create an unreasonable burden upon interstate or intrastate commerce.

(xi) **Delays in transportation**. No NRHM routing designations may create unnecessary delays in the transportation of NRHM.

(xii) **Climatic conditions**. Weather conditions unique to a highway route such as snow, wind, ice, fog, or other climatic conditions that could affect the safety of a route, the dispersion of the NRHM upon release, or increase the difficulty of controlling it and cleaning it up shall be given appropriate consideration.

(xiii) **Congestion and accident history**. Traffic conditions unique to a highway routing such as: traffic congestion; accident experience with motor vehicles, traffic considerations that could affect the potential for an accident, exposure of the public to any release, ability to perform emergency response operations, or the temporary closing of a highway for cleaning up any release shall be given appropriate consideration.

§397.73 Public information and reporting requirements.

(a) **Public information**. Information on NRHM routing designations must be made available by the States and Indian tribes to the public in the form of maps, lists, road signs or some combination thereof. If road signs are used, those signs and their placements must comply with the provisions of the Manual on Uniform Traffic Control Devices for Streets and Highways, published by the Federal Highway Administration (FHWA), particularly the Hazardous Cargo signs identified as R14-2 and R14-3 shown in Section 2B-62 of that Manual. This publication may be accessed free of charge on the Internet at *http://mutcd.fhwa.dot.gov/*.

(b) **Reporting and publishing requirements**. (1) Each State or Indian tribe, through its routing agency, shall provide information identifying all NRHM routing designations that exist within its jurisdiction:

(i) Electronically, by email to *HMRouting@dot.gov*; or

(ii) By mail to the Federal Motor Carrier Safety Administration, Office of Enforcement and Compliance (MC-EC), 1200 New Jersey Ave. SE, Washington, DC 20590-0001.

(2) States and Indian tribes shall also submit to FMCSA the current name of the State or Indian tribal agency responsible for NHRM highway routing designations. The State or Indian tribe shall include descriptions of these routing designations, along with the dates they were established. Information on any subsequent changes or new NRHM routing designations shall be furnished within 60 days after establishment to the FMCSA.

(3)(i) FMCSA will consolidate information on the NRHM routing designations, make it available on its website, *https://www.fmcsa.dot.gov/regulations/hazardous-materials/national-hazardous-materials-route-registry,* and publish it annually in whole or as updates in the *Federal Register*.

(ii) Each State or Indian tribe may also publish this information in its official register of State or tribal regulations.

(c) A State or Tribally-designated route is effective only after it is published in the National Hazardous Materials Route Registry on FMCSA's website at *https://www.fmcsa.dot.gov/regulations/hazardous-materials/national-hazardous-materials-route-registry*.

§397.75 Dispute resolution.

(a) **Petition**. One or more States or Indian tribes may petition the Administrator to resolve a dispute relating to an agreement on a proposed NRHM routing designation. In resolving a dispute under these provisions, the Administrator will provide the greatest level of safety possible without unreasonably burdening commerce, and ensure compliance with the Federal standards established at §397.71 of this subpart.

(b) **Filing**. Each petition for dispute resolution filed under this section must:

(1) Be submitted to the Administrator, Federal Motor Carrier Safety Administration, 1200 New Jersey Ave., SE., Washington, DC 20590-0001. Attention: Office of the Chief Counsel (MC-CC).

(2) Identify the State or Indian tribe filing the petition and any other State, political subdivision, or Indian tribe whose NRHM routing designation is the subject of the dispute.

(3) Contain a certification that the petitioner has complied with the notification requirements of paragraph (c) of this section, and include a list of the names and addresses of each State, political subdivision, or Indian tribe official who was notified of the filing of the petition.

(4) Clearly set forth the dispute for which resolution is sought, including a complete description of any disputed NRHM routing designation and an explanation of how the disputed routing designation affects the petitioner or how it impedes through highway routing. If the routing designation being disputed results in alternative routing, then a comparative risk analysis for the designated route and the resulting alternative routing shall be provided.

(5) Describe any actions taken by the State or Indian tribe to resolve the dispute.

(6) Explain the reasons why the petitioner believes that the Administrator should intervene in resolving the dispute.

(7) Describe any proposed actions that the Administrator should take to resolve the dispute and how these actions would provide the greatest level of highway safety without unreasonably burdening commerce and would ensure compliance with the Federal standards established in this subpart.

(c) **Notice**. (1) Any State or Indian tribe that files a petition for dispute resolution under this subpart shall mail a copy of the petition to any affected State, political subdivision, or Indian tribe, accompanied by a statement that the State, political subdivision, or Indian tribe may submit comments regarding the petition to the Administrator within 45 days.

(2) By serving notice on any other State, political subdivision, or Indian tribe determined by the Administrator to be possibly affected by the issues in dispute or the resolution sought, or by publication in the *Federal Register*, the Administrator may afford those persons an opportunity to file written comments on the petition.

(3) Any affected State, political subdivision, or Indian tribe submitting written comments to the Administrator with respect to a petition filed under this section shall send a copy of the comments to the petitioner and certify to the Administrator as to having complied with this requirement. The Administrator may

notify other persons participating in the proceeding of the comments and provide an opportunity for those other persons to respond.

(d) **Court actions**. After a petition for dispute resolution is filed in accordance with this section, no court action may be brought with respect to the subject matter of such dispute until a final decision has been issued by the Administrator or until the last day of the one-year period beginning on the day the Administrator receives the petition, whichever occurs first.

(e) **Hearings; alternative dispute resolution**. Upon receipt of a petition filed pursuant to paragraph (a) of this section, the Administrator may schedule a hearing to attempt to resolve the dispute and, if a hearing is scheduled, will notify all parties to the dispute of the date, time, and place of the hearing. During the hearing the parties may offer any information pertinent to the resolution of the dispute. If an agreement is reached, it may be stipulated by the parties, in writing, and, if the Administrator agrees, made part of the decision in paragraph (f) of this section. If no agreement is reached, the Administrator may take the matter under consideration and announce his or her decision in accordance with paragraph (f) of this section. Nothing in this section shall be construed as prohibiting the parties from settling the dispute or seeking other methods of alternative dispute resolution prior to the final decision by the Administrator.

(f) **Decision**. The Administrator will issue a decision based on the petition, the written comments submitted by the parties, the record of the hearing, and any other information in the record. The decision will include a written statement setting forth the relevant facts and the legal basis for the decision.

(g) **Record**. The Administrator will serve a copy of the decision upon the petitioner and any other party who participated in the proceedings. A copy of each decision will be placed on file in the public docket. The Administrator may publish the decision or notice of the decision in the *Federal Register*.

§397.77 Judicial review of dispute decision.

Any State or Indian tribe adversely affected by the Administrator's decision under §397.75 of this subpart may seek review by the appropriate district court of the United States under such proceeding only by filing a petition with such court within 90 days after such decision becomes final.

Subpart D—Routing of class 7 (radioactive) materials

§397.101 Requirements for motor carriers and drivers.

(a) Except as provided in paragraph (b) of this section or in circumstances when there is only one practicable highway route available, considering operating necessity and safety, a carrier or any person operating a motor vehicle that contains a Class 7 (radioactive) material, as defined in 49 CFR 172.403, for which placarding is required under 49 CFR part 172 shall:

(1) Ensure that the motor vehicle is operated on routes that minimize radiological risk;

(2) Consider available information on accident rates, transit time, population density and activities, and the time of day and the day of week during which transportation will occur to determine the level of radiological risk; and

(3) Tell the driver which route to take and that the motor vehicle contains Class 7 (radioactive) materials.

(b) Except as otherwise permitted in this paragraph and in paragraph (f) of this section, a carrier or any person operating a motor vehicle containing a highway route controlled quantity of Class 7 (radioactive) materials, as defined in 49 CFR 397.403, shall operate the motor vehicle only over preferred routes.

(1) For purposes of this subpart, a preferred route is an Interstate System highway for which an alternative route is not designated by a State routing agency; a State-designated route selected by a State routing agency pursuant to §397.103; or both of the above.

(2) The motor carrier or the person operating a motor vehicle containing a highway route controlled quantity of Class 7 (radioactive) materials, as defined in 49 CFR 173.403, shall select routes to reduce time in transit over the preferred route segment of the trip. An Interstate System bypass or Interstate System beltway around a city, when available, shall be used in place of a preferred route through a city, unless a State routing agency has designated an alternative route.

(c) A motor vehicle may be operated over a route, other than a preferred route, only under the following conditions:

(1) The deviation from the preferred route is necessary to pick up or deliver a highway route controlled quantity of Class 7 (radioactive) materials, to make necessary rest, fuel or motor vehicle repair stops, or because emergency conditions make continued use of the preferred route unsafe or impossible;

(2) For pickup and delivery not over preferred routes, the route selected must be the shortest-distance route from the pickup location to the nearest preferred route entry location, and the shortest-distance route to the delivery location from the nearest preferred route exit location. Deviation from the shortest-distance pickup or delivery route is authorized if such deviation:

(i) Is based upon the criteria in paragraph (a) of this section to minimize the radiological risk; and

(ii) Does not exceed the shortest-distance pickup or delivery route by more than 25 miles and does not exceed 5 times the length of the shortest-distance pickup or delivery route.

(iii) Deviations from preferred routes, or pickup or delivery routes other than preferred routes, which are necessary for rest, fuel, or motor vehicle repair stops or because of emergency conditions, shall be made in accordance with the criteria in paragraph (a) of this section to minimize radiological risk, unless due to emergency conditions, time does not permit use of those criteria.

(d) A carrier (or a designated agent) who operates a motor vehicle which contains a package of highway route controlled quantity of Class 7 (radioactive) materials, as defined in 49 CFR 173.403, shall prepare a written route plan and supply a copy before departure to the motor vehicle driver and a copy to the shipper (before departure for exclusive use shipments, as defined in 49 CFR 173.403, or within fifteen working days following departure for all other shipments). Any variation between the route plan and routes actually used, and the reason for it, shall be reported in an amendment to the route plan delivered to the shipper as soon as practicable but within 30 days following the deviation. The route plan shall contain:

(1) A statement of the origin and destination points, a route selected in compliance with this section, all planned stops, and estimated departure and arrival times; and

(2) Telephone numbers which will access emergency assistance in each State to be entered.

(e) No person may transport a package of highway route controlled quantity of Class 7 (radioactive) materials on a public highway unless:

(1) The driver has received within the two preceding years, written training on:

(i) Requirements in 49 CFR parts 172, 173, and 177 pertaining to the Class 7 (radioactive) materials transported;

(ii) The properties and hazards of the Class 7 (radioactive) materials being transported; and

(iii) Procedures to be followed in case of an accident or other emergency.

(2) The driver has in his or her immediate possession a certificate of training as evidence of training required by this section, and a copy is placed in his or her qualification file (see §391.51 of this subchapter), showing:

(i) The driver's name and operator's license number;

(ii) The dates training was provided;

(iii) The name and address of the person providing the training;

(iv) That the driver has been trained in the hazards and characteristics of highway route controlled quantity of Class 7 (radioactive) materials; and

(v) A statement by the person providing the training that information on the certificate is accurate.

(3) The driver has in his or her immediate possession the route plan required by paragraph (d) of this section and operates the motor vehicle in accordance with the route plan.

(f) A person may transport irradiated reactor fuel only in compliance with a plan if required under 49 CFR 173.22(c) that will ensure the physical security of the material. Variation for security purposes from the requirements of this section is permitted so far as necessary to meet the requirements imposed under such a plan, or otherwise imposed by the U.S. Nuclear Regulatory Commission in 10 CFR part 73.

§397.103 Requirements for State routing designations.

(a) The State routing agency, as defined in §397.201(c), shall select routes to minimize radiological risk using "Guidelines for Selecting Preferred Highway Routes for Highway Route Controlled Quantity Shipments of Radioactive Materials," or an equivalent routing analysis which adequately considers overall risk to the public. Designations must be preceded by substantive consultation with affected local jurisdictions and with any other affected States to ensure consideration of all impacts and continuity of designated routes.

(b) State routing agencies may designate preferred routes as an alternative to, or in addition to, one or more Interstate System highways, including interstate system bypasses, or Interstate System beltways.

(c) A State-designated route is effective when—

(1) The State gives written notice to the Federal Motor Carrier Safety Administration:

(i) By email to *HMRouting@dot.gov;* or

(ii) By certified mail, return receipt requested, to the Federal Motor Carrier Safety Administration, Office of Enforcement and Compliance (MC-EC), 1200 New Jersey Ave., SE., Washington, DC 20590-0001. Attention: National Hazardous Materials Route Registry.

(2) Receipt thereof is acknowledged in writing by the FMCSA.

(3) The route is published in the National Hazardous Materials Route Registry on FMCSA's website at *https://www.fmcsa.dot.gov/regulations/hazardous-materials/national-hazardous-materials-route-registry.*

(d) A list of State-designated preferred routes and a copy of the "Guidelines for Selecting Preferred Highway Routes for Highway Route Controlled Quantity Shipments of Radioactive Materials" are available upon request to Federal Motor Carrier Safety Administration, Office of Enforcement and Compliance (MC-EC), 1200 New Jersey Ave. SE, Washington, DC 20590-0001, or by email to *HMRouting@dot.gov.*

PART 397

Reserved

Emergency Phone Numbers

National Response Center: (800) 424-8802

Chemtrec®:   (800) 424-9300

Chemtel, Inc.:   (888) 255-3924

Infotrac: (800) 535-5053

3E Company: (800) 451-8346

U. S. Military Shipments
  Explosives/ammunition incidents: (703) 697-0218
  All other dangerous goods incidents: (800) 851-8061

Nationwide Poison Control Center: (800) 222-1222

NOTES

NOTES

NOTES

MARKINGS

ORIENTATION ARROWS	CONSUMER COMMODITY **ORM-D** Valid before 2021 **ORM-D**	keep away from heat **KEEP AWAY FROM HEAT**
OVERPACK **OVERPACK** **DOT–SP 01234** **SPECIAL PERMIT**	3 **EXCEPTED QUANTITIES**	**RQ** **REPORTABLE QUANTITY** **PG III** **PACKING GROUP III**
INHALATION HAZARD **INHALATION HAZARD**	**THIS PACKAGE CONFORMS TO 49 CFR 173.4 FOR DOMESTIC HIGHWAY OR RAIL TRANSPORT ONLY** **SMALL QUANTITIES**	HAZARDOUS WASTE ... HAZARDOUS WASTE – HANDLE WITH CARE **HAZARDOUS WASTE**
BIOHAZARD **BIOHAZARD**	**NON-ODORIZED** or **NOT ODORIZED** **UNODORIZED LPG**	**DANGER** THIS UNIT IS UNDER FUMIGATION WITH _____ APPLIED ON Date _____ Time _____ Ventilated on _____ **DO NOT ENTER** **FUMIGANT**
MARINE POLLUTANT	**Y** Air **LIMITED QUANTITY**	UN Number Here Telephone Number Here **LITHIUM BATTERY**

II MARKINGS

NON-BULK PACKAGE

Identification Number

Proper Shipping Name

SODIUM HYDROXIDE, SOLID
UN1823

CORROSIVE
8

J. J. Keller & Associates, Inc.
3003 Breezewood Lane
Neenah, WI 54957

(U/n) 4G/Y145/S/17
USA/RA

Package Manufacturer's Mark

Name/Address of Consignee or Consignor

Label

IBCs and Large Packagings

... kg max

Stacking Allowed

No Stacking

STACKING

HOT

HOT

HOT 3257

ELEVATED TEMPERATURE MATERIAL

10-17
V I P L K T
K-EPA27

CARGO TANK TEST/INSPECTION

1951

1824 8

3291

IDENTIFICATION NUMBER DISPLAY

BULK PACKAGE

PORTABLE TANK
<1,000 gallons capacity

Proper Shipping Name

ACETONE

1090   FLAMMABLE 3

Placard

Identification Number on orange panel, placard, or white square-on-point configuration.

J. J. Keller & Associates, Inc.
3003 Breezewood Lane
Neenah, WI 54957

Name of Tank Owner/Lessee

If labeled, instead of placarded on two sides, UN1090 may be displayed once in characters at least 0.47 inches (12 mm) high.

Tanks with ≥1,000 gallons capacity must have identification numbers displayed on all 4 sides.

CARGO TANK

1075 2   PROPANE

Identification Number on placard, orange panel, or white square-on-point configuration. Display on all 4 sides.

Common Name or Proper Shipping Name for Class 2 materials. Display on all 4 sides.

CLASS 1

** Division number 1.1, 1.2, or 1.3 and compatibility group letter.

* Compatibility group letter.

1.4 EXPLOSIVE * 1

1.6 EXPLOSIVE * 1

EXPLOSIVE ** 1

1.5 BLASTING AGENT * 1

Subsidiary

CLASS 2

FLAMMABLE GAS 2

NON-FLAMMABLE GAS 2

OXYGEN 2

INHALATION HAZARD 2

CLASS 3

FLAMMABLE LIQUID 3

CLASS 4

SPONTANEOUSLY COMBUSTIBLE 4

FLAMMABLE SOLID 4

DANGEROUS WHEN WET 4

CLASS 5

OXIDIZER 5.1

ORGANIC PEROXIDE 5.2

IV LABELS

PLACARDS

V

CLASS 1

EXPLOSIVES 1.1, 1.2, & 1.3

Placard any quantity of Division 1.1, 1.2, or 1.3 material.

∗ The Division number 1.1, 1.2 or 1.3 and compatibility group (when required).

EXPLOSIVES ∗ 1

CLASS 1

EXPLOSIVES 1.4

Placard 1,001 lb (454 kg) or more of 1.4 Explosives.

∗ The compatibility group (when required).

1.4 EXPLOSIVES ∗ 1

CLASS 1

EXPLOSIVES 1.5

Placard 1,001 lb (454 kg) or more of 1.5 Blasting Agents.

∗ The compatibility group (when required).

1.5 BLASTING AGENTS ∗ 1

CLASS 1

EXPLOSIVES 1.6

Placard 1,001 lb (454 kg) or more of 1.6 Explosives.

∗ The compatibility group (when required).

1.6 EXPLOSIVES ∗ 1

CLASS 2   Division 2.1

FLAMMABLE GAS

Placard 1,001 lb (454 kg) or more of flammable gas. See DANGEROUS.

FLAMMABLE GAS 2

CLASS 2   Division 2.2

NON-FLAMMABLE GAS

Placard 1,001 lb (454 kg) or more of non-flammable gas. See DANGEROUS.

NON-FLAMMABLE GAS 2

CLASS 2

OXYGEN

Placard 1,001 lb (454 kg) or more of either oxygen compressed or oxygen, refrigerated liquid. See §172.504(f)(7).

OXYGEN 2

CLASS 2   Division 2.3

POISON GAS

Placard any quantity of Division 2.3 material.

INHALATION HAZARD 2

VI

PLACARDS

CLASS 3

FLAMMABLE
Placard 1,001 lb (454 kg) or more of flammable liquid. See DANGEROUS.

FLAMMABLE 3

CLASS 3

GASOLINE
May be used in place of FLAMMABLE on a placard displayed on a cargo tank or a portable tank being used to transport gasoline by highway. See §172.542(c).

GASOLINE 3

CLASS 3

COMBUSTIBLE
Placard a combustible liquid when transported in bulk. A FLAMMABLE placard may be used in place of a COMBUSTIBLE placard on a cargo tank or portable tank or a compartmented tank car which contains both flammable and combustible liquids. See §172.504(f)(2). No placard is required for a combustible liquid transported in a non-bulk packaging (119 gal (450 L) or less).

COMBUSTIBLE 3

CLASS 3

FUEL OIL
May be used in place of COMBUSTIBLE on a placard displayed on a cargo tank or portable tank being used to transport, by highway, fuel oil not classed as a flammable liquid. See §172.544(c).

FUEL OIL 3

CLASS 4 **Division 4.1**

FLAMMABLE SOLID
Placard 1,001 lb (454 kg) or more of flammable solid. See DANGEROUS.

FLAMMABLE SOLID 4

CLASS 4 **Division 4.2**

SPONTANEOUSLY COMBUSTIBLE
Placard 1,001 lb (454 kg) or more of spontaneously combustible material. See DANGEROUS.

SPONTANEOUSLY COMBUSTIBLE 4

CLASS 4 **Division 4.3**

DANGEROUS WHEN WET
Placard any quantity of Division 4.3 material.

DANGEROUS WHEN WET 4

PLACARDS

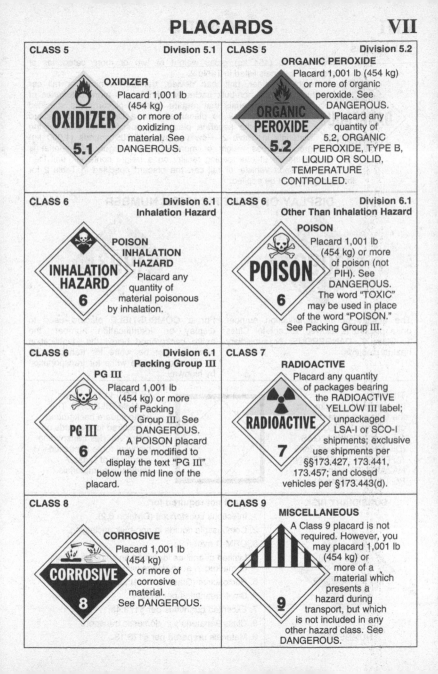

CLASS 5 **Division 5.1**	**CLASS 5** **Division 5.2**

CLASS 5   **Division 5.1**

OXIDIZER
Placard 1,001 lb (454 kg) or more of oxidizing material. See DANGEROUS.

OXIDIZER 5.1

CLASS 5   **Division 5.2**

ORGANIC PEROXIDE
Placard 1,001 lb (454 kg) or more of organic peroxide. See DANGEROUS. Placard any quantity of 5.2, ORGANIC PEROXIDE, TYPE B, LIQUID OR SOLID, TEMPERATURE CONTROLLED.

ORGANIC PEROXIDE 5.2

CLASS 6   **Division 6.1**
Inhalation Hazard

POISON INHALATION HAZARD
Placard any quantity of material poisonous by inhalation.

INHALATION HAZARD 6

CLASS 6   **Division 6.1**
Other Than Inhalation Hazard

POISON
Placard 1,001 lb (454 kg) or more of poison (not PIH). See DANGEROUS. The word "TOXIC" may be used in place of the word "POISON." See Packing Group III.

POISON 6

CLASS 6   **Division 6.1**
Packing Group III

PG III
Placard 1,001 lb (454 kg) or more of Packing Group III. See DANGEROUS. A POISON placard may be modified to display the text "PG III" below the mid line of the placard.

PG III 6

CLASS 7

RADIOACTIVE
Placard any quantity of packages bearing the RADIOACTIVE YELLOW III label; unpackaged LSA-I or SCO-I shipments; exclusive use shipments per §§173.427, 173.441, 173.457; and closed vehicles per §173.443(d).

RADIOACTIVE 7

CLASS 8

CORROSIVE
Placard 1,001 lb (454 kg) or more of corrosive material. See DANGEROUS.

CORROSIVE 8

CLASS 9

MISCELLANEOUS
A Class 9 placard is not required. However, you may placard 1,001 lb (454 kg) or more of a material which presents a hazard during transport, but which is not included in any other hazard class. See DANGEROUS.

9

VIII PLACARDS

DANGEROUS

Placard 1,001 lb (454 kg) gross weight of two or more categories of hazardous materials listed in Table 2.

A freight container, unit load device, transport vehicle, or rail car which contains non-bulk packages with two or more categories of hazardous materials that require different placards, as specified in Table 2, may be placarded with a DANGEROUS placard instead of the separate placarding specified for each of the materials in Table 2. However, when 2,205 pounds (1,000 kg) aggregate gross weight or more of one category of material is loaded therein at one loading facility on a freight container, unit load device, transport vehicle, or rail car, the placard specified in Table 2 for that category must be applied.

DISPLAY OF IDENTIFICATION NUMBER

The display of an identification number on a placard is allowed, except for Class 1, Class 7, DANGEROUS, or subsidiary hazard placards.

For a COMBUSTIBLE placard used to display an identification number, the entire background below the identification number must be white for transportation by rail and may be white for transportation by highway.

The white square background is required for the following placards when on rail cars: EXPLOSIVES 1.1 or 1.2; POISON GAS (Division 2.3, Hazard Zone A); POISON INHALATION HAZARD (Division 6.1, PG I, Hazard Zone A) and

for DOT 113 tank cars FLAMMABLE GAS. The white square background is required for placards on motor vehicles transporting highway route controlled quantities of Class 7 (radioactive) materials.

SUBSIDIARY RISK

NUMBERED

Placard not required for:

1. Infectious substances (Division 6.2).
2. Combustible liquids in non-bulk packaging.
3. ORM-D materials.
4. Limited quantities identified on shipping papers or marked in accordance with §172.315.
5. Radioactive (Class 7) I or II labels.
6. Small quantities per §173.4.
7. Excepted quantities per §173.4a.
8. Class 9 materials in domestic transport.
9. Materials prepared per §173.13.